ULTIMATE DE(

– How Stalin stole the Bomb –

By

Jerry Dan

RARE BOOKS & BERRY
SOMERSET, ENGLAND

This edition is published in 2003 by
RARE BOOKS & BERRY
High Street
Porlock
Somerset
England
TA24 8PT

www.rarebooksandberry.co.uk

ISBN 0-9539951-1-9

First published November 2003

Typeset in 10/12 pt Times New Roman
Printed and bound by Thanet Press, Margate, Kent, UK

*To everyone in Russia, the Ukraine, Britain, Germany and the United States
who has helped me research and produce this book.*

Enjoy the read!

Jerry Day

Back cover photo: The road between Taganrog in southern Russia to Mariupol in the southern Ukraine. Major Hans van der Velde travelled along this road in his Opel car on February 22, 1942 – destination Krivaya Kosa.
Cover design: Phil Macaulay.

Notes for readers

Terminology

Illegals: Soviet Intelligence agents who lived outside the Soviet Union under false identities. Moscow would often encourage taking on the identity of someone who had died. Illegals were vital to both the GRU and NKVD as talent spotters for potential agents.

KGB: The state security service has undergone a number of name changes since its inception – the Cheka [1917–1922], GPU [1922–1923], OGPU [1923–1934], NKVD [1934–1943], NKGB [1943–1946], MGB [1946–1953], MVD [1953–1954], KGB [1954–1994], FSK and FSB [1994–]. The author has usually referred to the NKVD, NKGB, MGB, KGB and FSB.

GRU: Russian military intelligence. During the early years of the war it gained substantial atomic intelligence, until Stalin decided that the NKVD would manage the programme.

SIS: Another name for Britain's MI6, the sister organisation of MI5.

Rezidentura: A Soviet Intelligence operation that resides in an Embassy. The *rezident* is the senior officer, usually First or Second Secretary or attaché. In certain cases the Ambassador can be the senior officer. Often, the term 'station' is used, such as 'London station'.

Case officer: An Embassy or Consulate officer who manages agents. Other terms – controller or handler. Contact with an agent can often be made through a courier, who, in turn, operates through a case officer.

Operation Enormoz: An NKVD operation, initially comprising four NKVD officers, established within the STI [the Science and Technology] department, reporting to Lt General Pavel Fitin, co-ordinating the gathering of atomic intelligence from the United States, Britain and Canada.

Manhattan Project: The US atomic bomb programme, also referred to as the *Manhattan Engineering District.*

Tube Alloys: The codename for the British atomic bomb project, set up in 1941. When America joined the war, and both countries agreed to co-operate, the codename continued in use in Britain.

CONTENTS

FOREWORD

I had heard about the 'atomic' notebook, discovered in the briefcase of an SS officer during a Red Army raid on Krivaya Kosa, a German and Rumanian-held Cossack village on the Ukrainian-Russian border in February 1942. Its existence was confirmed to me from a veteran KGB officer who had been a member of a specialist wartime team tasked by Stalin with stealing nuclear secrets from Britain, America and Canada.

Colonel Vladimir Barkovsky was an outstanding Russian spymaster of his generation. His long career had begun in Britain in 1941 where he operated under the guise of a diplomat in the London Embassy. It had ended as the deputy chief of the department in the Lubyanka responsible for all Western scientific intelligence. Only recently has Barkovsky emerged from the shadows, willing to impart some of his experiences before the veil is finally drawn over his life. In the many hours of taped conversations in Moscow we had discussed the role of the Russian intelligence services in building Stalin's bomb. Over two years he carefully guided me, prompting and hinting, and putting me straight when I was chasing up a dead end.

Most times when I travelled to Moscow we met, appropriately, at the Kurchatov Institute, the former Laboratory No. 2, the nuclear centre established by Stalin in 1942 where the development of the Soviet atomic bomb began in earnest. Once, we met in the National Hotel, near Red Square, where he was accompanied by his 'minders' who lurked close by. When I asked to visit the Lubyanka, Barkovsky arranged it and I had a fascinating four-hour tour of the KGB's history room with its archivist eager to explain many a covert KGB operation.

Barkovsky facilitated my contact with Colonel Ilya Starinov, a much-decorated Red Army and KGB hero who died in November 2000 at the age of 101 and was given an old-style Soviet funeral. Before his death Starinov gave me the true account of what had occurred in Krivaya Kosa and the subsequent events that followed in Moscow.

I met other Russian veterans and listened to their first-hand accounts on how Russia had stolen nuclear and other scientific secrets. Documents from the archives confirmed the staggering extent of Soviet penetration in Britain and America and some are included in the back of this book. The 'atomic' notebook had been a key factor in Stalin's decision to restart the Russian nuclear programme, curtailed so abruptly by the German invasion in June 1941. Equally important to that decision was received intelligence confirming that Churchill had abandoned his audacious plan for Britain to independently manufacture 36 atomic bombs and he had agreed to pool resources with America.

Everyone I met in my endeavours is very old, but what is remarkable is how clear and lucid most of them are. The idea of secrets, of not telling, becomes somehow ridiculous as their lives draw to a close. If they don't tell someone, how will the world ever know?

Is the ULTIMATE DECEPTION merely historical fiction or is it a genuine account of an extraordinary wartime episode?

Even after two generations innumerable files remain closed in London, Moscow and Washington, their secrets too dark and sinister ever to receive a public airing. The only measuring rod for truth is that which accords best with the facts, confirmed by authenticated documents. But once immersed in the murky waters of espionage there is information and disinformation, truths, half-truths and lies. There is no doubt of the telling contribution of Barkovsky and his colleagues in helping the USSR into the atomic age. Not in dispute, either, is the value of the 'atomic' notebook in ensuring that Stalin achieved his aim of ensuring that Russia had to be the nuclear equal of America.

CHAPTER 1

No. 10 Downing Street, the official London residence of the British Prime Minister – November 9, 2000

'Your news couldn't wait until my return?' the PM asked, wearily, without looking up from signing off official business in the Cabinet Room.

'Prime Minister, we are about to be acutely embarrassed,' replied the visitor, his quiet voice almost drowned out by the noise of the rain lashing against the windows. Dawn had yet to make an appearance. Just minutes earlier he had flashed his pass to the two armed policemen on duty at the back entrance to Downing Street, accessed from Horse Guards Parade.

MI5's director had remained at his club the previous evening, rehearsing in his mind how best to handle the meeting, which promised to be the most delicate since he had been appointed head of the British Secret Service. Relations between No. 10 and MI5 were often strained. After a restless night he awoke to skim through the headlines of the morning newspapers, full of the American presidential elections. There was no time for breakfast.

The club doorman had offered an umbrella given the inclement weather, which he gratefully accepted. St James' Street was windswept, the pavements littered from the overnight fall of leaves, creating a slippery hazard underfoot. Pall Mall was little better as he walked into the biting easterly wind. London was slowly waking up; a bus rattled by, its headlights cutting a swathe through the downpour.

Crossing the Mall, he cursed the fact that he had not rung for a 'company' car, despite the short distance to Downing Street.

He was to explain to the Prime Minister the full extent of Soviet penetration of the British establishment that had lasted for generations; known only to successive heads of MI5 and MI6. No Prime Minister since Churchill had ever received such a briefing. Echoes of the Cold War were to be visited on this Government, so often an administration desperate to conceal. In his pocket the director had a devastating document, given to him the previous evening by his head of Counter-Intelligence. In it were the names of 16 individuals – politicians, scientists and journalists – many publicly honoured, who had betrayed their country during the Second World War and in subsequent years. All but two were dead. There were to be further revelations for Britain's Prime Minister, unfortunately ferreted out of Moscow by a British publisher. The head of British Intelligence had no option but to admit that MI5 had arranged for the murder of Robert Maxwell, a Soviet agent since 1945. Furthermore, he would try to explain the full extent of Lord Victor Rothschild's extraordinary spying career for his Russian masters, beginning in 1934 and lasting to the days of the Edward Heath Government in the 1970s. The director chuckled to himself, despite the cold and driving rain. He wondered how the PM would take the news that a well-respected veteran KGB officer had finally admitted that Harold Wilson, the Labour Prime Minister of two Governments in the 1960s and 1970s, had been 'an agent of influence' recruited by the KGB during a secret wartime mission to Moscow.

Called to No. 10 the day after Labour's landslide election victory in 1997, an ebullient Prime Minister had made it abundantly clear to the head of MI5 that management from the centre would be a feature of his leadership. The PM demanded meetings on a regular basis, unlike the previous Tory regime that gave MI5 and MI6 a free hand in their daily responsibilities. The new war for MI5 would be against the drug barons, the Real IRA and the Triads, amongst others. After a year, the cosy relationship had changed and MI5 found itself organizing 60 per cent more wiretaps than under the John Major regime, many unauthorized. The listeners found themselves transcribing the conversations of ordinary citizens going about their daily lives. This Government was becoming increasingly paranoid. If its Ministers weren't briefing against each other in dark and dingy rooms in Whitehall, they were forever searching for more ammunition to use against opponents, not just in the opposition parties.

The meeting in the Cabinet Room had been hurriedly arranged just after midnight. A tired aide had answered the telephone. There was no opportunity at such short notice to see the PM, said the aide in his usual arrogant manner. The Prime Minister was about to embark on a three-day visit to Washington to meet America's recently elected President, he informed MI5's director. Irked, the director raised his voice. Some minutes later an irritated PM picked up the phone in his private quarters and reluctantly agreed to a 6.30am meeting, the only time he could spare before he took off from RAF Northolt, the airbase to the west of London.

* * *

A graduate from Cambridge, the head of MI5 joined British Intelligence in 1975 and had become a counter-terrorism expert. He was a popular director.

Thames House sits astride the north bank of the River Thames, just yards from Lambeth Bridge – a huge building, beautifully restored. While MI6 attracts most attention in its ostentatious pile on the South Bank, Thames House plays down its significance. It has no name, no number. Inside, in the large reception area, is a plaque commemorating the visit by John Major in November 1994 to open the headquarters of Britain's intelligence services. A receptionist behind a bullet-proof screen checks identification and provides receipts for mobile phones handed in on entry.

In his office enjoying panoramic views of the river, the director was relishing the opportunity of a long weekend, the chance to catch up on family matters and a leisurely perusal of the Sunday newspapers. He was packing his briefcase when there was a knock at his door. The head of Counter-Intelligence, a tall man with over 26 years' service to the firm entered.

'May I talk to you, I think it is important?' he asked his chief.

'Please, take a seat.'

'We may be in trouble,' said the director's colleague and long-standing friend.

'As you know, our files on the Soviet penetration into *Tube Alloys*, the wartime codename for the British atomic bomb efforts, remain open. The unmasking of the two physicists Allen Nunn-May and Klaus Fuchs confirmed to us that the penetration had been very extensive in the scientific community, but we never discovered all the guilty parties. In addition, we were never confident that Donald Maclean and John Cairncross supplied all the major atomic intelligence. When the KGB archivist Vasili Mitrokhin defected to us in 1992, with his extensive notes, more of our suspicions were confirmed. There were many others, most now dead, for whom we never had concrete evidence.

'Completely unbeknown to us, a publisher and former journalist decided to try to unearth evidence in Moscow on how Stalin achieved his bomb in 1949 and the level of NKVD and GRU atomic penetration in Britain. Nothing special here, many have tried and failed. However, this man, who is using the strange pseudonym of 'Jerry Dan' for his forthcoming book, seems to be rather more tenacious than others. He first came to our attention at a very specialised seminar last year in Laxenburg, Vienna, sponsored by the US Department of Energy. The delegates were mainly from Russia and the US, physicists and chemists, all experts on nuclear weapons. Since the collapse of Communism Washington has funded a number of initiatives in Russia, encouraging Russian scientists to recall their memories of a bygone age, with the apparent blessing of the Kremlin. This event was really a duplication of the Dubna seminar in 1996. For both seminars the agenda was very fluid, as ageing physicists described the events from 1939 to 1949 relating to the development of Russia's atomic bomb, built years ahead of the date the Americans, and we, had forecast.

'We weren't represented in Dubna. In fact we didn't even know about it. During the Cold War, Dubna, a secret scientific city constructed mainly for nuclear and rocket development, had been off-limits to any westerner. Some local visits were organized for the American delegates and apparently their hosts couldn't do enough to make their guests welcome. The Ministry of Defence didn't tell us and stupidly even prevented any British presence from Aldermaston, which was a mistake as we missed a unique opportunity to talk to some of the Russian scientists. The contents of the papers were quite startling and I understand that the FSB tried to prevent some speakers from giving their presentations. In five days the Americans, mainly from the nuclear laboratories, learned more about the historic Soviet bomb programme than in the previous half a century. The scientists had waited decades to tell their story without encumbrance from Soviet Intelligence. Unfortunately, only limited papers from Dubna have been released.

'When Washington repeated the seminar in 1999, in Laxenburg, this time we ensured we had a presence – two members from Aldermaston, including our senior nuclear historian who, as you know, enjoys an international reputation. The Russian

3

speakers were clever, never leaving their slides projected onto the screen long enough for the contents to be copied. Only the papers given by the American delegates from Los Alamos, Lawrence Livermore, Oak Ridge and the other nuclear labs were circulated. For the first time, detailed stolen western intelligence was presented. German Goncharov – one of the most respected scientists from that era, who still works at Minatom, the state atomic agency – gave an illuminating chronology of the timetable for the Russian bomb, and provided the audience with a sight of one of the handwritten reports sent by Fuchs to Moscow. It was the American design for the H-bomb, prepared in 1948. Goncharov's final slide was a timeline for the NKVD, NKGB and GRU acquisition of major atomic intelligence.

'The first item referred simply to the 'German atomic notebook in 1942', with no explanation. Goncharov didn't address this slide, he just left the audience to digest its contents for a few moments.

'Sitting at the back of the auditorium was our Jerry Dan, who never tired of taking notes. He was registered as a Russian delegate and a guest of the Kurchatov Institute, formerly Russia's premier nuclear institute. He spent hours interviewing the Russian speakers and delegates, knowing full well, just as we did, that never again would such a distinguished group be assembled under one roof. Within a few years they will be dead, or too infirm. During the coffee breaks our friend chattered with Colonel Vladimir Barkovsky, which is a name we are very familiar with. They appeared to know each other quite well.

'Barkovsky delivered his speech in perfect English, enthralling the audience. Dan stayed in the same hotel as a number of delegates, including the two from Aldermaston and people from Los Alamos, but he kept his distance and never socialised. One of our people asked him what he was doing in Laxenburg, at which he replied, research. There was a suspicion that he may be a member of our intelligence services. I checked him out, but no one claims responsibility. He certainly doesn't work for us.

'It was some months later when we learned that Dan had interviewed Barkovsky in Moscow, not just once but on four separate occasions. That was a real surprise as the colonel, now aged 86, has never really spoken to anybody, let alone an English journalist. In his long and illustrious career in the KGB Barkovsky has been anonymous and in retirement shunned any publicity. In the past 10 years or so, he was given the honour of writing the official history of the organization. He's prepared three volumes but he'll never finish, he is only up to 1945.

'Some weeks after the Austrian conference Dan had been in contact with the Ministry of Defence asking for a name with whom he could perhaps talk to, to clarify some of the Russian material he had acquired. The MOD contacted us and I decided to see him myself.

'An appointment was fixed up, here in Thames House, and I checked him out. He was very friendly and appeared quite genuine. I thought for one moment that he was taping our conversation as he left his briefcase open on a chair beside him for the couple of hours we spent together, but I was wrong. Dan had brought with him a photo album with photographs of many of the Russians he had tracked down, and some Germans, including Adolf Hitler's only living nuclear scientist, Professor Carl Friedrich von Weizsäcker. You will recall that von Weizsäcker was a key member of the team at the Kaiser Wilhelm in Berlin. We brought him and others to England for six months at the end of the war for debriefing on the German atomic bomb programme.

'I was really more interested in the Russians Dan had met, mainly Barkovsky. He was relatively forthcoming about the Barkovsky interviews without giving much away. It was clear from our first contact that people were giving him information, good information, too. Dan agreed to keep in touch and he asked for my direct phone number, which I gave him.'

'What's this publisher up to?' asked the director.

'He's writing historical fiction, he says, a book based on that German 'atomic' notebook which Goncharov mentioned in his presentation. Dan says it was found on a German SS officer with the name of Major Hans van der Velde, who was captured by the Red Army somewhere in the southern Ukraine in February 1942.

'Van der Velde was a physicist on a special mission in Russia to locate uranium oxide and nuclear laboratories. Dan asserts that British Intelligence is tied into this story of the notebook in some way. We had limited wartime contact with several German scientists, but our files don't mention any van der Velde.

'We tapped Dan's phone and one day a transcript of one of his calls to Barkovsky landed on my desk. I listened to the 35-minute tape, probably the first time anyone from MI5 has ever listened to a private Barkovsky conversation.

'They were discussing a number of names, Barkovsky speaking very softly, almost inaudible. Dan went over a number of issues from a previous interview. Fascinating. We continued to record all Dan's conversations. At one stage he had his phones 'swept'. Unfortunately for him he made contact with one of our free-lancers, who we use mainly to tap company chairmen and directors. In the time he was in Dan's home our man was able to break the code for the burglar alarm. In a phone call we heard that Dan was to meet up with Barkovsky again, not in the usual location – a room at the Kurchatov Institute – but at the National Hotel, near Red Square, which gave us an opportunity.'

'The thought must have crossed your mind that Barkovsky may have assumed that these conversations were being overheard?' interrupted the director. 'Despite his age, I hear he hasn't lost his touch.'

'Of course it did.'

'We had the meeting observed?'

'I sent one of our people from the Embassy. He arrived early and saw Dan and a Russian friend sitting at a corner table in the hotel coffee lounge, chatting. Apart from two waitresses, the place was empty. Not wanting to be seen hanging around, our man busied himself reading a paper in the lobby. Barkovsky arrived bang on time, at 4pm, shuffling into the hotel and Dan warmly greeted him. They sat down and ordered some drinks. Within moments, and on cue, two others arrived – one a young woman attired in a trouser suit, quite pretty, typical of the new breed of Russian Intelligence. They sat at a nearby table, keeping an eye on Barkovsky and his visitor.

'It was now pretty obvious that Dan and Barkovsky were quite friendly, the meeting lasting for two hours. Dan guided Barkovsky out to a waiting car, and we followed them to Barkovsky's flat in Baltiyskaya, a reasonably smart block by Russian standards, off the main highway into the capital from the airport. They shook hands in the road outside.

'Two months later Dan called me, he had just returned from another Moscow trip. He had been given access to more revealing KGB material. I asked him to come in and we lunched at the Tate Gallery, where he showed me his copies of the KGB documents, including his English translations. Obviously I wasn't allowed to keep any.'

'Were these documents genuine?'

'The ones he was prepared to show me looked pretty good, but it's difficult to tell without our people having a closer look. Dan doesn't strike me as the kind of person who is taken in easily. Pointedly he informed me that copies of his documents were also held in two locations in New York, for safe-keeping.

'Dan disclosed to me that some of his documents come from the KGB's First Directorate archives that contain substantial Stalin and Beria correspondence; few of these files have been released. Another source is the Presidential Archive, where access is almost impossible.

'Over lunch, Dan asked for a favour.'

'And?' enquired the MI5 chief.

'I was quite taken aback. He wanted me to locate our personnel files on Professor Yves-André Rocard.'

'Rocard?' replied the director, incredulously. 'Wasn't his name associated with that French press story some years back, that in the 1950s a scientist from Aldermaston covertly handed over our H-bomb research to the scientific attaché at the French Embassy?'

'True. MI5 countenanced the 'leak' with the French nuclear programme near to collapse. Sir William Cook, the deputy director of Aldermaston and scientific advisor to the Ministry of Defence, was authorized to provide the French with detail of much of our work. Not surprisingly, Whitehall's instruction to help the French went down really badly at Aldermaston and at Harwell. As usual we received nothing in return; so typical of de Gaulle and his people.

'Anyway, Rocard. Our dealings with him began in 1942 when he was a member of the French Resistance. SOE airlifted him out to London to be recruited into MI6, which was useful to us because de Gaulle needed Rocard as his scientific advisor.

Rocard also took charge of the research department of the Free French naval forces. For a short period he contributed to the British radar effort.

'Once Paris was liberated Rocard advised the French Admiralty, mainly on radio astronomy in the naval research centre in Marcoussis. But President de Gaulle had a further use for this brilliant mathematician and physicist. As we know, de Gaulle had been a nasty thorn in Churchill's side in the final years of the war, especially after he discovered we were co-operating with the Americans on the atomic bomb. There had been a French scientific team working side by side with us in America and Canada, so word was bound to leak out to de Gaulle, who insisted that when the war was over France would regain some of its pre-war nuclear lead.

'Rocard continued to work for MI6 in Paris in 1945; an ideal situation for Lt Commander Eric Welsh, the security officer in charge of *Tube Alloys*, as the Frenchman was to become central in de Gaulle's atomic project. A matter of days after Hiroshima and Nagasaki, Welsh and Michael Perrin, the deputy director of *Tube Alloys*, were in Paris for secret discussions with Rocard about establishing a centre, or bureau, to monitor Soviet nuclear developments. We didn't consult with the Americans on this Paris operation; there seemed little point as all nuclear co-operation had ground to a halt the day after Nagasaki.

'With Paris as its base it was natural that Rocard should be consulted on this British initiative. By this time Rocard was co-opted into the Deuxième Bureau. De Gaulle must have been aware of Rocard's double role.

'London financed the bureau but Rocard assisted in the recruitment of staff. I understand that MI5 was kept in the dark, on Welsh's instruction.'

'Is Dan suggesting that Rocard spied for Russia?'

'No. The reason for Dan's enquiry could, indeed, be very illuminating for us. I asked 'Six' for files on the Paris venture. Naturally they were curious but I declined to tell them the reason for my request. The existence of this Paris bureau has never been made public. After some reluctance 'Six' admitted to me that all the files had either been 'lost' or 'temporarily misplaced'. At least I was given the courtesy of a briefing. Substantial information was collected by the bureau but nothing has ever been shown to us. Curiously, I was also told that in 1947 a Russian nuclear physicist defected to us, whose name has been conveniently forgotten. Apparently Welsh flew over an American scientist, briefed him in the old SOE building in Baker Street, paid him £100 in expenses and dispatched him with an MI6 major to a town in West Germany to meet the Russian. Why didn't Welsh trust a British scientist for the debriefing?'

'Perhaps I can help you here,' responded the director.

'I've never heard of this Paris operation either, but I do know that MI6 distrusted British scientists at that time, thanks to Michael Perrin. In 1945 Perrin was convinced that some scientists involved mainly in radar, chemical warfare, atomic weapons and underwater technology were in regular contact with the Soviets.

Without consulting Welsh, Perrin drew up a list of suspects and handed it to Dr Reginald Jones, head of the scientific section of MI6 and Welsh's boss. Welsh was none too pleased to hear that Perrin had gone over his head. Jones was incandescent, especially as he had been deliberately omitted from the *Tube Alloys* project. Perrin's suspicions reached as high as Churchill, but with no hard evidence the names were not investigated. MI6 didn't let matters drop, at the insistence of Jones, which may explain why Welsh flew in the American for the interrogation of the Russian. I wonder what happened to the physicist? One shouldn't rule out the possibility that Welsh may have directed him to the US.'

'We'll never know, but I have more on Rocard, who enjoyed a long career with MI6,' replied the head of Counter-Intelligence.

'He died in March 1992. Michel, his son, served as the French Premier from 1988 to 1991. Rocard's involvement with MI6 in setting up the Paris bureau is described in an NKGB document in Dan's possession, dated August 23, 1945, and sent by Konstantin Kukin, the NKGB *rezident* in London, to Moscow. Undoubtedly the Paris operation was compromised.

'In his transmission Kukin clearly states that the source for all the detail in his cypher, is *Malone*, the codename for his British contact. As the senior NKGB officer, taking over from Colonel Anatoli Gorsky in 1943, Kukin had assumed responsibility for Philby, Burgess, Blunt, Maclean, Cairncross and other agents. From what Dan has told me, Kukin and two other officers, Barkovsky and Kreshin, ran *Malone* for the duration of the war. A KGB archivist has added a footnote to the Kukin cypher, describing *Malone* as a member of the SIS working in the second department on scientific and technical matters. That section operated from Shell-Mex House, working closely with RAF intelligence.'

'Have you seen this document?'

'I have and Dan is adamant that *Malone* is Wilfred Mann, one of the highest placed Soviet wartime agents, rated in Moscow as equal to Philby in importance.

'Dan has told me that if we locate the files on Rocard it may contain details of meetings he may have had with Mann. The loyalties of Welsh and Perrin have never been questioned and few in MI6 would have been aware of the Paris bureau. Mann was equally trusted, enjoying the confidence of his superiors, especially Professor Edward Appleton, MI6's scientific advisor and in charge of all technical aspects of *Tube Alloys*. In addition to the details of the bureau in the Kukin cypher, we could cross-check other facts against Mann's responsibilities.

'Wilfred Mann, a brilliant physicist, was part of our wartime *Double X* programme. Through him, we fed the Soviets some nuclear intelligence, sufficient to give a wrong impression that the nuclear issue wasn't high on Churchill's priorities. Of course, at the time we had no idea that Mann had been recruited into the NKVD after university, probably through blackmail. There had always been whispers about his homosexuality. After the war Welsh used Mann as his MI6 scientific officer in the Washington Embassy, advising Donald Maclean as Britain's representative on the Combined Policy Committee on Atomic Energy that we set up with the Americans. As soon as Maclean's treachery was confirmed we quietly fired Mann. We had our suspicions but we had nothing with which to nail him. To make matters worse, Mann had developed a strange friendship with James Angleton of the CIA for reasons we could never fathom.

'Dan tracked down Mann, now a very frail 92-year-old, to a Baptist retirement home in Owings Mills, Baltimore. There is a tape of the meeting. In our records we have next to nothing about Mann's role in Welsh's little group. Welsh, himself, was a real oddball. Known as the 'Admiral' to his staff, he had an office constructed on the fourth floor in Shell-Mex House, with steel bars that ran from floor to ceiling, such was his paranoia about secrecy. Colleagues called it 'the cage' and the secretaries were referred to as 'slaves'. By all accounts Welsh wasn't the most popular man in the service. He burned all his papers weeks before he died in 1954, which really annoyed MI6 at the time.

'When Blunt's treachery was revealed to the public in 1979, Mann came under intense suspicion from the press. You and I remember that time well; Fleet Street tried its damndest to get us to admit Mann had been a Russian spy. Mann wrote a book denying being 'the Fifth Man', the term he used in the title. For the past 20 years Mann has remained in the US, declining all interviews. From what we know, he only really had time for an American friend of his, someone he had worked with in Washington in the 1940s.'

'Have you imparted any of this news to 'Six'?'

'Certainly not. Why be in any hurry to tell them?'

'It may be prudent if this information suddenly leaks out and we are accused of not sharing important intelligence. It appears the *Malone* document may be the 'smoking gun'. No, you have to tell them immediately.'

'OK, I'll arrange it.'

'What have you told this Jerry Dan?' enquired the director. 'It's an odd pseudonym; and why do these two names sound familiar to me?'

'Nothing,' responded the head of Counter-Intelligence. 'Apart from inadvertently letting slip that the Paris bureau existed.'

'Is he still bringing out documents from Moscow?'

'Yes, on every trip and increasingly less on atomic matters. He seems to have access to several archives, which suggests his source, or sources, has the highest level of access to KGB files.

'One such file identifies an SIS employee, codenamed *Agent D*, who worked closely with Guy Liddell, head of 'B' section during the war. I asked Dan how many documents he's managed to obtain. He says it is near the 100 mark, which is staggering. About half refer to the atomic bomb development in Britain and America.

'The Americans may have a problem. One document, signed by Beria, confirms the recruitment of Robert Oppenheimer, the scientific head of the *Manhattan Project*, who resigned his position at Los Alamos in 1947 for a post at Princeton. From 1947 to 1952 he served as chairman of the General Advisory Committee of the Atomic Energy Commission, but there was always a smell about him. The FBI remains convinced that he was a traitor. Dan even knows Oppenheimer's secret financial contributions to the US Communist Party. In 1994 Barkovsky was tasked to prepare a note, for limited internal distribution, to clarify Oppenheimer's wartime role for the Soviets. Given that Barkovsky, before his retirement, was the deputy head of the department within the KGB that handled all scientific and technical intelligence, he alone would know. Not only has Dan unearthed the real Oppenheimer story, he knows the substance of Barkovsky's memo which names all the major American sources. Many of the names are completely new to us and, I daresay, even to the American authorities. Barkovsky also named *Fogel*, the codename of Russia's best wartime source at Los Alamos. That experimental physicist is still alive. He is the elusive *Perseus* – the agent spy writers have tried to uncover for years. The American newspapers would have a field day with that story.'

'Have we been inside?'

'Dan's home? Yes, this morning, when he travelled to London – which is why I felt I needed to talk to you. What was found is very disturbing. We copied transcripts of all his interviews, there were 35 of them, and the KGB material. Downloading all his files on his computer was no problem but we didn't locate any version of his book. It may be on the laptop he had with him on his trip to London today.

'It's very clear that Moscow has been of immense help. Dan has assembled a 70-page dossier on the Russian bomb programme from 1939 to 1949, naming every nuclear centre and listing more than 1,200 scientists, intelligence officers and party officials who participated, with acres of information on many of them. Our files are pretty incomplete by comparison. There are similar files on the British and the Germans that are just as comprehensive. God only knows where the British material came from, only limited information is available in the Public Record Office. The British file has 800 names, including details of MI5 and MI6 officers who worked on *Tube Alloys*.

'The file on Barkovsky is fascinating, complete with photographs. It runs to many pages and the content could only have come from Barkovsky himself, beginning with his selection for the NKVD officer training school in Malakhovka. There are details of his briefing with Molotov before being posted to London and his arrival at Liverpool docks an hour after a German bombing raid in February 1941. Barkovsky's career appears to be well documented. For the first time we have a real biography of one of Russia's greatest spymasters spanning a 30-year career.

'For years a story has prevailed that Barkovsky was asked by one of his agents to manufacture a copy of a safe key; as access to the key often proved difficult. Before joining the NKVD Barkovsky had trained as an engineer so he was able to fashion a copy in the London Embassy. Dan writes that the safe belonged to

Professor Sir James Chadwick who, from 1944, headed the British team in Los Alamos and maintained an office in one of our buildings in Washington. If that is correct, we must assume that very little was secure from the Soviets.'

'This just gets worse,' MI5's chief sighed, shaking his head. 'It is difficult to assess Barkovsky's motives. Why is he spending so much time with Dan?'

'It's not just Barkovsky. Other KGB officers are now in contact with Dan. In a very short space of time he's made some pretty powerful friends in Moscow. But, I did say he's pretty resourceful. Someone has given him a film and Dan allowed me to view it. In 1971 Philby was beginning to drink more heavily than usual in Moscow and he asked his case officer if he could have a holiday in Czechoslovakia. The KGB was horrified at the idea, it was still concerned that we, or the CIA, might still make a hit on him. Reluctantly permission was eventually granted, so Philby and Rufina, his wife, travelled to Prague with their case officer to be met by a team of Czech agents who were to be bodyguards for the next two weeks. One of the guards acted as cameraman. They visited every church in Prague on Kim's insistence, as he had read that they were famous for their wood-cut altars. I didn't know that Philby enjoyed such an affinity with churches. In the evenings, the Philby's, the case officer and the guards were steaming drunk. It had been agreed in advance that on the trip they would speak English, not Russian, whenever possible given the Czech antipathy to the Soviet Union. On one occasion they were in a bar which had a television showing a football game between a Czech and a visiting English team. Philby was jumping around, drink in hand, imploring the English to score. In the hotels Philby was often taken for a high-ranking Russian official, due to the presence of his bodyguards, and the film shows hotel staff reverently shaking his hand. I understand from Dan that the KGB had banned any photography on the trip so the film was kept secret.

'Recently Dan has a new contact, a KGB colonel active in Britain in the 1970s after we threw out the 100-plus Russians who we deemed to be intelligence officers. Dan and he correspond by email, which we intercept, and they always meet in Moscow. Dan has a number of recent photographs of him.'

'I wonder who is leaking these documents?' questioned the director.

'Barkovsky wouldn't dare, given his position. Someone is taking a big risk, and so is this so-called Dan. We did find some *Agent D* documents in his house. *Agent D* probably passed to his NKGB controller details of the top secret British and American peace overtures with Germany, held in the Vatican in 1944. One of the Vatican documents is dated July 24 and refers to Ernst von Weizsäcker, Hitler's Ambassador to the Vatican, and incidentally the father of the atomic bomb physicist. He received Francis Spellman, head of the American Episcopacy, and Myron Taylor, the president of United Steel, in the Pope's private quarters. Von Weizsäcker represented Generals Brauchitsch and Keitel, who said they enjoyed the support of a number of senior military officers, all anti-Hitler. The following month, on the 27th to be precise, the NKGB reported further talks in the Pope's quarters, this time with Churchill accompanied only by a personal secretary, and not Anthony Eden, the Foreign Secretary. Churchill presented von Weizsäcker with a number of peace proposals, leaving a defeated Germany in the hands of the Christian Democrats. An occupying Anglo-American force would eliminate any Soviet threat. The meeting was cordial, according to the NKGB cypher to Moscow. No record, as far as I know, has ever been made public of Churchill's meeting with Hitler's Ambassador to the Vatican just two months after D-Day.

'*Agent D* may be Philby, but I doubt it, as he wouldn't have been in the loop. The leak was someone much higher, with close contact with Churchill himself.'

'However, the most alarming find this morning in Dan's house was a listing of 27 names, with dates of their recruitment into Soviet Intelligence, their codenames and controllers.'

'Read them out to me.'

'OK. He has divided the list in two, Americans and Britons.'

'Give me the British, the scientists first.'

'Professor John Bernal, Professor Patrick Blackett, Professor Nicholas Kemmer, Wilfred Mann, Professor Keightley Eric Rideal, Lord Victor Rothschild and Joseph Rotblat. Two further names are annotated as still alive.'

'And the others?'

'The main ones are Harold Wilson, Lord Walter Layton and Robert Maxwell. Harry Pollitt, the head of the British Communist Party in the 1940s is on the list, which is no surprise. The codenames *Scott, Pirate* and *Agent D* are asterisked with no explanation.'

'By my estimation we know half were agents. And the Americans?'

'This begins with the Los Alamos physicist long suspected by the CIA and the FBI, who is still alive and threatens to sue if he is ever named as a Soviet agent. Robert and Katherine Oppenheimer are on the list, as is Edward Condon, the head of the US Bureau of Standards, America's top physics laboratory. Here, take a look.'

The director studied the 27 names – 16 British, 11 American. He got up, walked to a window and stared blankly in the direction of the MI6 building whose lights shone brightly in the darkness. His stomach was churning. He turned around to address his colleague. 'I fail to comprehend why Dan has been co-operative with you? Why doesn't he just publish and bask in the headlines for disclosing these names?'

'It's a question I've struggled with too. He insists his main story concerns this German officer, Major Hans van der Velde, and the unravelling of the subsequent events that took place in Moscow following the discovery of the notebook. Whether or not we had something to do with this notebook, which Dan claims, I can only conjecture. Barkovsky has been really helpful in Dan's search for the notebook. Dan has told me that his book has two threads running through it; the first is the notebook, the second is Soviet wartime penetration of Britain and, to a lesser extent,

America. The common denominator is Stalin and his overarching ambition to build an atomic bomb.'

'You don't think Dan's playing a double game do you, set up by Barkovsky, the wily old spymaster, to find out exactly what we did know about the Russian penetration during this period?'

MI5's head of Counter-Intelligence shrugged his shoulders. That thought had indeed preyed on his mind.

'Time for a drink,' said the director, resigned now to giving up his weekend. He listened to the copied tape of Dan's conversation with a veteran KGB officer, read Dan's account on how Robert Maxwell and Harold Wilson had been recruited into Russian Intelligence and how the notorious Maxwell had been murdered by the Special Boat Squadron on the orders of the Increment, the ultra-secret wing of the British Secret Service.

They continued talking for hours, pouring over the transcripts of Dan's tapped phone calls to Moscow, Washington, New York, Baltimore, Munich and Oxford, and the downloaded files from his computer. It was nearly midnight when they finished.

Dan had uncovered the truth about *Malone*, but more worrying was the evidence on Rothschild, codenamed *Valet* by his Soviet controllers. Rumours of clandestine activities had plagued Rothschild for years, right up to his death.

Despite the hour the head of MI5 knew he had to do his duty. 'No surprises,' the PM had said at their first meeting after the election. The director smiled at his colleague, gingerly picking up his scrambler telephone.

As both men left Thames House together, using the rear entrance, the director muttered something under his breath.

'Did you say something?'

'No, but I've just worked out the Jerry Dan pseudonym,' replied the director with a chuckle.

'Are you going to share it?'

'Later. I must go.' His chauffeur opened the car door to take him to his club.

It began to rain.

CHAPTER 2

No. 10 Downing Street – August 10, 1945

It was four days since the Americans dropped *Little Boy*, the world's first atom bomb produced with Uranium-235, on Hiroshima and the day after the more powerful plutonium bomb, *Fat Man*, exploded over Nagasaki.

Clement Atlee sat at the head of the table in the Cabinet Room, chairing a meeting with two of his senior Ministers and the former Chancellor of the Exchequer in the previous coalition Government. Atlee had been Churchill's Deputy Prime Minister since 1942. He had become PM after the General Election of July 26, 1945, when a war-weary British public voted in the first Labour administration since 1929. The European war at an end and the Japanese on the verge of capitulation, there was a sense of excitement in No.10.

Even as the votes of the British electorate were being counted, the 'Big Three' – Russia, Britain and America – had met in Potsdam, the capital of Brandenburg in southwest Berlin; the last of the inter-Allied conferences. Churchill and his Foreign Secretary, Anthony Eden, did not stay for the duration as the Prime Minister returned to London to tender his resignation. Atlee and Ernest Bevin, the new Foreign Secretary, replaced them in Berlin. Stalin was astounded that Churchill had been voted out of office after winning the war.

For US President Harry S. Truman, Potsdam was his first and last meeting of Allied leaders. He had taken over the Presidency after the death of Franklin D. Roosevelt on April 12, Truman having served just 82 days as Vice-President. James Byrnes, the former head of the Office of War Mobilization and now Secretary of State advised Truman at Potsdam. For Stalin, the only member of the original 'Big Three', and Molotov, his Foreign Minister, it was business as usual.

As Vice-President Truman had been told the barest minimum about the *Manhattan Project*, the American atomic bomb programme. Now President he was briefed and, while in Potsdam, he took Stalin aside to quietly inform the Soviet dictator that a new weapon of extraordinary force had been successfully tested in Alamogordo, in the desert of New Mexico, and that another might be dropped on Japan. Stalin had listened closely, his face registering no surprise at the news.

There was only one item on the agenda in No.10 – *Tube Alloys*, the codename for British nuclear development since 1941. The bombing of Hiroshima and Nagasaki heralded a new and destructive era, and Atlee needed to discuss how *Tube Alloys* should be treated now that the world knew the magnitude of such a weapon.

It was a select gathering, secrecy requiring that only those with immediate responsibility for Britain's post-war atomic bomb development attend. Days earlier, Sir Ronald Campbell, a member of the Combined Policy Committee for *Tube Alloys* in Washington, was requested by Atlee to provide ideas. Campbell had suggested an advisory committee, headed by Atlee himself, with Ernest Bevin, Sir Stafford Cripps and Sir John Anderson – all now present in the Cabinet Room. Atlee started the meeting by agreeing that the Foreign Office, so far deliberately excluded from the nuclear project, be fully briefed. He also insisted that the British should strenuously push for debate between the Foreign Ministers of Britain, the US and Russia on the advent of nuclear weapons at a forthcoming session of the Council of Foreign Ministers in London.

Bevin, to the point as usual, made a startling suggestion. He proposed that a secret committee be formed to consider whether the innermost secrets of the atomic bomb and its development should be shared with the Russians.

Anderson listened to the discussion, making no contribution despite his own crucial role in *Tube Alloys* tasked to him by Churchill in addition to being Chancellor of the Exchequer. There were no secretaries to take notes in the Cabinet Room, Atlee having agreed to Anderson's request that there be none.

The views of the Winchester-educated Cripps, who as a hard-line Socialist in the early 1930s had regularly flirted with Communism, were of interest to Anderson. Just two years after expulsion from the Labour Party for his extreme views, Cripps was the surprise choice in May 1940 as Ambassador to Moscow; a position he held to January 1942. Recalled, Cripps had joined the War Cabinet as Minister of Aircraft Production.

Bevin, in contrast, was new to the arena of international politics. A former powerful trades union leader, he enjoyed popular support throughout the country. The nine-day general strike of May 1926, when four million workers withdrew their labour in support of striking coal miners, had pushed Bevin into the limelight. Head of the Trades Union Council from 1937, Churchill appointed Bevin the Minister of Labour and National Service before bringing him into the War Cabinet in May 1940.

Atlee turned to Anderson, a politician held in high esteem by fellow members of Parliament. The Prime Minister looked perturbed that Anderson had been silent for the best part of an hour.

The son of an Edinburgh stationer, Anderson had studied mathematics and chemistry at the city's university, followed by a research year in Leipzig. A Government career beckoned for the young Scotsman, winning first place in the Civil Service examinations and choosing the Colonial Office, a traditional home for high-flyers. By 1932 Anderson was Governor of Bengal and during his tenure two assassination attempts were made on his life. Returning to England, he served in the Ministries of Shipping, Health and the Home Office. Entry into politics was an obvious move and in 1938 Anderson became an Independent Nationalist MP for the Scottish Universities. With war clouds looming over Europe, Anderson handled preparations for mass evacuation before the Prime Minister, Neville Chamberlain, moved him to civil defence. Within months the *Anderson Shelter* was designed and installed in gardens throughout the country. Anderson joined the War Cabinet in October 1940, became Chancellor of the Exchequer in 1943, and was considered the natural heir as Prime Minister if Churchill and Eden were killed.

'Prime Minister,' said Anderson solemnly.

'As you are aware, *Tube Alloys* has been my responsibility. With the deepest regret I would prefer to step down immediately from this position, my role is over. An advisory position would be accepted if it was offered but I want nothing to do with policy.'

Atlee appeared disappointed. 'I had a feeling that would be the case,' he said.

'However,' continued Anderson, 'it was important to use this timely occasion to share with you one wartime secret, an operation that was quite bizarre, which may have a bearing on the discussion today. When you called me yesterday, Prime Minister, I requested that no minutes be taken of this meeting by anyone. May I also remind everyone that we have all signed the Official Secrets Act.'

'You have my word,' replied a surprised Atlee, looking at both Cripps and Bevin, who nodded their agreement, aware of the enormous respect and responsibility that Winston Churchill had bestowed on Sir John Anderson.

'Thank you Prime Minister.

'But first, I feel I must comment on a proposal under discussion today. You are considering openly sharing our nuclear knowledge with Russia. Some people would react very negatively if it became common knowledge that we had even made such a suggestion given that the Soviet Union is our new enemy; a fact which will not be lost on you when you listen to what I am about to relate. That being said, I was always in the minority when I suggested that we should have made a greater effort in bringing Stalin more into our confidence in the final years of the war. In the hard years of reconstruction ahead it would have been more helpful to have Stalin as an ally, not an enemy.'

Anderson sipped his tea and shuffled his notes before speaking again. A sullen Bevin scribbled on his pad, now regretting his suggestion of the idea on nuclear exchange. He had readily accepted the view of a number of his former colleagues in the trade union movement that Russia be treated fairly and that Britain should trust Stalin. Cripps glared at the silent Anderson; there had been enmity between them for years. Intensely ambitious, Cripps long suspected that Anderson, with the ear of Churchill, had regularly briefed against him outside the confines of the Cabinet Room.

'When the Prime Minister invited me here today and told me the agenda, I was in two minds,' began Anderson. 'As you know, when I became a member of the War Cabinet I was put in overall charge of many secret tasks relating to the war effort, including the development of the British atomic bomb. Even you, Prime Minister, despite being in the War Cabinet, were informed in only the barest detail. In an attempt to disguise the real nature of *Tube Alloys* we let it be known in certain quarters that we were developing a new type of conventional bomb, never once disclosing that we were on the verge of building an atomic device with a destructive capacity beyond even proper calculation or comprehension.

'One night in March 1941, Churchill and I were alone in the bunker with a bottle of good malt for company. During the day, Professor George Thomson of Imperial College, head of a committee we established to look into the feasibility of building an atomic bomb, had been to see us. He was convinced that Britain understood the science and the technology to construct such a thing but it would take up to two years to develop. Churchill enquired of Thomson if that date could be any earlier, but this eminent physicist believed not. We drank more than a bottle that night.

'With the Americans insisting on staying out of the war, Churchill was reconciled deep-down, as indeed many of us were, that we were fast running out of time. The invasion threat of late summer and autumn in 1940 never really went away. We were never safe from a sneak invasion led by German paratroops. Germany was too strong. In War Cabinet meetings, as you recall, we discussed our tactics if Hitler invaded, but the options were few. The only real hope was that our forces not in the country, with American and Canadian military assistance, could evict the Nazis if the worst scenario happened.

'We did have one card up our sleeve. At Porton Down we were on the verge of perfecting biological weapons that could be dropped over hostile territory by the RAF. We had manufactured enough anthrax and other deadly substances to kill a sizeable proportion of Germany's urban population. This was all highly secret, of course, but it was in this country's interest to alert the Nazis, using our intelligence services, that we had no hesitation in poisoning Germany's cities if the threat of invasion became real.

'Many would argue that the British are best in adversity, whatever our shortcomings, and Churchill would do literally anything if it led to the defeat of Hitler. Our morale had sunk to its lowest point when the Prime Minister asked me to come up with some fresh thinking – ideas to help us spin the year out before what we hoped was the inevitable entry of America into the war. We had received good intelligence that Hitler had drawn up plans to invade Russia, but an invasion wasn't certain. Our relationship with Russia was cordial, despite Stalin's pact with Hitler. However remote, was there a possibility that Russia could become a British ally?

'Time was critical. We had ideas over the following weeks – most of them crazy. If I didn't reject them, Churchill did. One proposal we decided to take further. Prime Minister, I have to tell you that we set in train a covert operation for which, to this day, we have no confirmed reports of success or failure. If news of what we did were ever leaked to the Americans, our relations, now under some strain, might be seriously threatened further. We never told them and I believe we never should.

'With our country no longer under a coalition Government it is important this secret is shared with the three of you. If what I tell you ever makes it into the public domain I will vociferously deny it, as will Churchill. Given he was the Prime Minister of the day I strongly believed that he should tell you himself, but he insisted otherwise as it was my operation.

17

'No official records were ever kept of what we did.

'I took the liberty today of inviting two others to No. 10. They alone, with Churchill and myself, are aware of what happened. They should be outside this room as I speak. With your permission, Prime Minister, I will invite them in.'

CHAPTER 3

Russia gives up its secrets

Lavrenty Beria revelled in the trappings of high office. His Moscow mansion in fashionable Malaya Nikitskaya, formerly the home of a Russian Count, was exquisitely furnished. He entertained lavishly, drank the best wines, played tennis and, at his two dachas on the Black Sea, Beria loved the thrill of high-powered speedboats. Bodyguards accompanied him everywhere. As head of the Soviet intelligence services, no one challenged Beria over his main obsession – women. Mistresses were in abundance but that didn't stop his rape of literally hundreds of young girls procured by his bodyguards. Of those girls that dared to deny him his pleasure, some were lucky and were sent home, but others disappeared in the maelstrom of a vast country under tyrannical and murderous rule. Responsible for the great purges of the 1930s and the mass deportations, the Georgian-born chief of the secret police had killing in his blood. In a wood on the outskirts of the capital Beria even had his own killing ground where many of his enemies were liquidated and buried in the undergrowth. Some said that Beria was the real power in the Soviet Union, with even Stalin fearing this short, balding man with the pince-nez glasses and the piercing eyes.

In August 1944 Moscow was enjoying its summer. Muscovites revelled in the warmth and now the talk was no longer of defeat but of victory. On the warfront, the tide had long turned and the German Wehrmacht was being pushed back across the territories and borders so violently invaded in June 1941.

In his third floor office in the Lubyanka, a perturbed Beria studied summaries of the latest foreign intelligence provided by NKGB agents and controllers who reported into either Lt General Pavel Fitin, head of the 5th Directorate, or General Victor Kravchenko, chief of the 4th Directorate. Of particular interest were the reports from the Embassy in New York and the Consulate in San Francisco on the rapid expansion of the nuclear laboratory at Los Alamos in New Mexico. He scanned the grainy photographs of the heightened activity.

Lt General Vsevolod Merkulov, Beria's First Deputy and Minister of State Security, reacted immediately to the phone call. Utterly loyal to Beria, Merkulov, too, had blood on his hands; in 1940 he had issued the order to eliminate the elite of the Polish Army held in camps near Smolensk. More than 4,000 officers were executed by NKVD troops in the forest at Katyn, their bodies dumped in mass graves. Well educated and a first-rate speechwriter, a new task awaited the trusted deputy.

Stalin had charged his Foreign Secretary, Vyacheslav Molotov, with managing Russia's nuclear research – but the real power behind the building of the bomb rested with Beria as every member of the Politburo was too aware. Beria had one huge advantage over Molotov – he had already utilized the entire resources of the NKGB and the organization's Border Guards regiments to provide effective control over every secret scientific installation and laboratory throughout the country. Lack of commitment could be met with arrest, the farce of an impromptu trial, followed by jail or expulsion to the Gulag. Facing the firing squad was the ultimate punishment.

It was clear to Beria from the Los Alamos reports that America had accelerated its nuclear programme. The laboratory that the Americans had codenamed *Camp Y*, was surrounded by high wire fencing with troops patrolling the perimeter. Army engineers had constructed a communications centre and now more rows of huts were being added as living quarters. The report from one NKGB agent confirming that the FBI had moved in a special unit for surveillance of staff was enough to galvanise Beria to resolve an ongoing problem. Internal NKGB rivalries between Fitin and Kravchenko had resulted in poor co-ordination. It was bad enough that the GRU, the intelligence group of the Soviet military, continued to manage its own agent network, gathering nuclear intelligence despite Stalin's clear instruction that the NKGB would have overall responsibility. The scientist, Klaus Fuchs, had moved from GRU control in Britain to NKGB management upon his arrival in New York, but the GRU's reluctance to share other agents had led to friction.

Beria was not a man to cede full authority to anyone, but he felt comfortable in handing over day-to-day control of nuclear espionage to Merkulov. More importantly, Beria demanded of his deputy that greater penetration of *Camp Y* must be an immediate priority. That instruction also signalled greater urgency by the NKGB to acquire more intelligence material emanating from London. *Operation Enormoz*, the codename for the elite NKGB unit consisting of one officer in London, two others in New York and masterminded by a controller in Moscow, was given more resources and increased authority in its prime task of nuclear espionage. Established in 1941 *Operation Enormoz* had already tasted exceptional success. Churchill's War Cabinet had sat down on September 24, 1941, to discuss a proposal to independently build 36 atomic bombs. Nine days later the minutes of the lengthy meeting were covertly transmitted to Stalin, Molotov and Beria. Photographs of the lengthy report, taken by Vladimir Barkovsky, an attaché in Russia's London Embassy, would later arrive in the diplomatic bag.

The decision on the future control of the NKGB's most valuable asset in America took some time to resolve. Merkulov knew he had to temper more espionage activity in America with the greatest care given Stalin's decision to abolish the Comintern, an international association of Communist parties. The US authorities would not take kindly any disclosure that a number of its nuclear scientists had been approached by Soviet agents to carry out covert activities. Dr Robert Oppenheimer was the senior scientist in the *Manhattan Project* and it was vital he wasn't compromised. Oppenheimer was a secret member of the US Communist Party and Earl Browder, the head of the party, had often bragged to his colleagues about the membership of a highly-secret cell he had established. Six physicists were in the cell and all had been security cleared to work at Los Alamos or in the Radiation Laboratory on the Berkeley campus in California. Security was paramount, now especially as Elizabeth Zarubin, Oppenheimer's NKGB controller, was convinced that the physicist ran a great risk of exposure.

Merkulov sought Beria's approval in October 1944 for what he had decided. Given the nature of the internal memo, only three copies were circulated within the NKGB. Beria signed his agreement confirming that Gregory Kheifets, a much-respected NKGB officer in the San Francisco Consulate, would co-ordinate the relationship with Oppenheimer and the other secret cell members. With immediate effect the US Communist Party would cease contact.

Oppenheimer would not disappoint his Moscow masters, opening up a gateway for NKGB penetration into every key nuclear laboratory and establishment in America.

* * *

Yet, incredibly, it was the bravery and courage of a German SS officer who inspired Stalin to devote huge effort and resources to the building of an atomic bomb that was exploded on August 29, 1949, in Semipalatinsk, Kazakhstan – an event that stunned the world.

The real account of how Stalin stole the bomb lies in KGB files and in the memories of people who are now very old, and who have never been allowed to tell their stories. The KGB's operational files have been transferred onto microfiche and those documents relating to atomic espionage reside on the first floor below ground level in Yaseneva, a huge complex south of Moscow. Other archives in Moscow and elsewhere also reveal the extent of Soviet penetration in America, Britain and Canada during wartime. No secret was safe.

One relic of Stalin's rush to build his bomb is located half a mile from the dual carriageway linking Sheremetyevo international airport to the centre of Moscow. It is an underground nuclear reactor, the first to be built outside North America. The nuclear pile is without question the oldest working reactor in the world, and the most unstable. It measures 21 feet wide and 32 feet high, is air-cooled and comprises 430 tons of pure graphite and 48 tons of uranium, much of it taken by Soviet forces in 1945 from a defeated Germany.

Constructed as a stack with the graphite blocks placed at irregular angles, the reactor is almost identical to the prototype built by the Italian-born nuclear scientist Enrico Fermi in 1943 on a squash court at the University of Chicago. It was Fermi, the most influential nuclear scientist of his generation who, with Oppenheimer, served on the scientific panel of the Interim Committee on Nuclear Power, that recommended to President Truman the immediate use of nuclear weapons against Japan.

Igor Kurchatov, the physicist who Stalin placed in charge of the Soviet nuclear project, couldn't believe his good fortune when Beria personally brought the Fermi drawings to him in his private room at the Lubyanka, one of two locations at which he was permitted to view stolen western intelligence. At the time the Russian scientists were struggling even with the concept of a nuclear reactor. Beria immediately ordered the construction of a stack using the Fermi plans. There was one modification, however. More graphite was necessary as the Russian material was less pure than that available to Fermi. The foundation for Stalin's bomb was now underway.

Hidden in the wooded compound of the Kurchatov Institute, established as Laboratory No. 2 in April 1943, is the underground reactor. Few would guess its purpose from its now rotting entrance. The roof is lead-lined, poorly hammered into shape at the corners, and the height from the apex to the ground is no more than nine feet. In front a rusting gate is bent permanently open. A door leads to an underground corridor, its floor lined with a thick yellow plastic. The control room is basic, as it would have been in 1946 when the reactor was first fired into life, just some dials and a screen. Another corridor leads further underground to the reactor and, just outside the heavy metal door, is a periscope taken from a Soviet submarine, connected to a wire pulley system. That had been Kurchatov's idea. He wanted to view the reaction right inside the reactor and so control the uranium rods.

The reactor itself was built to last five years, but at the end of the twentieth century it remains in working order, its uranium having a half-life of 300 years. A metal staircase leads to a large room. In the middle lies a rectangular metal block – the head of the reactor. It measures five feet wide and four feet tall, with three uranium rods protruding and covered with beaten lead, nailed together and painted off-white. Loose layers of cadmium, resembling layers of very thin tin, lie on top and spent uranium is piled nearby. This nuclear monstrosity is held together by nails with their heads bent over. An application to the European Union for urgent funding to make the reactor safe has yet to be processed.

As most of Europe celebrated Christmas Eve in 1946 a group of eight men had gathered in the control room to witness Russia's first steps in the creation of its own super-weapon. Here an anxious Kurchatov started the reactor at 6pm, watched closely by Beria. The nuclear reaction was first measured at 11.53pm. Minutes later Beria left with his bodyguard to make an important phone call. Josef Stalin was asleep when the call was put through to his private quarters in the Kremlin. The self-proclaimed 'Man of Steel' smiled to himself and slowly replaced the handset. He would reward Kurchatov with one million roubles and the choice of a mansion anywhere in Moscow.

Once one of the most secret scientific locations in the USSR the Kurchatov Institute is now just a pale shadow of its illustrious and historic past. The yellow paint of the grand main building is scarred by the harsh Russian climate. A burnt-out car squats on the grass in front where, in 1944, three physicists set up rifles to experiment with uranium-tipped bullets in a bid to emulate American experiments on a gun-type trigger mechanism to detonate an atomic bomb. From the entrance staff come and go, many carrying plastic bags, a vital commodity in modern-day Russia. Scientists no longer command the eminence of yesteryear, earning a fraction of a taxi driver's wages. Inside the Institute is a small foyer, staffed by a stone-faced Russian woman and a security guard. The grey-tiled floor and the walls are dirty.

Across the 80-acre compound, buildings and machinery are in decay. Stray dogs scavenge for food. In April 1943, 11 scientists had moved into the newly constructed building that initially was to be used by the Institute of Experimental Medicine to manufacture the Russian version of penicillin. By 1946 that number had grown to 78. At the height of the Cold War in the 1960s some 4,000 scientists and technicians were employed at the Kurchatov.

The nuclear accident in Chernobyl in 1986 was the last time that the Institute played any real role. Some 600 staff members were sent to the Ukraine on Kremlin orders, led by its director Dr Evgeny Velikhov. From a helicopter, Velikhov surveyed the disaster caused when one of the four reactors went out of control, blowing off the top of the concrete and steel reactor. Velikov had told his wife he would be away for three days, but returned seven weeks later.

American scientists had advised Velikhov to quickly issue iodine pills to local children to limit radiation sickness, but the pills ran out. Sworn to secrecy the Kurchatov team's first task was to assess the condition of the plutonium in the reactor and to confirm whether it had melted or evaporated in the explosion. The second task was to prevent the plutonium from penetrating the soil and surrounding water resources. Most of the measures they took were unsuccessful and many members of staff are now sick and prone to heart attacks.

Hidden behind trees in the Kurchatov compound is Kurchatov's house, beautifully timbered and built in 1945 by Academician Shchusev, the famous Russian architect. On Stalin's instruction Kurchatov was to enjoy every luxury. When Kurchatov died at his dacha in February 1960, aged 58, having been nursed by his ever-loyal wife, the house became a shrine to the father of the Russian atomic bomb. In a corner of the living room is a 1950's Russian-made television. Memorabilia adorns the dining room where Kurchatov hosted dinner parties for his scientists, whom he would encourage to sing after overindulging in Georgian wine and vodka. Adjoining the dining room is a small balcony where, towards the end of his life, Kurchatov had whispered conversations with Andrei Sakharov, the Soviet scientist who was key in the development of Russia's hydrogen bomb, successfully tested in 1953. Kurchatov and Sakharov became vocal in warning the world about the dangers of nuclear power for military use.

On the cracked leather sofa in Kurchatov's study rests a wolf skin, the spoils of a shooting expedition held in celebration after the first nuclear test in August 1949. The mini snooker table remains in pristine condition. A fading black and white photograph shows the nuclear team. Despite being the senior scientist, Kurchatov is in the second row, easily identifiable. Some of his closest colleagues referred to him as 'The Beard', such was the long and bushy growth. Free time was scarce but Kurchatov enjoyed tennis on a court built in the grounds. A heavy smoker, he tried desperately to break the habit, failing each time.

Kurchatov met Stalin regularly and was often amazed by the dictator's knowledge of the work being carried out in the laboratory. Relations with Beria, who frequently turned up unannounced, were bad and the dislike was mutual. Typically Beria despised anyone who enjoyed the personal trust of Stalin, especially a scientist. When they met, Kurchatov found any excuse to keep their conversations brief. With a number of Jewish scientists working in the laboratory, Kurchatov always had to be on his guard against Beria who was renowned for his Jew-baiting.

The arrest of Browerman, a physicist in the electromagnetic isotope separation department, severely tested Kurchatov's skills. On Beria's order Browerman was interrogated in the political department in the grounds of the laboratory, falsely accused of subversive activity. Fearful, Kurchatov called Stalin to successfully plead for his colleague's life. On Browerman's release there was much celebration, but Beria fumed as Stalin warned him never again to interfere with the scientists.

Kurchatov won four major awards from Stalin but, remembering his own early hardship and humble upbringing, he gave away all the monies that came with such honours to local orphanages. He also had a terrific sense of humour. As a member of Nikita Khrushchev's party on the state visit to England in 1956, Kurchatov presented a paper at Harwell. For the first time ever, British scientists openly questioned the head of the Soviet atomic bomb programme. Protocol dictated that the paper be given in Russian, despite Kurchatov's excellent English. There was much good humour and laughter when he drew a picture of a contraption on the blackboard, built by the Soviets, that was capable of measuring up to one million degrees centigrade. The whole event was taped by MI5, edited and sent to the Prime Minister.

One of two sons of an uneducated peasant father, Igor Kurchatov was born in 1903 in a village near Ufa, about 900 miles east of Moscow. Both he and his brother Boris were destined to be ranked amongst the greatest scientific brains of their generation. Election to the elite Academy of Sciences is deemed the greatest scientific honour in Russia but it was Boris, two years younger than Igor, who received the achievement first. Boris perfected a device to demagnetise ships in order to avoid contact with mines, but he was later enrolled to work on the nuclear project.

The Kurchatov Institute is steeped in Russia's nuclear past and, with the passing of the Cold War, is now relinquishing some of its many secrets. Its dusty archives are bulging, not just with early Russian nuclear research. In the final days of the war three NKGB teams, which included many of Kurchatov's scientists, swooped into Berlin, Vienna and Dresden to grab uranium, files and German nuclear scientists. At the Kaiser Wilhelm Institute for Physics in Berlin the NKGB found the complete record of the Nazi programme to build an atomic bomb.

The name of Major Hans van der Velde, an employee of the Kaiser Wilhelm conscripted into a specialised SS unit just days before the invasion of Russia in June 1941, is not in any archive. Every record of his existence was systematically purged by the Soviets. At the end of the war his name was also purged from German archives under British control.

With the passing of time, the story of van der Velde now has greater significance, as does the role of Vladimir Barkovsky. These two men were key in turning the Soviet Union into an atomic power. Barkovsky rose to great prominence in the KGB and was given the highest intelligence honours. Even he is aware of the debt his country owes to van der Velde.

The 'atomic' notebook belonging to the SS officer contained Hitler's nuclear secrets. The contents of its 80 pages led to extraordinary events following its seizure. Colonel Ilya Starinov, the commanding officer of a celebrated group of Russian saboteurs that located the notebook in Krivaya Kosa, died in 2000 aged 101. His funeral in Moscow was worthy of a Soviet war hero, attended by past and present members of the Russian military. Before his death Starinov spoke openly about van der Velde, the first time he had done so in more than half a century.

CHAPTER 4

Hell on the River Mius

Stalin had inexplicably ignored the warnings of the impending German invasion, despite the disturbing reports emanating from Japan, Germany's ally. Richard Sorge, based in Tokyo and one of Russia's most accomplished undercover agents, enjoyed top-level contact within the Japanese Imperial Government. One source in particular fed Sorge with copies of radio transmissions from Berlin that included details of the forthcoming attack. The Soviet Premier trusted Sorge implicitly but for some reason never acted upon this devastating intelligence. The *Rote Kapelle* organisation, the *Red Orchestra*, had also provided ample advance warning of the impending *Operation Barbarossa*. *Albert*, the codename for one of its 200 members, transmitted a message to Moscow on February 21, 1941: *'Germany is concentrating 150 divisions in the East. According to a Swiss officer in the German Army, the invasion will take place in late May.'* The agent was Sandor Rado, an Hungarian living in Geneva, the host city for the League of Nations and home to intelligence agents from many countries.

All *Red Orchestra* members risked their lives to help Russia. Boisen Schultz, an aide to General Reinard Gehlen, the head of the Abwehr, Germany's military intelligence organisation, provided intelligence to Moscow and lived in constant fear of discovery. Almost the entire network was rounded up by the Gestapo in 1942 and strangled to death on meat hooks in the cellars of Gestapo headquarters, located on the corner of Wilhelm Strasse and Prinz Albrecht Strasse in Berlin. A Gestapo officer, Brian Tenbah, was one of the *Red Orchestra*'s longest-serving members but, compromised by a traitor, he was subjected to terrible torture before execution. The material passed to the NKVD from Arvid Harnak, a civil servant in the Economics Ministry, was of great use to the Soviets. He, too, died in the cellars; but, in Geneva, Rado was never discovered.

Operation Barbarossa was launched at 4am on Sunday, June 22, 1941, with 148 German and Rumanian divisions attacking the Soviet Union on a 1,800-mile front stretching from the White Sea in the north to the Black Sea in the south. At exactly 5am the German Ambassador in Moscow, Count von der Schulenburg, called upon Molotov, Russia's Foreign Minister, and informed him that a state of war existed between Germany and Russia. Molotov addressed 180 million Russians in a radio broadcast from the Kremlin immediately afterwards. At 5.45am Dr Josef Goebbels, the German Propaganda Minister, read out a statement composed by Hitler: *'German people. In this very hour a movement of troops is taking place which in its extent and magnitude is the greatest that the world has ever seen.'*

That night Stalin ordered a total blackout in Moscow – even the Kremlin switched off its lights. Civil defence services, thousands of men and women, took up positions around the city. Moscow Radio dictated that factory workers must work even harder in making munitions and aircraft. Three million German soldiers, battle-hardened from successes in Western Europe, supported by 3,350 tanks, 7,180 guns and 3,250 aircraft, were now pitched against 160 poorly equipped Soviet divisions. In the first hour of *Operation Barbarossa* German bombers brought terror to Kaunas, Tallinn, Kiev, Sevastopol and Odessa.

Winston Churchill spoke to the British nation on the evening of June 22 about the invasion: *'This was no surprise to me. I gave clear and precise warnings to Stalin of what was coming. I gave him warning as I have given warnings to others before. Hitler wishes to destroy the Russian power before the winter comes.'*

Field Marshalls von Leeb, von Bock and von Runstedt commanded three massive armies and the speed and ease of the advance in the first few days surprised even the German High Command. Berlin Radio announced daily successes on the eastern front, sometimes describing the heroics of the Soviet Army and its people. An ebullient Hitler broadcast on June 29, just one week into the invasion, that the Luftwaffe had annihilated the Soviet air force and that victory was in sight. He boasted that 4,100 aircraft had been destroyed, with the loss of only 150 German planes. Some 2,200 Russian tanks had also been smashed. *'Hitler's victory claim is a manifest lie and humbug,'* Moscow Radio retaliated.

Stalin kept his nerve but his military advisors, Zhukov, Timoshenko, Budenny, Voroshilov, Kuznetsov and Richagov, had already realised that the overwhelming German tide could not be contained. On July 3 Stalin spoke to hundreds of members of the Red Army in the Kremlin. *'Our country,'* said Stalin, *'has entered upon a death struggle with her most ferocious and perfidious enemy – German Fascism. Hitler intends to seize our land, bathed in our sweat, to seize our wheat and our oil, the fruits of our labour. Is it therefore a question of life or death for the Soviet State, for the people of the USSR – a question whether the peoples of the Soviet Union shall be free or reduced to slavery? We must not leave a single pound of grain or a single gallon of petrol to the enemy. Leave only the scorched earth for the invader.'* As the Soviet Army retreated, railways, fuel dumps, bridges and other key installations were ruthlessly blown up. The scorched earth order was obeyed without question. By the end of the first week in July the German advance showed no sign of slowing. Minsk, the capital of White Russia, fell after one of the biggest tank battles in history.

Urgent talks began in Moscow between Sir Stafford Cripps, the British Ambassador, and Molotov. Ivan Maisky, Russia's Ambassador in London, joined a Soviet delegation for discussions with Churchill about becoming allies. On July 12 a beaming Stalin signed the Anglo-Russian Alliance.

The first aerial attack on Moscow took place on the night of July 20. Leningrad was encircled by German and Finnish troops at the end of August. Kiev, Ukraine's capital, fell on September 18 and Hitler reaffirmed to his generals that he wanted the prize of Moscow before the Russian winter set in.

Moscow was already under a heavy blanket of snow by late October. The Red Army held their ground at Tula, a city south of Moscow, but Vyazma, to the east, was lost after a bloody battle. Odessa, Russia's main outlet to the Mediterranean, surrendered on October 15 and Kharkov was abandoned on October 24. The Luftwaffe's battle unit 'Hagen,' battered Moscow on a daily basis, attacking aerodromes west and south of the city, with munitions factories as secondary targets. Stukas flew over the Kremlin. Deteriorating weather was Stalin's saviour. German tanks increasingly failed in the snow blizzards and with the ground too hard to dig trenches the men were exposed in the open and to the bitter Siberian winds. The Wehrmacht's 258th Infantry held its position just 12 miles from the centre of Moscow, but would advance no further in this war.

German propaganda attempted to dispel British reports that severe Soviet conditions had halted the advance. Lord Haw-Haw, the English radio propagandist, in his weekly programme from Bremen, broadcast on December 28: *'The transformation from offensive to positional warfare proceeds according to plan. Churchill and his propagandists are still seeking to interpret the deliberate change by the German Supreme Command as a great Russian victory. Such a perversion of the truth can only be regarded with calm contempt. It stands to reason that when weather temporarily arrests the German and Allied offensive it becomes necessary for the attackers to fall back to positions that afford them better communications and supplies. It must be emphasised that as the German and Allied troops retire to winter positions they are inflicting very heavy casualties on the enemy, both men and materials. The Soviets are trying to force the pace and are failing to do so. That a winter campaign in Russia means hardships for the soldiers of our nation is no new discovery.'*

Of the three German armies, Army Group South had been given the vital task of capturing the oilfields in the Caucasus. Hitler's war machine, spread across the continent of Europe, was desperate for fuel. Access to the oilfields in Poland, Rumania and Hungary helped, but the mainstay of the Germany economy remained the output of synthetic oil.

Before the war the Caucasus had provided 90 per cent of Russia's oil output, as well as supplying a quarter of Germany's needs. The first German objectives were the oilfields and refineries of Maikop, Krasnodar, Grozny and Armavir. Second, were the major pipelines linking Grozny with the refineries of Tuapse on the Black Sea and extended northwest, through Rostov, to Trudovaya in the Donetz Basin in the Ukraine. Tuapse refuelled Russia's Black Sea fleet. Baku was the final objective – the Soviet jewel on the Caspian Sea and, outside America, the world's most productive oil producing region. In addition, at both Grozny and Baku, Russia had utilized American technology to produce 100-octane fuel for new-generation Soviet aircraft.

Pioneer battalions and more specialised Wehrgeologen units were attached to the two Waffen-SS divisions in Army Group South, charged with the prime responsibility of restarting the oilfields if they were torched by the retreating Soviets.

Trained oil engineers had been rushed into uniform to accompany essential drilling machinery and even distillation plants were transported in sections. The Germans were very hopeful that new wells in the Maikop area could be drilled quickly.

Berlin, still incensed at London's propaganda, made another announcement: *'In the southern sector of the Eastern Front the enemy, who had succeeded in making local penetrations into German positions, was thrown out again during successful counter-attacks. German, Italian and Slovak troops, as well as the SS Division 'Wiking' made up of Danish, German, Finnish, Flemish, Dutch and Norwegian volunteers, have again proved their valour in the battle. On all sectors of the front the German air force participated in the ground fighting by attacks against troop deployments, enemy supplies and the railway system. In the Straits of Kerch strong German bomber and dive-bomber formations continued their attacks against enemy shipping. Three transport vessels with a total of 2,800 gross registered tons were sunk while a gunboat and four other ships were damaged.'*

The Straits of Kerch is the gateway from the Black Sea into the Sea of Azov. 'Kosas', or long sand spits, litter the shoreline of the world's shallowest sea whose maximum depth is just 49 feet. The major port of Mariupol lies on the north shore, not far from the border that divides the Ukraine and Russia.

Anton Chekov's birthplace lies to the northeast at Taganrog, on Taganrog Bay, where in peacetime the town's population of 188,000 derived a living from fishing and shipping. East of Taganrog is Rostov-on-Don, the Cossack city so beloved by Stalin. Around the Bay temperatures fluctuated from stifling summers to biting cold winters when icebreakers were necessary to clear a passage for cargo ships. The River Mius flows into the Taganrog peninsular. Scattered on the shoreline lie small Cossack settlements, or 'stanitsas' as they are called in this region of Russia.

A radio report to Berlin on October 15, 1941, described the status of the German, Italian and Rumanian divisions as well as Luftwaffe actions. Seven aerial attacks had taken place on Mariupol and the city, with its important rail links to Moscow, was ablaze from incendiaries. To the east of Mariupol the Axis troops had taken large tracts of territory despite repeated counter-attacks from the Red Army and Ukrainian partisans. The Waffen-SS division, Leibstandarte Adolf Hitler [LAH], together with the 13th Panzer, established a bridgehead at Nikolaevka on the Mius. Tanks of the 14th Panzer were at Mtschus and their colleagues from the 16th had taken command of the villages of Grigorjewo, Kushnezowa-Mikhailowkaja and Koran.

Troops from the 1st Mountain Division and 'Wiking', the second Waffen-SS division in Army Group South, occupied South Krementschik, Gajtschul and Jcgorowka, with the 4th Mountain capturing St Hajpeskoje, Swjatoduchowka and Bogojalenkoje. The tough Slovakian Mobile division, renowned for its reluctance to take prisoners, was in control of Wolnowacha, Walerjanowka and Kirilowskoje. Nearby, the Italian Mobile [Celere] division advanced from Bol Janispol. Two other Italian units, Torino and Passubio, were part of the advance to Nikolaevka, as was

29

the German 198th Infantry.

The Red Army capitulated in Mariupol and, after ferocious fighting, Taganrog fell on October 22 to leave the road to Rostov and the gateway to the Caucasus open.

On November 21 the LAH took Rostov; but after just seven days the Red Army retook the city. This was the first defeat in *Operation Barbarossa* and a furious Hitler reluctantly agreed to von Reichenau's request that his troops retire to the banks of the River Mius. Between December 1941 and February 1942 much of the strength of Army Group South was under canvas in temperatures approaching –50°C. The oilfields of the Caucasus were safe, at least until the spring. Taganrog Bay froze over, as did the Sea of Azov all the way to the Kerch Straits.

Oberfeldwebel Hans Demleitner of the 1st Mountain Division had never experienced such cold, not even in the German Alps where he had lived before joining the Wehrmacht. On the Mius soldiers built shelters under the sparse trees, using thick branches. The German supply line from Mariupol to Taganrog was under attack from Ukrainian partisans so rations were limited, often taking days to arrive. Starving soldiers resorted to eating bark from trees, resulting in terrible sores on their faces. Scores died.

Photography was Sergeant Demleitner's hobby, so he had been given the responsibility of taking a daily photographic record for the division. Every battle honour from 1939 had been captured on film, from the 1st Mountain's participation in the triumphal march through Paris after its fall on the evening of June 13, 1940. Demleitner's camera captured the march into the city and the swastika flags adorning the Eiffel Tower. Postcards were made of his films for German soldiers to send to their families. Nicknamed 'Die Edelweiss Division' because it drew on men from the Berchtesgaden area in the Alps, battle honours had been won in the advance into France. In *Operation Barbarossa* the division was in the front line on the sweep through the Ukraine.

Demleitner's camera also recorded the horrific massacre of civilians in Lemberg in July 1941. Five German divisions had attacked the city, the Red Army no match for the Wehrmacht and Waffen-SS. Soon after Lemberg was taken, Demleitner had been ordered to find the city jail. Although a veteran, he felt sick as he took photographs in the cellars. Some cells had been bricked up, leaving the occupants to asphyxiate. Bodies were everywhere, shot through the head or mutilated, the walls splashed with blood. A naked woman had been sliced open, the knife plunged into her chest and forced downwards. An unattached umbilical cord was next to the dead woman.

From the smell and the state of decay Demleitner reckoned that the slaughter had taken place over several days. An SS officer appeared on the cellar stairs, peering at the carnage. Demleitner desperately needed fresh air and after passing a few words with the officer he fled outside. Both sides in this war were responsible for the slaying of 6,000 Poles and Ukrainians in Lemberg. The biggest atrocities were committed by the retreating NKVD, but the SS and the Einsatzgruppen, Himmler's specialized killing unit, were just as culpable. Tarnopol provided more photographic evidence of the sheer viciousness and total lack of rules of engagement. In Demleitner's unit, 10 of his men were taken prisoner and mutilated, held by their tongues as their genitals were sliced off, before being staked to the ground to bleed to death. The Germans retaliated in similar style.

In the vast encampment on the River Mius any moments of relief were precious. Passes into Taganrog were like gold dust, offering the chance of a hot bath and fresh clothes. A makeshift cinema in the town showed newsreels from home and brothels were popular, with many Russian women prepared to be ostracised for sleeping with the enemy. Great care, however, was needed in Taganrog as Russian snipers were holed up in the ruined buildings, picking off stray Germans. There were warnings, too, about messing with the local girls, risking the 'Caucasus revenge'. One unfortunate member of 1st Mountain didn't heed the warning and ended up stabbed to death, a cross gouged into his forehead. The young man's family was informed that the cause of death had been a fatal accident in an overturned VW Kubalwagen. No attempt was made to find the killer.

Camped near to the 1st Mountain was the Rumanian 5th Cavalry, notorious for its cruelty towards Ukrainians and Russians. Officers enjoyed roping prisoners by their necks behind horses, galloping them in circles until the bodies were torn apart on the rock-hard ground. Such events attracted large audiences, including Demleitner and his men who cheered loudly when the head was finally detached from the torso.

The LAH, after the beating handed out in Rostov by the Red Army, nursed its badly bruised pride and refused to mingle. Initially Hitler's bodyguard, the LAH had swaggered and bragged about its fighting ability after action on the Western Front. Morale had now hit rock bottom, especially as other divisions had blamed the LAH for being incapable of holding Rostov and panicking in the retreat.

Morale was a lesser problem for Wiking, the 5th SS division, however. One of the toughest fighting units in the German Army, the arrogant Obergruppenführer Felix Steiner, its commander, regarded every Soviet as being from a worthless underclass. To relieve the boredom Wiking officers raced each other on horseback along the river bank, resplendent in their white winter clothing with colourful flashes on their tunics denoting their nationality.

What distinguished Wiking from any other German division was the large number of foreign volunteers from mainly German-occupied countries. Its Nordland regiment included 294 Norwegians and 200 Danes, together with a great number of Finns, Swedes, French-speaking Belgians and even some Swiss. Most notorious was Westland, the regiment with its Dutch contingent of 620 men. All the officers in the division were German.

Fritz Hahl was an Obersturmführer in Westland. The fourth child of a Stuttgart railway official, Hahl joined up as a heavy machine gunner in 4th Company. Promotion to Unterscharfuhrer followed in August 1941 as did the award of the Iron Cross second class. Between July and November, Hahl's eight-man gun section was reconstituted no less than five times due to the very high death rate. Hahl was wounded on four other occasions during the battles of the southern Ukraine and Russia, but he survived the war.

Withdrawal was never a word used by Wiking. The division had hoped to capture the Russian town of Shakhty, a coal-mining city located 45 miles to the northeast of Rostov, by the end of 1941, but Steiner had to obey the order to fall back and help the LAH. *'We are only trained to attack, not retreat,'* wrote Fritz Stolz of the Westland, who maintained a daily diary.

Thanks to Wiking's rearguard action in Rostov the Red Army was unable to retake Taganrog. The Soviet 56th and 9th armies attacked Wiking and the LAH with overwhelming forces but the two Waffen-SS divisions held their ground in the terrible winter conditions. Stolz wrote: *'The Soviets have coats of fur but we are freezing in our shoes.'* Wiking at first withdrew to the Tuzlow, a river 30 miles north of Rostov, retreating again to hold the road from Rostov to Taganrog. On the Mius, it set up its defences to hold the villages of Alexejewka, Petropolje, Gustafeld, Berestowo, Alkazar, Ruskoje, Machmutzki and Marienheim.

Winter clothing from Germany either never arrived or was grossly insufficient for the huge numbers of men spending the winter on the River Mius. Featherbeds were collected from Ukrainian houses, straw too, which helped keep out the intense cold. By December the ground was so hard that trenches could no longer be dug. Soviet front-line positions monitored the discomfort of the German troops. At night German soldiers were guided back to shelter after just an hour in the open, as their mouths and noses froze. Daily food consisted of half a bowl of stacheldraht, a soup of dried vegetables turned ice-cold by the time it reached the front-line troops.

Meat was limited and, when available, it was nicknamed 'kleistwurst' by the troops, after von Kleist, the tank commander. The lack of vitamins led to grabenkrankheit, ulcers on the thighs. Cigarettes were rationed to three a day. The MGs, the heavy machine guns, froze in the extreme temperatures; only thinned oil and a yellow powdery substance, mainly sulphur, proved capable of lubricating the firing mechanism.

One soldier in the 'Zug', a forward MG position, recently on home leave had returned with a ziehharmonika, an accordion, and played 'Lily Marlene', which could be heard in the Soviet positions. This was the first time that the song was heard on the River Mius. On Christmas Day 1941, a 19th birthday celebration, hardly a party, was interrupted as news came through that a Soviet reconnaissance unit had overrun a local Westland position. The revellers, supported by a flame-thrower unit, wiped out the small Soviet group and returned to their Ukrainian beer. The whole German front on the Mius celebrated the New Year by shooting off spare ammunition. *'The sky was lit up like fireworks,'* wrote Stolz.

CHAPTER 5

The listeners in Moscow

Some of Stalin's foreign intelligence emanated from Moscow itself, from the British Embassy located on the south bank of the Moscow River facing the red brick walls of the Kremlin. NKVD staff listened through their headsets around the clock for any conversation, immune to the dull repetitive thud of the German bombardment on the munitions factories and aerodromes in the outskirts of the city.

It was November 1941 and the German Wehrmacht lay to the west and north of the city, freezing to death in the trenches. At the same time squads of Red Army engineers moved stealthily through the streets, setting mines in Government buildings, bridges and other key installations in what would be the greatest controlled explosion in history if Moscow was taken. Even the Kremlin, camouflaged in red, yellow and grey, was not to be spared. In the Embassy Russian soldiers helped British diplomats load boxes into lorries for temporary accommodation in Kuibyshev to the east, the proposed new capital. Sir Stafford Cripps, the British Ambassador, had decided to remain in Moscow. Since the abrupt ending of the Ribbentrop/Molotov Non-aggression Pact and the subsequent alliance with Britain, he knew it was imperative to stay close to Russia's leaders.

The listeners were familiar with Cripps' clear, well articulated voice, befitting someone of his rank. They had monitored many of his conversations since the day he had arrived in Moscow in May 1940, carrying his credentials from King George VI. Stalin read the daily transcripts, discussing each point with Molotov. He never trusted Churchill and these overheard ambassadorial conversations confirmed what he had known for many years – Britain had an innate fear of Bolshevism and would go to any lengths to undermine Soviet expansion.

Stalin had initiated his own intelligence service, based in the Kremlin, much to the annoyance of Beria and his generals at the NKVD. The most sensitive reports were kept in the office of Poskrebyshev, his secretary of long standing, including transmissions from Ivan Maisky, the Soviet Ambassador in London. With Maisky's source inside the British War Cabinet, Stalin was privy to Churchill's inner sanctum and had access to every major secret of the war.

Moscow was a hotbed of conspiracy in 1941 with Beria in constant touch with his own network of contacts in the city's Embassies, none more so than Stamenov, the Bulgarian Ambassador who had been in the paid employment of the NKVD since 1934. Stamenov played a dangerous game as a double agent. Unknown to Stalin, Beria had his own channel to Hitler, through Stamenov, and just weeks before the German invasion tried to avert military conflict. Hitler never took the overtures seriously, much to Beria's annoyance.

Every Moscow Embassy had been bugged, a policy started in the 1930s when the technology first became available. The NKVD had its own department that manufactured eavesdropping equipment. Listening devices in the German Embassy provided valuable intelligence on Joachim von Ribbentrop's mission to Moscow on August 23, 1939. Within one hour of landing, talks between Germany's Foreign Minister and Molotov began in earnest. Stalin joined the meeting later. When Ribbentrop retired to his Embassy, the listeners were waiting, instructed to pick up every word – nothing was to be omitted from the transcripts. Ribbentrop's long telephone conversation to Berlin was recorded. With the Non-aggression Pact agreed, a triumphant von Ribbentrop returned to Berlin to be hugged by a delighted Fuhrer. In the Kremlin, Russian leaders were briefed on the Embassy conversations.

Bugging the German Embassy had proved an easy task for the NKVD. Count Friedrich Werner von der Schulenburg, the Ambassador, could never resist a pretty face. Posted to Moscow in 1934, he eventually fell into the arms of Colonel Zoya Ribkina, a woman who turned heads in any company. Her pre-war missions for the NKVD included Sweden where she gained the confidence of the Wallenbergs, the influential family that arranged steel supplies to the USSR in exchange for platinum. When operating in Berlin, Zoya was ordered by Moscow to become the mistress of a top-ranking German general close to Hitler; although that particular plan failed to materialise. Returning to Moscow, Ribkina's German experiences were put to good use as head of the German desk at the NKVD. Handling the operations of the *Red Orchestra*, she alone knew the identities of its operatives.

The listeners first heard the codename *Operation Barbarossa* from the bug in von der Schulenburg's study in March 1941. The flow of transcripts from the listeners became frantic in the days leading up to the June invasion.

When Cripps had landed in Moscow to take up his Ambassadorial position, Molotov received him warmly. With the lax security in the British Embassy the NKVD had easily penetrated many of the palatial rooms. However, Beria gave little credence to the transcribed conversations, knowing full well that the diplomats were well aware that the Embassy was bugged. Too often the listeners reported whispered discussion. Furthermore, Beria suspected that the British used the bugs to plant disinformation. He preferred more traditional methods. Two Englishmen in Moscow were in the direct employ of the NKVD – one a journalist, the other a diplomat, an aide to the Ambassador, who reported on the real secrets within the Embassy.

The National Hotel was the favourite watering hole for foreign journalists ever since the Angliysky Club, the English Club, in Gorki Street, had been turned into a museum. The hotel's restaurant offered a panoramic view of two main entrances into Red Square. Lenin had once occupied a front-facing bedroom.

Ralph Parker, the Moscow correspondent of London's *News Chronicle*, enjoyed his new posting. In the first weeks of *Operation Barbarossa* the bar of the National Hotel was packed with journalists reporting endless radio broadcasts and newsreels from the Kremlin. Stalin announced great victories; but the real truth was elsewhere, in the Ukraine, as the Red Army retreated.

Many journalists in Moscow had departed by September 1941, worried about being taken captive if Russia fell to the onslaught. Parker was made of sterner stuff, which pleased his London editor, and he remained filing copy as best he could. On November 7 Parker reported from Red Square on the 24th anniversary of the Soviet Revolution, as the Red Army paraded and its troops marched straight out to the front line. The sky was alive with Soviet fighter aircraft in tight formation as Stalin took the salute.

Parker's apartment, off Gorki Street, was sparsely furnished but adequate. As a journalist he had taken advantage of new Soviet technology that allowed photographs to be electronically transmitted from Moscow to New York, from where they were then flown to London. For the first time Britain could see, in sometimes gruesome detail, regular photographs of the great war to the east. Parker was often taken with other correspondents to see downed German aircraft, inspect ARP units who were defending the capital, or watch as trenches were dug by thousands of women.

One evening in the National, lounging at the bar, he recognised a voice behind him, a contact from the Soviet Foreign Ministry. For the next hour or so they shared each other's company, the official reporting on the news from the front while Parker provided him with copious supplies of vodka.

There were subsequent drunken evenings – not in the National, but in other less salubrious establishments frequented by military officers with a ready supply of pretty Moscow ladies. Parker relished the entertainment, particularly as payment was never demanded. After one heavy drinking session both men stumbled down Gorki Street for a nightcap in Parker's apartment. With the biting wind sobering him up from the kvass, a drink made from black bread that passed as Soviet beer, Parker took in what was on offer. Each month, cash would be paid into his bank account in London on condition that he shared with the NKVD the details of his briefings in the British Embassy. At their next meeting Parker was asked to sign a document, an 'agentura', agreeing to the relationship with the NKVD. That document would haunt him for the rest of his life.

The British diplomat in the employ of the NKVD was of a different breed to Parker. At Oxford he had joined an association of fellow radicals. He later volunteered his services to a contact who fixed up a meeting with the head of the NKVD station in the London Embassy. Toning down his anti-establishment opinions he joined the Foreign Office and became a 'high flyer'. Beria was ecstatic when told that the NKVD recruit had been accepted to fill an important vacancy in Moscow. Contact was through 'dead letter drops' in Moscow's subway stations. The intelligence supplied was startling, including copies of decoded cables sent direct from Churchill to Cripps.

The content of one drop in September 1941 was read with keen interest in the Lubyanka. Sent from Lt Commander Eric Welsh, the MI6 officer, the cypher asked Moscow to check on the whereabouts of staff and apparatus from two specialized laboratories in Leningrad and one in Kharkov. In particular, Welsh needed details of the location of the cyclotron, an apparatus unfamiliar to Embassy staff, constructed in Leningrad's Radium Institute before the outbreak of war, now assumed to be dismantled. It would be most helpful, stated Welsh, if the Embassy could also provide London with any information about the current status of the Soviet atomic bomb project.

The scientists in Leningrad, the Russian scientific capital, had indeed been evacuated to Kazan, in Tartarstan on the River Volga. Meanwhile, in Kharkov, the great industrial city in the Donets Basin, plans were in progress to attempt an industrial evacuation and ransacking on a scale never before attempted. There was serious concern in the Kremlin for Kharkov's Physical Technical Institute, its valuable research, apparatus and materials. Colonel Joseph Cohen, the senior NKVD officer on the British desk in the Lubyanka, pondered the implications of Welsh's request as each of the laboratories named in the cypher had been important components in the now abandoned nuclear programme.

Hidden away in their dingy basement not far from Red Square, the listeners were instructed to listen for specific nuclear terminology. Cohen also met with Peter Kapitsa, the former Cavendish Laboratory physicist from Cambridge, for an opinion on how well versed the British were with the research in Leningrad and Kharkov.

The British Embassy became an invaluable source of information for the Russians throughout the war. On returning to London, Parker attempted to sever his relations with the NKVD, but his controller threatened blackmail and exposure of the 'agentura'. Parker had no option but to defect to Moscow where he later died. The diplomat, like Parker, was never discovered by British Intelligence. He enjoyed a long diplomatic career.

There had been surprise in MI5 when the appointment of Cripps as Ambassador was announced, but it decided against undermining the authority of Churchill. As Churchill addressed the House of Commons on May 13, 1940, for the first time as Prime Minister, MI5 decided against sharing with him their misgivings after observing several past clandestine meetings in London between Cripps and members of the Russian Embassy who were known to MI5 as intelligence officers. Moscow was vital to Britain as Churchill viewed Stalin as a potential ally. The Ambassador enjoyed convivial relations with both Stalin and Molotov, which pleased Churchill; however, British Intelligence only closed its files on Cripps upon his death in Zurich in April 1952.

CHAPTER 6

The raid on Krivaya Kosa

By Christmas 1941 those divisions from Army Group South whose tents were pitched on the banks of the River Mius were reduced to idleness. There was stalemate in this vicious and bloody war. German and Soviet forces faced each other over the frozen Taganrog Bay, waiting for the thaw and an increase in the exceptionally low temperatures. In Berlin, Hitler and his generals were planning the next phase of the campaign to take the oilfields in the Caucasus while, in Moscow, Stalin had issued orders that no oilfield, refinery or pipeline was to be left intact for the invader to utilize. London had offered its assistance and oil engineers had flown to Moscow with advice after successfully plugging the wells in Borneo and other locations in Asia that were under threat from the Japanese. The engineers of the Red Army, however, had their own immediate solution. In Maikop and Krasnodar they awaited the order to pour cement down the shafts. The refineries were mined, as were the pipelines.

Stanitsas, small settlements, dot the coast road south from Rostov – Batajsk, Semibalki, Margaritovo, Port Katon and Shabelskoye enjoyed tranquillity during peacetime as their citizens employed their artisan skills. Yeysk, further south, had a fishing fleet but was equally noted for its sulphur and mud baths, popular with Russians from the cities in the north for generations. But now every house provided a billet for the Red Army. Like the Germans freezing to death on the Mius, conditions for the poorly equipped Russians were hardly better. The war-weary Soviet 9th Army had been withdrawn, leaving the fresher 56th, its commander, Major General Tsyganov, in charge of a 180-mile line from Rostov to the Kerch Straits.

Colonel Ilya Starinov, the deputy head of the Red Army engineering staff in the 56th Army, had been based at Shabelskoye for less than a month. Already a Russian hero, he was an accomplished saboteur. When the Spanish Civil War began in 1936, Russia supported the Republicans against General Franco's Nationalists. Discretely, the Republicans were given the services of 10 explosives experts, under the command of Starinov who was codenamed *Rudolf Wolf*. Within 10 months the group expanded to 200 Spanish raiders, headed by the resourceful and ruthless Domingo Ungrier. Four subversive units created havoc for the duration of the Civil War, credited with derailing 87 trains. Manuel Belda, in particular, excelled under Starinov's training in laying explosives.

One derailment alerted the world's press and Ernest Hemingway, then a US newspaper correspondent, arrived in Spain to interview the wreckers. Starinov was forbidden by Moscow to talk to journalists, so Hemingway met Ungrier who introduced him to Alex, the young Jewish saboteur responsible for blowing up the train. As Hemingway moved freely around the camp, *Rudolf Wolf* hovered in the background avoiding the photographer whose pictures duly appeared on the front page of a number of New York papers. Hemingway caught the eye of the tall and well-built Russian. He had no idea that he was looking at the most wanted man in Spain with a reward of one million pesetas for his capture, dead or alive. Starinov, recalled to Moscow at the end of the Spanish Civil War, was awarded the first of his two Lenin decorations and permission was granted for up to 300 Spaniards, including Ungrier and Belda, to make their homes in Russia.

Starinov's experience in Spain proved invaluable as the Red Army retreated through the Ukraine. Under Stalin's scorched earth policy, bridges, railway lines and aerodromes were blown up using deadly delayed-action mines. The Wehrmacht feared for their lives as they warily felt their way along the empty streets of every taken city.

The Germans controlled the northern shoreline of Taganrog Bay, the Red Army the south. The ice was so thick that lorries and even tanks could cross without difficulty. Tsyganov, concerned about possible German attacks, instructed Starinov and his engineering team to drill deep ice holes and lay mines. One night the Germans mounted a raid, but the mines destroyed 12 troop carriers with a large loss of life. Those Germans not killed in the explosions, froze to death on the ice.

That failure gave Starinov an idea. He believed that Soviet sappers, more adaptable to the extreme cold, could cross the bay to mine the road from Mariupol to Taganrog, the main supply route for the German, Rumanian and Italian divisions on the Mius. The road was very exposed, surrounded by open fields that in summer were full of ripening corn and wheat but in winter, often impassable due to heavy snowfalls. Garrisons were stationed in the major settlements. The largest was at Budenovsk, on the Gruzski Elanchik River, where fuel supplies were stored. A short distance away was the sandbar of Krivaya Kosa, referred to as 'Crooked Spit' on pre-war Russian maps. The villagers of Krivaya Kosa eked out a living by wading out into the shallow waters of Taganrog Bay to cast their nets.

Troops from the Rumanian 5th Cavalry were the first to occupy the settlement and German troops followed. A large two-story house overlooking the bay was commandeered and a searchlight installed to spot any Soviet military activity on the ice. At the end of the Kosa stood a beacon, revolving every 16 seconds. It acted as a navigation point for the Luftwaffe but was switched off in the evening. In the centre of the village was the lifeboat station. Just outside, on the road to Budenovsk, the brick works provided a valuable source of employment.

More soldiers were billeted in Veselo Voznesenski, five miles to the east of Krivaya Kosa. The road continued to the Mius, where in pre-war days a ferry conveyed its passengers onto the Taganrog peninsular. Now, German engineers had erected a pontoon bridge strong enough to take tanks. The nearby ancient settlement of Lakedemonovka provided the German artillery excellent views of the widest stretch of the river. Not far away lay Nikolaevka, the centre for the military encampment that stretched all the way to the northern edge of Taganrog some 20 miles to the east. Hundreds of tanks were under camouflage, their engines regularly turned to stop them freezing up.

Using intelligence from the Ukrainian partisans and Soviet agents behind enemy lines, Starinov and his fellow officers had a very clear picture of the German Army's strength and location. He advised Lt General Malinovsky in Shakhty, or Comrade Malino as he was better known in the Spanish Civil War, on the intended plan. Malinovsky was delighted with the idea as were Colonel Egnarov, head of intelligence in the 56th Army, and Major Saltykov, head of operations.

Starinov put Senior Lt Nikolay Moklyakov, one of his best men, in overall charge who, in turn, selected a group of sappers for intensive training, including some of the Spanish saboteurs such as Manuel Belda, Domingo Ungrier and Mariano Chico. By the end of January 1942 a team of 80 was in place, comprising eight groups of 10 men.

The team members were equipped with new winter clothing, long white camouflage cloaks and PPSH submachine guns of 7.62 millimetre calibre, capable of firing 35 rounds from one magazine. Vicious-looking sapper knives, wire cutters and grenades completed their kit. In training, communication on the ice proved difficult as two-way radios were in short supply. Instead, flashlights with coloured glass were used.

After the German fiasco on the ice Starinov had rejected any idea of using motorised transport to cross it. Furthermore, engine noise would destroy any element of surprise. Starinov opted for the traditional Russian sleigh carriage, the sanya, pulled by two powerful Cossack horses. Local blacksmiths came up with the idea of fitting metal strips as runners for the sanyas to give better grip on the ice. Women in Shabelskoye sewed together white cloaking for the horses. Fishermen in Yeysk, more used to the winter conditions of Taganrog Bay, advised the sappers to attach iron crampons to their valenki [boots].

Fitness was key to survival. Each man would have to survive single runs across the ice of between 18 and 32 miles, be dropped off some distance from the shore and carry weapons and mines. There would then be the difficulty of a return journey, probably under German fire. Even on the proposed longer runs, a return trip overnight was ruled out of the question. The teams would have to leave during the day and stay out on the ice until nightfall before conducting operations. Blizzards, a regular feature on the ice, hampered movement. Yeysk was chosen as the base and communication centre for the sappers, with Lt Vladimir Kondrashev in charge.

Moklyakov questioned whether prisoners could be taken. Sanyas were not large, accommodating just six sappers and equipment. Starinov instructed that enemy dead and wounded would be stripped of any potential intelligence and then left. Prisoners would be interrogated on the spot, if time allowed, followed by swift execution.

The sappers undertook practice runs, their all-white camouflage undetected by forward German positions. Returning from one such probing mission, Starinov was summoned to the control centre to read an urgent message from Rear Admiral Sergei Georgyevich Gorshkov, the 32-year-old head of the Azov Flotilla. Before the ice had taken hold in Taganrog Bay and the Sea of Azov, two of Gorshkov's motor torpedo boats had regularly patrolled the northern shoreline. The weather was clear as Starinov took off in a reconnaissance biplane sent by Gorshkov, his destination the Russian naval port of Primorsko-Akhtarsk, 40 minutes flying time south of Yeysk. Coming into land Starinov saw the flotilla's warships stuck fast in the ice. One of Gorshkov's senior lieutenants, Tsezar Kunikov, stuck out a helping hand as Starinov climbed out of the cramped aircraft. Major General Tsyganov in Rostov had informed Gorshkov about the planned ice raids and the Rear Admiral suggested that some of his fittest seamen should join the sapper teams. Starinov readily agreed to the proposal and flew back to Yeysk.

The naval ratings trained hard with their new colleagues. The day before the first operation, on February 7, 1942, Moklyakov briefed the entire team in the Yeysk communication centre. Three sanyas were to be used, carrying a squad of 18 men. As Moklyakov handed over to Starinov, the hero of the Spanish Civil War looked around at the weather-beaten faces and grinned at the ever-loyal Spanish contingent. Chiko, a qualified pilot who had relished straffing trains in the Civil War, gave the thumbs-up.

The operation was a disaster, ending in death. The weather had worsened and the ensuing blizzard led to disorientation, with the sanyas becoming separated and one narrowly avoiding a fall into a Russian-mined ice hole dug a month earlier. Belda fell off and was lost in the blizzard. To compound the problems, when the sanyas finally made the steep northern shoreline of Taganrog Bay, the horses became stuck in the soft sand below the crumbling cliffs. German artillery spotted the sanyas and opened fire. The raid was aborted and the dispirited teams returned to base. Belda's body was found three days later, curled up in a ball and frozen solid. Without the benefit of a radio, Belda could make no contact as he had tried to walk back to Yeysk, hoping to be found by returning colleagues. He had fallen into an un-mined ice hole and, unable to climb out, quickly succumbed to the cold. Every sapper stood with bowed head in a howling gale as Belda was placed under a pile of stones, the ground too hard for a proper burial. For the rest of his life, Starinov blamed himself for Belda's death, as he had been unable to provide adequate radio equipment.

Mourning the loss of their comrade, in the following days the sappers hounded and terrified the enemy, sometimes raiding up to six times a night on the Mariupol to Taganrog road. Weapon trucks were ambushed, warehouses systematically destroyed and troop carriers and panzers blown off the road by delayed-action mines placed hours earlier with the sappers halfway back to Yeysk as they detonated. The Germans could do little to prevent the nightly attacks. Artillery fire was random and inaccurate. At one stage the German commanders in Taganrog even formed their own ice saboteur unit, but it was disbanded after two abortive sorties. The sappers took losses but nothing like that expected. Horses recorded the largest death toll, collapsing with sheer exhaustion on the ice. But even dead they had a good use. Cloaked in their white garb and frozen solid, they were positioned as 'dummies' near the shore to be shot at, the sharp stabs of light giving away the German positions.

Within a week the Germans had ceased any nightly movement on the road, spending the days trying to locate and disarm the well-hidden Soviet mines. During one raid a Russian sapper's leg became entangled in barbed wire adjoining a German minefield. Using hand signals he warned his colleagues of the danger and left his boot in the wire, wrapping a scarf around his exposed foot and lower leg and placing a mine in the boot. On a subsequent raid, out of curiosity, the sapper returned to the minefield and found remnants of his boot covered in human flesh. Another dead German had been added to the growing tally. There were celebrations in Yeysk the morning after a raid on February 14 in which two bridges had been blown up near Budenovsk, on the railway line from Odessa to Rostov, causing chaos.

That same day Tsyganov called a meeting in Rostov to review operations. Starinov arrived with Moklyakov, already present were Colonel Egnarov and Major Saltykov. Tsyganov read out Stalin's congratulations to Starinov and his team, and urged even greater success. Soviet reconnaissance had confirmed the extreme hardship in the encampment on the Mius caused by the raids. Furthermore, continued disruption to the supply lines would further delay any German advance towards Rostov and the Caucasus. Tsyganov looked agitated and didn't repeat to those assembled the remainder of his strange conversation with Russia's leader that morning.

Starinov agreed to a raid on February 16, with the sole purpose of taking prisoners for interrogation to find out if any date had been set for the German push. Four sanyas set off under the command of Lt Kozlov, three contained sappers, one ran empty for prisoners. A house on the edge of Krivaya Kosa was the target, based on intelligence from an undercover partisan in the village. Dismounting from their sanyas offshore, the sappers walked the remaining mile to the long sandy spit. The beacon was off, the night silent. Up in the watchtower edgy guards played their searchlight over the ice. Skirting the village the sappers easily located the Cossack house, its green painted shutters firmly closed. Noises could be heard inside. Kozlov couldn't detect how many voices, but he heard Rumanian being spoken.

Kozlov whispered to Sergeant Lipitski, gesturing for a frontal entry. The burly sergeant kicked in the door and was confronted by four Rumanians from the 5th Cavalry playing cards and a startled German sergeant awoken from his slumbers in a chair next to the fire. Lipitski shouted in German for the men to raise their hands, in vain as both table and cards went flying when the Rumanians reached for their weapons. Kozlov raced over to the German, pointing his silenced PPSH at his head. Lipitski had no option but to fire and three Rumanians fell dead, the final soldier pleading for mercy. Lipitski thrust the barrel of his gun into the back of the Rumanian's mouth, but didn't pull the trigger. More sappers burst through the door and frisked the dead soldiers for identification.

With rags bundled into their mouths and tightly bound, the Rumanian and the German were shoved, half running, towards the shore where the sanyas now waited with their drivers. Suddenly there was a commotion as the searchlight in the watchtower burst into light, its beam raking the frozen sea. Bullets smashed into the ice and the sappers fired back blindly at the gun flashes. The beam locked onto the sanyas, but by now the Cossack horses were engaged in their pull, the muscles in their huge necks bulging with the strain.

Egnarov, the intelligence chief, had travelled from Rostov to Yeysk to await the return of the sappers. He heard over the new two-way radios that Kozlov had been successful. In the communications centre binoculars were trained on the ice as the sanyas emerged, the sappers flashing their torches in celebration. Starinov shook their hands in congratulation.

Using Kozlov's limited translation skills, the Rumanian cracked first but offered no new intelligence to Egnarov. A better opportunity was the German sergeant with SS runes on his black tunic. With a wave of the hand the Rumanian was roughly marched out and immediately executed by a single bullet to the back of the head, the body left in the snow to be disposed of later.

The sergeant was given a chair and a cigarette. He, too, was familiar with the crack of a Russian rifle. Egnarov began by offering a prisoner of war camp in exchange for information. Hoping that was the truth, the sergeant was co-operative. He was a member of the LAH, he said, still shivering from his enforced journey over the ice, and had fought in both the capture of Rostov and the retreat. His hand shook as he raised the cigarette to his lips, looking warily around the control centre. Egnarov took his time but soon the German told him about the decision in the headquarters at Taganrog to strengthen the garrisons on the Mariupol to Taganrog road with LAH troops, as the unreliable Rumanian 5th Cavalry and units of the 13th Panzer division couldn't stop the Soviet ice attacks.

Egnarov grinned when the sergeant confirmed that these raids had sorely tested the patience of German commanders desperate to provision their men for the spring offensive. The Luftwaffe was unable to help given the continued adverse weather conditions. Krivaya Kosa, with its strategic importance and extended views of Taganrog Bay, was to be strengthened. Quite voluble now, the sergeant confirmed the strength of the garrison at Krivaya Kosa at 20, a figure that surprised Egnarov – he had expected more.

The interrogation at an end, Egnarov waved his hand to the guard. There was no transport waiting to take the sergeant to a PoW camp. His body was left in the snow next to the Rumanian. That cigarette had been his last.

As the shot rang out Egnarov called Tsyganov in Rostov. An order was given to Starinov to prepare for a raid using the entire strength of the sappers, about 125 men. Starinov questioned the wisdom of such an operation as there were other more important targets, but the decision was not rescinded. Krivaya Kosa was the target, the date confirmed as the early hours of February 23 – Red Army Day, an event to be celebrated by a show of military strength.

Only hours before the start of the raid Tsyganov had a second order for Starinov. Prisoners may be taken and, most importantly, any papers or identification tags found must be collected and sent to him for personal inspection.

It was a beautiful sunset as Starinov walked down to the harbour to wave off the 20 sanyas. The former *Rudolf Wolf* walked up and down the double row of saboteurs dressed in white camouflage with only their eyes visible – a fearsome sight for any enemy. He placed his hand on the shoulder of Ungrier, speaking softly to his comrade. Lt Maloletko, in charge of the raid, ordered the sanyas up to the start line and, on his whistle, every sapper stood to attention and saluted Starinov who had been ordered by Tsyganov to stand down from the mission. In a moment the sanyas were gone, pulled by 40 powerful horses on the 24-mile journey to Krivaya Kosa. Starinov watched them merge into the gathering evening gloom, unknown to him that the attack on Krivaya Kosa was to provide the Soviet Union with intelligence arguably unsurpassed in the entire war.

Out on the ice only the rapid panting of the horses and their muffled hooves could be heard. The sun disappeared, the temperature falling fast to –45°C. Sazalnik Sandbank, some 10 miles out of Yeysk, was the first obstacle passed. For the first time in days, no blizzard blew. Pschani Island, another protruding area of sand, was avoided as was the shipwreck, another landmark. Maloletko knew he would shortly have to signal the sanyas to stop, as the noise of horses' hooves must soon be heard on the shoreline.

The sappers dismounted and began walking to their holding point, weighed down with mines and weapons. At exactly 2am, on the morning of February 23, 1942, the long curved sandbar of Krivaya Kosa became visible. Maloletko checked his PPSH, glancing around him. Some sappers waved at him. The wind had dropped – it would be a great day for a raid.

With no cliffs to scale, the sappers walked directly off the ice onto land. Breaking into a run Maloletko waved the men towards cover, splitting into three pre-determined groups. Sergeant Major Maxim Repin remained with him. Maloletko was glad of Repin's protection. A gentle giant of a man, Repin had already proved to be a very able sapper and popular with it. He was destined to fight with great distinction and courage at Stalingrad.

Two groups moved wide to destroy communications lines. Maloletko's group stealthily made their way between the 'khattas', the fishermen huts, on the shoreline to the houses where the Germans and Rumanians were mainly billeted. Crouching, Repin saw the dark outlines of guards in the open windows of the two-story building that served as the watchtower.

Without warning gunshots rang out somewhere in the village and, within seconds, sirens wailed. Up in the watchtower the guards turned on their beam, frantically scouring the main street and the ice. Repin stepped out from behind the trees, pumping a whole magazine from his silenced PPSH into the searchlight. The doors of the billet homes were flung open and both officers and soldiers ran into the road, their eyes unaccustomed to the dark. Guns in hand they were unaware of how close the sappers were. It was an unequal firefight, the Germans and Rumanians never stood a chance. Explosions were heard, this time on the road to Budenovsk where the sappers had brought down telephone lines. Repin waved to his men to stop shooting, he had heard the sound of an engine but he couldn't place the source. It wasn't the deep roar of a heavy personnel carrier such as the Steyr or Horch, nor a VW Kubalwagen or one of the new Mercedes Benz 170 light personnel carriers.

The saloon car was upon them in seconds, careering at them from around a corner, its headlights on. Repin let loose a volley of fire and the car slewed into a snowdrift, its engine still running. The passenger from the Opel Kapitan ran blindly towards the watchtower, gun in hand, and was immediately cut down. Unbelievably, the driver remained in his seat, his hands on the steering wheel. Years later Repin couldn't explain why he didn't splatter the windscreen as he took aim but didn't squeeze the trigger. The driver slowly got out of the car, hands raised, in a blind panic. He was incoherently uttering a number of Russian names, including the name of a Professor Ioffe. Repin shone his torch into the terrified face of an officer – a major in the SS. Repin couldn't make out the pink piping of the Waffenfarbe and he had never seen the epaulettes before. The sapper pushed the German face down into the snow, ignoring the officer's gesticulation towards the car. Here was our prisoner, thought Repin, and a good one. Starinov will be pleased.

Maloletko terminated the operation, expecting to face reinforcements at any moment from the barracks at Budenovsk that must have heard the explosions. As far as he could ascertain from his radio the raid had been a success, but only one prisoner was a disappointment. It was too soon to assess losses. The sanyas had been brought to the shoreline. Climbing aboard his sanya with his prisoner, Repin looked back at Krivaya Kosa, observing the gun emplacements burning as well as the watchtower that he had torched, the sparks flying high into the night air.

As the sanyas sped towards the safety of the southern shore of Taganrog Bay the nervous tension disappeared and the talk was of an extra ration of vodka and a piping hot meal. The prisoner was quiet, but Repin could hear the SS officer's teeth chattering with the cold. His life will be short, thought Repin, remembering the bodies of the German sergeant and the Rumanian cavalryman still in the snow outside the communications centre. Repin clutched the briefcase he had grabbed from the Opel. His mind drifted off as he contemplated why the car had appeared in the middle of a gunfight. Halfway back to Yeysk, the snow began to fall.

CHAPTER 7

Starinov flies to Moscow

Much needed sleep was interrupted by a phone call from Major General Tsyganov. Starinov had already spoken to Colonel Egnarov before retiring, informing him about the capture of an SS officer with documents and photographs in his briefcase. The prisoner had been locked in a cellar pending Rostov's decision on what to do with him. Quiet had fallen over Yeysk, at least for a few hours. Surprisingly, all the sappers had returned safely from the raid on Krivaya Kosa – bar one. His body, shattered into pieces by a faulty hand grenade, had been left in the snow in Krivaya Kosa. There were no wounded.

Tsyganov seemed very agitated, asking Starinov numerous questions about the raid and the circumstances of the capture of the prisoner. All Starinov could do was to recall the short briefing he had been given by an exhausted Maloletko before he too departed to his billet. Suddenly, Tsyganov fell silent and for a moment Starinov thought the line was dead. But Tsyganov came back on the line and ordered Starinov to return to Krivaya Kosa immediately. Starinov was stunned but dared not dissent. In the past weeks political commissars had ordered the execution of countless officers for disobedience and cowardice in the 56th Army. High rank meant nothing to the NKVD firing squads that went about their task with relish, creating fear in every barrack. In one week alone one in five of the Red Army senior officer corps in Rostov and the surrounding area needed to be replaced as it was massacred by its own. Morale was rock-bottom. The political commissars who filed daily reports into the Lubyanka also feared for their lives, several having being found dead with their throats cut in the back streets of Rostov.

The order to return to Krivaya Kosa to evaluate damage troubled Starinov, even more worrying was that for the first time the sappers would be emerging from the ice in daylight. Lt Maloletko was angry. This was suicide, he argued fiercely. Starinov could only resignedly shrug his shoulders. An order was an order.

Conditions were atrocious as three sanyas left Yeysk. Only Starinov, Maloletko and Repin were aware of the destination, the others would guess as soon as the beacon at the tip of Krivaya Kosa came into view. Starinov shivered. Utter madness, he whispered to himself, ducking his head in a futile attempt to avoid the icy chill as visibility fell to almost zero.

This time the sanyas carried the sappers right up to the spit, risking immediate detection, but Starinov wanted the operation over quickly. The nervousness was visible in the men around him, including Ungrier, who had never shirked a fight in his life. Thankfully, German shore batteries hadn't spotted the sleighs in the blizzard. Nothing moved in Krivaya Kosa. Maloletko and one group provided cover on the road, Repin led Starinov to what was left of the watchtower, now reduced to a near ruin after being torched on the first raid, smoke still visible from the embers in its interior. Bodies lay covered by a thick layer of snow, as was the Opel, its engine now silent. There was no sign of any military presence and the terrified villagers remained in their homes, fearful of reprisals. Starinov could only assume that the road from Budenovsk was impassable with snow and that the Germans were worried about the delayed-action mines.

Wasting no time Repin and his men turned the bodies over, searching for identification and any intelligence missed in the earlier raid. Starinov walked over to the car, both doors hanging open, and Repin demonstrated how the Opel had raced towards them. Both men agreed it was a peculiar episode. Brushing the snow from the body of the passenger, Starinov saw the SS uniform. A brief search of the car came up with nothing new. Time to go.

The return to Yeysk was uneventful and Starinov's men retired to their bunks, exhausted after two raids in less than 24 hours. Sleep was not an option for Starinov. Given the odd phone conversation with Tsyganov he needed to sift thoroughly through everything found in the village on both raids. He wanted to be sure before he made his report, concerned that something might have been overlooked.

He carefully examined the captured German officer's ID, identifying him as Major Hans van der Velde, a member of the Wehrgeologen. What caught Starinov's eye were the Berlin telephone number and the address of the Heereswaffenamt, the German Weapons Office, on the reverse. The ID for the Opel's passenger bore no such detail, even though both men were members of the same unit. Curious, thought Starinov. On the surface there seemed no logical explanation for two members of the Wehrgeologen, a specialist SS group dealing with mining and petroleum resources amongst other duties, to be in Krivaya Kosa. Starinov turned to the stout briefcase found in the car. It was full of maps, mainly of the Caucasus, with some locations ringed. Heavily underlined was the village of Lermontev, north of Stavropol, a location Starinov was unfamiliar with. There were several photographs, landscapes with mountains in the background.

Lying in the bottom of the briefcase was a black notebook, quite thick with a shiny black cover. Starinov flicked through the pages but he couldn't understand the German content nor could he make any sense of the formulae and diagrams. The notebook was crammed with names of people and locations in Germany. Neatly folded in the middle were two loose pieces of paper – annotated drawings of devices, one almost spherical in shape with a bulbous head and a large fin. Tiredness was beginning to overwhelm him.

Tsyganov was attending to other matters when Starinov called so he asked for Egnarov. He, too, was unavailable. Starinov was put through to a lieutenant in the intelligence department and he meticulously itemised what had been found. Now it was time for sleep.

Some hours later Tsyganov called, demanding that no one should interrogate the prisoner. The NKVD would collect him and escort him to Rostov.

Buoyed by the daylight raid on Krivaya Kosa the sappers embarked on several such missions over the next two days. Teasing the enemy, dead horses and wooden tanks were dragged across the ice and left in open daylight for the German artillery positions to locate. As the shells tore into the dummies an even more spectacular operation was being contemplated in Yeysk. Starinov left his sappers to their planning and travelled to Rostov's anti-tank munition facility for a meeting. Engineers from the 56th Army, with help from civilians, had placed 50,000 anti-tank mines throughout the city and in the low-lying flood plain of the River Don. One development would be lethal to the Germans if they overran Rostov; its inventor, Lt Gridnev, called it *Bouncing Betty*. The 152-mm shell, triggered by a radio signal, jumped three metres into the air, exploding and throwing shrapnel in every direction.

On his return to Yeysk the next day Starinov was briefed on the new raid. For some weeks the number of oil convoys on the road to Taganrog had increased, confirming the expected spring offensive on Rostov and the push into the oilfields in the Caucasus. The thaw had set in and German naval units were moving ammunition barges east, with many moored at Veselo-Voznesensk, a short distance from Krivaya Kosa. Under the command of Lt Vladimir Kondrashev, the Russians took advantage of clear skies. Venturing over cracking ice using telescopic bridges they reached the cliffs of the village without discovery. Starinov had been promised a spectacular show just after 5am, when the 110th – and last – ice raid over Taganrog Bay was to begin. He was not to be disappointed.

Undiscovered, the team climbed aboard the barges, silenced the German guards and placed explosives amongst the store of artillery shells. With a huge grin on his face Kondrashev joined in the jog back to the sanyas. In Yeysk, 26 miles away, the Soviet Union's most distinguished and decorated saboteur trained his binoculars towards Veselo-Voznesensk. The time was 5.10am when Starinov saw the bright orange glow on the horizon followed by a roar like distant thunder.

There was no time for celebration as Tsyganov ordered Starinov to drive immediately to Shakhty to see Lt General Malinovsky with van der Velde's briefcase and ID papers. The German officer remained incarcerated in the cellar awaiting his escort. Within the hour Starinov and his driver were on the coastal road to Rostov, passing through the Cossack villages whose inhabitants had so warmly embraced the sappers over the last few months.

In Shakhty Malinovsky was his usual ebullient self and over vodka they discussed the likely timing of the new German offensive. An old-style Soviet officer who had come up through the ranks, Malinovsky knew he could share his thoughts and concerns with a fellow veteran from Spain. After downing the best part of a bottle, Malinovsky ordered his intelligence staff to join them.

Feeling quite mellow, Starinov laid out the contents of the briefcase for everyone to view. Malinovsky asked his officers for their opinions on the maps and photographs. One was aware that some mineral mining had been conducted at Lermontev before the war, but knew no more. Starinov passed the notebook around. There was speculation over the two loose diagrams. Everyone agreed that the strange-looking spherical object looked like a bomb, but nothing like anything in the Soviet arsenal. With regard to the other drawing, no one could hazard a guess as to the function of what looked like small metal cubes, strung together and dipped into a cylinder full of some substance. The German terminology was of no help.

Malinovsky concluded that Moscow should see the captured documents and offered to make the arrangements, including informing Tsyganov. A bed was made available for Starinov and he and Malinovsky shared more vodka, recalling more past experiences. By morning a cable had been received from General Mikhail Vorobyev, the new head of the engineering division of the Red Army – the fourth head of the division in less than six weeks such was the extent of the NKVD purges.

The flight to Moscow in an L1-2, a Russian copy of the American DC3 Dakota, took a bumpy six hours against a head wind. It was late afternoon when the aircraft landed on the bumpy runway at Vnukovo airport to be met by Vorobyev's adjutant. Moscow smelled fresh and welcoming as the staff car sped down Gorki Street to Vorobyev's headquarters near Red Square. Even though the immediate threat of a German attack had diminished there was a massive military presence in the capital.

Vorobyev courteously greeted Starinov and asked for a verbal report on the mining of Rostov and the ice operations in Taganrog Bay, which had been celebrated in Moscow. Starinov pleaded for more explosives, as stocks needed urgent replenishment, before handing over the notebook. Both men laughed loudly when the general joked about the paper compared to the usual poor Russian quality. Glancing at the drawings Vorobyev passed the notebook back to Starinov, with the suggestion that it should be seen by the GKO, Stalin's defence committee. The adjutant provided Starinov with the phone number and the names of the key scientific advisors on the committee, Sergei Kaftanov and Stepan Balezin.

Starinov thanked the adjutant and left the building. He walked past the main entrance to Red Square into the Moskva Hotel, Moscow's largest, where one of the best rooms had been booked for him as befitting a winner of Lenin's top military award. His luggage had already been delivered and a complimentary bottle of vodka left by the side of the bed. Starinov dialled the Moscow number. Balezin answered, he had expected the call. A meeting was fixed for the following morning at Rozhdestvenka 11, one of the GKO buildings located just a short walk away. Starinov rested well, very well, the bed the softest he had slept in for months.

After an early breakfast he decided to stroll around Red Square as he had plenty of time before his appointment. Even under camouflage the Kremlin looked a glorious sight. Russian workers were clearing away the previous night's snowfall from the cobbles. A procession of Army vehicles waited by the checkpoint at the main entrance. Starinov recognised Georgy Zhukov, the Commander of the Soviet

Army, in the lead car. He walked towards St Basil's Cathedral and the frozen Moscow River. Soon after, Starinov turned into Rozhdestvenka. Balezin, the senior of Kaftanov's four scientific deputies, couldn't help notice the impressive double row of ribbons on the engineering officer's tunic, especially the red and the gold of the Lenin award.

Born in the village of Volodinsk, not far from Ufa, Balezin was one of 16 children, of which only nine survived into adulthood. He attended school in Volodinsk and Birsk and, at the age of 13, had fought in the Civil War on the side of the Reds before continuing his education in Ufa. He graduated as a chemist from the Leningrad Pedagogical Institute and moved to Moscow to teach, becoming a member of the Institute of Red Professors; the renowned institution that taught and indoctrinated students from many countries outside the USSR. Before the outbreak of war with Germany he worked with Kaftanov on the management of the USSR's higher educational system with responsibility for the universities. As Germany invaded Balezin insisted on fighting at the front, but was immediately returned to Moscow on the orders of Kaftanov, who by now held a senior position on the GKO as the scientific advisor to Stalin.

Balezin took his time studying the notebook, page by page. He was deep in thought as he viewed the two drawings. After a while he asked Starinov for any clarification he could offer. Starinov shook his head and could only repeat the extraordinary circumstances of the find. Others must examine it, said Balezin, suggesting that Starinov should return to the hotel and take a few days leave.

That was the last time Starinov ever saw the notebook found in Krivaya Kosa.

Three days passed. Eventually Balezin called the hotel, insisting to a disappointed Starinov that the notebook contained nothing of interest while offering his services in the acquisition of the new and deadly plastic explosive for the mining teams in Rostov.

That explanation was far from the truth. Balezin believed the contents of the notebook were terrifying and he didn't need much knowledge of German to understand the formulae or the drawings. From his own experience as a chemist in Leningrad he had been aware of experiments on nuclear fission and was familiar with the term 'atomic' that appeared on a number of pages in the notebook. He consulted Nikolay Zhavoronkov, another of Kaftanov's deputies, for an opinion. There were numerous references to uranium and experiments at the Kaiser Wilhelm in Berlin. Ensconced in a meeting with Stalin, it was only after lunch that Kaftanov heard Balezin's oral report. Kaftanov agreed with Balezin's proposal that further evaluation was necessary and the highest level of secrecy. It was important not to alarm Stalin at this stage if the evaluation was wrong. Kaftanov called Vorobyev, it was time to give Colonel Ilya Starinov a new challenge.

Starinov received new orders. He was not to return south to Rostov and Yeysk, a new command had been found. His involvement with the notebook had terminated.

The remaining years of the war would be glorious ones for *Rudolf Wolf*, the hero of the Spanish Civil War and the ice raids over Taganrog Bay. Starinov was destined to lead thousands of Ukrainian partisans in harassing the retreat of the German Army and his men would blow up or derail more than 200 supply trains. With Hitler staring at defeat in the ruins of Berlin, Starinov was already in the city committing bloody mayhem and terror.

Academician Abram Ioffe, the foremost Russian nuclear physicist of his generation, was summoned to Moscow by Balezin from his temporary laboratory in Kazan. In addition, General Pokrovsky, an NKVD explosives expert, assessed the notebook as did Aleksandr Leipunsky, the reputable physicist who had worked on early nuclear experiments in Kharkov. None were prepared to endorse Balezin's view as the contents were inconclusive, just a hotchpotch of notes. Most certainly the notes detailed some of the nuclear work at the Kaiser Wilhelm, but no more. They dismissed the drawings out of hand, believing it to be impossible that German scientists had evolved nuclear fission to the point of being able to build an atomic bomb or a nuclear reactor.

Balezin wasn't satisfied so he spoke to Georgii Flerov, the scientist who had worked for Igor Kurchatov in Leningrad before the war. He had been aware of the bad blood between Flerov and Ioffe, and had seen some of the letters that the young and opinionated physicist had written to Stalin urging that Russia restart its nuclear research. It was no secret that Flerov had been nominated for the Stalin Prize for his research on spontaneous fission.

Prudently ignoring the comments of Ioffe, Pokrovsky and Leipunsky, and deeply worried after reading the more positive opinions from Flerov and Balezin, Kaftanov knew it was time to give Stalin the disturbing news – but first he needed to further his own investigations.

* * *

'Sergei,' enquired Stalin, sitting in his study talking to Beria, 'what do you have for us? You said the matter was urgent.'

'Comrade Stalin,' replied Kaftanov, 'I am in possession of a German document taken from an SS officer on one of the raids across Taganrog Bay by men commanded by Colonel Ilya Starinov, whose heroism operating in such awful conditions continues to amaze us. The circumstances of the find are curious. To celebrate Red Army Day Starinov's group raided the village of Krivaya Kosa. I must confess I needed a map to determine its location. The village rests on the border between the Ukraine and Russia. For some reason, and no one has yet offered a satisfactory explanation, this officer, probably a scientist, was found in the village during the raid. He immediately surrendered, which is most unlike a member of the SS. I have personally spoken to Major General Tsyganov and Lt General Malinovsky of the 56th Army, and Colonel Starinov himself.

'A briefcase was found in the car that this officer was driving, which included a number of items. The main one is a notebook. Being the excellent and loyal officer he is, Colonel Starinov personally flew to Moscow with this briefcase. I have to apologize for not advising you and Comrade Beria sooner but we felt we needed sufficient time to make an assessment of what was found. Comrade Georgii Flerov and my assistant, Stepan Balezin, concur that the contents of the notebook must be further evaluated. If Comrade Balezin is correct in his initial opinion, this document may be of great value to us. Two separate drawings, folded inside the notebook, are just as disturbing. They may be that of a prototype nuclear reactor and a new bomb with an unspecified destructive power.'

The reaction wasn't the one that Kaftanov expected. Beria glared at him, in obvious disgust at not being informed earlier. Stalin sat at his desk his face expressionless. Kaftanov immediately regretted not allowing Balezin to talk to Stalin and Beria himself. His deputy had offered but Kaftanov, as the GKO's senior scientific advisor, wanted to claim the credit for the find. Stalin broke the embarrassing silence, placing his pipe on his desk. 'Show me Sergei,' Stalin said quietly, stretching out his hand. 'Tell us what you know.'

'Thank you Comrade Stalin,' replied Kaftanov, now feeling more comfortable.

'Within two years Germany will have bombs so powerful they will wipe Moscow off the face of the earth and London with it. The bomb will initially kill tens of thousands of our citizens and many more will die of radiation.

'I will keep the scientific detail to a minimum. Two scientists, Irene Curie and Frederic Joliot, some years ago conducted experiments in Paris. They bombarded light elements – beryllium, boron and aluminium – with alpha particles, creating proton emissions that continued even after the bombardment stopped. In effect, radioactive particles had been created from normally stable atoms. It was clear to the international scientific community that radioactive isotopes could be made artificially – a discovery of enormous importance.

'An Italian, Enrico Fermi, duplicated and developed these experiments using more elements – 60 of them this time, both light and heavy elements. He bombarded these elements with neutrons, electrically neutral particles, discovered in Cambridge, England, by the British scientist Professor James Chadwick. Fermi achieved even better results using paraffin wax in his experiments, which contained hydrogen, and produced a higher emission of radioactive particles. One of the elements Fermi used in his experiments was uranium, the heaviest naturally occurring element.

'The internationally renowned Danish scientist, Niels Bohr, who many of our own physicists have met and respect, further stretched the boundaries of nuclear fission research from his institute in Copenhagen. With the German occupation he is confined to his institute and is in fear of imminent arrest as his wife is Jewish. The NKVD has confirmed that despite the war Bohr corresponds with scientists in Cambridge.

'Our scientists were not surprised that two chemists from the Kaiser Wilhelm

Institute of Chemistry in Berlin were able in December 1938 to split the uranium nucleus. This was pure scientific research, unrelated to any practical aim. The results were published in scientific journals and repeated in a number of laboratories in England and America. There was a worldwide conviction that an atomic bomb was feasible, the question was when and who would be the first?

'As Comrade Beria is fully aware, in 1940 the NKVD and GRU mounted major intelligence gathering operations in England and America to obtain details of their respective atomic research. In our possession in Moscow are documents photographed in our Embassy in London and obtained from several highly placed sources, alerting us to the extent of the British development. The NKVD has a team of officers dedicated to obtaining intelligence, codename *Operation Enormoz*, under Colonel Leonid Kvashnikov. Anatoli Yatskov and Aleksandr Feklisov are working in New York, Washington and in California. In London, Vladimir Barkovsky, the political attaché, has achieved a major success, guided by head of station Anatoli Gorsky.

'A British civil servant, sympathetic to our cause, provided one such document to Gorsky, which was immediately summarised and photographed by Barkovsky. These were the British plans for an atomic bomb and the construction of 36 such devices. This bomb will weigh 10 kilograms and have the destructive effect of 3,600 tons of TNT. Dropped by parachute from a British bomber, the bomb detonates before hitting the ground. The cost of the project, as discussed in the document, is in excess of £14 million.

'At that time, the British believed that a uranium separation plant could be ready for testing within 18 months, its units manufactured by a number of companies including Imperial Chemical Industries. The first bomb should have been ready by September 1944.

'Notice I used the past tense. Britain and America are now working on the project together, building the bomb in the United States using uranium supplied from Canada. Until recently the Americans had directed their nuclear efforts to the use of uranium for the production of energy for power, and not the atomic bomb. That has now changed, with Roosevelt's approval.

'This month, February 6th to be precise, the Deputy Peoples Commissar for Foreign Affairs, Andrei Vyshinsky, received from the temporary British Embassy in Kuibyshev an extraordinary request for scientific co-operation between our two countries. I deliberately use the word extraordinary. Not only have the British asked us to translate our scientific documents into English, but they asked for meetings and correspondence with just a limited number of our scientists, all chemists or physicists involved in our own nuclear programme which has been suspended. Sir William Bragg, head of the Royal Institute in London, wants contact with Professor Ioffe. A Dr Fleming, an engineer I believe, has requested meetings here in Moscow with Dr Stekolnikov, Dr Khariton and Dr Sinelnikov. Two eminent professors from the Cavendish Laboratory in Cambridge are keen to write to Peter Kapitsa.

'As you know from Flerov and his correspondence to you, Comrade Stalin, we clearly understand the principles of nuclear fission and a sustained chain reaction. Flerov and Konstantin Petrzhak conducted pioneering work at the Radium Institute in Leningrad in 1940.

'Let us also remember the event which took place here in the Kremlin, in the Hall of Columns on October 12, 1941, when our scientists gathered for an anti-Nazi rally. The event was covered by both *Pravda* and *Vestnik*, the journal of the Academy of Science of the USSR, and broadcast live on Moscow radio. I summarise what Peter Kapitsa, our physicist of international renown, said to such a distinguished audience: *'We are now provided with new opportunities to use atomic energy, whose use has only been described in science fiction novels. We are posing the question about the use of atomic bombs, which will have an enormous destructive force. Theoretical calculations show that if a present day bomb can destroy a whole city block, then an atom bomb, even small in size, if it is feasible, could easily destroy a large capital city with several million inhabitants.'*

'To date the Soviet work on the uranium question has been limited. The Uranium Commission, chaired by Vitali Khlopin, and the Praesidium of the Soviet Academy of Sciences, agreed and approved our proposals on October 15, 1940, amounting to 1.2 million roubles. The Soviet Academy of Sciences agreed to fund up to 400,000 roubles, the Ukrainian Academy of Sciences, 300,000 roubles, and the Peoples Commissariat for Finance of the USSR, 500,000 roubles. The largest applications submitted and approved were as follows: Radium Institute, 330,000 roubles; Ukraine Physical Technical Institute, 223,000 roubles; Dnepropetrovsk Institute of Physical Chemistry, 78,500 roubles; Mining Museum, Leningrad, 50,000 roubles; and the Biochemical Laboratory of Academy of Sciences, 35,000 roubles. However, all this was more than one year ago. Our work has ceased due to other war priorities and the loss or evacuation of our Kharkov, Dnepropetrovsk and Leningrad facilities.

'I will stop at that point and refer to the prisoner. He is a major in the Wehrgeologen, a specialised SS unit that reports into Himmler's department. As the name implies this unit is mainly interested in minerals, especially oil. Strangely, on the reverse of his ID is the Berlin telephone number of the Heereswaffenamt, the highly-secret organisation in charge of Germany's scientific and military development. That number did not appear on the ID of his dead colleague, also from the Wehrgeologen. On his capture – according to Sergeant Maxim Repin – he constantly repeated the name of Academician Ioffe. At this time we have no idea why.'

'Did you show Ioffe this notebook, I am interested in his comments as to its worth?'

'Comrade Stalin, I did, but Comrade Ioffe has little time for the handwritten notes of an SS officer.'

'And Flerov?'

'He agrees with Balezin. The notebook personally delivered to us by Colonel

Starinov confirms that Germany is far advanced in the design and manufacture of nuclear weapons.'

'Where is this Major Hans van der Velde now?' demanded Stalin.

'Still under close arrest in Yeysk, Comrade Stalin, awaiting collection for interrogation in Rostov,' replied Kaftanov.

'Bring him to Moscow, I want to speak to him personally,' Stalin pointed his forefinger at his trusted GKO colleague.

Kaftanov looked appalled. 'Comrade Stalin, I'm sure that is not necessary. He is an SS officer, guilty of terrible crimes against our people. We should extract everything he knows, torture him if necessary, and then execute him. That could be handled in Rostov.'

Stalin didn't respond, nor did Beria. Kaftanov left to return to Rozhdestvenka. Beria, too, had pressing matters, but he was puzzled. Moments later he returned to Stalin's study.

'You knew the name of this SS officer – how?' enquired Beria. 'I wasn't even aware of his capture.'

Stalin didn't look up, he was busy refilling his pipe. Beria turned on his heel. Back in the Lubyanka he picked up the phone and placed urgent calls to Shakhty and Rostov.

CHAPTER 8

Freedom and discovery

I owe my life to Stalin.

I am Hans van der Velde, and nearly 60 years ago I was captured in the Ukraine. I'm very frail now – my health is failing.

Stalin was in a jovial mood when I saw him in his dacha in Kuntsevo, a suburb to the west of Moscow, on August 31, 1949. It was two days after a momentous day in Russia's often-turbulent history – the exploding of its first atomic bomb. I had been arrested just hours after I had witnessed the test at Semipalatinsk in Kazakhstan. Members of Beria's bodyguard had bundled me aboard an aircraft bound for Moscow. My luck seemingly had run out. I, too, was destined to become yet another victim for the head of the Russian security services.

But not for the first time in my seven years in the USSR Stalin's intervention saved me.

I had been under guard on the long and tiring flight from Semipalatinsk but what awaited me at the base of the steps at Vnukovo airfield in Moscow was completely unexpected. An MGB officer, with two companions from the intelligence organization that had superseded the NKGB, brusquely ordered Beria's bodyguard aside. I was bundled into a car and we sped away across the tarmac. Relieved to be out of Beria's clutches I didn't dare ask where we were going. The car stopped outside a large wooden house, set back from the road and partly hidden by trees. A curious guard detail emerged from a hut, their machine guns at the ready. The officer got out of the car and walked over to them. No one had given chase, and the road was clear. In the guard hut I could see a guard talking on a telephone. Eventually the MGB officer beckoned me from the car and together we walked through the gates.

Never in my wildest imagination did I envisage meeting Stalin again. The first encounter had been in 1942 within hours of arriving at the Lubyanka from Rostov, followed by an interrogation several days later in his conference room in the Kremlin.

The housekeeper took us through the dacha and I marvelled at the highly-polished wooden floors and the fine furniture. Much to my surprise the walls in the hallway were covered with paintings of pre-Revolution Russia. Stalin was seated in the rear garden, under a copper beech, enjoying the warmth of a late summer evening. He waved me over to share his bench while the officer strolled casually back inside the dacha and sat in the study. A maid brought out tea and brandy.

'Velde,' Stalin began, not using my full name. 'I can no longer ensure your safety from Comrade Beria. He believes you fooled me but he can't figure out how and flies into a rage whenever your name is mentioned. From today you are free to leave. You will be given a new identity.'

Stalin looked me in the eyes. This was not the glare of a dictator, an absolutist who orchestrated tyranny on a scale the world had never seen, for he smiled and laid a hand on my shoulder.

'The officer will furnish you with the details,' said Stalin, pointing at him walking around the study viewing treasured mementoes of Russian history. 'He is a good man and carries my personal authority. I am relying on him to get you out of the country safely.'

'Where am I going?' I enquired.

'He'll tell you. But before you go I have something to give to you. Come.'

We walked into the study and from a drawer in his desk he produced a medal.

'This is my highest award,' he declared, pushing it into my outstretched hand. 'Where you are going you will never be able to wear it, but look at it from time to time and cherish the honour. It is Stalin's Prize, in the First Degree, my own personal recognition for what you have done for us – but you deserve more, which is why you have your freedom.' Stalin momentarily faltered. He returned to the desk and extracted a white box, in which he deposited the medal.

'I have another gift, Velde. Don't open it now, only later.'

He shook my hand.

'Goodbye,' uttered Stalin, finality in his voice. He gave a knowing wave of a hand to the MGB officer.

With that he returned to his bench. I remained transfixed. Stalin sat down and looked around his lovely garden before picking up the large brandy that the maid had poured.

The officer, a silent witness to this strange ceremony, was possibly unaware that the recipient of the State's highest honour was a former SS officer. At his feet was a small holdall, mine. Someone must have fetched my things from my room at the top-secret Elektrostal facility in Moscow, which we referred to as Plant 12, the location that manufactured pure metallic uranium for the nuclear project. Farewells to colleagues were obviously out of the question. A sensation of elation suddenly hit me but I wanted to linger longer in this room, taking in the framed photographs of Stalin and Lenin together in their more revolutionary days, when Stalin was little more than a notorious crook striving for political power.

The officer ushered me out and we returned to the car and his vigilant colleagues. I asked where we were going. Nowhere near the Lubyanka the officer joked, we were going to catch a train.

* * *

On that flight from Semipalatinsk, a dusty hovel of a town near to the border with China, my guards had offered me no food or water and prodded me awake if I lapsed into sleep. Beria had boarded the plane last in Semipalatinsk, a sense of triumph in his face, smiling at me over those pince-nez glasses of his.

I had been present at the testing of *RDS-1*, the codename for the bomb, one of eight privileged observers at NP-2, a point six miles south of the epicentre. The date was August 29. A bus had taken the eight of us, all personally selected by Igor Kurchatov, to NP-2, arriving at 2am. Essentially the observation post was merely a deep trench dug out of the sandy soil. We had been told the explosion would be at 7am but it was later changed to 6.30am. At first light we could see the tall metal tower holding the nuclear device with its deadly plutonium charge. I had kept my distance from the other members of the group but I overheard one of the scientists saying it was almost a replica of the American bomb dropped on Nagasaki.

In charge of our group was a colonel from Army intelligence. It was he who had given us final instructions, handing out protective glasses that were to be worn a minute before the explosion and removed after the flash. Shock waves would hit us 20 seconds later and we were to launch ourselves into the trench. A periscope had been crudely dug into the ground.

The explosion was both frightening and wonderful, resembling an arc of electric welding but a thousand times more powerful. After the ball of flame disappeared a column of dust and ash rose, grey-black in colour, rising and rising. Unexpectedly the sun emerged from the clouds. Within seconds the shock wave reached the trench, gathering speed and condensing into the hills of the Semipalatinsk desert. I stood up and stared with wonderment at the mushroom cloud rising into the sky. A second shock wave passed, not so intense as the first, and the wind increased in intensity. The ground felt warm to the touch.

For me there was no celebration. I saw the car coming from quite some distance away, moving at speed. My eyes stung and my face felt as if it had been rubbed with sandpaper as I was forced into the car. Radiation was the least of my worries. Time had caught up with me and Beria would exact his revenge.

I clutched the white box that Stalin had given me. The MGB officer looked anxious as we pulled up outside Moscow's Rizhsky railway station. He and his two companions quickly scanned the concourse but of Beria's men there was no sign. Only once on-board the train did the officer start to relax, in the belief that Beria could challenge Stalin's authority only so far. This was a special Government train, he had told me, its doors and windows sealed. Our destination was Helsinki in Finland. As the train sped through the woods that surrounded Moscow the two guards reported back that the other passengers were civil servants or members of the Embassy in Helsinki. No one untoward was on the train. The MGB officer briefed me about my new life and financial arrangements. He handed over a British passport with my photograph inside.

* * *

The village in England in which I live is dying – just like its villagers, some 140 inhabitants living quietly in beautiful countryside famous mainly for the Doones, a family that terrorised the area in long distant times. For exercise I walk down to the village to buy newspapers, a pretence really. I like to sit on the bench outside the shop and observe the daily life of our little community. On Sundays I like to hear the peal of the recently renovated bells of the Norman church. I made a small contribution to the fund.

My trip to London is the annual highlight of my life in England, a journey I make to the Russian-owned bank in Bishopsgate. The managers stay for a few years before moving to New York or returning to Moscow. The procedure has never varied. Ushered into a waiting room I'm given my customary envelope relating to a long-standing instruction from Moscow to debit an account in London and pay me the sum of £500 in cash on August 29 or the nearest working day. The date was a nice touch, coinciding with the Semipalatinsk test. Years ago that sum had seemed huge but inflation has eroded its purchasing power. That said, the money augments my meagre savings.

Exmoor is lovely throughout the year. Winter is my favourite time, when the European walkers have gone and the village drifts along as it has done for centuries. There is a little lane outside our back door, leading to a gate that is kept locked to stop the sheep roaming. Cold winter chills bite into my cheeks as I trudge up the gentle incline to the top of the first field to the 'kissing-gate'. When the wooden structure was constructed, a small sitting bench was attached to it. I can perch here and watch the Exmoor clouds go scudding by. My dark memories never go away, only death will provide relief. As the day lengthens into evening I slowly tread my way down the hill, wary of slipping on the sodden Exmoor grass. My wife and I have few visitors. We never had any children, a conscious decision I came to regret. I never wanted to be placed in a position where inquisitive children and grandchildren delved into my past.

* * *

My wife looked shocked as I returned from my walk one day in December 2000.

'What's wrong?' I asked, very concerned.

'A man phoned, asking to speak to Major Hans van der Velde,' she barely whispered the name.

'What did you say?'

'I didn't know what to say, but he asked again. Finally I said that you were out. He said not to worry, he will call later. I'm so sorry, he surprised me.' She burst into tears.

He did call back. We stared at the ringing phone, urging it to stop.

'Hello,' I croaked feebly, my hand shaking.

'Am I talking to Major Hans van der Velde, formerly of the Wehrgeologen?' asked the caller.

I said nothing.

'If you are, please believe me when I say I mean you no harm. May I come and see you?' he pleaded with some urgency.

'Who are you?' I whispered.

'A writer. I have been researching into the battles of the Caucasus and the capture of the Russian oilfields in the Second World War.'

'What has that to do with me?'

'I have made a fascinating discovery. I know about your notebook, the 'atomic' notebook, and its secrets.'

I put a hand slowly over the receiver and looked forlornly at my wife.

'Meet him, meet him here,' she said, gently squeezing my hand.

'What day would suit you?' I asked the caller, hesitantly.

'Saturday would be good. I'm coming down from London.'

'OK.'

'I will need some directions.'

'Junction 27 off the M5 will take you to Dulverton. Follow the signs out of the town to the village. We have the little house near the school, by the bridge, you can't miss it.'

The journalist thanked me and rang off. Only after I had put the phone down did I remember that I had not asked him for his name or phone number. He hadn't offered it.

Since the call I had been near to panic. I wanted to cancel the meeting but, of course, I had no number to call. On Saturday morning I was worse than ever. The door to that turbulent part of my life was about to be reopened. I took my coffee and climbed the rickety staircase to the spare bedroom that backed onto the patio. It was a lovely room with a wonderful view of the rockery that my wife had lovingly tended.

For the first few years after arriving in England I had committed some of my experiences to paper, but there was never any genuine intention to write a book. The last thing I wanted to do was draw the attention of the authorities who might look too closely at how I entered the country in 1949.

With my new identity provided by the MGB I was able to find a job reasonably quickly in the printing business, based on the experience I had gained in pre-war years. When anyone had queried my German accent I merely said that I had been born in London of German parents, spending childhood summers with grandparents in Munich. Within a few years I was the sales manager of a growing company in Taunton. As revenue expanded so did my travelling around the country. It wasn't until the 1960s, though, that I summoned up the courage to visit Germany for the first time since I left in 1942, to return to the Eastern Front.

My wife had declined the invitation to spend a long weekend in Berlin and Munich. She felt I needed my own space. After checking into a guest house in Meinekestrasse, in West Berlin, just two doors away from the bar where I had drunk with two dear friends many times in the early years of the war, I had caught an underground train to a station near the Brandenburg Gate. The East German border guards looked down on me from their guard post as I peered through to the Unter den Linden, entry 'Verboten'. Dahlem, with its open spaces and lakes, was in the Allied Zone. I retraced that walk I had first taken all those years ago from the station to the Kaiser Wilhelm institutes. I walked to the Kaiser Wilhelm Institute for Physics, its name still on the front entrance. The facility, once one of the most prestigious in Germany – founded initially elsewhere in Berlin by Albert Einstein – had been renamed the Max Planck Institute. Much of the building was now used by the Free University, established after the war when the University of Berlin in the Unter den Linden, in East Berlin, became the Humbolt University.

I tried the handle on the solid metal door of what was the underground nuclear laboratory in Harnack Strasse. A staff member enquired what I was doing. Flustered, I contemplated admitting that I was a wartime employee. I replied I was a tourist interested in the history of the Kaiser Wilhelm. He informed me that the Americans had sealed the chamber in August 1945, worried about radiation. Some years later the university decontaminated the rooms and converted them into a document storage centre. Offering many thanks I strolled over to the large circular building that had housed the van der Graaf particle accelerator, a valuable addition to the work of the nuclear physicists. I instantly recognised the Kältelaboratorium, the 'cold' laboratory where Dr Ludwig Bewilogua had conducted hydrogen experiments. As the Kaiser Wilhelm's administrator, Bewilogua had hired me in 1939. American military now utilized Harnack House, where I had been given accommodation, as an officers club.

There was so much to see in Berlin, so many memories to rekindle. In the evening I sat in the bar in Meinekestrasse and I raised a glass or two to my former drinking chums, both members of the *Red Orchestra*. Franz had told me on my leave from the Eastern Front in October 1941 that Helmut had disappeared, probably arrested by the Gestapo. The following day Franz and I had met in that airless and smoky bar, somewhere near the Berlin Opera House, off the Unter den Linden. Later I had walked for miles, cursing the suicidal plan that had been outlined. Dear Helmut and Franz, I still miss them. Nursing a thick head I caught the morning train to Munich.

For most West German cities, the 1960s marked the beginning of a new post-war affluence. Despite the aerial pounding in the last months of the war much of Munich had already been rebuilt. Outside the station I caught a cab in the same street where three decades earlier I had witnessed endless buses ferrying Jews and other helpless citizens to Dachau, Himmler's model concentration camp. Swarbing, the district where my father had run his academic printing business, was as lively as it had been in my student days. The name above the print shop had changed. From the other side of the street I observed a group of workers on the steps. One looked familiar. He returned my gaze. He was older but still recognisable as one of the Jewish workers arrested during *Kristallnacht*, the day Jews were made to suffer all over Germany.

I turned away and quickened my step towards the Schelling Salon. The man hesitated but didn't follow. In the bar a waitress informed me that the previous owner of the printing works had passed away shortly after the war, his wife two years later. There had been a son, she proffered, who had gone missing during the war, but was presumed dead somewhere in Russia. With no heir the owner had given over title of the company to his loyal staff a year before he died. Most of the staff had survived the war, and two had returned from Russia in 1955 after 10 years as prisoners of war working in mining settlements in Kazakhstan. From time to time the two came into the bar, she said, but they never spoke of the conditions that they had endured. The waitress enquired if I had known the family. I slowly shook my head, paid the bill and left. I never again returned to Germany.

Now, towards the end of my life, I was about to relive my past to a complete stranger. His car had pulled up outside.

My wife offered tea and we swapped pleasantries about the journey from London. 'Why do you want to speak to me?' I blurted out.

'Very little has been written about Hitler's quest for the Caucasus oilfields and how the Red Army prevented them from falling into German hands. In Moscow a year ago I met up with Nikolay Baibakov, the deputy to Lazar Kaganovich, Stalin's commissar in charge of the oil industry. In the spring of 1942, with great bravery, Baibakov and a team of engineers blew up the oilfields in Krasnodar and Maikop at the last possible moment. They were lucky to escape with their lives. Stalin then handed full responsibility for Soviet oil development to Lavrenty Beria. Digging into those archives I subsequently discovered that Beria played a major role in the Soviet nuclear programme.

'One day I received a phone call from my translator in Moscow. Completely out of the blue he had received a phone call from a retired KGB colonel, now well into his eighties, who suggested I should see him.

'We did meet and to my surprise he spoke excellent English. He mentioned a strange incident in the southern Ukraine in 1942 and the discovery of what he referred to as the 'atomic' notebook. A few days later he provided a telephone number for Colonel Ilya Starinov, a hero of the Soviet Union. Given Starinov's great age it was imperative to interview him as soon as possible. Before he died, Starinov related to me the real facts surrounding the extraordinary incident in Krivaya Kosa.

'So began my new quest, discovering the real truth about how Stalin developed his atomic bomb. While others received every Soviet honour, your role has never been acknowledged.

'If you will allow me, I would like to relate how Stalin achieved his goal, in which you played such a significant part. Your wife may want to listen.'

'And what will you do with your discoveries?' I asked feebly.

The writer smiled. 'Nothing will ever be published or repeated,' he said. 'I can't say why, but you have to trust me.'

CHAPTER 9

Interrogation in the Lubyanka

Beria was angry when he called the temporary NKVD office in Rostov, an austere, grey building in Bolshay Sadovaya, the city's main thoroughfare that had remained remarkably untouched by the bitter hand-to-hand fighting between November and December 1941. Calls were made to Lt General Malinovsky in Shakhty and to Sergeant Repin, in Yeysk, who was astonished to be called to the telephone to be quizzed by the Minister of State Security about the odd episode at Krivaya Kosa.

Perplexed, Beria asked Lt General Pavel Fitin, chief of the NKVD's 5th Directorate, to join him and together they studied a detailed map of Taganrog Bay. For several hours they debated why a German physicist, an employee of Berlin's premier scientific institute, should have been driving around in a saloon car in this particular theatre of the war, and, indeed, in the early hours of the morning. Krivaya Kosa had only limited strategic importance. Essentially it was a garrison village on the road to Taganrog that carried vital supplies from Mariupol. It offered nothing else. When Fitin departed Beria made a final important call. Kaftanov, uncertain as usual of Beria's motives, reluctantly confirmed that only a very small circle of people, mainly scientists, had known about the 'atomic' notebook and the capture of Major Hans van der Velde. Stalin had not been told until the meeting that day. Beria enquired why his office hadn't been told but Kaftanov replied that the issue was a 'scientific' matter that didn't at first sight need the help of the NKVD. Kaftanov heard Beria swear before the receiver was slammed down. Beria was left to contemplate how Stalin had been aware of the SS officer's name.

Events moved quickly. In Yeysk, two members of the NKVD arrived unannounced from Rostov at the sappers' communications centre. With Colonel Ilya Starinov still away, the remaining officers felt reluctant to hand over their prisoner. However, they were powerless to intervene and van der Velde was taken to Rostov, en route for Moscow and the Lubyanka.

Before the Revolution the Rusiya Insurance Company was regarded as the soundest insurance company in the world – more secure than Lloyds. Merchants never queried the word of a Rusiya broker. Later occupants of this imposing building that overlooked Dzerzhinsky Square had more sinister credentials. One was Nikolai Yezhov, the loathsome NKVD chief nicknamed the 'Dwarf', who executed the most savage of the great purges, infamy known as *Yezhovshchina*, in 1937–1938. Beria was head of security in Georgia at this time, perfecting his own murderous skills to such an extent that apparatchiks were forever in fear for their lives. Keen to utilize such talent, Stalin brought Beria to Moscow as Yezhov's deputy. Within months, however, Stalin tired of Yezhov and Beria fulfilled his ambition to become head of the security services in the USSR. Yezhov simply disappeared from his apartment one day, his body never found.

Under Beria the NKVD expanded considerably, the Lubyanka complex encroaching into surrounding buildings. The six-story prison in its centre was mainly occupied by enemies of Beria and Stalin, both of whom relished settling past scores. Most prisoners had no exercise, but for the luckier ones a lift took them, under guard, onto the roof for fresh air and a grandstand view of old Moscow. No one escaped.

There was a strict pecking order governing the use of the entrances to the Lubyanka. The imposing entrance, N1, faced Dzerzhinsky Square and could only be used by the head of the NKVD. Counter-Intelligence staff used N3; N5 and N6 provided general entry. At the rear, N4 was reserved for senior officers only. In the nearby N2 entrance there was a passage to the staff club and to the tunnel that ran under the road leading to the underground killing chamber. Security at the Lubyanka was entrusted to the Border Troops, a specialised NKVD unit.

From his cell van der Velde heard the screams circling the landings in the prison. Following his arrival in the early hours he had been left undisturbed. However, sleep was impossible given the intense cold. His SS tunic offered little warmth.

After what seemed like hours, the cell door opened. A guard escorted him out of the prison into Lubyanka 1, a building full of long corridors and large doors hiding their occupants. A woman came out of one office and stood aghast at the sight of an SS officer being half-dragged down the hallway. She scurried back inside and closed the door. On the third floor van der Velde was pushed by the guard into an office where two bored secretaries sat, trying to look busy. Loud voices could be heard in the adjoining room. Suddenly Beria appeared, dressed in a dark grey suit.

'So, you are Major van der Velde,' he sneered, more as a statement than a question. 'A Nazi has provided us with something useful, I understand. Comrade Stalin has requested that you meet him. Personally I would have spared him the trouble. Your Gestapo friends are exceptional torturers but we have greater talents… but that is for later. First, you are to be entertained in the Kremlin.'

Some 15 minutes later van der Velde and his guards were in Red Square, their vehicle passing through the Spasskaya Gate and under the Kurranty Clock, the timepiece symbolic not just for Moscow but for the entire USSR.

He stood dishevelled in the main entrance of the Kremlin. The minutes turned into hours as the guards awaited the summons from Stalin's office. Inquisitive military men came and went, verbally abusing the captive, some spitting in his face. Van der Velde begged for food but his guards only laughed. His bones ached with the cold, and he didn't rate the chances of his survival.

Finally the order came. With two gun muzzles prodding into his back he was taken through the Kremlin to Stalin's rooms. The Kremlin looked drab with some rooms completely devoid of furniture, their walls showing the dust marks of paintings and tapestries that must have adorned them in peacetime. Windows were boarded up and the glass taped.

At the end of a corridor stood Beria, a murderous smile on his face. A door was open. Stalin from his desk beckoned the German officer, a cigarette in his mouth. Dressed in military uniform displaying the Order of Lenin, Stalin's deformed left hand was tucked into a gap in the buttoned-up tunic. In the weeks holed up under canvas on the frozen banks of the River Mius, contemplating how best to engineer his capture, the thought never crossed van der Velde's mind that he would meet Russia's leader. Beria sat on the settee.

'We will keep this short – I am not used to listening to the lies of an SS barbarian, desperate to save his skin,' snapped Stalin, inhaling deeply. A seated officer translated.

'May I sit down?' van der Velde pleaded. 'I can barely stand.'

'What is this?' demanded Stalin, picking up the black notebook on his desk, ignoring the request. 'Explain.'

'That notebook is mine.'

The two loose sheets of paper fell out on the floor. The translator hurriedly picked them up. Stalin raised his voice. 'What do these drawings refer to?'

'One is a design for a prototype reactor, constructed from uranium and graphite, the other is a preliminary sketch for an atomic bomb. The notes in the notebook refer mainly to the nuclear process and some of the key German personnel engaged in the project.'

'Go on.'

'I'm sure, Sir, you know very well the capabilities of atomic fission. Your own scientists have been working on this question since the early 1930s. Academician Ioffe is eminent in his field, as is Peter Kapitsa. The Physical Technical Institute in Leningrad has been in the vanguard for Russian nuclear research for many years and shares the same international reputation as the Cavendish Laboratory in Cambridge and the Kaiser Wilhelm Institute for Physics in Berlin. Another Leningrad research centre, the Radium Institute, stands comparison with the Kaiser Wilhelm Institute for Chemistry in its work on radium and the properties of uranium. I am also familiar with the uranium isotope separation facilities in Kharkov, Dnepropetrovsk and Odessa.'

'You are well informed,' said Stalin, glancing in the direction of Beria but receiving no reaction.

'I had to be, that was my job at the Kaiser Wilhelm and the Heereswaffenamt.'

'Were you responsible for the ransacking of our institute in Kharkov and the murder of our scientists?' retorted Stalin angrily.

'No, I was part of a unit ordered into the city to locate the laboratories. We had been aware that in 1937 Mikhail Pervukhin, your Deputy Prime Minister, had proposed the construction of Russia's first cyclotron on the site. I understand if you don't believe the word of an SS officer, but I did not participate in either the interrogation of the scientists in Kharkov or the subsequent executions. In charge was Professor Eric Schumann, the head scientist at the Heereswaffenamt in Berlin, with Dr Fritz Houtermanns, a physicist known to your intelligence services who worked in Kharkov before the war. Schumann ordered me to take an inventory, which is exactly what I did. After I left the city a team of engineers dismantled the half-completed nuclear cyclotron, the van der Graaff accelerator and transported them to the University of Munich. The execution orders were given the day Schumann and Houtermanns flew out of Kharkov to Kiev.'

'Continue,' said Stalin.

'Many Russian scientists met with Niels Bohr in Copenhagen. Every year, before the onset of war, Bohr organized weekly lectures attended by scientists from throughout the world. Kapitsa was a regular visitor. Some of your people in July 1939 would have been delegates in Washington at a scientific conference held to debate the issues raised by the Berlin experiments on nuclear fission.

'Hitler has little time for science, despite his order for all the scientists in the country to prepare reports on their respective research. He initially provided a pitiful 30,000 Reichsmarks to fund fission research, a sum nowhere near enough. A conventional war with armies, planes and tanks will win this war, Hitler believes. There are some key Nazis, including Goering, who attended meetings at the Kaiser Wilhelm to listen to what the two main scientists – Werner Heisenberg and Carl Friedrich von Weizsäcker – had to report. More funds were made available without Hitler's knowledge. Since late 1939 the atomic bomb has been a top priority.'

'Assuming that Hitler can build this bomb, where will he drop it?' Stalin interjected.

'Two years ago, in 1940, the plan was simply to build a bomb and drop it on London's Docklands. This would have incapacitated the British for weeks, maybe months. That is no longer the case. The first device is to be dropped on Moscow, its epicentre the Kremlin. Goering wants to wipe Moscow off the face of this earth.'

Van der Velde suddenly felt desperately tired, rocking on his legs. The gun muzzle between his shoulder blades brought him swiftly back to his senses.

'Why would you be so concerned about the fate of Russia?' demanded Stalin, lighting another cigarette. 'The Waffen-SS has massacred its way through our beloved Ukraine, burning our cities and towns – and now an SS officer wants to compromise German secrets? Comrade Beria smells a different scenario. He thinks you are an Abwehr agent, conjuring up such a story to make us reallocate scarce resources from conventional military weapons. Can you convince us otherwise?'

Van der Velde swallowed hard, but his throat was dry. He desperately needed water.

'Germany has committed unspeakable atrocities, but none of this has been my doing, I swear,' he said hoarsely. 'I wear this uniform not through choice. I am a mere technician ensnared into war and with others want to see an end to Hitler's dream. Our nuclear technology must be shared with the Soviet Union. That is why I have risked my life, and I beg you to hear me out. A friend, a good friend, in the *Rote Kapelle*, the *Red Orchestra*, insisted my notebook must fall into Soviet hands and me with it to convince you of the seriousness of the situation your country faces. By now you must have verified its contents or else I wouldn't be here in

Moscow. I would have been shot in Yeysk.'

Stalin stood up.

'Velde, I will convene a meeting where a number of people, including scientists, will interrogate you. If we think you are lying your life will be terminated. I'm sure Comrade Beria will even carry out the task himself.'

The conversation with Stalin was at an end. Stalin left his desk and walked over to one of the large elegant windows, pulling aside the wooden shutter and deep in thought as the snow gently fell on the Kremlin. Van der Velde was returned to his cell, but before the door clanged shut he had an unexpected visitor. Beria pointed two fingers at the German officer, pulled an imaginary trigger, and left.

For several days the prisoner mentally struggled over how he would relate the contrived circumstance of his capture when the time came. He decided that the best course of action was to leave nothing out. The Border Troops guarding his cell were replaced by members of a highly-trained military unit that guarded Stalin, on orders from the Kremlin. Van der Velde was now under Stalin's personal protection, which infuriated senior NKVD officers and Beria. The word had got out that the Lubyanka was harbouring a special inmate. Although meagre, the extra food ration was welcome – but the cell light remained on.

The interrogation took place in the large conference room close to Stalin's office. Stalin sat at the head of the long table, the ashtray full. On his left, Molotov – the Russian Foreign Minister, to his right, Beria.

At the other end of the table sat Kaftanov, alongside him was Balezin. Next to him was Ioffe, the most senior and respected of all Russia's physicists, his work internationally recognised. With other leading figures from his Leningrad institute – Kurchatov, Alikhanov, Skobeltsyn, Artsymovich and Alikhanyan – Ioffe had sent a letter to Molotov on March 5, 1938, complaining that other countries had stolen a march on Russia in nuclear physics. The scientists stressed to Molotov that it was imperative to construct a cyclotron. Molotov agreed, allocating one million roubles to the project. Construction began in Kharkov but had ceased.

Ioffe had his critics, not least the young physicist Georgii Flerov who had despaired at the lack of resources in the country's nuclear programme, now terminated since the start of war with Germany. Flerov believed that Ioffe could have exerted greater influence with Stalin about restarting the project. Balezin had shown Flerov the 'atomic' notebook and had been annoyed and staggered at the level of detail in van der Velde's notes, confirming what he had guessed for months – Germany was well ahead of Russia. Flerov, in June 1941, had been conscripted into the Soviet airforce at Yoshkar-Oly as a lieutenant-technician. In what spare time he had he wrote letters, many of them displaying his anger at the futility of his situation, some sent in desperation to Stalin.

Also present was Igor Kurchatov, dubbed by Ioffe, his former professor, as 'First among equals'. Kurchatov had studied at the Polytechnic in Leningrad before being expelled due to the 'misdemeanours' of his father. He finished his education in Baku, but he soon returned to Leningrad – the centre for experimental physics – to study under Ioffe at the Physical Technical Institute. Kurchatov's first paper was an analysis of radioactivity in snow, which won acclaim throughout the scientific community. In Leningrad Kurchatov was never slow in speaking his mind, forever arguing that the State should not dictate scientific research. With the institute rife with informers Kurchatov was often arrested by the OGPU, the predecessor of the NKVD. Somewhat miraculously, he had survived and held on to his job. By 1930 he headed a department and two years later the Government awarded him a grant of 100,000 roubles from the Ministry of Heavy Machinery and Building for nuclear research. He acquired the nickname 'The General'. With his fame spreading across Europe, Kurchatov hosted seminars and conferences in Leningrad. Already fluent in French, German and English, and regularly reading Latin verse, he furthered his voracious appetite for languages. From time to time he would spend months at the institute in Kharkov.

With each Stalin purge Kurchatov was at risk and in 1936 a special session of the Communist Party criticised heads of industry for lack of effort and progress. The Russian scientists took the brunt of the blame, including Kurchatov. Powerless, he failed to prevent the arrest of many of his colleagues. Many stood trial and were exiled. For Kurchatov any further foreign contact was forbidden. Nuclear research in Russia ground to a halt.

Rejection by his peers followed. Twice, membership of the Academy of Sciences, which carried both academic and financial reward, was dismissed out of hand. Only after news reached Moscow of the Berlin and Paris fission experiments in February 1939 did Russia's premier academic body relent. Back in favour, Kurchatov rebuilt his team that was now accredited with the highest Government priority and funding. The Flerov and Petrzhak experiments, replicating the spontaneous fission of uranium experiments in Berlin, were conveyed to the Russian public for the very first time through *Pravda*, the official Government mouthpiece. Academician Nikolay Semyonov – the first Soviet scientist to win the Nobel Prize – informed Stalin's advisors on the military applications of Leningrad's achievements, arguing that if the 'European Fascists' developed a bomb it would be a catastrophe for Russia.

Upon the receipt of growing intelligence emanating from London, Kurchatov, in March 1940, pushed the Academy of Sciences to form a secret committee to examine the nuclear issues. Under the chairmanship of Academician Vitali Khlopin, from the Radium Institute, its members were the foremost nuclear physicists in the country – Vernadsky, Ioffe, Fersman, Vavilov, Lazarev, Frumkin, Mandelshtam, Krzhizhanovski, Kapitsa, Scherbakov, Vinogradov, Khariton and Kurchatov. The first meeting took place in April and Kurchatov warned his colleagues about the sinister developments in Berlin.

Those views fell on deaf ears in the Russian military. Following the German invasion the nuclear programme was abandoned and Kurchatov's scientists were dispersed throughout the country to work on the war effort or fight at the front. Disillusioned, Kurchatov volunteered for scientific work in the Soviet Navy. The news of the discovery of the document at Krivaya Kosa was a complete surprise to Kurchatov and, as he took his seat in Stalin's conference room next to Georgii Flerov, he pondered why Ioffe hadn't discussed the matter with him. Equally irritating was the fact that he had been excluded from Stalin's meeting with Flerov and Ioffe two days earlier.

Completing the group assembled for the interrogation of van der Velde were the two senior NKVD chiefs, Kravchenko and Fitin.

General Victor Kravchenko cared not a jot for the life of the German. As head of the 4th Directorate he controlled a group of 400 top scientists and technicians specialising in the development of new and deadly weapons in centres scattered throughout the country. Working conditions were horrendous and letters home banned. Breaches of discipline sometimes incurred immediate execution and many died from experiments that went wrong. A loose cannon was how NKVD colleagues described Kravchenko behind his back; but the quality of his international intelligence network was never in doubt, with well-placed agents scattered throughout Europe, America and Japan.

Concerned at the increased level of nuclear research being undertaken in London and Germany, Kravchenko had written to Beria on October 10, 1941, listing many of the research papers his agents had stolen. He stressed the urgency for Russia to immediately restart the Soviet effort, drawing on the experience of Kapitsa, Skobeltsyn and Slutskii. Despite the evidence Beria had rejected Kravchenko's proposal. Disgusted, Kravchenko circulated his report to some members of the Academy of Sciences for a second opinion. Again Beria brushed the proposal aside.

On the day of van der Velde's interrogation Kravchenko feigned other pressing matters, but Stalin insisted on his presence.

A journalist by profession, Lt General Pavel Fitin, chief of the 5th Directorate, the section that ran foreign Counter-Intelligence, had come to the Kremlin that day with an open mind. Before scientific intelligence had become a priority, Fitin's department had had a plethora of other tasks. Prior to the war his agents had chased down and liquidated Trotskyites spread throughout Europe. Fitin loved the ladies, entertaining and sleeping with wives of his officers at his beautifully furnished apartment in Milutinsky, a side street close to the Lubyanka, whenever his long-suffering family was away at the dacha. There were often complaints at Fitin's outrageous behaviour and on one occasion he was formally censured.

The German officer's capture was certainly curious to Fitin. Urgent checks had yielded little from sources in Berlin. As Russia's most senior spymaster he knew only too well that German intelligence had been deliberately laying false trails for the Soviets. Fitin stared in the direction of van der Velde as the prisoner was brought in. He looked gaunt and pale in his SS uniform. Surely not even the Germans were resourceful enough to invent this plot thought Fitin as he transferred his gaze to Stalin at the head of the table.

'Velde,' said Stalin, fingering his moustache.

'Your fate is in our hands. This is the very first time – probably the last – that an SS officer has been provided with such an audience. If we deem you to be a liar, within minutes of leaving this room you will be shot and your body thrown onto the frozen Moscow River for our starved dogs to eat. They will enjoy gnawing on your bones.'

'Where should I start?' asked van der Velde nervously.

'From the beginning.'

Hans van der Velde took a deep breath and looked around him. He felt Beria's eyes boring into him. Stalin lit his pipe, further polluting the already foul air.

CHAPTER 10

Vladimir Barkovsky's London mission

Flying was an obsession and after graduation from Moscow's Machine-Tool Institute Vladimir Borisovich Barkovsky had saved up enough money to fund some flying lessons at a local flying club. For years he had harboured ambitions to be a pilot, and with talk in Europe of another war he hoped that engineering would soon be in his past.

Barkovsky's life took an unexpected turn, however. A letter arrived on June 20, 1939. It was non-specific, from a unfamiliar Government department. But it was an order and it would be unwise to refuse.

Within 18 months Barkovsky would be in London, officially Russia's political attaché at the embassy and, unofficially, a fully trained NKVD intelligence officer specifically tasked with the stealing of atomic secrets. It was the first rung on a ladder that would make him one of the most renowned Russian spymasters of his generation.

The Moscow Metro took Barkovsky that sunny June morning into the centre of the city to an address he has long forgotten, to join 100 equally surprised candidates. All were men of Barkovsky's age group, in their middle twenties, graduates from technical institutes in a city famed for the number and quality of such establishments. Barkovsky kept his own counsel. It was foolish to express opinions to strangers.

Someone called for silence, ordering everyone into a large room to complete a questionnaire. Full family details were required – nothing must be omitted. The first interview was long, so was the second and the third. Each time an interviewer practised in such procedure rigorously tested every answer on political opinion, religion and family. Barkovsky could only guess that an engineering job was on offer. His real concern was the location – rumours had circulated about the new industrial cities opening up east of the Urals. Barkovsky wanted to remain in Moscow to be near his girlfriend Vera, soon to become his wife. Summoning up his courage he asked one interviewer as to the purpose of the selection. The answer was obscure apart from the cryptic remark that, if chosen, he would receive a diploma after a sufficient period of training. Finally, the exhausting day was over. On his departure Barkovsky was told that he would be contacted if needed.

Within days another letter arrived, again vague as to its purpose but confirming that the selection committee had been impressed. There were to be no more interviews, merely an instruction to assemble at a given time and place in Moscow.

Throughout Europe men mobilised for war. Germany, Britain and France courted Russia, with its huge Army but of an unknown size. The British, with an Army less than half the size of the French and much smaller than the 2.5 million men under arms in Germany, felt particularly vulnerable and Churchill pushed hard for an alliance with Stalin. In Moscow convoys of lorries rumbled down Gorki Street to unknown destinations. Even for Muscovites used to Stalin's purges and sudden arrest there was an extra frisson in the air. Queues lengthened outside official stores as the capital's citizens stocked up with foodstuffs with what little money they had. Barkovsky duly arrived at the assembly time, as did 19 others, to find two lorries waiting. Everyone was excited, but their accompanying NKVD officer was not prepared to offer any clues as to their destination. The lorries drove south into the suburbs of Moscow and pulled up 12 miles later, in Malakhovka, outside a two-story building surrounded by wire fencing with guards and dogs patrolling the perimeter. Passers-by lowered their eyes and walked on quickly. Malakhovka, the NKVD officer training school, was to be Barkovsky's home for a year.

It was the greatest day in his life, Barkovsky recalled 60 years later. Flying had been an ambition but he would have settled for a mundane engineering career, even as a machine-tool operator. Training began that day, accompanied by yet more interviews and testing for languages. He failed miserably at English, doing passably better at German, his second language at school. The 20 recruits were split into four groups of five, each specialising in one language only. A very surprised Barkovsky found himself in the English group. The other groups were French, German and Spanish.

Proficient NKVD tutors informed Barkovsky that he was expected to learn English to a moderate standard in a matter of months. Each day was tiring and intensive. Barkovsky's group was lectured on English customs, politics and constitution as well as English literature. Lt General Pavel Fitin paid a series of visits to review his new intelligence recruits and was impressed by Barkovsky.

Combat or physical training didn't figure in the programme, considered unnecessary for NKVD operatives who were expected to blend into their surroundings and culture. It was standard NKVD procedure never to wear uniforms, except for official Soviet functions where Barkovsky would be wearing the uniform of a Soviet political attaché. Former NKVD agents with experience of both London and Washington taught the recruits well-tried methods for making contact, including 'dead letter drops'. Photography was another skill taught at Malakhovka and, again, Barkovsky excelled with a German-made 35-mm Leica, the best camera available at that time. Barkovsky became friendly with a colleague in the English group, Pavel Yerzin.

Guest speakers complemented the comprehensive training. International relations, especially the economic situation in the United States that was recovering from the Wall Street Crash, was debated by the recruits. Leave was rarely granted, but permission to spend Sundays with friends and family, returning in the evening, was allowed. Inquisitive and inevitable family questions were met with excuses, or just silence. Barkovsky had taken the NKVD oath; not even family could be aware of his impending role. The months flew by as the recruits honed their new skills. Graduation loomed and there were no failures. Members of the English group were posted to mainly desk jobs in Moscow, to await assignments; Barkovsky taking up a temporary position at the Ministry of Foreign Affairs, in the English department. Within a month he and Yerzin were summoned to the Lubyanka to see Fitin and given their orders – London beckoned. Barkovsky would go first, followed by Yerzin a month later. The London *rezidentura* had had a turbulent history, culminating in the purging of its two NKVD *rezidents* in 1938. Beria, believing that the station was a 'nest of Trotskyites', recalled Adolf Chapskri, head of the *rezidency*, and his colleague, Grigory Grafpen. On arrival in Moscow they were arrested and imprisoned in the Lubyanka. Chapskri was executed in the underground killing chamber, but Grafpen was spared the bullet in the head and was dispatched east to an overflowing labour camp, only released years later. With war looming Beria had a change of heart and put the London station back into operation under Colonel Anatoli Gorsky, who controlled Kim Philby, Anthony Blunt, Guy Burgess, Donald Maclean and John Cairncross – the 'Cambridge Five'.

With little time left in Moscow Barkovsky continued his English studies. Such a high-profile posting frightened the new political attaché. Fitin briefed Barkovsky on his role as an intelligence agent for the most secretive unit within the NKVD.

The Science and Technology Department – the STI – had long-established origins, dating back to when Lenin needed Western technology to rebuild Russia's industrial base after the devastation to the economy caused by the Great War. Lenin had no desire to pay for such knowledge and insisted on stealing it. The All-Union Economics Council, VSNKH, was told to acquire industrial secrets from Europe and the United States by whatever means necessary. This agency bypassed official channels of communication and stolen material was evaluated by the newly-established Academy of Sciences. It wasn't long before the STI was established and by 1920 cells operated throughout Europe, North America and Japan. Recruitment policy changed and only graduates with scientific and engineering backgrounds became STI officers.

On Lenin's death in January 1924 Stalin, as the new head of the Soviet Central Committee, allocated greater resources to the intelligence services – especially the STI. In the years leading up to the outbreak of the Second World War the flow of scientific intelligence to Moscow had turned into a flood.

With so much material Stalin and Molotov insisted on short summaries. One such summary in 1936 reported more than 500 stolen documents on aircraft technology, radio engineering, chemical discoveries and warship design. London was the most lucrative hunting ground for STI activities, followed by Berlin and New York. In 1937 a document passed to Gaik Ovakimian, the senior NKVD *rezident* in the US and codenamed *Gennady*, greatly excited Moscow's chiefs. A US Navy scientist, a lieutenant commander, met an STI agent in a bar in New York and passed over the top-secret plans and designs for America's liquid-powered rocket programme. At the time Russia was many years behind America in rocket technology. Within days the report had been photographed and dispatched to Moscow in the diplomatic bag. Ovakimian had been in the US since 1933, operating from the Amtorg Trading Corporation, the largest of the clandestine Russian companies. There were three others – the Soviet Trading mission, the Tass news agency and the World Tourists Corporation. The FBI arrested Ovakimian in May 1941.

Copenhagen was equally productive. The Niels Bohr annual summer seminars attracted the cream of the world's physicists, chemists and mathematicians. They sat like students on wooden benches and debated nuclear theories and discoveries. Contact was made with delegates who displayed Communist sympathies and a number became NKVD or GRU agents.

The news from Berlin about the Hahn and Strassman nuclear fission experiments conducted in December 1938 had shocked senior STI officers, coupled with the knowledge that international scientific journals had suddenly ceased coverage of nuclear issues. Intriguingly, the names of regular editorial contributors disappeared from the mastheads and contents pages of such publications. Nuclear science was no longer in the public domain, scientific papers dried to a trickle.

In the Lubyanka the NKVD established a specific STI operation, *Operation Enormoz*, to obtain nuclear intelligence. Leonid Kvashnikov, an engineer by profession and codenamed *Anton*, was chosen as its head. In the US STI officers Anatoli Yatskov, *John*, and Aleksandr Feklisov, *Calistratus*, were designated to plunder secrets from the laboratories and universities. England awaited Barkovsky to play his role as *Jerry*. He would not be aware that the GRU, Soviet military intelligence, was already running Klaus Fuchs, the German-born physicist, at the University of Birmingham.

In the weeks leading up to his departure Barkovsky studied the daily military intelligence from London. The expected invasion of Britain had failed to materialise, the Germans beaten by the weather in the English Channel and lack of air supremacy. America had offered limited financial and munitions assistance, believing a German victory was imminent. That said, the RAF, for months battered by the Luftwaffe, was fighting back. In October 1940, 484 raids on 200 targets were mounted on German and enemy-occupied territory and a further 380 in November. The Commonwealth had rallied to the mother country – the Canadians providing over 200,000 men, Australia and New Zealand, 350,000 and India in excess of half a million men. South Africa provided 100,000 men in uniform.

Molotov lectured Barkovsky on Soviet foreign policy towards Britain. The Soviet Foreign Minister explained to him that Britain was on its knees but its Prime Minister – Winston Churchill – was made from a different mould to Neville Chamberlain his predecessor. Under Churchill, Molotov said, Britain would fight to the bitter end.

* * *

Almost two generations later Barkovsky's name was added to the select list of operatives recorded on the large stone plaque in the history room of the Lubyanka, the highest KGB honour. From the time he arrived in England in 1941 to his departure in 1946 Barkovsky established a network of 20 contacts supplying scientific intelligence. Much of this material related to the nuclear programme. There were rings in Birmingham, Cambridge, Oxford, Liverpool and London – mainly in the universities that supplied the scientists, engineers and technicians to the war effort. Barkovsky helped in the control of agents with the codenames of *Moor, Alkit, Ellie, Agent D, List, Pirate, Valet, Scott* and *Malone*.

After London, Barkovsky had two spells of duty in the United States. From 1949 to 1950 he was commissioned to work in the Washington Embassy; he remained in the capital for less than a month before being sent to New York. These were trying times for the Soviet Intelligence services. The treachery of Fuchs had been discovered, as had Theodore Hall, the youngest scientist employed at Los Alamos. Fuch's confession led the FBI to Julius and Ethel Rosenberg, Harry Gold and others. Barkovsky and three other KGB operatives were hastily recalled to Moscow, the KGB angry that some of its best agents in the US had been discovered. The organization conducted an enquiry and Barkovsky was cleared. This period coincided with purges within the KGB, with officers urged to testify against each other. Many officers lost their rank and were given menial tasks in the new industrial cities or the labour camps. For Barkovsky, however, his star continued to rise. In 1956 he returned to New York as KGB *rezident* for seven years, spent mainly replenishing the huge losses caused by the defection of Elizabeth Bentley who had defected to the FBI in 1948.

From 1963 to 1969 Barkovsky was deputy head of the STI department, in control of KGB scientific espionage in the Western Hemisphere. This was a period of enormous gain to the Soviets throughout Europe and the US. Civil servants, scientists, politicians and journalists were targeted as recruits. In his role as grand spymaster Barkovsky became reacquainted with *Valet*, now an advisor to large corporations and to British Prime Ministers. *Valet*, one of the highest placed agents the KGB had ever recruited, had become the puppet master in charge of the circus.

CHAPTER 11

Early years – Munich and Berlin

Within weeks of starting at the University of Munich Hans van der Velde regretted his decision to study theoretical physics. However, he persevered. At school he had enjoyed science and maths, but it was only because his father was a printer of scientific papers for the university that he had chosen the course. Although Hans had been born in Munich his parents were of Dutch origin, emigrating from Amsterdam the year before the onset of the Great War. The family business almost collapsed years later when in 1923 hyperinflation reached its peak of 4.2 trillion Reichsmarks to the US dollar; only regular work from the university helped it survive. The van der Velde home was in Schwabing, close to the printing works. Located north of the city and close to the university, the area was frequented by artists and students throughout the 1930s. With Hans an only child, his mother fussed over him. His father quietly longed for retirement, hoping that his son might eventually take over the business.

Schwabing offered Hans many attractions. Billiards at the Schelling Salon in Schellingstrasse, in particular, was a favourite pastime – played on French tables with no pockets, unlike the more common English version. In the late 1920s Adolf Hitler and his friends were regular customers, not to play billiards but to talk National Socialism. The proprietor, Englebert Mehr, asked Hitler, Ernst Röhm and others to drink elsewhere when credit remained unpaid and bills mounted. A generation earlier, Lenin, who had apartments in both nearby Querstrasse and Kaiserstrasse, enjoyed frequenting this renowned Munich drinking spot that had been named after the German philosopher Friedrich Wilhelm Joseph von Schelling, who died in 1854.

Maria, a fellow student, was both a girlfriend and long-time companion for Hans. While he was quiet, Maria was quick-tempered and often loud in expressing her opinions. But she was beautiful and his parents hoped that after graduation the couple would marry. Fluent in French and English, Maria studied Russian and was already displaying a mastery of the language. Home was a grand house in the affluent suburb of Grünwald. Her father, an industrialist, had directorships in several German chemical companies; her mother was long dead.

Students revelled in Schwabing's bars. Munich was the political hotbed of the new Germany that had grown out of the Weimar Republic, the post-war system of Government that had finally collapsed in 1933 bringing Hitler and his National Socialists, the NSDAP, to power. Marching songs were sung with great gusto, especially the Horst Wessel song 'Raise High the Flag', a celebrated number adopted by the NSDAP to commemorate a poem written by a murdered party member. Another favourite was 'Erika', which began 'Auf der heide blüht ein kleines blümelein und das heisst Erika', loosely translating as 'On the moor is a little flower called Erika'. Maria loved singing that song.

In the Schelling Salon NSDAP supporters eagerly read first editions of the *Völkischer Beobachter*. Once an independently minded newspaper its headlines now screamed hatred for the Jews. The Ulter Simpl pub in nearby Törken Strasse attracted more liberal students who read *Simplicissimus*, the Munich-based satirical magazine that enjoyed a wide circulation. With its traditional bulldog drawing always on its cover, the editorial and lampooning cartoons of Hitler and his henchmen infuriated the NSDAP. There was real dismay when it closed after the Nazis imposed strict editorial censorship throughout the country.

Hans graduated in 1934, pleasing his father by agreeing to lead the sales team in expanding the business into other university cities. Selling came easily to him and new contracts were won. Extra staff were hired and a new state-of-the-art Heidelberg press installed. The travelling was tiring and Hans spent few weekends with Maria. Increasingly she spent weeks away in Moscow, accompanying her father on his business activities, acting as translator.

Munich's hauptbahnhof, the city's central railway station, was already packed when Hans arrived to catch the early morning train to Nuremberg one balmy early September day in 1935. He cursed not cancelling his appointment. Hitler was in Nuremberg at the annual rally of the NSDAP, known as Party Day, and the city would be packed. Rallies had been held in Nuremberg in 1923, 1927, 1929 and then each year from 1933. Deciding to take a later train home Hans joined the throng making their way to the Reichparteitagsgelände. This was the rally area where Hitler Youth, members of the SA, the SS, various German regiments and other organisations such as the Labour Corps, some 100,000 in total, had gathered to hear Hitler speak.

Wagner blared out over the public address system as those on parade marched and wheeled while awaiting Hitler's arrival. Newsreel cameramen captured the intensity for their domestic and international audiences and giant Nazi swastikas and banners festooned the stage. This was Hollywood, German style, with many more extras. Hitler arrived in his open top Mercedes to a fanfare, surrounded by his SS bodyguard, the Liebstandarte Adolf Hitler, known as the LAH.

Hitler's speech was amplified around the Reichparteitagsgelände, confirming Nazi policy on citizenship, race and the purity of the nation. Goebbels and Himmler also addressed the fanatical audience. Day turned into night, with a torchlight procession at one stage resembling a huge Hakenkreuz, the swastika. The rally ended with a breathtaking firework display. Hans disagreed with the political message, but he couldn't help but feel enthralled by the sheer spectacle – Hitler was a showman and his adoring public loved him.

Hans was to come face to face with the Fuhrer seven months later in a meeting that, unbeknown to him, would change Maria's life forever.

The date was April 16, 1936, and Hans had driven his parents and Maria to Lake

Walchensee, on the road to Garmisch-Partenkirchen, for lunch at the famous Café Bucherer. Maria, home after a long trip to Leningrad, had insisted on coming so Hans collected her from Grünwald. She wasn't ready when he arrived so Hans struck up a conversation with her father, enquiring about life in Moscow and Leningrad under Communism. He was an old-school German, lucky to have come through the Great War alive. The long-retired colonel described Stalin's new ideas about re-invigorating the Russian economy and the introduction of the first five-year plan that offered fantastic opportunities for foreign firms in providing machine tools and the latest technology. German intellectuals, like those in Britain such as George Bernard Shaw, openly welcomed Stalin's efforts towards modernisation.

The Café Bucherer, often frequented in the evenings by rowdy and arrogant SS officers from the training school in Bad Tölz, backed onto the lake offering stupendous views. That spring day the sun shone and the lake appeared emerald green. With such fine weather Anna Bucherer, the owner, put chairs and tables out on the lawn for the first time that year. Her daughter, Norma, and Gretel, her young niece, laid the tables. Hoping for some good custom Anna had baked extra cheesecake, a house speciality. The Bucherer family had owned the coffee shop since 1927 and it was a favourite spot in this part of Bavaria.

The good weather had brought other unexpected guests to the Café Bucherer. Maria was chatting to his parents in conversation when Hans saw the convoy of vehicles slow and halt outside the café. The heads of all the diners on the lawn swivelled towards the road as SS men leapt from the front two vehicles. Hans recognised them as the LAH, conspicuous in their black uniforms with a badge on the left arm, a shield with a key in the middle. Also recognisable was the huge Mercedes with its three occupants. Hitler emerged first, followed by Heinrich Himmler and Reichsjugendfuhrer Baldur von Schirach, the head of the Hitler Youth movement who knew the café well as he owned a lake-side chalet in nearby Urfeld. Anna, terrified, stared at her unexpected guests.

Hoffman, Hitler's photographer and personal assistant, strode towards her, demanding a table with privacy. Thinking quickly Anna offered the party the veranda, which overlooked the lawn. She could only peer down at her feet in apprehension as Hitler walked past, waving at the other astonished guests before climbing the stairs. Hans had read in the Munich paper that Hitler was to visit the city from Berlin for talks with NSDAP party officials.

His parents sat paralysed in their seats, witnessing the new arrivals being seated in the veranda right above them. Maria, as usual, took it all in her stride and carried on talking but could not resist glancing upwards in Hitler's direction. Hoffman hurried off into the kitchen to provide clear instructions on the Fuhrer's dietary requirements. No alcohol must be offered as Hitler wanted water and, as a vegetarian, he preferred a plain salad. Himmler got up from his seat and strolled to the edge of the lawn, smiling at everyone – but no one had the courage to smile back at the head of the SS. Norma greeted Hitler with a hushed *'Sieg Heil'* and checked that the table was properly laid. Hitler spoke to her, courteously asking her name.

Maria's voice could easily be heard on the veranda, chatting about her travels with her father. Hans' parents, however, were desperate to leave. Tucking into his salad Hitler laughed and joked with von Schirach who had just returned from a month-long trip encompassing 11 German cities, starting in Berlin and ending in Garmisch, whipping up support for the Hitler Youth. The chubby von Schirach tucked into the cheesecake, but Hitler declined a slice offered by Norma. Himmler picked at his meal, not really entering into the conversation and more curious about the lovely woman below him who was regaling her party with stories of Stalin and Russia.

After what seemed an eternity to Hans, Hitler's party made moves to leave. Hitler chided Hoffman into paying the bill and leaving a decent gratuity. As a memento to the Café Bucherer he signed the official photograph of himself that hung on the wall, adding an appreciative remark and dating the photograph April 16, 1936. Hitler stood up and looked over the veranda. In that moment he caught the eyes of Hans. He looked at him again, but this time Hans had hastily turned towards the mountains. Maria saw it though and grinned back, ruffling her long hair with her hands in her usual seductive manner. Ambling back to the Mercedes Hitler turned to savour the view a final time, looking at Maria once more. He said something to Himmler before climbing into the car.

Inside the café the collective sigh of relief turned into a babble of noise. One customer rushed onto the veranda to sit in the chair Hitler had just vacated. Days later an inscription was crudely painted on the reverse of the chair to commemorate the visit, but a souvenir hunter promptly stole it.

The next two years flew by as Hans increasingly spent time in Berlin seeking extra revenue for the printing works. To much of the German lower and middle classes Hitler could do no wrong, but to Hans and his parents he was a political bully and they were disturbed by the rumours emanating from nearby Dachau. The Anschluss, incorporating Austria into Germany, had met with universal approval in greater Germany after a plebiscite recorded that 99 per cent of the population agreed with Hitler's actions.

There was a distinct buzz in the air one January morning in 1938 as Hans walked through the Brandenburg Gate, the triumphal archway through which Napoleon Bonaparte had marched with his victorious soldiers in 1806 and Otto von Bismarck with his in 1871 following the Prussian victory over France. He had an appointment at the Friedrich Wilhelm University, further down the tree-lined Unter den Linden, opposite the State Opera House.

Hans hovered outside the Adlon, on the corner of Parisier Platz, promising himself that one day he would treat Maria to afternoon tea at the city's finest hotel. Rolls Royce and Mercedes cars cluttered the entrance. In the university, students wearing the uniform of the NSDAP excitedly raced around the corridors. Hans had once witnessed a student being assaulted for not wearing the uniform but he had refrained from seriously intervening as several burly young men jostled him away. On this occasion Hans was told that during the afternoon the Unter den Linden was to be closed, to mark the annual anniversary of Hitler becoming Chancellor, and the students were excused lectures. After lunch with his business contact Hans joined the crowds to watch the goose-stepping LAH and witness Hitler, with Rudolph Hess by his side as usual, take the salute.

Back in Munich Hans passed over the newly signed contract and related the news from Berlin. His parents, aliens in Germany, were continually worried that Germany seemed obsessed with racial purity. Often they considered a return to Amsterdam but were reluctant to leave behind a company so painstakingly built up.

As that year progressed Hans travelled the country on business, but he could never forget the night of Wednesday, November 9. Staying overnight in a boarding house near the Unter den Linden he awoke to the sound of gunfire and ran into the street to see trucks full of SS and SA race past. Close by two SS smashed a shop window on which 'Juden' and the Star of David had been crudely daubed. The mayhem continued until dawn. This was *Kristallnacht* or *Reichkristallnacht* as the German newspapers referred to the event. Berlin awoke to a pall of smoke hanging over the city. Every synagogue had been looted or destroyed. The two largest, in Fasanenstrasse, near the Kufurstendamm, and in Oranienburger Strasse, were completely gutted.

A German diplomat, Ernst von Rath, the third secretary at Germany's Embassy in Paris, had been gunned down the previous day by Herschel Grynszpan, a 17-year-old Jewish boy. Hitler had despatched Dr Karl Brandt, his own personal physician, in a fruitless bid to save the life of the wounded diplomat. The news of von Rath's death reached Hitler as he was enjoying lunch at the Hotel Vier Jahreszeiten in Munich with NSDAP colleagues. Himmler and Goebbels cynically used the assassination as an excuse to let SS and SA thugs loose to systematically destroy more than 7,000 Jewish businesses throughout the country.

Later that day, on a noisy train to Munich, Hans heard more about the night's events from other passengers. Berlin Radio, expressing not the slightest remorse, broadcast that Jewish owners would have to pay for the damage themselves. On arrival in Munich the full realisation of what had occurred hit Hans. In the past four years he couldn't help but notice the extra trains from Munich to the picturesque town of Dachau, home of numerous landscape painters, and the growing presence of SS guards and their dogs on the platforms herding frightened passengers into the carriages. Hans, in common with other Munich citizens, had heard that the camp at Dachau was being utilized for 'political undesirables'. After the events of *Kristallnacht* Munich station was packed – not with commuters and tourists, but with frightened families with screaming children, old and frail men and women, the Jews of the city. Over the din Hans heard someone shout his name, a senior employee from the printworks, but the worker was swiftly bundled into an overflowing train.

Outside the station, in Arnulfstrasse, further chaos ensued as scores of buses transported Jews up Dachauer Strasse to KL Dachau, the Konzentrationslager built in the marshland.

As quickly as he could Hans ran to the printing works but found it locked. At home he found his mother crying. Ashen-faced, his father described what he had witnessed in Munich, including the arrest of his five Jewish workers who were taken to Dachau. In the streets broken glass littered the pavements and blood flowed like rivulets. At the university, where Jewish lecturers had been taunted for years, students had rampaged and beaten up anyone they believed was of the faith. Swimming pools, libraries, restaurants, bars, even park benches were now forbidden to Jews. The *Völkischer Beobachter* loudly proclaimed Germans as 'Herrnvolk', or 'Master Race', and that all Semites were inferior.

In the following days Hans witnessed further anti-Jewish activity. The trains to Dachau increased, now leaving from a dedicated platform with nosy bystanders kept away. The civilian authorities in Munich didn't oppose the outrage and most citizens were now fully aware of the true purpose behind the growing camp that needed more local labour to expand its facilities.

Maria was in Leningrad during *Kristallnacht* but Hans hoped that he might enlist the help of her father, by using his connections, to secure the release of the five print workers. When she returned to Munich she was aghast at the turn of events, but declined to see Hans despite the urgency. More than ever Hans was convinced that their relationship had cooled. In recent months Maria seemed distant when they went out together, no longer engaging in political conversation and never once confiding in Hans about the nature of her Russian visits. Furthermore, Maria felt disinclined to meet in Schwabing where they might bump into old friends.

Finally, Maria returned one of his desperate phone calls and Hans suggested they meet at the Rheinischer Hof. That evening, sitting in the hotel's empty coffee lounge, Hans was horror-struck as he saw Viktor Lutze, the burly chief of staff of the SA and successor to the murdered Ernst Röhm, entering the lobby. The waiter whispered to him that the leadership of the Sturmabteilung had unfortunately adopted the hotel for its meetings.

Hans buried his head in a newspaper, contemplating leaving, but he decided to remain. An hour later Maria showed up, flustered and looking tired. She told Hans that she had to catch the midnight train to Berlin, declining to say why. Over a brandy, Maria asked for news on the print workers. Hans replied that every request to see them had been rejected. Maria then threw Hans with her knowledge of the German Konzentrationslager system. Many camps, she explained, had been built since 1933 primarily for the imprisonment of political dissidents, Left-wing adversaries, liberals, union leaders, Catholic priests and Jews. Small camps were closed during 1935 as six were considerably expanded – Dachau, Lichtenburg, Sachsenhausen, Esterwegen and two in Berlin, Oranienburg and Columbia House.

Buchenwald had opened in 1937, followed by Mauthausen and Flossenberg. Maria reported another Berlin camp was under construction at Ravensbruck, for women only. Himmler planned further camps. Dachau, the model for the concentration camp system, now had 35 feeder camps in the Munich area, as far south as Bad Tölz and Tutzing.

Maria glanced at her watch and pulled on her coat. She asked for the names of the five print workers in Dachau, promising to give them to her father when she next saw him. Hans kissed and hugged her but she gently pulled away, said good-bye, and disappeared into the night. That was the last time he would ever see her.

A week later Hans' father received a curt phone message from the Dachau commandant's office, instructing him to be at the railway station within the hour. Not knowing what to expect, Hans drove his father to the station. A train pulled in, the regular service from Dachau, and the occupants alighted, including his father's employees, looking sullen and gaunt. They had been released without any explanation and given fresh clothing.

After initial reluctance, as a release condition included no discussion with anyone about the activities of the camp, they told their story. On arrival at Dachau an admission index card was completed by a member of the SS and checked against any information known to the Gestapo. Each inmate was issued with the standard KL Dachau uniform of blue and off-white tops and trousers, with caps and wooden clogs. On a sleeve was a chevron of differing colours denoting the type of prisoner; red for political, green for criminal, black for the assumed work-shy, violet for religious inmates and Jews, and pink denoting a homosexual. Work for new arrivals included the gravel pit or in the plantation, which doubled as an execution area for the SS guards. It was common practice for handcuffs to be nailed into the trunk of a tree where the guards would leave inmates hanging for hours, their arms behind their backs and feet unable to touch the ground.

A grateful Hans telephoned Maria's house hoping to speak to her father and thank him for his intervention, but there was no answer. He tried again with no success. Instead he wrote a letter, also enquiring after Maria. He received no reply.

War fever gripped Europe after SS units marched into Prague on March 16, 1939, on Hitler's order that Czechoslovakia no longer existed. Hans contemplated the news, fearing his conscription as many friends and business acquaintances were already in uniform. Lacking any will to fight for the Nazis he awaited his conscription letter with dread. Surprisingly, by July no such instruction had arrived – but he knew it must be imminent. He visited the Friedrich Wilhelm University to see a contact who shared with him the news that a number of Berlin's more specialised technical institutes were taking on researchers who may be exempted from conscription.

As a physicist, although somewhat lapsed, Hans hoped he might just stand a chance. Within days his contact reported that the Kaiser Wilhelm Institute for

Physics, based in Dahlem, was hiring for unspecified positions. The institute, established with a grant from the Rockefeller Foundation in 1936, was the newest of the world-renowned facilities set up after 1912 as a 'German Oxford' by Kaiser Wilhelm II in this smart and leafy suburb located south-west of Berlin that featured many Ambassadorial homes.

Hans wrote a letter to the institute and was surprised to be granted an interview. The area of Dahlem with its parkland was new to Hans as he exited the U-Bahn underground station of Thielplatz. From the Faraday Weg he mistakenly walked into the Kaiser Wilhelm Institute for Chemistry, the first of the Kaiser Wilhelm institutes and built on a grand scale. He was redirected past the biology and physiology institutes to Boltzmannstrasse, to the austere and grey entrance of the Kaiser Wilhelm Institute for Physics.

Dr Ludwig Bewilogua had two responsibilities. He ran the Kältelaboratorium, or 'cold' laboratory, and he conducted the interviews for new, less-qualified recruits. Initially disdainful that a physics graduate from a respected faculty had wasted his vocation in the printing business, Bewilogua did not reject Hans out of hand and promised a quick response. Hans asked what positions were on offer but Bewilogua declined to answer. Nor did he respond to Hans enquiring as to the purpose of the tall, circular structure attached to a corner of the institute. Within days Hans received an offer. The pay was pretty dreadful in comparison to what he had been earning but at least conscription had been avoided, for the time being anyway. Bewilogua didn't specify what the job would entail.

In the Munich City Library Hans read up about the Kaiser Wilhelm institutes. Not all was positive. During the Great War chlorine and phosgene manufactured in the chemical institute were tested with horrific consequences in the trenches, its director, Fritz Haber, employing 150 scientists and 2,000 staff on gas warfare. Haber narrowly avoided prosecution by the Allies for war crimes. During the war Haber, being Jewish, was given the military rank of corporal, but the Kaiser personally intervened, insisting on the rank of captain. By 1920 the department of atomic physics opened under the internationally renowned James Franck. The early 1930s became the 'Golden Age' with enormous strides achieved in the new discipline of physical chemistry, unhappily brought to an end by the NSDAP demanding the dismissal of Jewish scientists. Haber emigrated to England in 1933, dying the following year in Switzerland. With war again looming, every institute in Dahlem had geared up for the military effort.

On August 27, 1939, four days before Germany's invasion of Poland, Hitler addressed the Reichstag Deputies and the nation in the Ambassadors Hall of the New Chancellery in Berlin to wild acclaim. Blackouts were already in force in Berlin but even at this late stage some western diplomats hoped that Hitler would pull off the Polish coup, as he had the Anschluss and the dismemberment of Czechoslovakia, without foreign intervention.

That same day Hans began his still unspecified employment at the Kaiser

Wilhelm Institute for Physics. The institute's administrator handed him his security pass and informed him that a bedroom in Harnack House, a large conference and entertainment centre shared by all the institutes in Dahlem, had been allocated to him. Photographs of prominent Nazis, including Hitler, adorned the restaurant and bar areas of Harnack House in commemoration of party gatherings.

German stormtroopers invaded Poland on Friday, September 1, and Hitler again addressed the Reichstag. In Washington President Roosevelt appealed to Germany, Britain, France, Italy and Poland to refrain from all military action. In the bar at Harnack House the residents listened to Berlin Radio, awaiting any news. Berlin anticipated an immediate response from Britain which had clearly pledged to support its long-time ally Poland. All work in the institutes came to a halt in the crisis.

Hans was at a loose end as Bewilogua rushed around the institute attending endless meetings of senior scientists and military officers. He spent time in the library, catching up on key developments in physics since he had left university. The librarian provided journal articles on the experiments in Paris, led by the eminent scientist Professor Joliot, that involved uranium and heavy water, and papers by Otto Hahn and Fritz Strassman, whose work on nuclear fission had truly excited the international scientific community. Hans read with interest the work of Lise Meitner, the Jewish chemist who worked with Hahn for 30 years before escaping to the Netherlands and Sweden in 1938 to avoid the clutches of the SS.

That weekend the Mozart Lounge of Harnack House offered relief from his reading, but not from the conversation on the war that was unfolding. Berlin Radio reported that the British had delivered a note to Hitler demanding the withdrawal of troops from Poland. Hans called his parents, who were equally anxious as to the turn of events. Harnack House descended into chaos as Berlin Radio announced that Neville Chamberlain, the British Prime Minister, had declared that his country was at war with Germany.

Europe was at war, for the second time in the century. Berlin's newspapers reported that Chamberlain had selected a War Cabinet that included Winston Churchill, an opponent of any measure of appeasement with Hitler. France had presented Germany with an ultimatum that was rejected. President Roosevelt declared that America would remain neutral.

There was a heavy and subdued atmosphere amongst the 250 scientists and technicians in the institute on Monday. At midday, Peter Debye, the director, addressed the staff stating that the Kaiser Wilhelm Institute for Physics was now on a war footing and would make a vital contribution to winning the war – but he didn't elaborate on what type of work it might perform. He introduced members of the Heereswaffenamt, the Army Weapons Office, who would be managing much of the institute's secret work. From now on the institute would be under SS guard and all its work strictly classified. Passes would be checked at all times, with harsh punishments for those found breaking the rules.

Debye, a Dutchman, feared for his own safety. As a physics professor in Leipzig,

the Kaiser Wilhelm Society in 1936 had chosen him to head the institute. That decision had angered Hitler who had wanted a German scientist as director. Himmler
ordered Debye to take out German nationality, but Debye, liked and respected by
his staff, strongly resisted. He infuriated Himmler further by employing Jewish
physicists and, just months before the outbreak of war, Debye found himself conscripted into the Wehrmacht as a private as punishment. After just 14 days the more
pragmatic Wehrmacht informed the SS that the coming war effort would be best
served by sending Debye back to Berlin to run the physics institute. He was
released and a dispirited but relieved Debye returned to his house on the Kaiser
Wilhelm estate. He kept the title of director but no longer held the responsibility.

With his fellow physicists, Debye threw himself into his work. Together with
Willem van der Grinten and Wolfgang Ramm, he spent most of his time in the tall,
circular building that Hans now knew was a van der Graaff nuclear particle accel-
erator. Other specialists were hired. Fritz Rogowski studied electron diffraction in
gases while a group tested thermodiffusion in fluids under the direction of Horst
Korsching and Karl Wirtz. Bewilogua was immersed in his hydrogen research and
Max von Laue ran the highly prized team studying X-ray diffraction with Jürgen
Beck, Gerhard Boormann and Georg Menzer. The spectroscopic group, under
Hermann Schüler, investigated atomic nuclei, assisted by Heinz Gollnow, Heinz
Haber, Theodor Schmidt and Adalbert Woeldike. Rumours abounded that top
nuclear physicists were being transferred from laboratories in other parts of
Germany to the Kaiser Wilhelm Institute for Physics or to the Heereswaffenamt's
experimental laboratory in Gatow, supervised by Kurt Diebner, the
Oberregierungsbaurat, or head of civil engineering, and his assistant Erich Bagge.

After the Debye incident Diebner was given overall charge of the atomic bomb
project. Another scientist, Heinz Pose, a uranium isotope separation specialist,
helped in the administration. Diebner was a hardened Nazi party member and never
trusted by his scientific colleagues who rated him a poor physicist. He claimed he
was a Freemason and not a member of the NSDAP, but that was a lie. Professor
Erich Schumann, the scientific head of the Heereswaffenamt, had seen his potential
to push ahead the nuclear programme and to wave aside protestations from any
recalcitrant scientists.

Werner Heisenberg, a winner of the Nobel Prize for Physics at the age of 31,
became the chief architect of Hitler's bomb, sharing his time between the
University of Leipzig and the Kaiser Wilhelm. Otto Hahn, from the Kaiser Wilhelm
Institute for Chemistry, and Carl Friedrich von Weizsäcker, the experimentalist
from the Physical Chemistry Institute, joined the team. Under the watchful eye of
the Heereswaffenamt, the Kaiser Wilhelm Institute for Physics was gearing itself up
for intensive nuclear research.

For von Weizsäcker, if it hadn't been for the personal intervention of Peter Debye
he would have spent his war in the Wehrmacht. He had studied first in Berlin and

then in Leipzig under Heisenberg, joining the Kaiser Wilhelm in 1936, a year before Karl Wirtz, the institute's heavy water specialist. Conscription had threatened many of the scientists, but von Weizsäcker served just 14 days. This tall, blond-haired, theoretical physicist was regarded as the brightest of his generation and his opinions were well regarded. The Heereswaffenamt was impressed when von Weizsäcker told the military that Germany had the expertise and capability to manufacture nuclear weapons, only tempered by his view that given German military successes the war would be long won before such a bomb was built. In the Institute for Physical Chemistry in the University of Hamburg, chemists Paul Harteck and Wilhelm Groth were just as enthusiastic and pursued their isotope separation trials.

Within the Kaiser Wilhelm fear stalked the corridors – no one knew who was a friend, who an informer. The disquiet deepened with the constant presence of the SS. Scientists were a breed not to be trusted according to the Nazis. Heisenberg had been a celebrated victim of a smear campaign accusing him of being anti-German. It was common knowledge that the Gestapo had built-up a card index of several million names, not just of aliens, but of anyone suspected of working against the state.

For Hans there was no news of his responsibilities. He expected to be a low-level lab technician but Bewilogua still hadn't found time to see him. When Hans was finally summoned he was completely unprepared for the task assigned to him. Bewilogua explained that he was to research and identify the location of proven and potential uranium oxide supplies as well as other rare materials, such as beryllium, boron, cadmium, zirconium and graphite, not just in Germany but all over Europe and the Soviet Union. Bewilogua stressed the importance and urgency of the job and suggested that Hans should first fully acquaint himself with the territory by obtaining maps and source material from Government Ministries and industry.

Now aware that his work was part of the nuclear fission project, Hans found back copies of international mining journals helpful for recording mineral discoveries and he introduced himself to the respective Ministries. He poured over maps and read, and re-read, countless press cuttings. As a relief in the evenings Hans frequented the bars of the now-blacked out streets of Berlin. One bar in particular, in Meinekestrasse, near the Kufurstendamm, offered a convivial atmosphere, cold beer and friendship with Helmut and Franz, two civil servants.

A momentous meeting took place at the Kaiser Wilhelm on September 26, 1939, as Diebner debated with the country's top scientists the feasibility of constructing an atomic bomb. Heisenberg flew in from Leipzig to join von Weizsäcker and Hahn. Also present were Paul Harteck from Hamburg and Walter Bothe from Heidelberg. Organized by Erich Bagge, this was the first of the *Uranvereins* as these meetings were called. The meeting became quite acrimonious with Hahn rejecting the concept of any nuclear weapon, bitter that his pioneering fission work could be turned into a super weapon. Von Weizsäcker's comment silenced the room: 'If atom bombs are going to be built, then Germany may as well be ahead of everyone,' he said in his quiet and unassuming voice. Heisenberg readily agreed to prepare a progress report in a matter of weeks.

Diebner couldn't be more pleased and he enthusiastically reported to his Heereswaffenamt masters who in turn updated both Hitler and Goering on developments. Hitler authorised a budget of 30,000 Reichsmarks, hardly sufficient, but no one had any clear idea on the level of expenditure necessary to develop such a thing. The authorisation to proceed with the bomb was received at the Kaiser Wilhelm on October 5. By early November Harteck was separating the uranium isotope using the Clusius-Dickel method, a technique developed by Claus Clusius in the chemistry laboratories of the University of Munich.

Heisenberg didn't mince his words when he handed to the Heereswaffenamt the first part of his report on December 6, 1939, the day that the RAF flew over northern Germany in a show of force. German scientists, he wrote, were capable of building an explosive device with a destructive power greater than any explosive yet known. A reactor would enrich the uranium isotope U-235, but the scarcity of uranium oxide and other essential materials was a problem that needed addressing urgently. Heisenberg delivered his second report the following February.

Oblivious to the top-level discussions taking place around him, Hans, in the space of a few months, had become quite an expert on the properties of uranium. The largest supplies were in Canada and in the Belgian Congo, well outside the reach of Germany. However, such ores were being transported from the German-occupied territory of Czechoslovakia in the Erzgebirge mountain range, referred to as the Ore Mountains. The Erzgebirge was also rich in gold, silver, lead, copper and pitchblende, a variety of uranium ore. At the base of Mount Klonovec in the Erzgebirge lay the small town of Joachimsthal, where uranium and radium had been mined since 1908 and which had been utilised in Paris by the acclaimed Pierre and Marie Curie. Production of pitchblende averaged 20 tons a year in the inter-war period but, by 1939, output had slumped to just six tons. Other uranium deposits, although smaller, were found in the area of Aue, not far from Joachimsthal, in the Thuringian Forest.

In the library Hans came across a paper written by a petroleum mineralogist in 1936, prompting the thought that uranium oxide may exist in oil producing areas – an intriguing theory given the considerable Soviet oil production activity in the Caucasus region. Details of uranium production in the Soviet Union were scant, although the search for radium had led to the discovery of uranium ores in the Ferghana Valley in Uzbekistan at Tyuya Muyun and near Lake Baikal in eastern Siberia. Hans discussed with petroleum engineers from Gewerkschaft Elverath in Hanover, operator of the prolific Nienhagen oilfields producing 75 per cent of Germany's crude oil output, the possibility of whether uranium could be located near oil finds. The company had taken strategic shareholdings in a number of foreign oil companies and it shared with Hans confidential information.

The Heereswaffenamt needed more evaluation on mineral sources in central and eastern European countries, including the Soviet Union, and Hans worked tirelessly. Geological prospecting in Romania suggested reasonable quantities of uranium. In southern Hungary there were reported discoveries near Pecs in the Mecsek Hills. For a number of years uranium ore had been mined in Poland from shafts in the Sudeten Mountains in Lower Silesia. Uranium had also been found in Bulgaria to the north-east of Sofia, the country's capital. Each week Hans wrote reports on his findings, carefully differentiating what was proven and what was unsubstantiated information. The resources of the Ministry of Economics were helpful, as were the staff under Major General Loeb, head of the Department for German Raw and Working Materials.

Despite his workload the Heereswaffenamt considered it helpful if Hans attended the top-secret lectures on the nuclear programme that were given by Heisenberg, Hahn and others either in the Kaiser Wilhelm or in the lecture theatre of Harnack House. These always attracted quite an audience, especially among senior military officers. The scientists were careful never to divulge the full extent of their work yet provide enough to give the impression that the project was fully underway. Hans made copious notes.

Christmas 1939 was a dismal affair with festivities kept to a minimum. The British and French navies' blockade of the Belgian and Dutch ports had been successful in preventing ships from unloading their cargoes destined for Germany. Some US supplies, however, got through via Russia. Basic items, such as soap, were scarce – a bar of soap substitute had to last an adult German for one month and was only available on ration. The Reich Regulations Bureau affected the lives of all Germans, even prohibiting the sale of Christmas trees.

Curiosity took Hans into the city centre to see how Berliners were faring. At the Adlon nothing appeared to have changed, although most of the guests alighting from their vehicles now wore a uniform. In nearby Voss Strasse, the new Reich Chancellery designed by Albert Speer looked modern and resplendent. Hans walked into Prinz Albrecht Strasse, stopping momentarily outside No. 8, the Gestapo headquarters, and a former school whose classrooms had been converted into cells. The building opposite housed Heydrich's Sicherheitshauptamt, the secret police, whose reputation was even worse than the Gestapo. He walked the length of the Unter den Linden down to the Spree. People hurried by. The pre-war flower sellers had gone and the windows of the shops were boarded up. Hans caught a train back to Dahlem and slept badly, worried at what was in store.

On the war front Europe was experiencing the 'Phoney War' period, a term invented by the British. It was a war of words, fought mainly in the newspapers and on the radio, each army rattling its hardware and firepower. German forces threatened the French, the Belgians and the Dutch but declined any full-scale attack. In the North Sea and north Atlantic, however, German U-boats stalked British merchant shipping. Finland had become a war zone with the heavily outnumbered Finns holding off the Russian army. In Czechoslovakia, martial law imposed by the

SS in Prague was accompanied by daily executions. Poland's capital, Warsaw, was effectively a ruin administered by the Gestapo.

In Munich, Hans' parents had no idea as to the important nature of their son's work and given the high level of security at the Kaiser Wilhelm Hans couldn't enlighten them. The printing business had slumped as the publication of scientific papers and reports needed special Government clearance. A short trip home by their son temporarily lightened their spirits.

As winter turned into spring the office Hans shared with another physicist was piled high with maps, magazines, papers, and cuttings – anything that might be of use in the search for strategic materials. More precious materials had been added to the growing list, including niobium and tantalum after Hans was informed that the Soviets had been experimenting with them in its nuclear centre at Kharkov. His request to visit Joachimsthal and Aue to review the level of uranium oxide production was agreed with the Heereswaffenamt. Stopping over in Leipzig Hans met some staff in the theoretical physics department of the university. Heisenberg, it was rumoured, had gone to Berchtesgaden for an appointment with Hitler. In Joachimsthal Hans was horrified at the condition of the workers, mainly Jews and gypsies. He discussed his concerns with the Heereswaffenamt on his return to Berlin but was ignored.

Increasingly Hans reported directly to the Heereswaffenamt, no longer Bewilogua, and sat in on briefings hosted by Dr Wirth, the chief scientist at the Auer organisation, the industrial and mining entity entrusted with producing the bulk of the metallic uranium necessary for the Kaiser Wilhelm and other laboratories. Wirth had become an expert on the corrosive characteristics of uranium and was widely respected by fellow scientists. Such briefings were useful to Hans.

The RAF was about to bring the war directly to Berliners. Bomber Command carried out a sortie over the city on March 1, 1940, but dropped no bombs, only anti-Hitler leaflets. Further west the Allied and Axis armies continued to face each other across the concrete defences of the Maginot and Siegfried Lines. By March 10, Finland, after a desperate struggle, surrendered to Soviet forces. In the first week of April Germany invaded Norway and Denmark.

On Norway's surrender the Heereswaffenamt assembled a scientific task force to travel immediately to the Vermork plant in Ryukan, operated by Norsk Hydro, the world's sole commercial supplier of heavy water. At the same time scientists at the Kaiser Wilhelm grew concerned for the safety of Niels Bohr, their mentor, who ran his celebrated institute in Copenhagen. With his Jewish wife Bohr was at risk.

As well as the Norwegian heavy water, the Heereswaffenamt attempted to requisition supplies of uranium oxide that it knew to exist in Belgium. However, Diebner, responsible for the operation, did not secure all the stocks from the offices of the Union Minière, the mining company active in the Belgian Congo, and the British managed to ship out some consignments before Germany invaded Belgium on May 10, 1940.

Activity at the Kaiser Wilhelm was pretty frenetic. Von Weizsäcker had demonstrated how the use of paraffin wax could increase the speed of nuclear fission and had progressed the design for a nuclear reactor using uranium and graphite.

Hans had struck up a strong friendship with Helmut and Franz, his drinking pals from the bar in Meinekestrasse. The three often sat at a table quietly discussing the war, careful not to be overheard. They soon became aware that in the building next door an underground Jewish organisation forged passports and other documentation for those Berlin Jews in hiding, but said nothing. Their respective work was never discussed, but Hans had the feeling that Franz had precise knowledge of the type of research being undertaken at the Kaiser Wilhelm Institute for Physics. One evening Franz had hinted to Hans that a visit to the Propaganda Ministry might be helpful in his work. Dr Goebbels' office maintained comprehensive files on the Soviet Union, including mineral production, compiled by undercover Abwehr agents. They were updated very regularly and Franz knew them as *Die Grünen Akten, The Green Files*. The next day Hans typed a memo to Diebner, omitting his source, suggesting greater co-operation between the Kaiser Wilhelm and the Ministry. Diebner's secretary later confirmed that her boss had written personally to Dr Goebbels.

The Kaiser Wilhelm was given access to the files and, at first sight to Hans, the contents of the light green folders appeared extensive. Franz had been correct about the level of detail of Russian pre-war mining. In addition, coverage of the oil sector was comprehensive with photographs of the infrastructure of many oilfields. Maps identified the location of every other known mineral in the Soviet Union. One map particularly grabbed his attention, showing the barely explored hills of Lermontev in the north Caucasus as potentially rich in uranium oxide.

Hans took the opportunity he had in the Ministry to study a number of other files. He was curious. One included the biographies of Stalin, his ministers and generals, and their personal habits, even detail on their wives and mistresses. The Abwehr certainly had been thorough. Another file related to chemical manufacturing in Leningrad and Hans was stunned to read a report relating to chemical exports to Russia, signed by Maria's father. Flipping quickly through the numerous files he found one on Soviet nuclear research and development that included a gallery of photographs of scientists, each with a biography. Included was additional detail of the experiments conducted by Abram Ioffe, Peter Kapitsa, Igor Kurchatov and the young physicist Georgii Flerov, the experimentalist behind much of the fission work in Leningrad.

A recent note on Kharkov, dated June 1940, caught Hans' eye, written by Dr Fritz Houtermanns, a scientist in the Baron von Ardenne laboratory not far from the Kaiser Wilhelm. Houtermanns' opinion had been sought on an intelligence report that two Soviet physicists, Maslov and Shpinel, from the Kharkov Physical Technical Institute had submitted an application to the People's Defence Commissariat, to the department dealing with scientific invention, that an atomic bomb could be built using Uranium-235. Two signed riders accompanied the report. The first stated that Houtermanns was unreliable. He had worked in Kharkov but had been arrested by the NKVD on spying charges and deported – the Gestapo remained convinced that Houtermanns was a double agent. The second confirmed the rumours circulating in the Kaiser Wilhelm for some weeks. Russian and British attempts to build a bomb were way behind Germany, it read. Diebner, Heisenberg and von Weizsäcker had had a series of private meetings with Schumann at the Heereswaffenamt to hasten development of the 'Uranmaschine' and discussions on the bomb's possible design had begun.

As he gratefully returned *The Green Files* to an aide of Dr Goebbels Hans knew the nuclear race was on and that he had been charged in helping source the very material needed to build the super weapon.

CHAPTER 12

The nuclear race begins

The nuclear race had begun in Europe well before leading scientists from many countries gathered in Washington on January 26, 1939, for what would be the last such conference before the outbreak of war. With dismay and alarm, the American scientists had greeted the nuclear fission experiments conducted by Otto Hahn and Fritz Strassman at the Kaiser Wilhelm Institute for Chemistry in December the previous year. The results published in *Nature* magazine confirmed that the US lagged far behind the Germans and probably the British. Sponsored by the George Washington University and the Carnegie Institute, the Washington event created huge coverage in the American newspapers. Nuclear fission became headline news and the public equated this discovery with the possibility of building an explosive device greater than the world had ever seen.

In the conference hall speakers refrained from mention of an atomic bomb, stating only that three elements – uranium, thorium and protactinium – bombarded by neutrons, split into approximately equal fragments and unstable fission fragments, releasing enormous kinetic energy that could be harnessed to provide an alternative supply of energy. Privately, many delegates believed that fission could be put towards a deadlier use.

A body of US scientists, including many who emigrated from Europe in the 1930s, grew concerned at the continued antipathy of both Government and military in seriously debating the deadly potential of nuclear fission and the possibility that Hitler might be the first to achieve it. Such alarmists were discounted in a country that since the end of the Great War had lapsed into isolationism. In March 1939 Professor George Pegram, head of the physics laboratory at Columbia University and president of the American Physical Society, personally contacted the Navy to set up a briefing with himself and the Italian physicist Enrico Fermi. Navy scientists and senior officers listened attentively as Fermi reported that a nuclear chain reaction was both sustainable and controllable with 'slow' neutrons and that up to 100 kg of the uranium isotope U-235 could be the critical amount needed for a bomb. Plutonium, created by bombarding uranium with neutrons and chemically separated, may be an even more fissile alternative Fermi declared.

Assessments were urgently made on the availability of uranium in the US. Only one uranium mine operated in the country, in Colorado, its oxide used in the ceramics industry. Throughout the US other production was negligible. There were, however, some proven discoveries in Idaho. Larger supplies were more readily available in America's northern neighbour, Canada, but the British had cornered its production. For other materials used in the fission process the news was better. Thorium oxide was found in high concentrations in monazite sands located in the US and

Brazil while high quality graphite, essential as a moderator during the nuclear reaction, was abundant. Beryllium, an alternative moderator, was also available. It was suggested that an invitation be extended to Niels Bohr to visit the US. It was in his Copenhagen laboratory that Lise Meitner, Hahn's former Kaiser Wilhelm colleague, and her Austrian nephew, Otto Frisch, had replicated the Hahn-Strassman experiments.

In July 1939 two Hungarian scientists living in America, Leo Szilard and Eugene Wigner, together with the celebrated Albert Einstein warned the Navy that an atomic bomb in the hands of Adolf Hitler would have catastrophic consequences.

US physicists collectively agreed to cease contributing articles on nuclear fission for public consumption, imposing an informal censorship, quickly copied by their British counterparts. The French, to everyone's dismay, continued to publish, with the two foremost chemists, Professor F. Joliot and his wife Irene Curie-Joliot, publishing revealing papers in *Physical Review*.

Einstein, on holiday at Peconic on Long Island, New York, decided to make a last ditch plea directly to Roosevelt on the seriousness of the matter. In his letter dated August 2, the German Nobel Prize winner for physics in 1921 gave a dire warning.

'This new phenomenon would lead to the construction of bombs, and it is conceivable – though much less certain – that extremely powerful bombs of a new type may be constructed,' wrote Einstein, a life-long pacifist. *'The United States has only very poor ores in moderate quantities. There is some good ore in Canada and the former Czechoslovakia, while the most important source of uranium is the Belgian Congo. In view of this situation you may think that it is desirable to have some permanent contact maintained between the Administration and the group of physicists working on chain reactions in America.'*

This two-page plea unfortunately took two months to be delivered to Roosevelt by Alexander Sachs, the President's Economic Advisor. It ended: *'I understand that Germany has actually stopped the sale of uranium from the Czechoslovakian mines, which she has taken over. That she should have taken such early action might perhaps be understood on the grounds that the son of the German Under-Secretary of State, von Weizsäcker, is attached to the Kaiser Wilhelm Institute in Berlin where some of the American work on uranium is now being repeated – Yours very truly, Albert Einstein.'* Reluctantly Roosevelt agreed to the appointment of a uranium committee to oversee limited nuclear experimentation, but with a derisory budget of $6,000.

Alarm bells had rung much earlier in Britain with its strong network of intelligence sources in Berlin and, indeed, the Kaiser Wilhelm. None of this knowledge was shared with the Americans. The Nobel Prize winner George Thomson, Professor of Physics at London's Imperial College, had been seconded to the Royal Aircraft Establishment in Farnborough, with David Pye, the chief scientist at the Ministry of Aircraft Production, to head Britain's attempt to develop an atomic weapon. However, with a hard-pressed Treasury battling to provide funds for a conventional war the initial work was low priority.

Thomson knew his letter, dated August 9, 1940, to Professor Franz Simon, the chief scientist at the Clarendon Laboratory in Oxford, would not be welcomed in many quarters. Simon was one of a clutch of Jewish scientists who had evaded the Nazis to make England their home, but their loyalty remained questionable. No alien scientist had access to secrets and major war projects, such as radar, jet propulsion or work on nuclear development. Oxford and the Clarendon had attracted the German émigrés, several of whom had honed their skills in the renowned physics faculty at Göttingen.

In 1933 Professor Frederick Lindemann, a great friend of Winston Churchill and the charismatic director of the Clarendon who annually toured Germany in his Rolls Royce interviewing threatened Jewish scientists, had offered Simon a position supported by a £300 bursary from one of Britain's largest industrial companies, Imperial Chemical Industries. After graduation Simon had been conscripted, suffered mustard gas poisoning in the Great War and was awarded the Iron Cross, first class, for gallantry. But even a war hero was not exempt from SS persecution. Simon had taught in Berlin and Breslau before the NSDAP effectively prevented Jewish lecturers from teaching.

No one doubted Lindemann's loyalty. Schooled in Scotland and Germany he had fled to England in 1914 and within years had become the director of the Royal Air Force Physical Laboratory, working specifically on aircraft stability. Later he was elected Professor of Experimental Philosophy at Oxford and head of the Clarendon. Lindemann's friendship with Churchill extended back to 1921 and, with Churchill now Prime Minister, he frequently attended War Cabinet meetings as a scientific advisor. Personally vouching for the integrity of Simon, Lindemann, like Thomson, thought it folly to continue to exclude the Clarendon's German and East European scientists from the war effort.

Thomson's letter to Simon, marked '*Secret*', could not have been clearer.

'*I should very much like to see you to discuss the possibility of using the fission of uranium as a source of energy for a bomb. A committee of the Ministry of Aircraft Production is considering this, and work is being done in several centres. If you are willing to help we could talk the general problem over, and I am sure that there are several aspects of it with which you could help us greatly.*

'*As regards arranging a meeting, I am up in London fairly frequently, and if you could let me know possible dates, I am sure we could arrange one that would be convenient for both of us. Yours sincerely, GP Thomson.*'

That meeting took place at Imperial's science library, South Kensington, on Thursday at 11.30 in the morning. '*I chose this rather queer place because it is next-door to my laboratory, and the object of meeting there is so that I can take you into the laboratory for which one needs a pass.*' Thomson had written.

For months Simon had been annoyed at the high-handed disdain meted out to him and his colleagues, especially as they knew more about nuclear physics than many of their British equivalents. He was pleased to receive Thomson's letter. Trains in wartime Britain invariably were late or never ran, so, with his access to petrol coupons as the Clarendon had some Admiralty work, Simon preferred to drive to his appointments. This time, however, he caught the train into Paddington and spent the night at the Mayfair Hotel, insisting on a ground-floor room.

Simon hardly needed Thomson's briefing. For months the Clarendon had assisted Imperial College on uranium separation techniques. Wilfred Mann, one of Imperial's physicists, had utilised the Clarendon's expertise in developing different types of membranes essential in the process.

Imperial had conducted secret research into the properties of graphite as a moderator, involving Professor James Chadwick at the University of Liverpool. Chadwick's reputation was universal, having worked with Ernest Rutherford at the Cavendish Laboratory in Cambridge on the emission of gamma rays from radioactive materials. Interned for the duration of the Great War as he was in Berlin at that time, Chadwick had returned to the Cavendish to work with Rutherford. He bombarded beryllium with alpha particles emitted by polonium, a natural radioactive element, creating a highly penetrating radiation. These radiation particles had a mass that was almost that of a proton, but carried no electrical charge. Chadwick called them neutrons. Rutherford in 1920 suspected the existence of the neutron but it was Chadwick who confirmed that the neutron had a major role in nuclear transformations. There were two ways of producing neutrons – mixing radium or polonium with beryllium or by means of a cyclotron, a device using large circular magnets pioneered by Ernest Lawrence at the University of California in Berkeley. Chadwick moved to Liverpool to embark on the construction of a cyclotron.

The real impetus to British efforts to build an atomic bomb had come in March 1940 when Thomson was handed the *Frisch-Peierls Memorandum*, the contents of which were startling. In the University of Birmingham the Austrian Otto Frisch, now in Britain, and Rudolf Peierls, a former colleague of Heisenberg in Leipzig, rocked the scientific community by preparing what was in effect a blueprint for a bomb. They believed that a slow neutron chain reaction would produce explosive effects no greater than those obtained with ordinary explosives, but fast neutrons could achieve an explosion of enormous power. Ordinary uranium naturally contained only 0.7 per cent of U-235 but, if this isotope could be artificially separated, just a few kilograms could produce a bomb equivalent to many thousands of tons of TNT. The super weapon would be in two parts, with a mechanism or trigger to collide both parts together in a critical mass. Another Birmingham scientist, the Australian Mark Oliphant, concurred with Frisch and Peierls, adding his weight to the growing clamour that Britain needed to redouble its efforts. Sir Henry Tizard, the Government's senior scientific advisor, agreed to talk to Churchill now that there was a real worry that the Germans in the Kaiser Wilhelm may have reached the same conclusion.

Peierls, however, had his detractors. Despite his undisputed brilliance as Professor of Mathematical Physics at Birmingham there were aroused misgivings in a number of quarters because of his German background. To inflame the situation further, Peierls had a Russian wife, Genia, a loud and outspoken woman. Many found her deeply irritating, especially at parties when her shrill voice echoed around the room.

Simon and Thomson met again in London on September 17, just weeks after Tizard and John Cockcroft, head of the Cavendish Laboratory in Cambridge, returned from a secret trip to the United States. They had attempted to solicit American assistance in its nuclear fission research without admitting that Britain's real intention was to build the bomb. Thomson informed Simon that the Clarendon was to take the lead in development of membranes essential to the separation of U-235. Within a short period of time this work would spill over to the laboratories of nearby Jesus College, to a converted staff theatre at the ICI facility in Birmingham and to a secret location in north Wales, codenamed *P6*.

Through its growing cells in the United States and in Britain, Russian spy chiefs monitored all these developments. The NKVD sent missives to Embassies and Consulates in London, Washington, New York, San Francisco and Ottawa, demanding an immediate focus on nuclear intelligence. There were two priorities – locating the research laboratories and identifying key personnel, including those further down the chain of command, a strategy that historically served the organisation extremely well. Soviet military intelligence, the GRU, had its own well-established channels. Both organisations had increased their efforts in Oxford.

On the ground floor of the Clarendon the isotope separation experts occupied rooms 15 to 19, their corridor facing the laboratories given over to the scientists and technicians working on radar. The two groups hardly socialised with each other, never speaking about their work. They played cricket against each other in the summer months on a college playing field, but intense secrecy prevented any further fraternisation.

However, one NKVD agent with the codename *Scott* had already penetrated radar, the invention that could help to win the aerial war against Germany. This Briton wasn't alone, *Scott* ran the espionage cell within the Clarendon that provided the Soviet Union with the country's radar secrets.

Vladimir Barkovsky, recently graduated from the NKVD's training centre at Malakhovka, was to spearhead his organisation's efforts to steal Britain's atomic secrets, orchestrated in Moscow by Lt General Pavel Fitin, chief of the 5th Directorate.

Britain's industrial cities and ports suffered terribly badly in the last months of 1940, as German bombers turned their attention away from the airfields, the Battle of Britain lost. Coventry was blitzed on November 14 when 400 bombers razed this medieval city to the ground. In retaliation, on November 20, the RAF launched a six-hour bombing raid on Duisburg-Ruhrort, the largest river port in the world, linking the Rhine with the Ruhr. Southampton, Bristol, Birmingham and Liverpool were bombed; London suffered on almost a daily basis. Incendiaries and high explosive bombs devastated the City of London on December 30 in one of the Luftwaffe's worst attacks.

Only hours after a Heinkel raid on Liverpool in February 1941, Barkovsky, carrying his credentials as the USSR's newest political attaché, arrived by boat at the smouldering George Dock. Ironically, one of the few port buildings to survive in the raid was the head office of the White Star Line, the owner of the ill-fated *Titanic*.

The journey from Moscow to Liverpool had taken an exhausting 70 days, as travelling west from Moscow through war-torn Europe was impossible. First stop was the Middle East, followed by Japan and Hawaii. A cargo ship transported the party to San Francisco and a train took them to New York to await a ship to Ireland. Barkovsky was unaccompanied, a NKVD policy reversed 18 months later when Vera, his wife, joined him in London. In Liverpool Barkovsky encountered war for the first time, the sight of the bombed city would haunt the 26-year-old for the rest of the life. Clutching heavy suitcases the small group of Russian diplomats picked their way through the streets to Lime Street railway station to be told that due to the raids, trains to London's Euston station ran only in the early hours of the morning. Weary, they checked into a hotel, had a meal and ventured out to see first-hand how Britain was coping with war.

Practising his English Barkovsky chatted amiably to members of the Home Guard, none of whom had ever met a Russian, and drank pints of Guinness and brown ale with British soldiers. When the air raid siren blared he and the rest of the people in the pub ran for the underground shelter. The warning was a false alarm, the German bombers were making for Bristol.

At 2am the London-bound train picked up speed, steaming through the Lime Street tunnel. On board, Barkovsky slept. Before his return to Moscow in 1946 he would be consuming plenty more Guinness in Liverpool, picking up atomic secrets from the university laboratory and transmitting them to his grateful masters in Moscow.

In America the search was on to identify a scientist who could lead the country's effort in nuclear research, despite its pathetic lack of budget. The FBI and other Government entities would not allow a foreign physicist to fill the role. Robert Julius Oppenheimer had yet to fit the frame but he had been recommended as one of the brightest physicists in the country and was more than capable.

In Berlin the scientists at the Kaiser Wilhelm were working at a frenetic pace, encouraged by the Heereswaffenamt, the Army Weapons Office, and Goering. An underground nuclear laboratory had been constructed adjacent to the Kaiser Wilhelm Institute for Physics. Otto Hahn continued to have reservations but carried on, pressured to do so by his colleagues. Von Weizsäcker progressed his research into fast and slow neutrons in a mixture of heavy water and uranium. Walter Gerlach from the University of Munich had joined the nuclear group as an advisor, but his regular entertaining of SS officers only engendered further fear and uncertainty amongst the staff. In Lichterfelde the independent Manfred von Ardenne

Laboratory, run by the mercurial Baron of the same name, built nuclear accelerators and electromagnetic isotope separators.

The Auer company in Oranienburg had delivered its first delivery of metallic uranium in January 1940 and was now struggling to cope with demand from the Kaiser Wilhelm and Leipzig, where Heisenberg had built his model reactor. A brilliant scientist, Nicholas Riehl, had been put in charge of production at Auer and tried to substantially increase output by subcontracting to other Berlin companies who manufactured the precious metal under the guise of leather and tanning factories. Siemens equally struggled to produce high-grade graphite with its plant at Mansfeld, south of Magdeburg, working to full capacity. Unfortunately, its director of research, Dr Hans Mayer, and some of his colleagues were under close surveillance by the Gestapo for possible connections with the *Rote Kapelle*, the *Red Orchestra*. Mayer was later arrested and sent to Dachau.

Von Weizsäcker had reported to the Heereswaffenamt in July 1940 that a large-scale reactor would produce element 93, neptunium, decaying into element 94, the highly fissionable plutonium. In the US the scientists Edwin McMillan and Philip Abelson at Berkeley in California had reached the same conclusion.

Heidelberg, principally the Kaiser Wilhelm Institute of Medical Research run by Walter Bothe, became Germany's centre for research into neutron absorption by graphite. Laboratories in Celle and Freiburg researched isotope separation. Mass spectroscopic studies were conducted in Kiel. The highly respected chemists in Munich also contributed to the atomic bomb programme, with a number of its scientists visiting Dresden to supervise the building of a new laboratory. Its purpose was known only to a few.

Annexed Austria had secretly joined the project. Vienna's Radium Institute, directed by Gustav Ortner, and the Physics Institute led by Georg Stetter, experimented with fast neutrons and isotope separation. A more specialised facility, the Neutron Institute, was set up and funded directly by the Heereswaffenamt. Signed orders from Hitler himself adorned the main reception area, threatening harsh penalties for any disclosure of the institute's work. The able Josef Mattauch was ordered to the Kaiser Wilhelm as deputy to Otto Hahn. All three Vienna facilities relied on a small Austrian uranium producer, Treibacher Chemische Werke, and its mines in Treibach and Foorlach, near Klagenfurt.

Heisenberg and von Weizsäcker assured the military that German scientists understood the theoretical science, the only constraint being the shortage of materials. Throughout the remaining months of 1940 and in the early months of the following year the project progressed, but by July there was an impasse.

Professor Erich Schumann of the Heereswaffenamt reported to his superiors his disturbing conversations with a number of the key Kaiser Wilhelm physicists. They had tried to convince him that Germany would win the war against Britain and Russia with conventional weapons well before the atomic bomb was even ready for testing. Schumann took this to mean that the scientists were deliberately slowing down the programme. One evening von Weizsäcker returned home and greeted his wife with the words *'We don't have to work on the bomb anymore.'* In London, studying the latest intelligence from Berlin, the War Cabinet breathed a sigh of relief and immediately redoubled its own nuclear efforts.

The Germans, however, were far from relinquishing their early lead on nuclear fission. Uncertain as to the motives of both Heisenberg and von Weizsäcker, the military took the necessary measures to replicate some of the Kaiser Wilhelm work in a far more secure facility, well away from Berlin and using scientists whose dedication was unquestioned.

CHAPTER 13

The Russians penetrate the War Cabinet

In the House of Commons on the evening of February 7, 1940, a Select Committee convened to agree an important item of Government spending. At 7.21pm the Financial Secretary to the Treasury, Captain Crookshank, read out the motion:

'*That a supplementary sum, not exceeding £2,880, be granted to His Majesty, to defray the charge which will come in course of payment during the year ending on the 31st day of March 1940, for the salaries and other expenses in the department of His Majesty's Treasury and Subordinate Departments, the salary of a Minister for Co-ordination of Defence, the additional salary of the Chancellor of the Duchy of Lancaster as a member of the Cabinet, and the salary of a Minister without Portfolio.*'

The man in question was Lord Maurice Pascal Alers Hankey, who had had a long and very distinguished record of public service. Britain's Prime Minister, Neville Chamberlain, needed Hankey's skills and he confidently expected the motion to be carried with no opposition.

Crookshank described Hankey as a man of exceptional experience enjoying the fullest backing of the Prime Minister. '*He has been invited to join the War Cabinet and because he cannot get a salary unless this Supplementary Estimate is agreed to by the House of Commons, I come forward today to submit it to the Committee,*' explained the Financial Secretary.

Every member agreed, bar one – Hugh Dalton, the Labour MP, who three months later would join the new Churchill Cabinet as Minister of Economic Warfare with responsibility for the Special Operations Executive, the SOE. Dalton refused to let this motion be carried 'on the nod' and stubbornly demanded a debate. Crookshank was rattled.

If others had spoken out against Hankey's appointment, Britain's War Cabinet secrets would never have been compromised to the extent they were to be for the next three years. Stalin and Beria could not believe their good fortune.

Born in Biarritz in April 1877, Hankey was schooled at Rugby, one of the toughest of Britain's public schools. After the Royal Navy, Hankey entered the civil service rising to Assistant Secretary in the Committee of Imperial Defence in 1908. Within three years he had assumed the role of Secretary at the relatively young age of 35. Two years into the Great War, Lloyd George became Prime Minister and he appointed Hankey to serve as Secretary to the five members of his War Cabinet. Prior to the appointment, no War Cabinet minutes had ever been taken. Henceforth Hankey insisted on full records. At the Paris Peace Conference in 1919 he was included in the British delegation as Secretary. Throughout his long Governmental career Hankey was to serve seven Prime Ministers: Herbert Asquith, Lloyd George, Bonar Law, Stanley Baldwin, Ramsay MacDonald, Neville Chamberlain and Winston Churchill.

The outspoken Dalton didn't mince his words that night in the House of Commons, in a desperate week for Britain with shipping losses mounting in the North Atlantic. Opposing Hankey's appointment, he railed:

'There was a period during which he was Secretary to the Committee of Imperial Defence in addition to being Secretary to the Cabinet, during the whole period from 1931 until his final retirement, when grievous errors were made in British policy in matters of armaments and defence. He held this office during the fiasco of the Disarmament Conference. He was then a civil servant and not subject to criticism. He had a very long close season, but we are now entitled to say – and he is entitled to reply to us – that he must take his share of responsibility for gross errors of policy when the Government was failing to co-operate in disarmament by agreement, and also in the later period when the Government was failing to re-arm in the face of the German menace. We have the very greatest doubt of the competence of Lord Hankey to advise today on questions of defence.'

His words were to have little effect. The motion was carried on a majority vote.

Hankey was in an ebullient mood as he arrived at Richmond Terrace, London, SW1, on October 10, 1940, to chair his first meeting of the Scientific Advisory Committee, the SAC, and address the group of six top scientists appointed its members. Among them were Sir Henry Dale, president of the prestigious Royal Society, and Sir Edward Appleton, head of the Department of Scientific and Industrial Research which managed many of Britain's scientific war efforts. Using his title of Chancellor of the Duchy of Lancaster, Hankey outlined the SAC's terms of reference. Five days later the members assembled again in the Privy Council Office in Whitehall with Sir John Anderson, Lord President of the Council, in the chair who announced that the committee would report directly to the War Cabinet.

Hankey went to work with gusto, instructing all Government departments to provide the SAC with precise details of research capabilities, locations and staff. Nothing was too secret to be omitted. Sir Archibald Sinclair, the Secretary for Air, was the first to respond with information on the Royal Air Force and the Ministry of Aircraft Production. Sinclair identified the presence of the most secret RAF experimental establishment, headed by Sir Frank Smith and Sir George Lee – the experimental jet engine facility at Swanage in Dorset.

Other early respondents included the Radio Research Board and the Post Office, reporting the existence of a radio branch that was working closely with the Air Ministry, Admiralty and the War Office on special portable devices to detect illicit transmissions from the United Kingdom.

A document discussed by Hankey and the SAC on October 30 was to have far-reaching implications. The Central Register Advisory Council had named every secret wartime committee, the most comprehensive scientific directory ever compiled.

Terms of reference for the SAC expanded to food production both in Britain and the Commonwealth, training, recreation, education, sewage and many other areas of the economy, including details of committees that specialised in rodent control, pig and sheep diseases and mastitis. The SAC even requested details from a committee that had reported on bed bugs in boys' boarding schools. This information flow didn't slow as Hankey continued to press the Ministries. Given Hankey's remit it was difficult to decline the SAC's requests but Anthony Eden, the Secretary of War, refused through lack of available time.

The use of alien scientists, mathematicians and engineers interned in either Britain or Canada became a priority of the SAC. Professor Lander of Imperial College was asked by the committee to assess every internee that could be used in the war effort, especially well-qualified Germans, Russians and East Europeans who had settled in Britain in the 1930s. Helped by an Imperial colleague, Dr Paul Rosin, Lander compiled an extensive list of 250 names for Hankey, including 80 already approved by the Royal Society who had joined Government departments. Klaus Fuchs, an experimental physicist who would create his own place in the history of atomic espionage, was one. He had been interned in the Isle of Man and later in Canada.

By March 1941 Hankey's Committee, as the SAC was now informally known, had spread its tentacles to Washington and Ottawa. Sir Charles Darwin, head of the United Kingdom Scientific Mission based in K Street in America's capital, provided regular input to Hankey. In Canada, Sir William Bragg, from the Cavendish Laboratory in Cambridge and a former president of the Royal Society, often flew to London to address the committee. In the meeting on March 18, held in Hankey's room, No. 55, Whitehall, Bragg brought with him General McNaughton, president of the Canadian National Research Council. McNaughton reported that *Camp X*, the top-secret scientific facility, had been expanded for British research into gas warfare in addition to being a vital radio listening post. Bragg also discussed his progress on scientific exchange between America and Britain with Dr Vannevar Bush, head of America's National Defence Research Committee.

Information obtained by British Intelligence was included in SAC discussion – such as the secret German plan for its engineers, using expendable PoW and slave labourers to build a tunnel under the English Channel from France to further an invasion.

Russia, an ally after June 1941, was often on the SAC agenda. Sir Stafford Cripps in February 1942, in one of his last chores as Ambassador in Moscow, was asked to comment on potential scientific exchange. However, the original two-page document, circulated several weeks before, was already in the hands of the NKVD and the Russian Academy of Sciences. Its contents, detailing the personal requests of a number of eminent British scientists, had been cabled to Moscow by Philip Kislitsin, the NKVD's cypher clerk in the London Embassy on February 2.

Bragg welcomed contact with Abram Ioffe, Yuli Khariton and Aleksandr Leipunsky, three of Russia's premier nuclear scientists, as did Professors' Cockcroft and Fowler from the Cavendish. Appleton wanted to receive the results of Soviet work on the ionosphere from Leonid Mandelshtam. Cripps knew that the British request would be declined. The Russians laughed at the British naivety in the final paragraph of the cable – *'We would be very glad if you would ask the Soviet organisations whether they would be able to print in English a useful series of extracts from their recent works on applied sciences. We are very keen on finding out about the latest Soviet successes in this field,'* the SAC had requested of Cripps.

Throughout his tenure as chairman of the SAC and of other committees Hankey bristled with indignation over his exclusion from Churchill's small circle that received all War Cabinet papers. An annoyed Hankey on May 16, 1941, wrote to Sir Edward Bridges, Secretary to the War Cabinet:

'My dear Bridges – a year ago when the Prime Minister asked me to accept my present office, he said I was to have a full distribution of War Cabinet papers – exactly the same papers as the Secretary of State for War. I have never pressed to have this promise fulfilled to the letter, partly because it makes such a mass of reading, including some matters in which I am not specially concerned, and partly because, as a former Secretary of the Cabinet, I appreciate how important it is in matters affecting operations to limit the distribution.

'Formerly, however, I used to receive a much larger distribution than I do now. At present I am getting practically nothing from the Chiefs of Staff of Defence organisations, with the result that I often find myself, as Chairman of my Committees, at a disadvantage as compared with some of my members. This is really essential to my work as Chairman of the Committee for the Co-ordination of Allied Supplies. I think you have always kept me informed about anything bearing on German oil and I am sure you will continue to do so. The same applies to the various uses of burning oil as anti-tank and defensive weapons. I do not think that at present anything arises in connection with either my Scientific or Engineering Advisory Committees.

'I do not ask to keep any of the papers you send, except copies of my own reports and decisions bearing thereon, as I dislike having large accumulations here. I shall just read them and send them back unless in any particular case it is useful to keep a paper for a time, in which case I will let you know – yours ever, Hankey.'

Bridges replied, offering better news for Hankey who put pen to paper and thanked the Cabinet Secretary:

'My dear Bridges – Thank you for your letter of the 28th May about Cabinet documents. First let me thank you for the documents that I am now receiving, which have already proved of the utmost value. I should certainly be glad to have the papers of the Committees you mention, namely: Night Air Defence, the Far Eastern Committee and its Economic Sub-Committee, and the North American Supply Committee as affecting the Middle East or other Allies. Night Air Defence will be particularly useful because departments frequently ask me to investigate and decide problems bordering on that subject, and I am sometimes doubtful whether I ought to tackle them myself or not.

'I am keeping these secret papers entirely to myself and returning them immedi-

ately after I have read them – Yours sincerely, Hankey.'
In addition, Hankey's name had been put on the distribution list for all papers relating to civil defence, co-ordination of Allied supplies, bacteriological warfare – including the secret work at Porton Down – and on preventing oil from reaching the enemy.
Still far from satisfied, Hankey tried a new tack. He bent the ear of Sir Rupert Haworth, a friend in the Privy Council Office, who agreed to write to Bridges on his behalf. Headlined *'Top Secret'*, Haworth's note on December 1, 1941, stated: *'...that he [Hankey] is greatly handicapped by not having seen papers which had been circulated to Chiefs of Staff. He has no intention of taking the matter up formally and if it is a question of being smothered with papers or the reverse he would prefer to be smothered and to pick out for himself what was of interest to him. He has always returned papers as soon as he has read them.'*
Hankey requested a private meeting with Bridges over another request for papers which had been declined – the complete Great War Cabinet records from 1916 that he himself had helped compile.
Bridges wrote to Haworth: *'When I was seeing Lord Hankey this morning he said that he thought he would have to question my 'ruling' about Cabinet minutes. He gave me a long story, the gist of which was that when he had been invited by Mr Chamberlain to join the War Cabinet it had been largely in order that he might inform the Prime Minister about past history, and he had therefore regarded it as his duty to have with him a full set of the War Cabinet minutes of the last war [the Great War]. I told him that we had never made any difficulty about letting him see minutes on matters of current business.*
'While the discussion was thus largely inconclusive, I think that the episode has served to make it clear that we do not regard Lord Hankey as having a complete run of War Cabinet records for all and any purposes. There is thus every possibility of there being more fun in the future – though I shall do my best to avoid it.
'To tell the truth I cannot get an idea into my head as to how to improve matters, if indeed it is possible to make any improvement – I am not at all sure that it is.'
The fun did continue and the situation worsened, this time over the highly sensitive papers, coded WP, distributed to only five members of the War Cabinet. Lesser categories received WP (G) and WP (R) codes. Churchill, growing weary of Hankey's complaints, instructed Bridges to fully investigate the position. A War Cabinet minute on December 8, 1941, confirmed that from September that year, 95 documents had WP codings. Hankey had seen 15, including the defence plan in the event of a German invasion.
Hankey's private secretary phoned up the War Cabinet offices, quoted five WP numbers and demanded that Lord Hankey receive them – all five concerned Britain's sensitive relations with Russia. This request was rejected out of hand. But that had not always been the case. Private secretaries had a wide circle of contacts, often better than the masters they served. That April he had written to a Mr Harris

at the War Cabinet, marked *'Secret and Personal'*:

'Dear Harris – many thanks for your letter of the 11th April enclosing a copy of WP 69, which Lord Hankey has returned directly to Bridges.

'In this connection I should add that Lord Hankey has frequently felt some uneasiness as to whether he is receiving, in accordance with the assurance given to him by the Prime Minister when he took up his present office, the same papers and especially the same Cabinet papers (of which he is on average sent only about two-thirds) as the Secretary of State for War. Lord Hankey has refrained from making enquiries with a view to confirming his fears, but in one instance at least (that of Lord Beaverbrook's last report to the Cabinet, WP40) he was not put, unlike the Secretary of State for War, on the circulation list. Unless there is a specific directive from the Prime Minister on the distribution of this paper, Lord Hankey would be glad if he could be sent a copy, which, of course, could be returned if so desired.

'The only persons to see such especially secret papers sent to this office are Lord Hankey and myself. It would be very helpful if you would confirm to me, subject to the reservation already made, that the Prime Minister's assurance to Lord Hankey is being complied with.'

By the end of 1941 Hankey won as Churchill conceded. Bridges wrote to Hankey's private secretary on December 13: *'I am writing to let you know that we have recently been reviewing the circulation lists of certain Cabinet documents and that, in this connection, we have arranged that Lord Hankey should in future receive copies of all papers and minutes of the Lord President's Committee. Hitherto he has been sent only selected papers and minutes which were thought to be of direct concern to him.'*

From the time that Hankey was appointed Britain's war effort was compromised. The spat over the minutes of the Lloyd George War Cabinet was resolved and the volumes were released to Hankey, adding to his existing pile of unread material. However, in Moscow, the events of the Great War were not a priority and were ignored.

Hankey had an inexhaustible thirst for detail but he could never possibly digest the volume of paper that filled his Whitehall in-trays. However, his ever-conscientious private secretary, John Cairncross, ensured the supply never stopped. As Hankey chaired the innumerable committees and attended War Cabinet meetings, Cairncross diligently attended to business.

No one ever noticed Cairncross placing these documents into his leather standard issue briefcase with the gold Royal emblem on the front after he cleared Hankey's desk well before the security officers conducted their rounds. Russia now had access to Britain's top table and was privy to almost every secret of the war. Sir Henry Dale took over as SAC chairman in March 1943 but by that time the damage was devastating.

Cairncross never admitted the full extent of his treachery to MI5 during the interrogations. The Russians had given him several codenames, including *Molière* as the

Cambridge-educated civil servant was fluent in French and had an affinity with the seventeenth century French actor and playwright. Often in cyphers Cairncross was coded as *Liszt*, after Franz Liszt, the Hungarian virtuoso and composer. However, when such cyphers were decoded in Moscow and retyped for circulation, *List* was the usual format.

His Soviet controller was Anatoli Gorsky, the NKVD *rezident* in the London Embassy whose codename used on his cyphers to Moscow was *Vadim*, but to Cairncross, Philby, Blunt, Burgess and Maclean he often used *Professor Nikitin*. Cinemas, which during the war were often open all night, coffee shops, pubs, even public lavatories were used as drops. After a pick-up Gorsky would return to the Embassy in Kensington Gardens as quickly as he could. The new political attaché, Vladimir Barkovsky, using his skills taught at the NKVD training school in Malakhovka, carefully photographed every document. Out of the 'Cambridge Five' Cairncross was easily the most prolific agent. The NKVD even gave a codename to the unwitting Hankey – *Boss*.

The level of compromise was staggering. Thanks to Hankey's insistence on receiving information from every Government department and committee the Russians knew every secret location, every address and the names of every key individual involved in the scientific war against Germany. Cairncross, with access to the Lander report on alien scientists, provided the NKVD with one of its major coups. Moscow was able to sift through each name for any possible Russian or East European connection to exert pressure or blackmail. On many occasions Cairncross had to be bullied by Gorsky into sifting what was passing through Hankey's office. Moscow had no need for the minutes of committees researching into bed-bug infestation, school epidemics or mental disorders, which often took up Hankey's time.

Fluent in German Cairncross, in 1942, was posted to the Code and Cypher School at Bletchley Park as editor of German decrypts. Moscow Centre was ecstatic. The British believed that their code breakers were safe from eavesdroppers, but each week Cairncross met Gorsky as regular as clockwork. He remained at Bletchley Park for a year before joining Section V at MI6 where he stayed for the duration of the war before returning to the Treasury. The defection of Burgess and Maclean led to frenetic investigation of their college friends and close colleagues. Cairncross had never been careless but given the volume of intelligence he had stolen there was always the danger of disclosure. An MI5 officer, Arthur Martin, was convinced that Cairncross had been treacherous and in 1952 conducted the first of several interrogations. Convinced of Cairncross' guilt Martin tried hard to establish the truth but failed. A prolific writer of poems and books, Cairncross became a correspondent for *The Economist* and later an FAO representative in Asia for the United Nations. After his final interrogation in 1964 Cairncross was not prosecuted, MI5 allowing him to leave for Geneva to teach.

Gorsky, on orders from Lt General Pavel Fitin, chief of the NKVD's 5th

Directorate, was initially instructed to tell Cairncross to steal all that passed through the hands of *Boss*. For a while Moscow digested every morsel of detail, but it soon instructed Cairncross to be more selective. That decision turned out to be a very profound mistake, to Moscow's cost. Cairncross had little idea about what scientific information was needed and he missed many documents that the NKVD knew Hankey must have received.

Fitin, codenamed *Victor*, identified several areas on which he wanted Gorsky and his fellow NKVD colleagues in London to concentrate. In one cable to Gorsky, dated March 15, 1942, Fitin said that intelligence on bacteriology, Britain's chemical warfare programme and the Uranium-235 project were vital. Fitin had added a rider: *'In questions of technical intelligence please be very careful,'* he wrote, referring to the need for attention to detail.

If Cairncross was prolific the person who introduced him to scientific espionage was of equal value for the Soviets. James Klugman, a Cambridge contemporary, was arguably one of the most respected of all the agents recruited into the NKVD before the war. In 1936 Klugman had travelled to Paris for a meeting with Arnold Deutsch, the OGPU 'illegal'. The OGPU was the predecessor of the NKVD. Klugman, secretary of the International Students Association against Fascism, needed no convincing to work for Russia. Deutsch, a homosexual, had slept with both Burgess and Maclean but blackmail was not necessary with Klugman who had been recommended by Harry Pollitt, the talent spotter for both the OGPU and GRU, and the London head of the British Communist Party. In Paris, another OGPU talent spotter, Olga Halpern, joined the meeting and she immediately took to Klugman.

Deutsch and Halpern asked Klugman to identify any friends who might be helpful. He suggested that Cairncross may be receptive to a Soviet approach but it was agreed in Paris that Klugman himself would handle the recruitment. Initially Cairncross wasn't as keen as Klugman in betraying his country, but this view soon changed. Both men met at regular intervals and shared Gorsky, and later Konstantin Kukin, as their controller. Fluent in Serbian and Croatian, Klugman distinguished himself in army intelligence during the war, working for MI6 and SOE in the Balkans. Stalin and Beria were delighted to receive, through Klugman, Churchill's ideas on a post-war Yugoslavia and the Prime Minister's private discussions with Tito.

If other members of the Treasury Select Committee that met on February 7, 1940, in the House of Commons had voiced their doubts over bringing Lord Hankey out of retirement to advise Chamberlain, and later Winston Churchill, events may have taken a different turn. Hankey's obsessive requests for detail, much of which he would never read or, indeed, act upon, provided the Russians with an unprecedented intelligence source. The cunning Cairncross was in his element. The chemical and biological secrets of Porton Down, the revolutionary jet engine and radar were just some of the scientific inventions passed by Cairncross to his Soviet controller. Given Hankey's access to American secrets, these too found their way to Moscow. Contrary to Hankey's claim that the highly classified documents, the WP papers, would be returned as soon as he read them, nothing could be further from the truth. In August 1952, Hankey, finally departing from public service, contacted Sir Norman Brook at the Cabinet Office, from his office at the Ministry of Labour and National Service. *'I am gradually getting rid of the chairmanship and membership of a number of committees, all of which I have held for many years, and I am engaged in getting rid of the papers that have accumulated in connection with them,'* wrote Hankey. *'In nearly all cases I am able to clear these up with the departments concerned and only a small proportion were ever secret.*

'Somewhat to my surprise, however, I have found in the safe a number of files dating back to the days when I was a Minister and which, for some reason that I cannot account, were never returned and I have never looked at them until today.

'The most important of these are a series of files and correspondence connected with an enquiry on German oil over which I presided from 1939 till my retirement in 1942, which was known from its Cabinet Office lettering as the P.O.G. Committee. These papers deal with every phase of that subject. Many were extremely secret at that time and probably some are secret still.

'In the course of my examination it is possible I may find other files which emanated originally from my connection as a Minister, or even later, with the Cabinet Office.' Three large parcels were later sent with a short note from one of his secretaries. *'He would be grateful if you could arrange for them to be destroyed, unless you wish to retain any of them'*, she said. Every file in the packages was marked *'Top Secret'*.

One document stolen by Cairncross from the office of Lord Hankey had the same impact on Josef Stalin as the discovery of the German 'atomic' notebook in Krivaya Kosa. Some 30 pages in length and delivered to only a select few in the War Cabinet, Hankey's private secretary confirmed receipt to the motor-cycle courier from the Ministry of Aircraft Production. Through Cairncross, Britain's greatest scientific secret was conveyed to Moscow in two parts – the first, a summary by coded cypher on September 20, 1941; the second on October 10, via a speeded diplomatic bag, were photographs.

Gorsky, intrigued by the diagrams, insisted that Barkovsky summarise the report in addition to photographing every page in the normal way. After reading the introduction, Barkovsky's heart leapt. Cairncross had handed over to the Soviets the blueprint of Britain's bomb – the plan to manufacture 36 atomic bombs to devastate Nazi Germany and win the war.

CHAPTER 14

Rudolf Hess offers more than peace initiatives

Professor Carl Friedrich von Weizsäcker, a key architect of Germany's plan to build an atomic bomb, was working late in the Kaiser Wilhelm Institute for Physics when the telephone rang – the operator from the Reich Chancellery was on the line. It was early April 1941. After one of the coldest winters on record Berliners strolled during the day around the gardens and city parks, enjoying the weak sunshine. But at night they hid in their underground shelters as searchlights picked out the RAF bombers whose crews meted out the same death and destruction that the Luftwaffe wreaked over England.

The State Opera House in the Unter den Linden, the Prussian State Library, the Bellevue Palace and the New Palace at Potsdam were ablaze as Berlin suffered its heaviest attack of the war to date on April 9. In the city centre many Government buildings were reduced to rubble by high-explosive bombs. The Luftwaffe retaliated with even greater force *'as a reprisal to British air attacks on cultural and residential centres in Berlin'* broadcast Berlin Radio as more than 500 German aircraft hit London on April 16 in one of the biggest single raids of the war.

In other theatres of war the Greek army surrendered at Larissa to overwhelming German and Italian forces after stubborn and brave resistance. Nazi jackboots paraded with the Italians in Athens on April 27, as 55,000 British and Commonwealth troops made a run to safety. In North Africa, news of Rommel's victories was heralded in every German newspaper. Miraculously, the British held out at the strategically important town of Tobruk. The victory was still with Germany – Britain was barely hanging on, its army stretched to the very limit. Meanwhile in America, war only touched the lives of its citizens through the newsreels in the cinemas. The public appeared reluctant to become enjoined with another European conflagration. American industry was booming and its people danced and drank while across the Atlantic the German terror machine respected no border.

Von Weizsäcker was delighted that he was to meet Rudolf Hess at last, a good friend of his father, Ernst, the Secretary of State in the Foreign Office. He looked forward with anticipation to the visit to the Reich Chancellery in Voss Strasse in the final week of April.

The tall Hess, conspicuous for his square jaw and sunken eyes, held an absolute loyalty for Hitler. Born in Alexandria, Egypt, in 1894, Hess had studied in Munich before joining the National Socialist Party in 1920. From the outset Hitler and Hess hit it off and their friendship grew. At Landsberg Castle in 1923, where Hitler, Hess and others spent six months in jail, he provided considerable input into the writing of *Mein Kampf*. When the Nazis came to power in 1933 Hess was never far from Hitler's side. On April 20, 1941, the Fuhrer's

52nd birthday, it was Hess who broadcast to the nation offering greetings.

Such reverence confirmed the public persona of Hess but privately his relationship with Hitler had cooled since the onset of the war. Increasingly Goering, Himmler and Goebbels deliberately sidelined Hess from any decision-making.

In reality, however, Hitler's deputy built up a network of informants in every Ministry. He was regularly briefed. Officially he had been provided with the barest of detail about the secret war work undertaken by the Kaiser Wilhelm institutes in Dahlem. He had never been invited to the meetings that Werner Heisenberg had had with Hitler and Goering but thanks to his network Hess was completely up to date on the project that might deliver a bomb.

Hess, wearing the uniform of the 'Totenkopf', the 3rd SS-Panzer Division, warmly welcomed von Weizsäcker at the Reich Chancellery. It was to be a private, informal meeting. They drank coffee in Hess' sitting room and chatted amiably for quite some time about the pace of the war.

The conversation switched to Britain and Hess explained to von Weizsäcker why Germany should continue its attempts to forge some alliance as the real enemy lay to the east – the Soviet Union. Von Weizsäcker didn't disagree. He was impressed with the vision and integrity of Hess and enjoyed the lively discussion.

Two weeks later, on May 10, Hess, a qualified pilot, strode across the tarmac of an airfield in Augsburg, the testing centre for the Messerschmitt manufacturer. He was wearing his leather flying kit and no one deemed it unusual that the Deputy Fuhrer wanted to take to the air nor that during the day Hess had telephoned to request that extra fuel tanks be attached to the ME 110.

That evening the debating chambers of London's Houses of Parliament were bombed as German incendiaries brought to an end the three-week lull in the air raids over the city. Some distance to the north a lone Messerschmitt was detected, destination unknown. An RAF Defiant night-fighter was scrambled to give chase and intercept. Hess never saw the Defiant as the bullets ripped into the ME's fuselage to the south of Glasgow – a distance of 800 miles from Augsburg. The Defiant pilot witnessed the ME pilot bale out. He radioed through to control to register his 'kill'.

Hess broke his ankle on landing. A local Scottish ploughman, David McLean, apprehended him with a pitchfork but helped the pilot to his cottage to await the arrival of the police. The plane had crashed some 200 yards away.

With their prisoner declining to say anything, the police quickly handed over the pilot to the military. Hess provided a false name and demanded to be seen by the Duke of Hamilton, a Wing Commander pilot in the RAF whom he claimed to have met at the Olympic Games in Berlin in 1936. The Duke, who had three brothers in the RAF, was instructed to visit Hess, now in the military hospital at Buchanan Castle receiving treatment for his ankle. According to the newspapers the Duke failed to positively identify the prisoner, or 'Nazi No. 3' as the British press labelled him after Hitler and Goering. That was the official line fed to the press. The Duke knew full well of course who the man was, photographs of Hess had adorned English newspapers and magazines for years. Air Marshal Sholto Douglas, Commander-in-Chief, Fighter Command, told the Duke that Churchill wanted to see him immediately in London. After landing his Hurricane at RAF Northolt the Duke was driven to Ditchley Park, Churchill's favourite wartime retreat.

Initially there was silence from Germany, but the next day, May 11, Berlin Radio issued a statement. *'Party Member Rudolf Hess, who, as he was suffering from an illness of some years' standing had been strictly forbidden to embark on any further flying activity, was able, contrary to this command, again to come into possession of an aeroplane. On Saturday, May 10, at about 6pm, Rudolf Hess set out on a flight from Augsburg, from which he has not so far returned.*

'A letter which he left behind unfortunately shows by its distractedness, traces of a mental disorder, and it is feared that he was a victim of hallucinations. In these circumstances it must be considered that Party Member Rudolf Hess either jumped out of his aeroplane or has met with an accident.'

Thereafter Berlin's propaganda machine went into overdrive, questioning the state of mind of Hess and also denouncing any peace initiatives that Hess may be making to the British. Given the massive international press coverage, a cypher from Churchill, dated May 13, 1941, and marked *'Most Secret and Personal'*, was cabled to British Ambassadors in Canada, Australia, New Zealand and South Africa.

'Following for secret and personal information of Prime Minister begins.

'As reported in the press, Rudolf Hess landed by parachute from a Messerschmitt near Glasgow on the evening of May 10. He was seen and finally identified early this morning by Mr Ivonne Kirkpatrick, formerly serving in His Majesty's Embassy at Berlin [Kirkpatrick had known Hess when he was Counsellor at the Berlin Embassy]. *In lengthy harangue with Kirkpatrick, Hess declared that he had left Germany without the knowledge of the German Government, that he had not been sent on any mission, and that he merely left behind a note for Hitler. He said, speaking for himself, that German morale was unbreakable, that Germany was immensely strong in armaments (he instanced enormous growth in the submarine fleet and the air force) and that German victory was absolutely certain. He feared, however, that if the war were to continue much useless destruction would result. He advocated a settlement on the all too familiar lines that Hitler wished to live in harmony with the British Empire provided he were given a free hand in Europe.*

'Hess appeared to be completely calm and collected and gave no sign of insanity.

'Further interviews with Hess will take place later and you will be kept informed of any developments. Please treat above as secret. In the meantime, the line being taken with the press is given in my Guide telegram Z No.169 of today. You will see that it has been thought best at this stage to suggest that the flight is due to disagreement with other Nazi leaders. Ends.'

Berlin was in turmoil despite its statements to the contrary, as was the physicist from the Kaiser Wilhelm Friedrich von Weizsäcker. He was panicking that he may be asked to explain the circumstances of his recent trip to the Reich Chancellery, especially as the conversation had switched to nuclear fission and the atomic bomb. Hess had been particularly keen to hear more about the potential of plutonium.

'Are you happy in your work at the Kaiser Wilhelm?' Hess had suddenly enquired.

'Yes, of course,' replied the scientist.

'Please explain to me that secret report you wrote for the Heereswaffenamt in July last year proposing that reactors can be used to create neptunium for the manufacture of atomic bombs,' asked Hess solemnly. 'I understand it caused quite a stir, even amongst some of your colleagues.'

Taken aback that Hess was not only aware of his paper but also familiar with neptunium – a material very few outside the Kaiser Wilhelm would have even heard of – von Weizsäcker briefly outlined his proposals.

'How would this reactor look?' enquired Hess. 'Could you draw a diagram for me?' Von Weizsäcker carefully sketched a schematic for Hitler's deputy, labelling each component part of what crudely resembled a circular, irregular lattice of graphite with uranium cubes placed inside.

'I understand that not everyone at the Kaiser Wilhelm is in agreement about developing this new bomb, is that true?'

'It would be unfair to answer that question,' replied von Weizsäcker, thinking that Hess must have heard about Otto Hahn, the senior chemist, who had contemplated suicide.

'Tell me more about those experiments you conducted in March using layers of uranium oxide and paraffin wax in a cylindrical tank. Are you close to a sustained nuclear chain reaction?'

'The results were rather poor, I'm afraid, but I and my colleagues really believe that within months our experiments will be successful,' said von Weizsäcker.

'Is it true that Heisenberg conceded that deuterium oxide, heavy water, is considered no longer essential in your work and that Paul Harteck and Wilhelm Groth, in Hamburg, have had mixed success in their uranium isotope separation trials. Correct?'

Within days of his flight to Scotland, British Intelligence had spirited Hess to London and onward to 'safe' houses in Hampshire and Abergavenny in Wales, well away from German agents who desperately tried to locate his whereabouts. Contrary to newspaper opinion Hess was no fool, neither was he insane as German propaganda went to such lengths to suggest. The international press speculated that Hess carried photographs of himself, in his flying suit, for identification purposes. None were necessary, the Deputy Fuhrer's features were unmistakable.

Hess had a formidable memory but he had known that to really prove his value in England he needed to be armed with intimate knowledge of a number of Germany's deadliest secrets. In his flying suit he had several documents, some of them taken from the Heereswaffenamt, the German Weapons Office. As soon as Hess mentioned the Kaiser Wilhelm the interrogation took on a more urgent turn. During the first few weeks of his capture London's newspapers suggested that *'Hess was singing like a bird'*, but Churchill insisted on a complete news blackout. In the House of Commons, even MPs were oblivious to the intensity of the Hess interrogation, their questions met with obscure and inaccurate responses.

As Hess pulled back the canopy of his burning Messerschmitt, flinging himself out into the darkness, he had in his leather flying suit not merely a proposal for peace with Britain. Safely tucked away were two drawings. One was a schematic of a prototype nuclear reactor. The second would prove to be even more invaluable to the British.

Before Hess had concluded his informal discussion in the Reich Chancellery he had a final question for the theoretical physicist.

'If your team at the Kaiser Wilhelm Institute for Physics is successful in developing an atomic weapon, what would it look like?' Hess had enquired quietly. The mild-mannered and articulate von Weizsäcker walked slowly around Hitler's deputy's desk, picked up a blank piece of notepaper and drew his second sketch. The drawing was nothing like Hess had imagined.

Both drawings would shortly be in the hands of Winston Churchill and his close War Cabinet colleague, Sir John Anderson. They would ponder very carefully how to make the maximum use of such an intelligence coup.

CHAPTER 15

Barkovsky photographs the Maud Report

No one had met Vladimir Barkovsky and his colleagues as the train from Liverpool drew to a halt in Euston Station. They were expected to find their own way to Kensington Gardens. At the Embassy Russia's new political attaché presented himself to Ivan Maisky, the Ambassador, handing over his credentials.

London was under incessant German bomber attack in February 1941, but within weeks Barkovsky had found his bearings using the London Underground and the buses – when they ran. More often he walked. There was an Embassy car but Maisky had first claim, scuttling backwards and forwards to the British Foreign Office and to numerous social functions. Only on rare occasions was Anatoli Gorsky, the head of the NKVD London station, allowed to use it, but, as he couldn't drive, Maisky's driver drove him to clandestine meetings in and around London.

One of Barkovsky's first tasks was to buy himself a suit. He had his uniform for official receptions, but for his NKVD role a suit was the preferred choice. Expenses were limited but enough for Barkovsky to purchase a decent woollen suit from Austin Reed, the respectable tailor on Regent Street in the West End.

Gorsky was delighted with his new assistant, especially as Barkovsky had photographic skills that were vital given the volume of gathered intelligence coming into the Embassy. The codename *Jerry* was assigned to Barkovsky; sometimes he used *Dan*. With Gorsky as his mentor Barkovsky learned the ropes of the Embassy that had been savagely purged by Beria in 1938, eliminating two-thirds of its professional staff.

The resilience of Londoners and the daily difficulties caused by the level of bombing impressed Barkovsky greatly as he familiarised himself with the capital's landmarks. He dearly missed his wife, Vera, whom he was forced to leave behind in Moscow. Wives could not join their husbands in overseas postings, a ruling that changed in 1943. Gorsky instructed his new charge to be an active participant in the Soviet Society for Cultural Relations with England – an already proven source for useful contacts. Membership provided the perfect cover to travel around England and Scotland without causing suspicion. The rail network, still only really functioning at night because of the raids, regularly took Barkovsky to Liverpool, Birmingham, Oxford, Cambridge and Edinburgh to meet the growing NKVD network of intelligence providers in the scientific community.

Barkovsky's ultimate superior, Lt General Pavel Fitin, had made it very clear to Gorsky on which areas of espionage to concentrate; but the first priority was to increase the number of agents in the field and this was achieved with great effect. Lord Hankey's office had become a veritable goldmine, identifying every secret scientific location and the name of every scientist, British or foreign, that worked on the war effort. Barkovsky's trainers in Malakhovka had been very specific on recruitment methods, suggesting that contact with people well down the chain of command could yield the best opportunities.

The NKVD station grew. In March 1941 Pavel Yerzin arrived from Moscow to join Gorsky, Barkovsky and Andrei Grauer, an intelligence officer who had been in London since 1940. Within the year they were to be joined by Boris Kretensheild, who used the names of Kreshin or Krotov and the codename *Bob*. Kreshin had been in the United States running the Cambridge-educated spy Michael Straight, before transferring to London to help Gorsky manage Philby and the other Cambridge agents. Also active were the GRU officers. Captain Nikolay Aptekar, codenamed *Sergei*, arrived in the summer of 1941 to help evaluate Fuch's material from the University of Birmingham. His colleagues Major Simon Kremer and Captain Andrei Dubonosov had established several GRU cells throughout the country. Regular reports were communicated to Lt General Ilyichev, the GRU chief in Moscow.

In Moscow, Joseph Cohen, who ran the NKVD's British desk, was delighted with the flow of stolen intelligence from Britain, as was Fitin. Cairncross had provided the Russians with full details on Britain's biological and germ warfare programme at Porton Down, arguably the most advanced in the world at that time. More importantly, he had filed information to Moscow on protective measures developed by the British against this new form of attack – that had been a major revelation. Radar, another British invention, was intensely penetrated despite the edict by MI5 that no alien scientist should work on the project.

An internal NKVD note, written in Moscow and dated January 26, 1943, praised the efforts of the London *rezidency*:

'Altogether in the course of 1942 we have received about 3,000 sheets of material from the agents dealing with various technical questions. In the main the materials stand out to be valuable,' the memo reported. At the top of the list of agents who were passing intelligence to NKVD controllers was *List* – Cairncross. In second place was *Ellis* or *Ellie*, the codename for Melita Norwood, the secretary who worked in the Non-Ferrous Metals Research Association as secretary to the eminent metallurgist George Bailey. She provided her controller with documents on uranium research. For his work on stealing the radar secrets from the Clarendon Laboratory in Oxford, *Scott* came in for special praise. Of mention, too, were *Pirate, Alkit* and *Valet* – three agents of the highest value to Russian Intelligence.

Barkovsky enjoyed strolling through Hyde Park but he never used it for meeting his contacts, preferring Kew Gardens. The London pubs always provided good cover, as in wartime they were noisy and full of people conversing in foreign languages, given the international war effort concentrated in the capital. The hustle and bustle of the London Underground system was also ideal for passing over papers. However, his meetings with *Alkit* had a more specific location.

The choice of *Alkit* as a codename was one of the more unusual to be given to an agent. In the 1930s it was the name of a gentleman's tailoring firm that supplied uniforms to Britain's armed services, with outlets in London, Oxford and Cambridge. At chosen times Barkovsky would meet Eric Keightley Rideal, the Professor of Colloid Science at Cambridge since 1930. Rideal's department was one of the first university departments to be funded directly by the Ministry of Aircraft Production to experiment on centrifuges to separate uranium. Barkovsky would meet Rideal outside an Alkit outlet and they would find a café to talk.

Rideal's small team in Cambridge was highly respected by George Thomson and other scientists involved in the early British efforts to design and build an atomic bomb. Not destined to be part of the large British teams that arrived in Los Alamos and Oak Ridge in the latter years of the war, Rideal did, however, travel to the United States on a number of occasions. In Washington he developed a strong friendship with General Groves, the American officer in charge of the *Manhattan Project*. Through his work on the nuclear project, Rideal was also in close contact with scientists in the Kellex Group at the University of Columbia and with Sir Hugh Taylor, the British-born physicist at Princeton and Los Alamos.

The identity of *Pirate* was hidden from everyone, including the Ambassador. *Pirate* had been a 'walk-in', using his knowledge of how the NKVD operated in London to arrange a first meeting. An army officer, scientific training and language skills had brought him to the attention of MI6 where he soon impressed. The NKVD preferred to use codenames that had some association with their agents and *Pirate* certainly fitted the bill. A childhood accident had led to *Pirate* losing an eye, although few would notice the glass eye that had been fitted. At the end of the war *Pirate*, in consultation with the CIA in Washington, would shock his hosts by taking out the glass eye to give it a polish before popping it back in.

In the Embassy not all NKVD contacts were kept as closely guarded as *Pirate*. It was difficult to conceal the identity of *Valet*, who everyone knew to be Lord Victor Rothschild. Increasingly, Rothschild had become an agent of great value to the Soviets and Stalin was amused that an English peer had been recruited. The codename *Valet* was symbolic as Rothschild employed a valet, or manservant. In Russian there can be another meaning – valet is a 'Jack', a high value card in a pack of cards, denoting status. Often *Valet* was transmitted in coded cyphers from London as *Wallet*, somebody with money. Rothschild was not directly involved with nuclear intelligence, but as an officer in MI5 he was employed on domestic anti-sabotage duties that included security in key locations now being utilised for the atomic bomb project. His peerage gave him status within MI5, an organisation that thrived on social connections. Friendship with Churchill and other Cabinet Ministers always ensured that Rothschild was well informed and his opinion was sought in unrelated areas of state defence.

Often Barkovsky travelled from London to Moor Street station in Birmingham where he met a resourceful physicist that the Russians had codenamed *Moor*.

Barkovsky never had to leave the busy terminus – the physicist was always on time, waiting in the tearoom, and few words were exchanged. On the return journey Barkovsky, now fluent in English, would read the results of the latest uranium separation tests that were beginning to excite nuclear physicists in Moscow. During the war *Moor* would never disappoint, but he would eventually be unmasked by MI5.

Working with *Malone* became a delight for Barkovsky but meetings were infrequent as Wilfred Mann, the Imperial College physicist who by the end of the war had access to memoranda written by the head of Britain's secret service, Brigadier Stewart Menzies, divided his time between Washington and London. Mann, recruited in the late 1930s, was one of three NKVD agents in MI5 and had been given the codename *Malone* because of the strong Irish connection that ran through the family. Given the importance of the uranium separation developments at Imperial between 1940 and 1941 it was agreed with Professor George Thomson that Mann be transferred to the Ministry of Supply in Shell-Mex House in the Strand, where the atomic efforts were co-ordinated by Lt Commander Eric Welsh, the MI6 officer.

Moscow encouraged Gorsky and Barkovsky to penetrate deeper into the better universities, especially those that had offered employment to Jewish German scientists in the 1930s. East Europeans also interested the NKVD, especially Hungarians and Poles. Scientists with Russian or eastern European connections were targeted and blackmail was regularly used. False promises were made to look after relatives caught up in the war.

Barkovsky was proving indispensable to Gorsky, photographing much of the material obtained by the 'Cambridge Five'. This was enormously time-consuming as he developed several frames of each film taken by his Leica to ensure that his work was up to standard. However, Barkovsky still found the time to establish his own extensive network of contacts. If the MI5 'watchers' trailed Barkovsky around London and elsewhere he wasn't aware of it, although he took every precaution. It became standard practice that before every meeting with an agent a colleague would observe from a distance to ensure that no one had been followed. It was an advantage that Anthony Blunt, an officer in MI5, managed the 'watchers' and did as much as he could to lessen the surveillance of his Soviet controllers. Furthermore, the war was against Germany and MI5 had more pressing responsibilities.

At that time Barkovsky did not know the names of the other three NKVD agents involved in *Operation Enormoz*, the codename for the acquisition, by whatever means, of the nuclear secrets of both Britain and America. Kvashnikov, Yatskov, Feklisov and Barkovsky were destined not to meet each other until 1956, when a gathering of the Science and Technical Intelligence, the STI, in the Lubyanka brought them together. Only in 1943 did Moscow decide to pool the efforts of the GRU and the NKVD in obtaining nuclear intelligence under the NKVD umbrella for greater efficiency. However, the GRU didn't fully comply with the directive and maintained contact with a number of its agents.

As soon as nuclear intelligence was received in Moscow it was passed to Igor Kurchatov. Initially he was prevented from knowing the source, but that restriction soon changed as Kurchatov requested further clarification from London. Kurchatov made copious notes and circulated them to three close colleagues, Khariton, Zeldovich and Kikoin. Khariton was very worried about the potential security risk, at one time sending out a memo to his staff that his safe and office were out-of-bounds if he was away. When Laboratory No. 2 was constructed in Moscow, a NKVD officer delivered the latest intelligence to Kurchatov's home in the grounds to read at his leisure in his study.

Sometimes the diplomatic bag yielded unexpected gems for Kurchatov. In 1945 microscopic samples of U-235 and U-238 were included, courtesy of the British scientist Alan Nunn-May, codenamed *Alek*, who was working with the Anglo-Canadian team in Montreal. He had passed the material to his Russian controller, Senior Lt Pavel Angelov, in return for a bottle of Canadian whisky and $200. The one-milligram of enriched U-235 was contained in a small glass phial; the one-tenth of a milligram of U-238 was attached to platinum foil and wrapped in silver paper.

Normal communications channels across Europe from London could not be used during the war years and the diplomatic bag was the only way for Barkovsky's films to reach Moscow. The bag followed a long and complex route. It would be flown first to New York, where documents from the Consulate would be added. A courier then caught the train to Washington, America's capital that provided the Russians with incredible riches from the Gregory Silvermaster network of agents. This included Harry Dexter White, a senior official in the US Treasury who also provided highly classified material from the White House.

The diplomatic bag continued on its way, this time to Canada, another intelligence goldmine. In Ottawa, Colonel Nikolay Zabotin, the Soviet military attaché and head of all GRU activities in Canada, ran a number of networks, including the one in Montreal where Nunn-May worked on the British atomic bomb project. After Ottawa, the courier then boarded a Russian ship, docked in Seattle, with Vladivostok the next destination. The train journey from Vladivostok to Moscow took nine days.

There were a number of times, however, that Moscow received legitimate intelligence from Britain. On September 20, 1941, with Leningrad encircled, a cable to the London Embassy conveyed intelligence that Germany would try to take Moscow before the onset of the Russian winter. Bletchley Park was the source, an *Enigma* decode. That message was radioed directly from the Ambassador to Stalin and Molotov.

That same day another London transmission, this time from Gorsky, was greeted with incredulity. General Victor Kravchenko, the head of the NKVD's 4th Directorate and responsible for every top secret scientific and military establishment throughout the Soviet Union, called an urgent meeting of his colleagues and advisors. From Lord Hankey's office Cairncross had acquired the *Maud Report* – circulated to Churchill and the War Cabinet. Kravchenko urgently met with Fitin and together they briefed Beria.

Decades later Barkovsky recalled the moment in the Embassy when Britain's plans to build 36 atomic bombs were passed to him by Gorsky. *'I was at my desk when Gorsky brought over some papers for me to look at. In the pile that he had collected from Cairncross was a large report. I began to read it and immediately called Gorsky over when I realised what it contained. Gorsky said I should prepare for him a telegraph for Moscow summarising as much as I could. Some of the terminology was completely unknown to me but I used my English to Russian dictionary and did my best. After several hours I had written the summary, which I gave Gorsky.'*

The full title was the *Report by the MAUD Committee on the use of Uranium as a source of power*, dated July 15, 1941. In two parts, the least interesting to Barkovsky was the section on the use of uranium in the production of atomic energy for domestic use. Of greater interest was the considerable detail of Britain's planned weapon of mass destruction. In a matter of hours Barkovsky and Gorsky had prepared a summary that they handed to Philip Kislitsin, the NKVD cypher clerk, for immediate transmission. Stalin was aware of the British plans even before Churchill and his War Cabinet had specially convened on September 24 to discuss whether to proceed.

Not every member of the War Cabinet was in agreement, but the decision was made – Britain, on its own, would go ahead with developing the atomic bomb. The minutes of that meeting were also shared with Moscow, transmitted from the London Embassy on October 3. The source came from within MI5. Barkovsky's photographs of each page of the *Maud Report* arrived in Moscow on October 10, via a special diplomatic bag that excluded the usual stopovers in order to speed up delivery.

Kravchenko and Fitin had faith in the London station and the quality of its intelligence. They both believed that the *Maud Report* was genuine but Beria, as ever, needed convincing, even suggesting to Stalin that Cairncross had been compromised and 'turned' by MI5 and that the document was an elaborate hoax. Thanks to Barkovsky's photographs, Russia was now in possession of Britain's blueprint. Stalin was in a quandary. Although he deeply distrusted Beria, his deputy's instincts could usually be trusted.

There had never been any doubt in Professor Thomson's mind that Britain had the will and commitment to build a bomb, even if the War Cabinet didn't entirely share his conviction. Few outside a close circle of top scientists in spring 1941 were aware of the secret meetings held either at Imperial or the Royal Society. James Chadwick, John Cockcroft, Mark Oliphant and Phillip Moon were Maud members, joined later by Patrick Blackett, Charles Ellis, Norman Howarth and David Pye. Wilfred Mann was an advisor. None of the scientists could really be spared from other wartime projects. Cockcroft and Oliphant spent most of their working time with the RAF, developing radar.

Despite their sensational memorandum on the small amount of U-235 necessary for an atomic explosion, Rudolf Peierls and Otto Frisch were excluded from the committee because of their nationalities, as was Franz Simon from the Clarendon. The omission of Simon had been a major surprise to everyone concerned. With the relaxation of this policy, perversely only for the atomic bomb project not for radar, Simon was cleared by MI5 and he, in turn, helped in the vetting of his deputies in the Clarendon. Nicholas Kurti, born in Budapest, who had arrived in Oxford in October 1933, had already distinguished himself by perfecting a technique whereby metal splinters could be removed from the brain by magnets. Simon provided a reference for Kurti to the Ministry of Aircraft Production, the Government department tasked with handling the bomb's development. *'Kurti has a mother still living in Hungary, but no relations in any part of German occupied areas. I can absolutely guarantee his anti-Nazi attitude,'* Simon wrote.

Thomson had also asked Simon to vouch for the loyalty of Heinrich Kuhn, the physicist who left Germany for England in August 1933. Kuhn was a former assistant to James Franck, one of Germany's most distinguished scientists at the University of Göttingen, the 'Mecca' for physicists. Lindemann, head of the Clarendon, on a trip to Göttingen to visit Franck was made aware that the Nazis had suddenly withdrawn Kuhn's *venia legendi*, the right to teach in the German university system. Simon's third reference was for an American, Shull Arms, who was writing his thesis at Jesus College.

This team, under the direction of Simon, built uranium separation models, aided by Oliphant, Peierls and Fuchs from the University of Birmingham. The early Clarendon work attracted minimal financial support from Government, despite the best efforts of Thomson and Simon. Thomson wrote to Simon to inform him that the Air Ministry was to award Oxford University a special contract, enabling the Clarendon to talk to Government suppliers and other firms on an easier and less bureaucratic basis.

Permission was also granted to the Clarendon to use disused Government buildings owned by the Ministry of Supply at Rhydymwyn in Flint, north Wales, to undertake large-scale modelling work. Codenamed the *P6* experimental station, Imperial Chemical Industries contributed most of the 200 staff, mainly Army engineers and technicians. Arms, the Rhodes scholar from Idaho, never stopped refining the sketches for a prototype isotope separation plant, sharing his ideas with physicists and chemists in Liverpool, Birmingham and Cambridge. More scientists in the universities were co-opted, with Chadwick nominated as the senior scientist in charge of all laboratory research.

The scientists were working in a brave new world, a research environment where theories could only be proved after a test, the size of which the world had never before witnessed. In May 1941 Thomson wrote to Simon, in need of advice.

'Could you help me with a point of some importance?' enquired Thomson. *'I*

have been calculating the temperature that would be reached by the portions of the bomb when they hit after being shot together, and taking a speed of 6,000 feet per second, it works out at about 5,000 degrees absolute, which is rather formidable. I have made a calculation to see whether the resulting vapour pressure would be so great as to blow the halves apart before they could explode, assuming that for any reason the initiation of the explosion was delayed for a fraction of a second.

'I do not know what to assume for the heat of vaporisation of the uranium metal, but the lower of the two figures in the calculation seems fairly safe and in that case we are all right. I should be very grateful if you would look through it and criticise. I have had the algebra and arithmetic checked, but some of the assumptions are a little rocky.'

During that summer expert opinion was sought throughout the country. In early August 1941 the first draft of the *Maud Report* was finalised and submitted to Sir Henry Tizard, Churchill's special advisor. By August 27 it was with Lord Hankey, the chairman of the Scientific Advisory Council, personally delivered to him by Colonel Moore-Brabazon, the Minister of Aircraft Production. Churchill, too, received his copy.

Given the stringent wartime conditions, the project provoked the sternest questioning on cost grounds as radar had already sucked up so much cash and human resources. There was also scepticism as to whether Britain had the expertise to build such a thing. Churchill and Sir John Anderson never waivered from their contention that the bomb must be developed, but with American money. Testing remained a stumbling block as nowhere in Britain would be suitable for an explosion on such a scale.

Lord Hankey's committee met on seven occasions and solicited written and oral opinion from Tizard, Anderson, Lindemann and many others. Lindemann argued that a uranium isotope plant on the scale proposed by Simon could only be constructed in Canada. The level of radioactivity released by an atomic explosion was a question unresolved – no one had any real idea of the level of devastation.

In the second week of September Hankey and his SAC members recommended to Churchill that Britain should proceed with haste and build the separation plant in Canada, near the uranium resources at Great Bear Lake. It was now up to Churchill to convince the War Cabinet. He convened a meeting for September 24 in the bunker, an underground command centre near Downing Street where he spent most of his days and nights in the first years of the war.

In the Russian Embassy Barkovsky struggled with the 30-page *Maud Report* that was liberally annotated with formulae and diagrams. He started by translating, word for word, the introduction: *'Work to investigate the possibilities of utilising the atomic energy of uranium for military purposes has been in progress since 1939, and a stage has been reached when it seems desirable to report developments,'* it began.

'We should like to emphasise at the beginning of this report that we entered the project with more scepticism than belief, although we felt that it was a matter that had to be investigated. As we proceeded we became more and more convinced that

release of atomic energy on a large scale is possible and that conditions can be chosen which would make it a very powerful weapon of war. We have now reached the conclusion that it will be possible to make an effective uranium bomb, equivalent to the destructive effect of 1,800 tons of TNT.

'Large quantities of radioactive substances would be released, which would make places near to where the bomb exploded dangerous to human life for a long period. The bomb would be composed of an active constituent, U-235, present to the extent of about 1 part in 140 in ordinary uranium. Owing to the very small difference in properties, other than explosive, between this substance and the rest of the uranium, its extraction is a matter of great difficulty and a plant to produce 2 1/4 lbs (1 kilogram) per day (or three bombs a month) is estimated to cost approximately £5,000,000. A considerable proportion would be spent on engineering of a highly skilled character for making turbines.

'In spite of this very large expenditure, we consider that the destructive effect, both material and moral, is so great that every effort should be made to produce bombs of this kind. As regards the time required, Imperial Chemical Industries, after consultation with Dr H. L. Guy of Metropolitan Vickers Company, estimates that the material for the first bomb could be ready by the end of 1943. Dr Ferguson of Woolwich Arsenal estimates that the time required to work out the method of producing high velocities required for fusing is 1–2 months. Even if the war should end before the bombs are ready the effort would not be wasted, except in the unlikely event of complete disarmament, since no nation would care to risk being caught without a weapon of such decisive possibilities.

'We know that Germany has taken a great deal of trouble to secure supplies of the substance known as heavy water. In the earlier stages we thought that this substance might be of great importance for our work. It appears in fact that its usefulness in the release of atomic energy is limited to processes that are not likely to be of immediate war value, but the Germans may now have realised this. It may be mentioned that the lines on which we are now working are such as would be likely to suggest themselves to any capable physicist.'

This reference to the value of heavy water would create alarm in Moscow. There was also a realisation that Russia was nowhere near the British level of progress in harnessing the potential of nuclear fission, lacking even any facility that could manufacture a mere fraction of the required U-235. According to the *Maud Report,* an isotope separation plant designed and built by Imperial Chemical Industries would produce 360 kilos of U-235. In total the British estimated that the project would cost £8,510,000, considerably cheaper than the forecast £14,150,000 to produce TNT bombs of equivalent destructive power.

Within 30 months, said the report, by the end of 1943, the first atomic bomb would be ready. One estimate suggested each bomb could weigh up to 10 kilograms, with the destructive power of 3,600 tons of TNT. The world-renowned explosives expert,

Professor Geoffrey Taylor, had given his estimate on the expected blast damage. Barkovsky carefully translated one of the final parts of *Maud*, which focused on an issue the Soviets had suspected for some time – British atomic co-operation with the Americans.

'We are informed that while the Americans are working on the uranium problem, the bulk of their effort has been directed to the production of energy, rather than to the production of a bomb. We are co-operating with the United States to the extent of exchanging information, and they have undertaken one or two pieces of laboratory work for us. We feel that it is important and desirable that development work should proceed on both sides of the Atlantic, irrespective of where it may be finally decided to locate the plant for separating the U-235. For this purpose it seems desirable that certain members of the committee should visit the United States.'

The conclusion was clear.

'The scheme for a uranium bomb is practicable and is likely to lead to a decisive result in the war. Work should be continued on the highest priority and on the increasing scale necessary to obtain the weapon in the shortest possible time, and the present collaboration with America should not only be continued, it must be extended.'

At last Barkovsky was finished with summarising and taking photographs. Gorsky sped away to return the *Maud Report* to Cairncross while Barkovsky retired to his bed, conscious that his real task in London was only now truly beginning. The *Maud Report* had identified every secret location and the names of a number of the key scientists involved.

Barkovsky and Gorsky wasted no time in attempting to flesh out more detail on what Cairncross had acquired for them. Over the next three months both men determined the real extent of Britain's nuclear weapons programme. Rideal had become an advisor to the Maud Committee and proved invaluable, as did Mann. Some months earlier Barkovsky had met Mann for the first time. The location was Covent Garden. The nuclear scientist queried whether Barkovsky would be up to the mark. *'Look here,'* he stated in a clipped accent, *'if I am to pass secrets over to you, you will need to understand some nuclear physics.'* Mann pointed in the direction of a local bookshop in nearby Long Acre, where Barkovsky could purchase a standard textbook on nuclear physics written by US physicists E. C. Pollard and W. L. Davison. That book was to become heavy bedtime reading for the Russian political attaché. Within months Barkovsky had built up a rudimentary knowledge of nuclear physics, understanding electrons, protons, neutrons, photons, the workings of a cyclotron and the configuration of a van der Graaff high-energy particle accelerator.

The Soviets activated another scientist, a 'confidential contact' who had been of use for some time – Professor Patrick Blackett from the Cavendish Laboratory in Cambridge, who had given evidence to the Maud Committee on the feasibility of constructing a nuclear device. Recruited by the Comintern in the 1930s Blackett was involved with the 'illegal' apparatus of the British Communist Party. The suggestion for Blackett to join the British League of Free Europe, the centre for the struggle against Communism, had been the idea of Arnold Deutsch, the homosexual and great blackmailer who recruited many of his sexual conquests into Soviet Intelligence. The League attracted a broad church of members including Trotskyites that had fled Russia after Trotsky sought refuge from Stalin. Names of Trotskyites were passed to Russian controllers and throughout Europe many were liquidated. Blackett proved to be a successful talent spotter. However, he had no luck in trying to lure one young German émigré physicist in Oxford to Moscow with the offer of a handsome salary. Given his friendship with Churchill and his access to top-level scientists Blackett proved very useful.

Rideal, Mann and Blackett confirmed to Gorsky and Barkovsky that Churchill intended to build his bombs in a last-ditch attempt to stave off defeat against Adolf Hitler. In the Kremlin, however, Stalin contemplated that in the event that America joined the war those weapons might also be turned on the Soviet Union to eradicate Communism once and for all.

General Kravchenko wrote to Lavrenty Beria on October 10, 1941, strongly urging the head of state security to consider two main options to counter the British lead in developing a military use for nuclear fission.

'I would consider as urgent,' wrote Kravchenko, *'to task the foreign agents network of the NKVD in collecting materials relating to the building of apparatus and experimental plant in the manufacture of uranium bombs. Furthermore, a special commission of Soviet scientists should be established, attached to the Defence Committee of the USSR, to implement our own use of atomic energy for military purposes.'*

In his corner office on the third floor of the Lubyanka Beria contemplated Kravchenko's missive, as well as enclosed attachments from Gorsky in London and Anatoli Yatskov, the Soviet Vice-Consul in New York. Stalin had already set in train his own measures, contacting the Embassy in London. Ambassador Maisky, several weeks earlier, had suggested to Stalin through one of his sources that Britain was working on a super weapon but he had little detail. In the Kremlin the cypher clerk in Stalin's personal intelligence service sent an urgent dispatch to Maisky. In addition, a cypher had been sent to *Maxsim*, the codename for Colonel Vasily Zarubin who used the name Zubilin in New York where he was the NKVD *rezident*.

Zarubin was to fly to Moscow for a personal meeting with Stalin and some advisors. Beria was not invited to the conference that took place on October 12 in Stalin's study. The Russian dictator ordered Zarubin to exert every pressure on the NKVD's 'agents of influence' in the United States to share nuclear intelligence. Under Zarubin's efforts the Communist Party of the United States had developed into a large subversive organization with secret cells established all over America. Stalin told Zarubin that his wife Elizabeth Yurieva, a highly-competent NKVD officer in her own right, should step up her contact with a number of respected physicists, above all Robert Oppenheimer.

Within days of returning to New York Zarubin met up with Earl Browder, the head of the Communist Party, and stressed that Stalin had a new priority.

No atomic secrets in America or Britain were now safe.

CHAPTER 16

A decision for Roosevelt

In September 1941 the *Maud Report* was legitimately in another diplomatic bag – this time attached to the wrist of a Foreign Office employee travelling to Washington. There had been a lengthy debate at War Cabinet level about whether the Americans should have a copy. But as two members of the US National Defence Research Committee [NDRC] had been invited to attend Maud meetings as observers since April that year, the decision had been taken to give the Americans sight of the document.

Sir Charles Darwin, the head of the British Central Scientific Service in Washington, carefully scrutinised the report, already aware of much of its contents. Picking up the telephone, the former head of Britain's National Physical Laboratory in Teddington called Vannevar Bush, Director of the Office of Scientific Research and Development [OSRD] and chairman of the NDRC, requesting that they urgently meet. He knew that the people over at the OSRD would take the news badly. Bush would be miffed, knowing that the British, technically at least, were well ahead of the Americans.

Locking his office at 725–15th Street NW, Darwin hailed a cab. Little was said as Darwin handed over the *Maud Report* to Bush, who immediately rang James Conant, his deputy at the OSRD and president of Harvard. Despite the hour in London Darwin, back in his office, called Imperial College where Professor George Thomson waited patiently. After a short conversation Thomson dialled a number – known only to a few outside the War Cabinet. Churchill's face lit up when he heard the news, pouring himself a large whisky and not forgetting to replenish the empty glass of Sir John Anderson, the keeper of many secrets of this war. It was well into the evening, London time, and just hours away from a major RAF raid on Berlin and Kiel that would employ the latest four-engine Stirling and Halifax aircraft. That night the Berlin raid cost the RAF 20 of its new heavy bombers and their crews.

Bush and Conant spent some days in digesting the *Maud Report*, their suspicions confirmed that Britain had made great strides in developing an atomic bomb. Even worse, Bush now had to brief Roosevelt.

This was the second time that Darwin had acted as the courier. A month earlier and before the *Maud Report* had been proofed, an advance copy was safely aboard a Pan-American Clipper, stored in the overhead luggage rack above the head of a British naval officer, a chain-smoking Lt Commander. The 15-hour flight to New York, which included a short refuelling stop at Gander in Newfoundland, proved uneventful. The MI6 operative always enjoyed his flights across the Atlantic. Pan-American treated their passengers well, the food was excellent and the Californian wines very drinkable. Arriving in Washington the officer delivered his charge to

Darwin before heading for the Willard Hotel to catch up on sleep. He returned to London the following day.

Darwin had delivered the draft to Lyman Briggs, director of the US Bureau of Standards, the national physics laboratory. Briggs had little time for the British, disliking their quirky traditions and clipped accents. Furthermore, he had scant regard for Britain's uranium research. There were whispers that he even perceived little use in America's effort. As Darwin closed the door to Briggs' office he saw the director open his bottom drawer and throw the *Maud Report* into it. That night Darwin reported his reception to a very disappointed Downing Street.

The bottom drawer is where the report remained, even after a visit from the highly respected Australian physicist Mark Oliphant, who headed a team at the University of Birmingham and was a prominent figure in the implementation of Maud. Deaf ears greeted Oliphant's emphatic argument that the Americans must assist in whatever way they could. In his conversations with Conant and eminent scientists Arthur Compton and Ernest Lawrence, Oliphant stressed that the Americans should take the *Maud Report* seriously. The weeks passed – still Briggs sat on his hands.

This inaction had convinced the British to sideline Briggs and go higher, this time to Bush and Conant, ultimately Roosevelt. Bush had been well aware of the *Maud Report* and the intensive work of its component committees, but Briggs was a problem. As head of the newly formed Uranium Committee, Briggs had to make any recommendation. Now with the second copy of the *Maud Report* in his possession, Bush had been passed the ball and he knew he had to by-pass the roadblock. Roosevelt confirmed a private meeting in the Oval Office at the White House on October 9, Bush insisting on Conant's attendance. Bush enquired if Vice-President Wallace should be present, a suggestion greeted with a derisory response.

Rocking back in his chair, Roosevelt skimmed through the document, stopping at the page with an illustration of a cylindrical object.

'Is this it – is this the British bomb?' FDR enquired of Bush.

'Not quite, Sir. What you see is a drawing of a machine designed by a Professor Simon and others from the Clarendon Laboratory in Oxford, to separate uranium using a gaseous diffusion process through gauzes of very fine mesh,' replied the head of the OSRD.

'Are you telling me that the British, with their German scientists, have finally managed to put all the theory together and can build the thing?'

FDR's two most trusted scientific advisors shifted uncomfortably in their armchairs. Conant nodded his head.

'OK, how soon?' responded the President.

'Could be two years – could be three. They plan to build 36 bombs, the first to be ready before the end of 1943. They probably have the technology but their problem is space. It is going to be very difficult to camouflage an industrial-scale separation plant from German bombers, but that is a problem they may have solved.

'As you know, Mr President, there have been meetings both here and in London with some of our scientists swapping theories and ideas. Both sides always knew that a bomb was feasible. The British are exploiting the substantial uranium resources in Canada in the Great Bear Lake region. Already a group of Canadian scientists has been assembled in an expanded physics laboratory in Montreal's McGill University. We understand that British physicists and chemists may soon join them. The FBI has confirmed that engineers are constructing research facilities at Chalk River, some 130 miles west of Ottawa, with living quarters at an Indian reservation in nearby Deep River. The British have banked on their past imperial relationship with Canada to put this project together.

'Everything is not yet in place but given some luck, which is something the British could do with right now, they may just get their bomb. The first will be dropped on Hamburg, the second on Leipzig, and if the Germans don't capitulate, the third and largest will be exploded over Berlin. The bombs will be slung under a Lancaster bomber, only now coming into service with the RAF and the only air-craft in the world large enough to carry such a device. Initial casualties for each bomb could be 10,000, but we have no idea about how many would be affected by the radioactive fallout. Nor indeed do the British. I understand that the third bomb will have an explosive capacity of 3,800 tons of TNT equivalent. Much of Berlin will literally be wiped off the face of the earth.'

Roosevelt had ceased rocking his chair. 'Have you any idea what this thing will look like?' he asked.

'Nothing resembling a conventional bomb, it may be round and stubby,' inter-ceded Bush. 'For it to have the highest explosive effect it will be in two halves which need to come together at very high velocity, using ordinary explosives, in the form of a double gun. The gun will be heavier than the bomb itself but the whole device should not be more than one ton. The British say the bomb will be dropped by parachute and the gun fired by a percussion device when it hits the ground. According to the *Maud Report*, the time of drop can be made long enough to allow the Lancaster to escape from the danger zone.'

'How can the British assess damage?'

'That assumption is very vague,' replied Conant. 'Some of their analysis is based on a monumental explosion which took place on a British ship moored in Halifax, Nova Scotia, in 1917. Onboard was a veritable cocktail of explosives including 450,000 pounds of TNT, 122,000 pounds of guncotton and nearly 5 million pounds of assorted acids. There was a fire and, as you can imagine, a hell of an explosion. There were no survivors and the vicinity was devastated. Given the fact that a substantial part of the cargo was below the water line, and that damage was seen up to 61 miles away in one direction, the British have made some measure of the devastation.'

'Apart from the *Maud Report*, what else do we know?'

'Enough. You may not be aware of what I am about to tell you, Mr President.

Every time a British scientist or Government Minister enters this country, the FBI taps their phone lines and bugs their rooms. Remember when their two senior people, Tizard and Cockcroft, came over to talk to us in August last year? I have read the transcripts of their phone conversations. Mr Hoover set up a monitoring and surveillance unit in 1939 as soon as the Brits starting to come here in numbers for talks, especially over weapons purchase. At any one time there are countless meetings taking place here in Washington and New York.

'The British are creatures of habit, once they choose a hotel they never change. Most like the Hotel St Regis on East 55th Street in New York, others stay in the Barbizon Plaza in Central Park. The switchboard operators are discrete and paid good overtime by the FBI. Here in Washington, the favourite hotel is the Willard. That, too, is bugged. I understand that the FBI is assembling a large file on the backgrounds of the British scientists we have dealt with in recent months, just in case our present, very limited, co-operation turns into something more substantial. FBI people have been to London, quietly asking around.'

'You are right,' retorted Roosevelt, angrily. 'I didn't know this was happening and I find such underhand tactics despicable.'

'Perhaps I should also inform you, Sir,' continued Conant, 'that this practice is even more widespread. The FBI has covertly observed every German or Eastern European scientist who has fled to the United States since Hitler assumed power.'

'Even Einstein?' Roosevelt uttered, looking furious.

'Yes,' replied Conant quietly, 'including Albert Einstein. Edgar Hoover has never trusted Einstein, from the day he arrived in New York in 1933 to work in Princeton. Einstein is a self-confessed pacifist and the FBI felt he could be a danger to this country. His letters are intercepted and read, and his phone is bugged.'

'Einstein's letter to me in 1939, warning about Germany's intentions to build a nuclear weapon – had Hoover seen it, before me?'

'I am afraid that was the case,' Bush cut in, upset with how the conversation had turned, and annoyed with Conant for bringing up the issue over Einstein. 'I must tell you that it is only in recent days that we have heard about this surveillance,' he said, quickly covering his back and Conant's. 'Our source isn't Hoover, it is a deputy unhappy that the FBI Director had played this operation too close to his chest.'

'Did Einstein actually write the letter?' asked Roosevelt.

'No, it transpires that he merely signed it,' responded Conant cautiously. 'Two other physicists, Edward Teller and Leo Szilard, instigated the letter to push you to spend some money on the nuclear fission programme. Szilard considered that your sanctioning of $6,000 for uranium and graphite experimentation was derisory.'

The conversation stalled. A silence hung over the three men in the Oval Office. FDR looked thoughtful.

'I feel I've been deceived,' he said finally. 'We bug our British friends, we read the letters of our scientists and now I find out that Einstein didn't even write this letter to me. I do just happen to be the Commander-in-Chief around here. Is there anything else I should be aware of?'

Conant hadn't finished, he had yet more revelations.

'Mr President, our FBI source has said that there are taps within the British Embassy including the private phone line of the Ambassador. Apparently we have been listening into Churchill's phone calls to Washington. With regard to Britain's nuclear fission programme it also transpires that the FBI has gathered considerable intelligence from these Embassy taps which it has never deigned to share with us.'

FDR's face looked thunderous and Bush regretted including Conant in the meeting.

'Let us continue,' stated the President. 'The Germans – how far are they from their super weapon?'

'That's a tough question,' said Bush, anxious to quieten his deputy. 'Basically it boils down to whether Berlin's scientists are better than Britain's German émigrés. Hitler has left the project under the control of Hermann Goering but, from what we hear, the head of the Luftwaffe appears more enthusiastic about rockets rather than anything unconventional. The key team is based in the physics institute on the Kaiser Wilhelm compound in Berlin. The names of most of the older scientists we know as Einstein worked with many of them. However, the Kaiser Wilhelm is employing the best young talent in the country. One physicist, Professor von Weizsäcker, is regarded as one of the brightest scientists of his generation. His father, incidentally, is a senior and well-regarded Minister in Ribbentrop's Foreign Ministry. There are also unconfirmed reports that another secret nuclear centre has been established in Vienna.

'Our British friends inform us that special units have been attached to SS divisions within *Operation Barbarossa* to find uranium supplies, which can only mean that the Kaiser Wilhelm is deadly serious – even if Hitler doesn't appear that bothered. So far very little of the Russian nuclear effort has been captured by the Germans, apart from the Dnepropetrovsk Institute of Physical Chemistry in the eastern Ukraine. I doubt if the Russians would have left anything of substance – usually what they can't dismantle and carry, they burn. There is also a small laboratory in Odessa, on the Black Sea, but at the moment Soviet troops are holding out. The serious worry is the nuclear institute in Kharkov, just weeks, even days, from falling into German hands. According to our intelligence this institute was the furthest advanced in any Soviet uranium research.'

'Will the British beat the Germans to the bomb?'

'It is only conjecture that the bomb has a low priority with the German High Command, as we have been told by the British. What the *Maud Report* has confirmed is that the British have more or less discounted the use of heavy water in such a bomb, but the Germans may not have done so.

'I don't think we should trust our British friends completely. British Intelligence has a first-rate undercover operation in Berlin, placing agents deep inside military and scientific institutes before the war. True to form, little has been shared with us. Yet just a week ago, in London, one of our NDRC scientists on a liaison visit was taken aside and for an hour briefed about the Kaiser Wilhelm and its current work status, including the nuclear capability. Has an agent reported from Berlin that events in Dahlem are moving ahead quicker than expected and Britain now needs our scientific assistance?'

'It is common knowledge,' interceded Roosevelt, 'that Churchill is desperate for us to join the war. I personally believe that we should do so, but the American public is divided. Hitler must be stopped but memories linger over the Great War where we lost so many troops on the battlefields because we were ill-equipped and unprepared in coping with the carnage of trench warfare. When we agreed to go to war in 1917 we had just 100,000 enlisted men in uniform and 5,000 officers. The Europeans had years to gear up, we had just months. The British love conflict, it's in their nature. Is there any possibility that this *Maud Report* is really designed for us, to bring us out of our isolationism?'

'Close-up, Sir, it always appeared on the surface that the British were keen to work with us. Churchill set up this Scientific Advisory Committee under the chairmanship of Lord Hankey, and when I or Conant visit London he always makes us welcome. Recently I have had considerable personal contact with a Professor Fowler, the liaison officer between our two countries on scientific matters, who is based in Ottawa, and Cockcroft who works out of the British Embassy.

'In the first week of March this year we were asked by Hankey to make a specific presentation to his committee on our own scientific efforts at the NDRC. As well as myself, I asked two of our scientists, Dr Hovde and Dr Wilson from the small NDRC office at the US Embassy in London, to attend. Two days later a senior British scientist, Appleton, chaired a meeting on Anglo-American Scientific Co-operation on defence matters and Conant was invited. Within weeks the British agreed to a number of American missions to Britain to assess what work had been achieved in certain areas. Professor Tolman, a key NDRC member in charge of armour and ordnance development, led one. He talked to the scientists and engineers working on jet propulsion engines and anti-aircraft devices, particularly acoustic and radio proximity fuses.'

'How is our nuclear programme progressing, or is progressing too strong a word?' asked Roosevelt, sarcastically. 'I am aware the NRDC has purloined further funding from other sources, including the military. Are we being left behind by the Europeans?'

'The line we have fed to the press, after those headlines in 1939 concerning the Hahn-Strassman experiments, has been fairly non-committal but we have stressed that any developments underway in the United States will be purely for peaceful uses. Nuclear power could over a very long period of time completely transform our country.'

'Yes, I remember the policy – exactly where are we in the manufacture of an atomic bomb… or are we nowhere?' The President glared at Bush.

'I would be grateful, Sir, if you would allow me to review what we have done in the past year or so, it may be useful?'

'Go ahead.'

'After you received Einstein's letter you agreed that a Uranium Committee be set up under the directorship of Lyman Briggs. At the time we felt that both the Navy and Army should be represented and we appointed Colonel Adamson of the Army Ordnance Department and Commander Hoover of the Navy Bureau of Ordnance to assist him.

'Budgets are tight but we feel we have done a huge amount of work with the limited funding. At the first meeting of the Uranium Committee on October 21, 1939, there was input from some of our scientists, mainly Teller, Szilard, Wigner, Roberts and Mohler. You insisted that your economic advisor, Alexander Sachs, attend.

'I thought we moved pretty quickly because by November 1 the committee handed you its first report with eight recommendations. One of the recommendations was the immediate procurement of four tons of graphite and 50 tons of uranium oxide, sufficient supplies for our experiments.

'On the agenda for the next full meeting of the Uranium Committee on April 28, last year, there were just two items. The first confirmed our research on the U-235 isotope and our capability in manufacturing a uranium bomb. Secondly, we reviewed our intelligence on the German efforts, including the latest British information. An MI6 intelligence officer in the British Navy briefed us but it was pretty clear to Briggs and company that the committee was hearing only a fraction of the story. However, the upshot was that the Kaiser Wilhelm Institute for Physics had almost completely been set aside for research into uranium on the personal instruction of Goering. That news had quite a profound effect on the Uranium Committee, I can tell you, especially on the military.

'It was clear that we needed to beef up our own intelligence, but we shouldn't expect immediate results. We have kept in touch with the Lt Commander, 'the Admiral' as his colleagues refer to him, who I understand has intelligence responsibility for the entire British project.

'The Uranium Committee now reports to the NDRC and myself. Briggs, as you know, remains chairman, but Pegram, Urey, Beams, Tuve, Gunn and Breit – all very capable scientists, have now joined him. Wigner and Teller have both agreed to serve as consultants but Teller, in particular, is keeping the committee on its toes.

'The Navy funded the award of the first contract by the Uranium Committee. Columbia University received $40,000 for Urey's work on isotope separation. And after our meeting in the spring of this year, more contracts were agreed. We now have 16 contracts totalling $267,000 on the study of the uranium question; at Columbia, Princeton, Cornell, the Carnegie Institute of Washington, John Hopkins, the National Bureau of Standards, Purdue, Iowa State College, the universities of Minnesota, Virginia, Chicago, California and Indiana and, lastly, the Standard Oil Development Company.

131

'At Columbia, Fermi, Szilard and Anderson, under the leadership of Professor Pegram, are researching the use of graphite as a neutron moderator. Fermi now wants to construct a trial atomic reactor. Chain reaction experiments were also conducted at Princeton and in Chicago. To avoid replication Pegram has now co-ordinated efforts into a single programme headed by Columbia.

'We awarded a contract to Princeton, which ran from January to August this year, to investigate the increase of neutron production when an atomic pile is wrapped in beryllium. Initially that was worth $9,500 but we have bumped it up to $30,000 because the work is important. Dr Allison is the project head. In addition, at Princeton, theoretical work by Louis Turner points to plutonium having better fissionable qualities than U-235. Just a month after Turner announced his work two scientists from Berkeley, Philip Abelson and Edwin McMillan, demonstrated that neutron bombardment of U-238 produced neptunium that quickly decayed into plutonium.

'This breakthrough generated further research into plutonium, notably by Glenn Seaborg and Emilio Segrè, leaders of the nuclear physics group at the University of California. The Berkeley work, co-ordinated by Ernest Lawrence, has expanded considerably. There is now a pretty definite view that plutonium, like U-235, is fissionable.

'In March, we had some interesting news from England. Two scientists, Otto Frisch and Rudolf Peierls, have calculated how much U-235 was needed for an atomic bomb – four to eight kilograms, depending on how it was finally constructed, was their conclusion. Such a small amount caused annoyance amongst our military people, who questioned how the British got to that conclusion before we did.

'We can now produce microsamples of U-235 and U-238 for analysis. Alfred Nier, from the University of Minnesota, has become pretty expert in this process and is highly rated in the nuclear community. Our British friends have asked for some of our U-235 samples, which we have provided.

'With regard to heavy water, or deuterium, at first we felt it was quite promising as a moderator because of its low absorption and its slowing-down properties. In February, Urey initiated work at Columbia on possible methods of large-scale production but we have to wait and see. We also have a small programme running at the Frick Chemical Laboratory at Princeton. The scarcity of good graphite remains a difficulty. Columbia sources from a company in Saginaw, Michigan, but it is insufficient.'

'Thank you for that summary, but are we less advanced than the British and Germans?'

'On the theoretical side we are certainly up to the mark of the British and on the issue of plutonium we are well ahead. On application, the *Maud Report* has shown we lag well behind. The British are already thinking of a bomb design and even how to drop it – our scientists and military aren't even on first base. The jury's out on the Germans, but we shouldn't underestimate them. If we believe the British, the Nazis, too, could be just two years away from building an atomic bomb.'

'OK, should the United States buy-in to the British project and, if we did, what would the public reaction be if any of this leaks out to the press, given our very vocal anti-war lobby?'

'Sir, I believe we should extend our co-operation with the British but we should try to take the lead and direct the project – if any country builds atomic weapons, it must be us. I suggest we form a Top Policy Group to take us further, with as few people as possible to avoid leaks. It should consist of you, Vice President Wallace who can deputise, the Secretary of State for War, the Chief of Staff, Conant and myself. Perhaps we can add some scientists later.'

'Briggs, what about him?'

'Definitely not Briggs.'

'If we climb further into bed with the British, doesn't that imply that America's common enemy is Germany, even though we haven't declared war?'

'I'll leave that thought process to you, Mr President.'

'One final question to both of you.'

'Yes?' enquired Bush.

'Should I be worried about a Russian atomic bomb?'

'We can forget Russia. It doesn't have the technology or the uranium. Even if somehow they acquired the expertise my people confidently tell me they are at least 10 years behind us. No, the Soviets are no threat to the United States.'

Conant paused for a moment, debating whether he should offer his opinion. He stayed silent. His FBI source had recently passed him some very worrying information. According to an FBI agent in London every East European scientist experienced in nuclear research and living in America or Britain was a target for the NKVD and GRU.

'You had better draft me a letter for Churchill,' said Roosevelt returning the *Maud Report* to Bush.

Winston Churchill received that letter from Roosevelt, dated October 11, 1941, suggesting complete co-operation on the building of an atomic bomb – two months before the Japanese attack on Pearl Harbour and the American declaration of war.

CHAPTER 17

Stalin sets Maisky a task

Ivan Maisky read the decoded cypher several times before he fully understood what Stalin wanted him to do. There would be a monumental risk, but the tone was unequivocal. Stalin's note had been written in a dictation style, not the usual missives transmitted daily from Moscow. Poskrebyshev, Stalin's personal assistant, must have taken it down and passed it directly to the cypher room within the Kremlin, where the staff worked around the clock.

It had been a long and somewhat tedious day, culminating in a useful and entertaining dinner with Anthony Eden, the British Foreign Secretary. Maisky had earlier reluctantly accepted an offer of drinks as a guest of one of the innumerable Soviet friendship groups that had sprung up since the German invasion of the Soviet Union. Even the most hard-nosed of the Embassy staff were touched by the overwhelming support of the British as the gigantic battle for survival was being played out in the battlefields of the Ukraine and Russia in late October 1941. People queued everyday outside the Embassy offering food and clothes. Wives of British politicians, including Clementine Churchill, organized charity events and collections. Maisky wrote warmly about the donations in his communications to Stalin.

Such generosity brought new difficulties. Maisky was often approached at social gatherings where other more delicate offers were made. Nearly all were rejected out of hand as the Russians were unable to distinguish which were genuine, false or MI5 'plants'.

When Maisky arrived in London in 1932 relations with Britain were strained due mainly to the revelation in 1927 that Arcos, the USSR's main trade agency, was merely a cover for the OGPU, the predecessor to the NKVD. Officers from Special Branch raided the Bishopsgate offices in the City and discovered boxes of incriminating index files relating to espionage in Britain over a 10-year period. Staff had been caught in the act of burning files and documents in the basement. The raid made sensational headline news for days. Two years later British patience could be tested no further and Arcos was closed down. Maisky tried hard to mend the diplomatic fences, at the same time establishing his own intelligence network whose information he shared with no one but Stalin, much to the anger and chagrin of Beria.

The Ambassador and his wife adored the social whirl of London, the favoured posting in the Soviet Foreign Service – such a contrast from the austerity and blandness of life in Moscow. At times, however, he hated his job. When Moscow's tentacles of terror struck in London in 1938 he had felt impotent as Embassy staff were recalled on trumped-up charges, to be jailed or executed. Maisky had cultivated a wide circle of political and social contacts and his wife revelled in playing her part. She loved to lecture Embassy staff on etiquette, and was unpopular because of it.

In her spare time she played the piano, skilfully tutored by a Russian émigré who lived in Streatham, south London.

During the urgent negotiations that took place in London in June 1941 with the advent of *Operation Barbarossa*, Maisky was part of the delegation that negotiated the alliance with Britain. But Maisky doubted this new friendship would stand the test of time.

One ambassadorial duty was to attend the intelligence meetings that took place in the Embassy. These were stilted affairs, with the NKVD and GRU reluctant to share secrets, but often they were necessary as talent spotters, such as Harry Pollitt, the head of the British Communist Party, recruited for both organizations. It was common knowledge that Maisky had his own channel into the Kremlin and the cypher clerk in the basement of the Embassy had explicit instructions to destroy all the Ambassador's communications after transmission. Maisky never got on with the NKVD officers as he hated the organization and everything it stood for. However, he was duty bound to help when needed.

Colonel Anatoli Gorsky, the NKVD *rezident*, worked around the Ambassador as best he could but Barkovsky couldn't help but detect the spiky atmosphere soon after his arrival in London. If at all possible Maisky favoured the GRU, enjoying the friendship of its *rezident*, Major Simon Kremer. He had no hesitation in alerting Kremer after a phone call from Jürgen Kuczynski, an active member of the Anglo-Soviet Society and a co-founder of the German League of Culture. Kuczynski's news was most welcome – the German-born physicist Klaus Fuchs had agreed to supply British nuclear secrets.

The cypher to Maisky that cold October 1941 morning was unambiguous. Stalin needed Maisky to bypass NKVD and GRU officers in the Embassy and with the utmost urgency confirm personally that Britain and America were seriously investing money and manpower in the production of an atomic bomb. Moscow had received conflicting signals. In America, NKVD agents suggested that the US was dragging its feet about co-operation while in Britain Churchill debated whether to curtail the country's independent nuclear research and hand over part management of its programme.

In recent weeks, continued Stalin, documents had fallen into Russian hands that confirmed British scientific advances and he alluded to German progress on the same matter. Maisky, of course, knew exactly what Stalin was referring to. Despite attempts by Gorsky and his deputy, Barkovsky, to down play the significance of the *Maud Report* to the Ambassador, Maisky had clearly understood its shattering content.

For several days Maisky considered his options.

By any standards the house was a stately pile, a large estate in a picturesque village nestling in the gentle landscape of the Oxfordshire countryside, close to Henley-on-Thames. Deer roamed the grounds, the saplings fenced off to prevent them gnawing at the bark. During the pre-war years the village attracted walkers of all nationalities, exploring the Chiltern Hills. But now it was quiet, like thousands of other villages throughout the country. The able-bodied men were at war, leaving contractors to till the extensive wheat acreage. In the great house the servants had been conscripted or had voluntarily joined up, leaving only the elderly chef and butler to perform their now numerous duties. The giggling young maids were in the front line, maturer now and manning heavy anti-aircraft guns on the Norfolk and Suffolk coastlines as members of the ATS.

Less than a mile away the village cricket field was overgrown, the pavilion boarded up, its paint peeling. The sound of a leather ball on English willow hadn't been heard for two summers. An estate gardener had lovingly tendered the cricket square, but he had perished, left behind to die on the beaches of Dunkirk with shrapnel wounds as the last ships left for English shores carrying the defeated British Army.

The owner's somewhat younger wife preferred to spend her time in London, visiting Oxfordshire as little as possible. Such lengthy absences had taken their toll on the marriage. In polite company her husband explained away as best he could another non-appearance of his wife; but privately he relished the peace and quiet and the chance to pursue other, more clandestine, interests.

Once a month, after dinner, he pressed money into the hand of his butler with the instruction to disappear for the evening with the chef to the village pub. The worse for wear, the servants would stagger back through the rear garden and past the study. Through a crack in the drawn wooden shutters they could glimpse the master of the house in conversation with his guest, brandies in hand. At the front of the house the guest's Russian manufactured car was parked on the shingle, only the glow of a lit cigarette giving away the presence of the chauffeur. The butler, who had made up a spare room, never saw the guest who usually left for London as soon as it was light.

What Maisky had in mind would break the long-held golden rule of Soviet Intelligence, but he had been left with no other choice. In his office on the first floor of the Embassy he dismissed his personal staff for the day. He carefully drew up a list of names, deliberately excluding any GRU contacts, and settled on four possibilities. Maisky had met them all socially – one he knew in a more private capacity.

The night was drawing in as he left his desk to draw the curtains of his office – even Ambassadors observed the rules of the 'blackout' against bombing. He stared at the large building opposite, also in darkness, well aware that it was rented by MI5 for surveillance. Maisky smiled to himself, musing on how Britain and the Soviet Union remained deeply distrustful of each other.

If everything went to plan Maisky would introduce three agents of the NKVD to each other, an act that Beria, Fitin and Kravchenko would consider treasonable and that could only result in a firing squad if discovered. Stalin would never support him. He had thought about individual meetings to lessen the risks but decided against it – the situation was too urgent. Maisky shuddered as he reviewed his final shortlist. It was vital that each man could be trusted.

He finally deleted the name of John Desmond Bernal, the physicist from London University labelled by one London newspaper as *'the wisest man in the world'*. Founder of Birkbeck College's reputable crystallography department, Bernal had become involved in Britain's scientific war effort, but Maisky was uncertain as to whether that included the atomic bomb. Furthermore, Maisky felt that Bernal was too devoted to the Soviet cause, too vocal for his liking. Moscow initially believed that Bernal was a MI5 'plant' but it soon became clear that British Intelligence would not have dared feed the scientist with the quality of the material he had misappropriated for Russian consumption.

His mind finally made up he waited until later before he made his phone calls. Maisky had no fears about his phone being tapped; an MI5 officer in the employ of the NKVD had informed the Embassy that MI5, despite its sophisticated technology, was unable to listen to calls scrambled by the device recently installed by Moscow engineers.

Patrick Blackett was the most reluctant of the three in accepting the offer to spend part of the following weekend in Oxfordshire. The Cambridge scientist sounded disbelieving over the telephone as Maisky cited a recent Churchill report suggesting that further Anglo-Soviet co-operation might be helpful in progressing the bond between both countries. Maisky's final call was to Oxfordshire.

Shortly after Friday lunchtime Maisky and his driver were on the now familiar A4, the trunk road to the west of London, passing through Slough and Maidenhead before taking the Henley road. Maisky wanted to be early. The first houseguest arrived, paying off the taxi from Henley railway station, the signal for the Ambassador's most helpful host to retire for the remainder of the day.

Maisky greeted Walter Layton, the respected editor of *The Economist* from 1922 to 1938 and who still conducted vital foreign policy probes for the Soviet Ambassador. Layton had been perceptive in his analysis that the British Union of Fascists, under the leadership of Oswald Mosley, would find it difficult to expand its power base beyond the East End of London and would lose its popular support. After the new public order bill came into being in 1936 following the East End riots, Layton had correctly judged that the Prime Minister, Stanley Baldwin, was more worried about the movement to the Left in Britain than the Fascist group who supported Mosley. Stalin had read Maisky's report in 1938 on the Conservative Party and his conclusion that the Tories had lost touch with both the middle classes and the upper working classes, and was unlikely to win another general election in the foreseeable future. Maisky had paid Layton well for that information.

With his huge international experience Layton had been an excellent catch for the Soviets. He had first visited Russia in 1917, as a member of the Milner Mission, and in the 1930s he had become an economic advisor to the League of Nations. On the outbreak of war Layton joined the Ministry of Supply to produce propaganda and his abilities were well-respected in Government circles. Maisky had chosen well in Layton, who was noted for his contacts and tact.

Next to arrive was Blackett, in whom Maisky had taken a calculated risk, aware that he had met recently with Barkovsky to discuss the *Maud Report*.

The final guest, Lord Victor Rothschild, arrived late, pulling up in the drive in his sports car and looking forward to a jolly dinner with the Russian Ambassador. He knew both Layton and Blackett and after accepting a drink quizzed Maisky about the war on the Eastern Front before reminiscing with Blackett about Cambridge. Maisky refreshed everyone's glasses. The manor house was empty apart from the occupant in another wing. The two members of staff had been given the weekend off, but the chef had prepared a cold meat dinner for the expected guests. Outside, the burly Russian chauffeur prowled around the immediate grounds checking for intruders.

Rothschild was vital to Maisky. Before leaving the Embassy Maisky had read his NKVD file – it was both fascinating and extensive.

There was much detail on the Rothschild family and its influence in Russian matters after the Russo-Japanese war between 1904–1905, when a victorious Japan ended Russian attempts at hegemony in the Far East, especially Manchuria. The family provided funds to Russian revolutionaries leading up to 1917 and became involved with two American bankers, Gomberg and Rubin, who had a crazy idea to found an alternative power base in Odessa. In more recent years the Rothschilds' were used in Hitler's speeches to whip up hatred of the Jews and Jewish-owned banking institutions.

At the age of 20, Victor went up to Cambridge to read biology, never short of money and the envy of fellow students with his throaty Mercedes. Studying at Trinity, he became friendly with Peter Kapitsa, the Russian nuclear physicist from the Cavendish Laboratory who had travelled to Moscow on holiday and had his exit visa cancelled on Stalin's personal order. Other friends included current and former members of 'The Apostles', the Left-wing Cambridge club that included Burgess, Blunt and Alastair Watson, the brilliant scientist employed by the Admiralty in war work but who shared naval secrets with Moscow. Philby, also a Trinity man, was the conduit for the recruitment of Rothschild in August 1934, but the first attempt was bungled. Unexpectedly Rothschild received a theatre ticket through the post for a play in Cambridge – with no clue as to its sender. He discarded it. Several days later he received a short letter, signed by Philby: *'Dear Victor, haven't you received an invitation recently?'* it read, with another ticket enclosed.

Moments before curtain-up a tall blue-eyed man, with bushy hair, occupied the seat next to Rothschild. During the break they shared a drink and talked about music, the stranger introducing himself as Paul Hart, a Hungarian by birth. Others would know him as Theodore Mally. Moscow referred to him as *Otto*, an 'illegal' who had arrived in Britain as a recruiter for Russian Intelligence in the top universities. Other 'illegals' who had proven success throughout the country and in the universities were Arnold Deutsch, Samuel Kahan and Henry Christian Peake. Their controller in the Russian Embassy was Aron Schuster.

Hart made a favourable impression on Rothschild and met the budding biologist in the pubs in and around Cambridge. The recruitment was a formality, as Rothschild didn't need convincing that Fascism in Europe had to be fought against. Rothschild was instructed to terminate all contacts with the British Communist Party and tone down his strongly held anti-Fascist opinions. In 1937 Victor took up the family seat in the House of Lords and regularly met Churchill, still in his 'wilderness years' after falling out with Stanley Baldwin by opposing the granting of any measure of future independence to India.

During the Spanish Civil War Rothschild had proved his worth with his connections. Through Rothschild, Soviet Intelligence was able to establish a secret London-based weapon supply to the Republicans that later extended to Paris, Brussels and Warsaw. The young member of the House of Lords showed promise.

Maisky put down his glass.

'Gentlemen, thank you for coming,' said the Ambassador, his voice sincere in its tone. 'Forgive me for being dishonest. I found it necessary to bring you here together on false pretences.'

Blackett swore and got up to leave but Maisky pushed him back hard into the deep leather armchair. Layton looked petrified, Rothschild appeared calm.

'I have taken a great risk bringing the three of you together but I am in need of some answers to some important questions. Equally, you must now feel very exposed.'

His three guests looked astounded, realising the terrible significance of Maisky's inference.

'Unfortunately I could not afford the luxury of seeing you personally. This little gathering never happened and you will never speak of it to your individual case officer within the Embassy. I trust I make myself very clear?'

No one spoke. Layton averted his eyes to the ceiling in what looked like silent prayer. Blackett's face was thunderous. Rothschild now glared at the Ambassador.

'If anyone breaks this confidence there will be great risks for us all, but I will personally ensure that whoever is responsible will be dealt with – however, that threat, I'm sure, is unnecessary.

'This large house is empty, with the exception of the owner, and I have every reason to trust him implicitly. The only other person in the vicinity is my driver and he has orders that no one leaves until the morning. Dinner has been organized and rooms prepared. Gentlemen, refresh your drinks and let us retire to the dining room where our kind host has left us some excellent wine from the cellar.'

During dinner the silence was palpable. The guests merely picked at the contents of their plates.

Maisky dispensed with the dessert. He felt he needed to make a start.

'Britain is building a bomb,' he began, 'but not of the conventional variety. It will have the explosive equivalent of nearly 4,000 tons of TNT and will be constructed of a new material, a derivative of uranium, referred to as U-235.'

The Ambassador paused, hoping for a response. There was none. He continued.

'It is imperative that two weeks from now I have a full briefing which will be reported directly by myself to Comrade Stalin. Using extreme caution I expect you to use your contacts to provide me with anything you think important to include in my assessment for Moscow. Take great care in writing anything down.

'Mr Layton, sorry, Walter; I hate formality, I have to put up with it every day.

'You have acquaintances that reach into the War Cabinet. Furthermore, your friendships in the Civil Service, those private secretaries who delight in gossiping about their respective Ministers, have been a veritable gold mine in your long journalistic career. I need to know if there is a political will to really push the development of this bomb through.

'Patrick, you are an advisor to the very committee that has produced the *Maud Report*. The British aim to build a plant with the capacity to separate uranium oxide in industrial quantities to produce the necessary U-235. Can Britain really manufacture metallic uranium in such quantity and where could it be hidden from German bombing? Could its location be Canada? There is even suspicion that Britain is working on an even deadlier weapon, a bomb of even greater devastation, using another uranium isotope, U-239. I need to know more about this plutonium.'

Maisky turned towards Rothschild.

'Lord Rothschild, I won't share your precise role with my other guests, but in all probability they know exactly what you do. Cambridge could never keep its secrets. It isn't just your scientific skills that are well regarded in the organization that now employs you.

'Your country claims its first bomb will be ready by the summer of 1943. The Americans by then will be part of this war and, if that is the case, Hitler, even with Japan on his side, knows that his vision of world mastery will be under major threat. Given America's huge economic power the tide will surely turn and we must also assume that at some time our own Red Army will be resurgent. In my opinion Britain and America will combine their nuclear research and build a super weapon together. However, I need to know that fact categorically.

'Assuming defeat for Germany, will the Americans and British then declare war on Communism? Will Soviet cities become the ultimate targets to test this atomic bomb – an important consideration for Stalin, I think you'll agree?

'It may also be useful if you could confirm the name of the scientist in America who is likely to head the joint American and British nuclear efforts.

'So gentlemen, I need some answers, and fast. I will excuse myself and leave you alone for a while.' Maisky left his guests in the dining room, keeping the door ajar. Blackett's raised voice could easily be heard.

Inwardly, Rothschild was angry too, very angry at being compromised, his relationship with Soviet Intelligence now known to Blackett, a man he disliked intensely. Maisky had forced him into a corner with no alternative but to comply. Since leaving Cambridge Rothschild had assiduously tried to divest himself of his Communist friends. It was bad enough that his mother had befriended Guy Burgess, a drunk at the best of the times. To add insult to injury, his mother paid Burgess to advise on her investments, ignoring the usual banks that dealt with the Rothschild fortune. Pure chance had led to Burgess picking up the tip on Argentina's nationalisation plans, ensuring that his mother withdrew her investment whilst other investors caught a cold. Rothschild looked at the ashen-faced Layton, nursing his drink – he didn't look like a threat.

When Rothschild had informed his Russian controller about his employment within MI5 he had hoped that the NKVD would leave him alone not wanting to inadvertently compromise either Blunt, who was already in a good position within the organization, or Philby in MI6. For a year that was the case, until Philby had contacted him to relay a message. The NKVD wished to re-establish the relationship. Reluctantly Rothschild agreed, but the Embassy case officer regularly admonished him for the relatively low level of intelligence he handed over.

Rothschild needed some air, and he walked alone into the garden. To give Maisky what he wanted was going to be difficult. He knew little about the specific MI5 unit set up with RAF Intelligence to supervise the project. There had been an almighty row after Reginald Jones, the chief scientific advisor already in charge of radar, was passed over in favour of Lt Commander Eric Welsh of MI6. That was a very unpopular decision. Rothschild decided he would try and pump Roger Hollis, who was vetting the nuclear scientists, for information. There was also his friendship with Churchill, but that was a hand that would need to be played with great care.

After returning from the garden Rothschild had steered Maisky into the study, slamming the door behind him and venting his anger at the Ambassador, threatening to discuss what had happened with Philby. Maisky could only hope and pray that that eventuality would not occur. Blackett and Layton continued drinking well into the early hours. It is doubtful if anyone slept in the great house that night, apart from the owner. Outside, the chauffeur kept a watchful eye over the house and its immediate grounds.

In the morning Rothschild was first away, avoiding any farewells. Layton caught the train to London and Blackett caught a taxi into Oxford to meet friends at the Clarendon Laboratory. Maisky, standing at his bedroom window, observed them leaving.

Matters didn't go to plan. The deadline was too short, all three calling to express the need for more time. They met again in Oxfordshire almost a month later, but this time individually.

Blackett was first. His technical report of progress was very thorough, including detail on the discussions with the Americans and the plans to build a uranium separating facility on the banks of the Chalk River in the Canadian province of Quebec. Moscow would find that information very useful. Before he took his leave the sullen Blackett thrust a piece of paper into the Ambassador's hand – a scribbled copy of the minutes of a technical committee convened to discuss the latest research into the explosive properties of plutonium.

An hour later Rothschild arrived. From the inside pocket of his jacket he handed an envelope to the Ambassador and left without saying a word. Rothschild strode back to his car, the rear wheels skidding on the shingle as he raced down the long drive to the gates of the estate.

Layton, as usual, did not disappoint. The War Cabinet, he imparted, was split over the bomb, putting Churchill in a dilemma. His advisors had urged that greater pressure be placed on the US Ambassador to Britain and for Churchill to visit Roosevelt and persuade him to bring America into the war, which would surely be won with conventional weapons. Layton had prepared a short synopsis of the views of each member, which Maisky found extremely illuminating. Atlee had argued fiercely that scarce funds should not be wasted on a non-conventional bomb. The military, mainly the Army, remained unconvinced that an atomic bomb could even be manufactured. The RAF, on the other hand, seemed more positive. Intriguingly, Sir John Andersen had stimulated discussion over offering limited nuclear exchange with Russia. Maisky thanked Layton and gave him an envelope, money drawn that day from the Ambassador's own contingency fund at the Embassy.

The Ambassador settled back in his seat as the car slowly made its way through the confined streets of Henley. The river looked serene and calm, some young boys paddled a canoe under the historic bridge, impervious to the war. As the car engaged first gear up Remenham Hill towards Maidenhead, he read Rothschild's short note.

'Roosevelt has written to Churchill agreeing to the Prime Minister's proposal that atomic research and technology be shared, but the detail has yet to be worked out. Robert Oppenheimer is likely to head any American programme. The decision to move all research and development across the Atlantic has not been discussed. However, Churchill is pushing for that to happen, despite strong opposition from a number of quarters.

'Our scientists are far too optimistic in even suggesting that a nuclear bomb could be built within two years on our own and mainly in Britain. If America enters the war, the war will be shortened and we must be optimistic as to a favourable outcome. In this event no such super weapon may be necessary. Publicly, Churchill has been profuse in his support of our ally, Russia. In private, he is thankful that the second front for the Germans provided Britain with much needed breathing space. He knows that America will eventually be engaged in the war, he just doesn't know when. Britain's natural ally is America, certainly not the Soviet Union, a country Churchill has detested ever since the 1917 Revolution. Churchill has asked the RAF to draw up a list of potential German targets for the bomb, and queried whether it *would be possible to modify the new Lancaster, increasing the range of the bomber's Rolls Royce engines, sufficient to enter Russian airspace.'*

Maisky spent a day drafting his communication to Stalin, careful to omit any statement that the NKVD in Moscow could trace back to its agents in the event that a copy fell into its hands. Satisfied, the Ambassador walked downstairs to the basement, to the cypher room, standing over the clerk as the coded transmission went out. Back in his office he tore up his report into tiny pieces and left the Embassy – he was late for a drink at the Athenaeum and his host never liked to be kept waiting.

A week later the Japanese attacked Pearl Harbour. America was now in the war against Germany and Japan. Irrespective of the cost, it now forged ahead in a late attempt to build its own weapon.

CHAPTER 18

Tube Alloys *is born, but compromised*

In Britain, Roosevelt's letter to Churchill to assist in the development of an atomic bomb was greeted in some quarters with scepticism, even contempt. With Britain effectively bankrupt and with the war sapping all available resources there were loud accusations that the Americans were attempting to snatch what could be one of the greatest inventions the world was ever to witness.

Churchill overruled dissension within his War Cabinet, arguing that British-American collaboration was paramount if the war against Hitler was to be won. Some members had different views but secrecy prevented them from airing their grievances over this issue. David Pye, the senior research scientist at the Ministry of Aircraft Production and a member of the Maud Committee, managed to sway the War Cabinet, suggesting that Britain should push on as the level of American co-operation was as yet unspecified.

Professor George Thomson's Maud Committee was replaced by the Department of Scientific and Industrial Research [DSIR] and the Ministry of Aircraft Production relinquished its lead role. Sir Edward Appleton, already in charge of the radar programme, was handed overall scientific responsibility. Much to the annoyance of the key university laboratories involved in the atomic project Imperial Chemical Industries [ICI] demanded, and won, a lead role in its management. That decision was justified as ICI committed hundreds of the company's best scientists, engineers and technicians, and agreed to construct the uranium separation plant once the Clarendon had carried out sufficient testing on the diffusion models. The responsibility for producing the metallic uranium was given to ICI's general chemicals division in Widnes, with input from another ICI plant at Winnington, as well as the Clarendon and Cavendish laboratories, and the Non-Ferrous Metals Research Association. Metropolitan-Vickers, one of Britain's largest ordnance companies, also tooled up in readiness to take the project further.

The question for Churchill was who at War Cabinet level should have the ultimate sanction. He took advice from Lindemann, now Lord Cherwell, and Sir John Andersen was his choice – a recommendation that was readily accepted. Churchill asked the Chiefs of Staff Committee to endorse that decision. *'Although personally I am quite confident with the existing explosive, I feel we must not stand in the path of improvement, and I therefore think that action should be taken in the sense proposed by Lord Cherwell, and that the Cabinet Minister responsible should be Sir John Anderson. I should be glad to know what the Chiefs of Staff Committee thinks,'* he wrote to General Ismay, head of the committee.

With ICI now in the driving seat it was a mere formality that Wallace Akers, an ICI director, was given day-to-day control. He had successfully managed the company's

Billingham research facility in County Durham and pushed through an innovative process for deriving oil products from coal. The plant was also producing heavy water on a laboratory scale. Anderson summoned Akers to London and offered him the job as controller of atomic policy. An ICI colleague, Michael Perrin, a chemist by training, was appointed his deputy and Britain's atomic bomb project now operated out of an office in Old Queen Street, London. For months Perrin had co-ordinated the meetings between Professor Simon and Lord Melchett, an ICI director, who had been instrumental in ensuring that the Clarendon received sufficient samples of metallic uranium for its experiments.

The diminutive Perrin established several co-ordinating committees. Akers chaired the Diffusion Committee, comprising Simon, Peierls, Arms and representatives from ICI and Metropolitan-Vickers, with Perrin as secretary. Professor Norman Howarth from Birmingham University chaired the Chemical Research Panel with administrative support from Perrin. The only committee on which Perrin did not participate was the Metal Panel, a group of seven scientists chaired by Edward Colbeck, head of ICI's alkali division. Perrin and Akers awarded all research contracts and issued patents.

The codename *Tube Alloys*, or *TA*, was applied to the atomic bomb project. Perrin – whose appointment had surprised everyone except Akers – added intelligence and security responsibilities to his tasks. Given the secrecy of *TA*, Perrin moved to the fourth floor of Shell-Mex House on the Strand, a London landmark that was linked into the underground warren of tunnels in central London. Narrow channels that conveyed the mail for the Post Office throughout the area had been in use for decades, while other, wider passages including rooms free from eavesdroppers, were now used by the military, Government departments and the intelligence services. Entrances were either in key buildings such as Shell-Mex House or through heavy metal doors in a number of streets. One such entrance can still be found in Holborn, right on the pavement, which is connected to a lift that leads underground. In Shell-Mex House the nameplate in the foyer described the Government tenants of the fourth and fifth floors as the Ministry of Supply, but in reality the occupants were specialist MI5 and MI6 departments.

A high-level visit from two American scientists was arranged in October 1941 to mark the greater co-ordination between the two countries. Vannevar Bush, head of the NRDC, selected George Pegram, the President of the American Physical Society and Director of the Physics Laboratory at the University of Columbia, and Harold Urey, also of Columbia, to assess the full extent of atomic development in Britain. The American Embassy in London made the travel arrangements and confirmed to Perrin that the two would be leaving the US by PanAm Clipper on October 14.

Bush was naïve in assuming that the British would fully co-operate. Appleton laid down the ground rules for the appointments, writing to Simon: *'I hope it may be possible to arrange for them* [Pegram and Urey] *to visit you in a few days' time.*

Mr Perrin will probably be telephoning you about this. It will be very useful for the US authorities and us if a full record is made of all the discussions with Professors Pegram and Urey, and I have asked Mr Perrin to do this. At this stage of the work I think it will be sufficient to confine the discussion to the scientific possibilities and results. The questions of the larger issue have not yet been definitely settled and I feel it would be wiser not to discuss them at present.' The 'larger issue' was, of course, the atomic bomb and Perrin personally contacted everyone who would be meeting the two scientists to remind them to adhere to the hard line on secrecy.

Vetting was one of the most difficult tasks for Perrin. The rule had been established before the war that only British-born scientists and engineers could be enrolled in secret work such as the radar programme, but given the urgency of *Tube Alloys* and the experience of the European and German scientific émigrés, a special dispensation was allowed. The Royal Society helped Roger Hollis, the MI5 officer, as best it could in the vetting but the main check was by character reference. The nuclear scientific community was a small one so everyone knew each other. In most cases the more experienced scientists were quite prepared to provide written references for the younger ones, some just a few years out of university. The DSIR and MI5 did run some background checks, but there wasn't the time or the manpower to investigate every employee. One physicist, newly hired by Simon, had Russian ancestry that included a mother who had been a valued employee in London for Arcos, the notorious Soviet trade mission raided by Special Branch in 1927.

Rudy Peierls, the German-born physicist working in the University of Birmingham was cleared but there were misgivings about Genia, his Russian wife. It had not gone unnoticed how Genia loved to cultivate key nuclear scientists such as Simon, regularly questioning them about their respective research. Genia also took to 'mothering' some of the younger physicists that her husband had employed in his laboratory, such as Fuchs. Usually they had little money, as their salaries were poor despite the importance to the nation of their work. She invited them home for dinner, advised them on personal matters and generally took them in hand.

Dr Klaus Emil Julius Fuchs, born December 29, 1911, in Russelheim, Germany, had been desperate for British citizenship, canvassing colleagues and friends to help in his application. His father was a pastor and an academic, dismissed as Professor of Theology at the Pedagogische Institute in Kiel by the Nazis as politically unsuitable. Political persecution led his mother to commit suicide at the age of 60 and a sister took her life at 30. Fuchs had attended the University of Leipzig from 1930–1931, followed by two years in Kiel. As a student he had joined the KDP, the German Communist Party, openly wearing a hammer and sickle badge. Ever since March 1930 the country had been in political chaos, with the coalition Government that had ruled the Weimar Republic since the end of the Great War in disarray. Dr Brüning, the 'Hunger Chancellor' and head of the Catholic Centre Party, increasingly came under pressure from the National Socialists and the KDP to improve the chronic economy. By 1932 these two parties in total accounted for 52% of the voting amongst the electorate.

When the Reichstag was set afire in 1933 and the blame placed on the KDP, Fuchs went on the run, hiding in 'safe houses'. The Gestapo put out a warrant for his arrest, the field office in Kiel holding the file *'Klaus Fuchs, Student of Philosophy, Born December 29, 1911, Russelheim, RSHA-IVA2'*. Desperately keen to study for his doctorate Fuchs knew, however, that no German university would dare offer him a place. Funds were made available by his Communist friends to study in Britain and in 1933 Fuchs arrived at the University of Bristol. Funds were channelled to him each year. After obtaining his doctorate in 1937 Fuchs had a real problem, as he was unable to return to Germany. He enlisted the support of Professor Max Born, the German physicist at the University of Edinburgh, who offered him a research post. Born was internationally renowned for his award-winning research on the scattering of atomic particles and in Germany he had worked with Robert Oppenheimer on the structure of molecules. At Edinburgh Fuchs met up with a number of old friends and impressed his colleagues by his aptitude for experimental physics. On the outbreak of war Fuchs was interned as an alien but Peierls wanted him in his group in Birmingham. Perrin was assured by Born that Fuchs was beyond reproach. His activist background was never discussed or discovered.

Nor was the Communist background of Alan Nunn-May ever disclosed. Educated in Birmingham he had won a scholarship to Trinity Hall at the University of Cambridge in 1930, and had been tutored by Patrick Blackett. He joined the Communist Party of Great Britain and after graduating worked at the Cavendish Laboratory before taking up a lectureship at Kings College, London. On the outbreak of war Nunn-May was recruited as a member of the radar group but he was evacuated to the University of Bristol with his colleagues to join a group under Neville Mott. Brought back to the Cavendish by James Chadwick, the scientist in overall charge of co-ordinating the input into the *Maud Report*, Nunn-May was asked to evaluate reports emanating from Germany that 'dirty weapons' were being proposed. Such a process was indeed under review at the Heereswaffenamt, the German Army Weapons Office. With the V-rocket programme on the drawing board plans were afoot to irradiate the rocket heads and so contaminate the area with radioactivity wherever they exploded. Nunn-May was actively involved with reactor studies at the Cavendish and the use of heavy water.

Throughout the war Nunn-May would compromise British scientific secrets to the Russians with complete disdain. Even on his deathbed he would not disclose the full extent of his treachery or the name of the man who recommended his recruitment to the NKVD.

Perrin quickly grew into his job, striking up a solid working relationship with Lt Commander Welsh who took the son of the Bishop of Willesden into his full confidence. Welsh had established a major MI6 network in Germany managed by

Frank Foley, who worked in the British Embassy in Berlin from 1929 to 1939 under the guise of Passport Control Officer. Foley made innumerable contacts including running *The Griffin*, the codename for the German scientific editor and publisher Dr Paul Rosbaud. Through Rosbaud contact had been maintained with several contacts at the Kaiser Wilhelm. Otto Hahn regarded Rosbaud as a friend, as did others who worked on the German atomic bomb project. During his time in Berlin Foley was able to grant visas for hundreds of Jews fleeing the Nazis. As war with Germany was imminent MI6 moved Foley to the Embassy in Norway where he continued to monitor his Berlin network. When Rudolf Hess fled to Britain Foley travelled to London and was a key member of the interrogation team.

Under Akers and Perrin *Tube Alloys* gathered momentum, both in Britain and Canada, but Churchill and Sir John Anderson were keen to foster a greater sense of realism amongst Britain's scientists that the country couldn't go it alone. The US had to be a full partner; despite the fierce objections from some scientists who remained dead set against any such proposal.

In America, however, events were moving quicker than even Churchill supposed. Roosevelt had countenanced proposals for a nuclear programme whose funding would dwarf any previous project undertaken during his long Presidency. He was now convinced that America had to be the first to manufacture an atomic bomb, leaving the British behind to pursue their own efforts if need be.

The decision had yet to be made to make the young, but brilliant, Robert Oppenheimer the chief scientist; but he was a strong candidate among the shortlist. Earl Browder, head of the US Communist Party and controller of a secret cell that included Oppenheimer and his wife, Katherine, had already imparted the promising news to the NKVD in New York.

As Britain entered 1942 confidence heightened following Roosevelt's decision to commit America to fight on two fronts – Europe and the Pacific. Matters were yet to be finalized on the atomic bomb but it was clear to his close colleagues that Churchill had thrown in Britain's hand and given the Americans what they wanted – full control. Begrudgingly America had felt it prudent to utilize the nuclear efforts of its ally but minimizing the scale of collaboration.

In Moscow Stalin remained in a quandary. Wehrmacht troops still occupied positions not far from Moscow and only the severe winter cold had held them at bay. He guessed that in the coming spring Hitler, whatever the cost in manpower, would order another advance. Yet each week Beria briefed the GKO, the State Defence Committee of which Stalin was Chairman, on the nuclear discussion in Washington and London. Stalin was undecided about recommitting his nuclear scientists to the pre-war fission programme and sought the advice of Peter Kapitsa, the former physicist from the Cavendish. Kapitsa didn't underestimate the skills of the scientists in Britain but he advised Stalin that the British could never develop an independent nuclear capability by 1943. America's decision to suddenly invest in its own nuclear programme was a far more worrying development and one that needed to be carefully monitored.

The GKO digested further reports emanating from *Red Orchestra* agents in Berlin but the news was contradictory. There had been unwillingness by some scientists at the Kaiser Wilhelm to pursue work on a weapon of mass destruction, but research in other more secret locations throughout Germany was progressing.

In Britain the year 1942 was to mark a watershed in Soviet scientific espionage. Rideal, Blackett, Mann and Rothschild added to the exceptional volume of material already being passed to NKVD controllers from *List, Ellie, Pirate, Scott* and *Moor*. On a number of occasions the flow was so high that Stalin insisted on mere summaries. The recruitment of *Agent D* in December 1941 would add to the surfeit of secrets received in Moscow. Within months Stalin would also be in receipt of one of the most far-reaching documents of the war. It wasn't a stolen document passed to a Soviet Intelligence officer, but a notebook. In February 1942 the 'atomic' notebook was to be found in the briefcase belonging to a German SS officer in a village in the Southern Ukraine.

CHAPTER 19

Enter Agent D

Bach's piano composition wafted through the open doors as the NKVD officer climbed the steps of the National Gallery, in pre-war times the home of one the world's greatest collections of European art. The more valuable paintings had been moved to underground storage in Wales and the galleries were now bare. Adorning the north side of Trafalgar Square, this grand neo-classical building now fulfilled another pleasurable purpose, coming alive at lunchtimes with music, an idea that quickly caught the imagination of Londoners who spent endless hours in air raid shelters. Open to all, the concerts were organized by Dame Myra Hess, the renowned pianist, often accompanied by Irene Scharrer, another top performer in her day. The orchestra comprised musicians in military uniform, who considered the invitation to play at the National Gallery a great honour.

Positioned close to the main viewing gallery used for the concerts was Poppy's, a tearoom and popular rendezvous. Poppy, the proprietor, was tall with gaunt eyes, voluminous black hair and heavily rouged lips. Her customers perceived her as a 'Mayfair lady', the term usually assigned to 'a woman of the night'. She chatted to her customers before they retired to the gallery to listen to the concert. Not for Poppy the monotony of Spam and dried egg sandwiches; during the summer months she had access to fresh tomatoes and cucumbers, while in the winter she provided all varieties of English cheeses. Poppy's was a London institution during the dark days of the war.

The days leading up to Christmas 1941 had brought no cheer to Britain and its leaders. London's evening newspapers for December 21 were already on the streets, reporting the probable loss of Malaya to overwhelming Japanese forces with six of the 11 RAF airfields captured. The island of Penang, some 400 miles from the British fortress of Singapore, had been abandoned. Burma was a new target for the continued Japanese onslaught in South East Asia.

As the Russian listened to the velvet touch of Dame Hess his thoughts drifted elsewhere, to another theatre of war and the safety of his wife in Moscow. Married just months before his posting to London, she was upset about him living and working under the menace of German bombing. Now it was his turn to worry. For the past two months Stukas had bombed and strafed Moscow, with thousands of civilians reported dead. Only the bitter winter conditions had halted the German advance on Moscow. There had been some comforting news in the Embassy that the crack Siberian divisions, withdrawn from the Manchurian and Russian Siberian borders, had counter-attacked in recent days, defeating the Wehrmacht at Klin to the north-west of the capital. Accurate assessments of the fighting were scarce and unreliable, the Embassy relying instead on BBC reports.

The cold of the unheated National Gallery chilled the Russian to the bone as he buttoned up his overcoat. He hadn't been followed; MI5 had more pressing engagements.

'Shall we go to Poppy's?' asked a voice from behind, in a whisper.

Turning slowly around, the Russian faced the man, whose features were muffled with a heavy woollen scarf.

They stood in silence as they queued for tea before moving away to a quieter area.

'Have you been here before?'

'No, never, but I've read about these concerts, they're famous,' responded the NKVD officer.

'Dame Hess is quite a virtuoso. Do you recognise the piece?'

'Yes, Bach – its one of his piano concertos but I can't name it. I'm more familiar with Rimsky-Korsakov.'

'Ah, Rimsky-Korsakov, what a composer. Russia has given the world so many talented musicians. Dame Hess and her orchestra are performing 'Jesu Joy of Man's Desiring', a great favourite of the audiences here. Do you play the piano?'

'I wish I did,' replied the Russian, sipping his tea, 'but in Russia your life is usually ordained for you. If you show early talent as a musician you are sent away to a special school, but my piano skills were barely rudimentary. As a boy I yearned to be a pilot in the Soviet air force. My father thought I was just a dreamer and pushed me into mechanical engineering. Then, in a very roundabout way, I found myself becoming a diplomat.'

'So, engineer to diplomat, and now an intelligence agent. That's probably not unusual. Soviet agents have had all manner of backgrounds.'

'How would you possibly know?' asked the Russian.

'I was part of the interrogation team that grilled Alexander Sheinman, who defected to us in October 1937, an event which I'm sure was part of the briefing you received on the London *rezidency* before leaving Moscow. Sheinman was the director of the London office of Intourist, having previously held a number of senior positions in the Soviet Union, including Commissar of Foreign and Internal Trade and chairman of Vneshtorgbank, the state trade and finance entity. After his defection you very wisely recalled a number of intelligence agents as Sheinman blew the covers of every operative within Vneshtorgbank, worldwide. We guarded him well, especially after the NKVD killed Dimitri Navashin, another defector, in Paris in January of the same year.'

'I've never heard of Sheinman, or Navashin,' replied the Russian.

'Of course you haven't, any good intelligence officer denies everything. And what about Alexander Orlov, who spent time working for Russian Intelligence in Spain and Britain? He defected in July 1938, finally making his way to the United States. Do you recollect that name?'

The NKVD officer sensed he was being provoked. 'Exactly what do you do in military intelligence?' he ventured.

'Some years ago I was assigned to a special military course on the activities in Britain of GRU, your sister organization. There had been attempts by GRU officers to infiltrate key Army bases, mainly by bribing young privates and sergeants who had access to sensitive information. My superiors, for some reason, believed I would make a good intelligence officer and I landed up in a secret group that operates in parallel with the British Secret Service. The work is never dull but the pay is poor.'

'You met my Embassy colleague, I understand?'

'Yes, in a noisy pub in Tottenham, in north London. He introduced himself as Professor Nikitin. That was obviously one of his cover names, he certainly didn't strike me as academic. We didn't talk long, it was more of a polite introduction.'

'He acquainted me with what you discussed. Do I take it that you want to just talk from time to time or is something else on offer?'

'That really depends on you. Given my position any accusation of treachery would effectively kill my career, and possibly end my life. There wouldn't be the formality of any trial, I would be quietly dispatched, permanently. We British are secretly experimenting on some pretty powerful drugs these days, 'hallucinogenic' I think is the word that accurately describes them. These drugs come from mushrooms found only in Mexico and they affect the flow of serotonin, a chemical substance that occurs in the brain. Captured Abwehr agents make excellent guinea pigs and after this stuff has been directly injected into their bodies, their minds are wrecked. We drop their bodies from reconnaissance flights over the North Sea, a tradition of Britain's intelligence services. No one is ever any the wiser.'

The audience clapped as Dame Hess came to a long pause in her recital.

'Are you an idealist?' asked the Russian.

'My opinions hardly matter, since from June the USSR and Britain have been allies. For what it is worth, my view of Stalin is that he ranks higher than Hitler in the megalomaniac stakes. Even if you exclude the mass murder of the labour camps, collectivisation alone killed millions through starvation. In Kazakhstan in the 1930s this so-called lynchpin of Stalin's new economic policy never stood a chance of succeeding, with political cadres from Moscow having zero knowledge of agriculture in charge of enforcing the collectivisation. For centuries Kazakhs lived on the plains, not in tiny economic units living on subsistence.

'Did Stalin have any humanity in the Ukraine when he effectively expropriated the grain harvest for three years, exporting most of it for hard currency to purchase imported technology in industrial centres in Kharkov, Leningrad and Kuibyshev?

'He didn't care a jot. I daresay that the Russian newspapers haven't reported the retreat in the Ukraine in recent months. The people have welcomed the Nazis as saviours, thrown garlands over the heads of the SS bastards and littered the broken streets with flowers. Berlin Radio has broadcast interviews with Ukrainians, expressing unequivocal hatred towards Russia.

'We are providing you with Infantry Mark II and Churchill Mark I tanks as well as Hurricane and Spitfire aircraft. Even some RAF pilots are based in Russia. Does our generosity change the deep-down enmity that has existed between us since you declared a revolution in 1917 and subjugated your once proud nation? I think not.'

'So, why did you agree with my colleague to meet me here today? Why risk a watery grave in the North Sea if you find our system so contemptible?'

'Money, greed, call it personal capitalism. I will provide you with the best intelligence, in return I need money and plenty of it. You see, my Russian friend, I merely wish to trade.'

'I would need approval from my superiors, but you need to tell me what material you are privy to.'

'Didn't Professor Nikitin tell you? I am loosely connected to one of our most classified projects – the atomic bomb programme.'

'Go on,' prompted the Russian.

'My department has been asked to help in vetting scientists, especially those with European backgrounds. A small group has been formed under the chairmanship of Michael Perrin, who is in charge of administration. Since 1938 it may seem that we have concentrated on German espionage in Britain – but we haven't ignored your organisation, or the GRU. Perrin's no fool. He understands full well that your people have already compromised the project. The focus of this group is to try and limit Soviet penetration as best we can, ring-fencing the work that's going on in laboratories around the country.'

'Who else is in this group?'

'Can't say, but I will know soon enough as I'm due to attend my first meeting this afternoon. Perrin has a list of names who have been given contracts by the DSIR, the Government department that two weeks ago took over the management of all secret scientific research and development. Their academic qualifications are impeccable, their references excellent, but Perrin is troubled about gaps in their backgrounds that were not discovered during the MI5 and Special Branch vetting procedure. Some hard questions should have been asked, but weren't.'

'Do you have access to this list?'

'I do. It has 12 names on it but I'm only prepared today to give you the names of three. They work at the Clarendon, the University of Birmingham and the University of Liverpool.'

'Will I ever see the full list of Perrin's suspects?'

'Maybe. These three are on account. Next time we meet you will need to give me £300 for today. The full list will cost Professor Nikitin £1,000. Thereafter we can agree a further payment schedule for other intelligence material. Is that a deal?'

'As I said I will need approval from my superiors, but I'm sure the request will not be denied if your intelligence is as good as you tell me it is.'

'Digest this while I buy some more tea to keep out this damn cold,' said the man, handing the Russian a crumpled piece of paper.

The NKVD officer examined the names. Klaus Fuchs wasn't on it, which was a surprise given his Communist activist past. Two names were instantly recognisable. Joseph Rotblat, the Polish experimental physicist born in Warsaw in 1908, had been a natural for the NKVD to approach due to his Eastern European background. In the University of Liverpool, Rotblat researched into deuterium oxide, heavy water. The second name was just as concerning. A new NKVD recruit at the Clarendon was under suspicion. The third name the Russian had never heard of.

'So, recognise any names?'

The Russian gladly accepted the fresh tea.

'No,' he lied.

'I wouldn't have expected any other answer,' replied the man, chuckling behind his scarf.

'This man at the Clarendon, why is Perrin suspicious about him?'

'I don't know. He was born in Britain and educated at a top public school and one of our best universities. Perrin has uncovered some interesting facts about him that MI5 strangely missed. I can't elaborate further than that at the moment.'

'When can we meet again?' asked the Russian. 'We need to develop a rota of meeting dates. If you don't make one, I'll turn up at the next determined time.'

'No, I'll lay down the ground rules. Each Monday you will have to read *The Times*, in particular the personal column. Monday is always full of strange messages, people celebrating anniversaries, looking for old friends that may have joined up and they would like to hear from, that kind of thing. From time to time I will be in contact.'

'How?'

'My codename will be *Agent D*. We are aware that the NKVD is keen on using codenames that bear some relationship to the person, but *Agent D* has no relevance whatsoever to anything or anybody.'

'Why *Agent D*?'

'I hope anagrams are part of your training. For example, I could place an advertisement in the newspaper saying – 'Congratulations to A. D. Gent on celebrating his 50th birthday', with some suitable words, or 'Best wishes to D. T. Egan on becoming a grandfather', etc. No return address will be necessary, which is typical of many of the messages. When any derivation of the name *Agent D* appears you will know that I need a meeting a week later. Next time we'll again meet at Poppy's as I feel safe mingling with the crowd and the delightful Bach nicely stifles our conversation. Thereafter we will find another location. I am right handed and will always carry a briefcase or newspaper. If you see me holding anything in my left hand, that will be a danger signal.'

It was the Russian's turn to laugh. 'So I have to become a *Times* reader?'

'If after I place a message and you don't show I won't be too concerned. You may have missed it, equally you may well be out of London. After a suitable lapse of time, it may be even months, I'll place another message. I guess you will now report the bones of this meeting to your NKVD head of station?'

'Yes, that is standard procedure, but only he and I will be aware of you.'

'What about the Ambassador, Ivan Maisky – I understand he keeps his finger on the intelligence pulse?'

'No comment. Is he tailed by MI5?' responded the NKVD officer.

'In the beginning we did, when he was first posted to London, but now hardly ever. One final little gem for you before we go our separate ways.

'The Politburo has a traitor in its midst. We recruited him on a trade mission to London in the 1930s. Contact with him is difficult at the moment given the state of the war. Intrigued?'

'Of course, but it's no good without a name.'

'Oh, no. That's for the long term, when I want a really big pay day. Don't bother trying to find him – literally hundreds of Russians have been involved in these trade missions.'

With that he bade farewell and disappeared into the crowd as Dame Hess played her final bar, another concert at an end. After a suitable period the Russian departed, heading down the steps into Trafalgar Square where he caught the eye of a man casually reading a copy of the *London Evening News* on the bottom step, who shook his head so slowly only his colleague noticed. No one had observed the rendezvous in Poppy's.

The military intelligence officer had walked quickly down the Strand, his mind in turmoil despite the calm exterior he had earlier projected. Suddenly he was paralysed with guilt, but there was no turning back now. He had made his bed, and in that bed he must lie – a comfortable retirement beckoned and he was to commit treason for large bundles of cash.

Rummaging in his suit pocket for identification he walked into Shell-Mex House, flashing the card at the military policeman on duty.

'I have an appointment with Mr Perrin.'

'I know, Sir, you are expected. You are the last to arrive. Please make your way up.'

He slowly climbed the stairs to the fourth floor. A secretary walked with him to Perrin's office, where he paused outside the closed door before striding confidently in.

'Good afternoon Major,' said the bespectacled Perrin. 'I think you know everyone here apart from Flight Lieutenant Barrows, a member of the RAF Intelligence Section, who has been seconded as a full-time member of our little group.'

The Major shook Barrows' outstretched hand.

'Gentlemen,' said Perrin, 'I believe you are aware of the Major's position in the Secret Service. He is an advisor on the security committee that briefs Winston Churchill from time to time. More to the point he is an authority on the methods employed by the Soviet Intelligence services that operate in Britain and he directly reports to Guy Liddell, who runs Section B of Counter-Intelligence. I am grateful that we can use his undoubted expertise in our subsequent investigations and he is to shortly assist Roger Hollis, head of F Section, in the vetting procedure for *Tube Alloys*. Major, please take a seat.'

In the Russian Embassy the NKVD officer wrote up his notes on the meeting at the National Gallery, beginning a new file marked *Agent D*. The revelation that Perrin had reservations about 12 scientists with DSIR contracts was troubling and great care was now necessary from both him and Gorsky. For a while he considered why Gorsky had handed *Agent D* over to him, which was out of character. He could only surmise that Gorsky had a hunch that *Agent D* might be an agent of MI5's *Double X* Committee and wouldn't want to take the responsibility if that assumption later proved correct.

He contemplated talking privately with Simon Kremer, the senior GRU officer in the Embassy, but decided against it. There was also the question of the Politburo source. Gorsky's advice needed to be sought over that very delicate issue.

The phone rang. 'How did it go, do we have him?' enquired the Ambassador. 'I think so,' replied the NKVD officer, surprised that Maisky had even been aware of the meeting. The Ambassador would have good news to include in his daily report to Stalin.

A jubilant Gorsky sent his own cable to his superiors with the news of the NKVD's latest recruit. That same day, December 21, 1941, Gorsky provided Moscow with the news that after some considerable absence Kim Philby wished to re-establish contact. Philby had joined Section V, the counter-espionage section of the British Secret Service, to work in the Iberian department. Based at a country house near St Albans, the department specialized in monitoring the increased flow of U-boats through the Straits of Gibraltar.

Moscow welcomed *Agent D*'s recruitment but Gorsky was warned that he needed careful monitoring. In addition, the recently received information on Philby concerned the NKVD chiefs greatly. A meeting was hastily convened in the Lubyanka to assess whether Philby may have been discovered by British Intelligence and turned. An urgent cypher was transmitted to the London Embassy, but Gorsky was not the recipient.

CHAPTER 20

Into uniform and into battle

The interrogation of Major Hans van der Velde in the Kremlin had become tedious for everyone in Stalin's conference room. Beria led the initial questioning in his usual abrasive and abrupt manner, the translator struggling to keep up. The SS officer tried as best he could to provide answers but invariably he was interrupted. Stalin appeared disinterested as his deputy spat out his questions. He perked up as van der Velde recalled much of his life in Munich, grinning as the captive joked that he had often drunk in the same bar in Schwabing that Lenin had done several decades earlier. However, such mirth only served to increase Beria's annoyance that this interrogation was taking place at all. Never before had an SS officer taken up such valuable time – yet Stalin had inexplicably insisted.

At one point Stalin had silenced the translator with a wave of his hand and walked towards the window to stare out towards the frozen Moscow River.

The tide was turning in the war, and for the better. In February 1942 the Red Army had retaken the city of Dorogobuzh, 50 miles east of Smolensk, and launched a ferocious offensive in an attempt to break the German encirclement of Leningrad. At Staraya Russa to the south of Leningrad, the Red Army had smashed the German 16th Army and to great joy in the Kremlin, the Totenkopf, the renowned Waffen-SS division that referred to itself as the 'Deaths Head', was almost decimated. For the first time since the German invasion in June the previous year Stalin felt optimistic. More troops from the Transbaikal Military District on the Mongolian border, together with the First and Second Red Banner armies with their headquarters in Vladivostok, were transferring west to add a fresh impetus to the fighting as the threat of a Japanese invasion had receded.

Returning to the conference table Stalin picked up the black notebook that had been found in the briefcase of the German officer in Krivaya Kosa by Russian saboteurs under the command of Colonel Ilya Starinov. Stalin carefully thumbed through it. While he lit his pipe he studied the two drawings tucked inside the notebook. His scientists had informed him they were diagrams of a nuclear reactor and an atomic bomb.

Stalin gestured to Beria, inviting him to continue.

With a glint in his eye Beria asked van der Velde whether he was homosexual. That accusation stirred the tired German to tell of his relationship with Maria, describing her physical characteristics for Stalin's benefit. He recalled to the assembled a strange episode in Berlin in a packed bar in the Unter den Linden with his two friends, Helmut and Franz. The beer had flowed and the room had erupted with the singing of the Horst Wessel song. Through the cheering and stamping crowd van der Velde noticed a woman, tall, well dressed, with black hair rolled up in a bun

– he was positive it was Maria. She was talking to two military officers. He lurched towards her, pushing aside other drinkers. Suddenly the woman saw him, muttered some words to her escorts and in a moment all three were gone. The last time he had met up with Maria was in the hotel in Munich when he tried to enlist the help of her father in the release of the print workers from Dachau.

It was Stalin's turn to loudly interject. He was keen now to hear how the German officer had joined the SS and become involved with *Operation Barbarossa*.

* * *

The banging on Hans' door in Harnack House, the Kaiser Wilhelm's guesthouse and recreational centre, at 6am on June 17, 1941, had set in train a sequence of events that had changed his life forever. Professor Eric Schumann, the scientific head of the Heereswaffenamt, had unexpectedly summoned him to Gatow. It was a Sunday but war was no respecter of weekends. The driver and his passenger swept past the aerodrome at Gatow, formerly a Luftwaffe training airfield. Now rows of transport aircraft queued to take off into the red morning sky, their engines revving in a cacophony of sound. At the Heereswaffenamt Hans observed the chaos. A weary secretary told him to wait. Only several hours later was he ushered into Schumann's office and commended on his work at the Kaiser Wilhelm and the comprehensive research into the mineral wealth of the Soviet Union. Schumann did not remark on the regular access that Hans had now been given to the invaluable light-green folders in the offices of Dr Goebbels.

The conversation with Schumann had remained etched in Hans' mind.

'In a week's time Germany will invade the Soviet Union, our former ally but now our enemy,' said Schumann in a hushed voice. 'The forces ranged against Stalin will be so overwhelming that within months, possibly weeks, he will sue for peace. Our intelligence has confirmed that the Red Army is poorly equipped and trained, and the air force is no match for the Luftwaffe.' That news was hardly a surprise to Hans, it was common knowledge around the Kaiser Wilhelm compound that the invasion was imminent. However, Hans was curious as to why Schumann had disclosed to him the date.

'Uranium is scarce,' continued Schumann, 'a situation you comprehend all too well. It is paramount that Germany finds more uranium oxide for our project. Supplies at Joachimsthal are barely adequate for the Kaiser Wilhelm, but here in Gatow and in our other laboratories throughout the country stocks are virtually depleted.'

Hans reeled at what Schumann said next.

'Given your newly attained Soviet expertise, you will be part of the invasion. There is every possibility that our troops will find secret research facilities where work on nuclear fission has been conducted. The last thing we want is the Wehrmacht tearing them apart. I have arranged for you to join the Wehrgeologen.

It is a specialized SS unit compromising mainly of conscripted petroleum engineers and technicians whose objective is the capture of the Soviet oilfields. In your case, your role is more exclusive and you will carry an ID linking you with the Heereswaffenamt. Hans, you are going to war to sniff out uranium.'

Schumann grinned.

'Not solely uranium, of course, other minerals too. Don't forget to take your maps, they could be useful,' he ventured with a touch of sarcasm. 'You are to report back in Gatow in two days for a uniform, papers and a full briefing, so I suggest you enjoy yourself until then.'

Stunned, Hans made to leave. 'Oh, I forgot to mention,' said Schumann, 'your rank is Major.'

As Hans left he overheard Schumann instructing his secretary that he wanted her to place an urgent call to Obergruppenführer Felix Steiner, the commanding officer of Wiking – the elite Waffen SS division.

In the car back to Harnack House his mind raced. Schumann's decision to conscript him was a real body blow, especially as Hans had taken steps to make himself indispensable to avoid being drafted. He had made countless trips to the Auer Company in Oranienburg, which manufactured metallic uranium and enabled supplies to reach a number of laboratories scattered throughout Germany. On one occasion a grateful scientist had provided him with entry into the underground facility at the Kaiser Wilhelm Institute for Physics, its entrance via a heavy steel door in Harnack Strasse, to witness some of the very first German nuclear reactor experiments. Small cubes of uranium were loosely connected together, dangling into circular drums with graphite linings. External tubes connected these devices with heavy water.

All his efforts to avoid conscription had been in vain.

There was a frisson of excitement in Harnack House and Hans observed more scientists than usual in uniform. He sat alone in the dining room, glumly picking over his lunch and listening to the conversation. It was clear that others also knew the timing for *Operation Barbarossa*. In the evening he phoned Franz at his apartment to impart the news. Franz sounded equally disappointed and suggested a beer in the usual bar in Meinekestrasse. By the time Franz and Helmut arrived they found Hans drowning his sorrows. Franz suggested a quiet corner.

Despite being sworn to secrecy, Hans no longer cared and disclosed to his two friends the invasion date.

'Can we trust you?' responded Franz abruptly.

'Trust me?' retorted Hans angrily. 'I should be asking you two that question. I could be shot for repeating what Schumann told me earlier today.'

Franz took a gulp of beer and spoke in barely a whisper.

'Just listen. There is a group of us, people in powerful positions throughout the country – in the military, Government and civil service – and we share a common goal. Hitler and Nazism must be beaten, and we are sympathetic to any nation that believes the same, including Russia. The Molotov-Ribbentrop Pact was worthless; six months ago it was clear Hitler's war agenda differed to Stalin. Our so-called Fuhrer is obsessed with Communist and Jewish plots as a threat to his National Socialism. You know full well where Auer gets its labour. It is from the nearby concentration camp. After *Kristallnacht* more than 10,000 Jews were thrown into Oranienburg and many have died from radioactivity through the uranium production process.'

'Yes, I am aware of the barbaric conditions at Auer,' replied Hans.

'Let me continue,' explained Franz.

'Since January the German High Command has been secretly planning *Operation Barbarossa*, which may turn out to be the biggest war in history. Some 150 Wehrmacht divisions, including four Waffen-SS divisions, are on standby according to an aide to one of Hitler's closest Ministers and contacts in the Abwehr. The invasion signals the beginning of an orgy of wanton killing. Himmler has established a new wing of the SS, the Einsatzgrüppen, that will be behind the main invasion force creating a holocaust, exterminating Jews.'

Suddenly Hans felt very sober. 'This group you talk about, who are you, and where have you heard about the uranium experiments?'

'I can't say much as we run a constant risk of being given away to the Gestapo and SS,' answered Franz, looking furtively around the bar. 'However, given we may have little time left with you we should elaborate. We call ourselves the *Rote Kapelle*, the *Red Orchestra*, and we are in contact not just with Russia but also the British. The invasion date was passed to Moscow through contacts we have with the NKVD, the Soviet Intelligence service. As best we could, we detailed the strengths of each division and the first targets. In the first hour 12 cities in the Ukraine are in for a Blitzkrieg similar to the devastation the Luftwaffe rained down on Rotterdam. And how are we aware of the precise role of the Kaiser Wilhelm Institute for Physics? Memos have circulated for months about the atomic bomb project in Government departments. You can't keep something like that quiet forever.'

'Why haven't you taken me into your confidence before?'

'Quite simple. We were never fully sure of you, but I think that was a mistake. Heydrich has informers everywhere and he knows full well there is a Soviet spy ring operating here in Berlin with access to the most confidential of information. I'm certain we have been infiltrated but none of our group has yet experienced the cells in Prinz Albrecht Strasse, thank goodness. We have to be very careful with the Kaiser Wilhelm, given its secret war work and the fact that some of the scientists are Nazi party members. When we first met you hinted that you worked in Dahlem, so we guessed it was the Kaiser Wilhelm. Another time you mentioned an interest in very rare minerals. That alerted us to the fact that you were looking for uranium oxide. At some stage, when we felt ready, we were planning to recruit you.'

Hans grinned and ordered another round of drinks. 'Count me in, but with such a short time before the invasion how could I be of any use to the *Red Orchestra*? I might never return to Berlin, I'll probably be bayoneted to death in a back street somewhere in the Ukraine.'

'True, but in the next few days you could detail for us precisely the full nature of what has been happening at the Kaiser Wilhelm Institute for Physics, especially in the underground laboratory in Harnack Strasse.'

'So, you know about that laboratory?'

'Have you been inside it?' countered Franz.

'I have. One of the senior physicists, Professor von Weizsäcker, spends most of his time in there.'

Helmut spoke for the first time. 'Is there a chance we could establish contact with someone?' he asked.

'Hardly, I have no real friends in the institute; it is not the type of place where friendships are easily made,' replied Hans.

'Have you in your possession any notes or documents about the nuclear project we could have?' Franz cut in.

'Very little is circulated, and certainly not to me, but I have kept a notebook of all my work, which includes many key points from seminars I was allowed to sit in on.'

'What was the nature of these seminars?'

'They were mainly updates on the project, given by Heisenberg, von Weizsäcker and Hahn, and very enlightening they were too.'

'Why were you invited?'

'The Heereswaffenamt thought it beneficial, useful for my work.'

'Was the military involved?'

'Yes, the Wehrmacht and the Luftwaffe.'

'Does Goering ever put in an appearance?'

'I only saw him once, and then he looked disinterested and left halfway through.'

'All very interesting,' stated Franz, drinking his beer. 'So, your notebook is a pretty good record of the Nazi attempts to build an nuclear bomb?'

'I wouldn't say it was comprehensive but, yes, it is a good documentary of what I have done from the time I arrived in Dahlem. It also includes details of meetings I have had in Hamburg, Heidelberg, Leipzig and other centres, including my trip to Joachimsthal.'

'You visited the uranium mines?'

'I did. On my return I reported on the awful labour conditions but to no avail. I think it's my turn to ask a question. You two are not junior civil servants, are you? I always felt you were being economical with the truth.'

'We didn't lie, but we're more middle-rankers in reserved occupations,' said Helmut. 'I work in the Air Ministry in Wilhelmstrasse and Franz is nearby in the Propaganda Ministry, working for Dr Goebbels. Franz had seen the *Green Files,* those excellent records on the Soviet Union. It was a calculated risk telling you, but call it a test if you like. You never did tell us if you found their contents useful.'

'They were, too useful it seems. Schumann is of the opinion I'm some authority on Russia and for that reason I'm to join the war.'

'A final drink?' smiled Franz. 'We'll see you tomorrow and talk further. I have some petrol coupons so I suggest we take a trip outside Berlin and visit one of the lakes. The weather promises to be fine so we can sit on the grass and talk without being overheard. Hans, please bring your notebook with you, I would like to study it. My friends, a toast.'

Hans never made it to the lakes. He was not to see Franz for five eventful months and he would never see Helmut again.

That night a thumping on the door rudely awoke him, the grumbling night manager thrusting a note into his hands – he was expected in Gatow within the hour. Two earlier arrivals, chemists from the Kaiser Wilhelm Institute for Chemistry, sat waiting patiently in Schumann's office and introduced themselves. Schumann began his briefing.

All three, as members of the Wehrgeologen, had a mission of great importance to the Third Reich, the Heereswaffenamt's chief scientist explained. He had attached them to Waffen-SS divisions in the vanguard of *Operation Barbarossa*.

One chemist would be part of Army Group North, the force invading through Lithuania with the ultimate aim of taking Leningrad. It was imperative that three key nuclear institutes in the city, the Leningrad Physical Technical Institute, the Radium Institute and the Mining Museum, were captured with as little damage as possible. The Abwehr had reported unspecified supplies of uranium oxide stored at these three locations. Furthermore, given the nuclear expertise concentrated in Leningrad, the capture of physicists and chemists would be a priority.

Hans saw the chemist stiffen as Schumann explained that he had been assigned to the Totenkopf, its commander, Gruppenführer Theodore Eicke, agreeing to provide a small insurgent force to take the Leningrad institutes as soon as it was practical.

The institutes in Kiev and Kharkov were the objectives for the second chemist, seconded to Army Group Centre, whose route would include Minsk and Smolensk en route to Moscow. Schumann stressed the importance of the Kharkov Physical Technical Institute, which Hans knew from the *Green Files* figured prominently in Russia's nuclear research. On this occasion Das Reich, led by the influential Oberführer Paul Hasser, the officer instrumental in the formation of the Waffen-SS, would provide the military force. The division had been well rested and was now spoiling for a fight, its last campaign on the Maginot Line preventing French troops escaping from the concrete fortress.

When the facility in Kharkov was secure, Schumann informed the chemist that Dr Fritz Houtermanns, a former employee at Kharkov and now working at the Baron von Ardenne laboratory in Lichterfelde in Berlin, would be immediately despatched to the Ukrainian city to provide a thorough assessment. Again, Hans remembered that Houtermanns had figured in the files in the Propaganda Ministry, recalling the note stating that the NKVD had arrested him, accusing him of being a spy and later deporting him to Germany.

Schumann at last turned to Hans. There was a third prong in the invasion, perhaps the most vital. Army Group South would wheel further south to the Rostov-on-Don area, the gateway to the Caucasus and the world's richest reserves of crude oil. However, Hans was to locate the laboratories in Dnepropetrovsk, where uranium isotope and heavy water experiments had been reported by Abwehr agents, and accompany the group into the north Caucasus. Lermontev, where pre-war Soviet exploration had revealed a rich source of uranium oxide – as unearthed by Hans in his research – was an objective. In the initial phase he was assigned to Wiking, the SS division under Felix Steiner, a Great War veteran and a fervent anti-Communist. There was every probability, explained Schumann, that within weeks, if everything went to plan, he would transfer to LAH – the Liebstandarte Adolf Hitler, the second Waffen-SS division in Army Group South.

Every division commander in *Operation Barbarossa* had received orders to urgently report any nuclear or chemical weapon facility found in the advance. The Kaiser Wilhelm Institute of Chemistry had become a world leader in developing chemical weapons, especially mustard gas, tabun and sarin. Mustard gas caused blistering, lung damage and death within hours. Tabun led to spasms in its victims and death within minutes. Sarin was just as deadly. Schumann believed the chemical facilities in Leningrad and Odessa may be manufacturing similar chemical agents. Anthrax, the biological agent, was another concern; but Schumann doubted whether the Soviets were that far advanced.

The briefing ended with Schumann vigorously shaking the hands of the Kaiser Wilhelm employees, wishing them luck. Hans felt nauseous. Schumann's secretary directed them to an office where uniforms were piled on a table; standard black, with SS runes on the right collar, a patch denoting the rank of major on the other and the light pink 'Waffenfarbe' piping around the shoulder straps of the Wehrgeologen. Carefully rolled up was the infamous leather belt, the SS motto 'Meine Ehre Heisst Treue' – 'My Loyalty is Honour' – inscribed on the circular, nickel-plated steel buckle.

There were no goodbyes and no time for any phone call to Franz or his parents in Munich as a car took Hans and the two chemists back to Dahlem and waited whilst they collected some items. Hans' involvement in the *Red Orchestra* was on hold. At Gatow airfield the Wehrgeologen conscripts received their final orders and within the hour they were airborne to join their respective Waffen-SS units on invasion standby.

Wiking had been combat ready since April, concentrated at the Truppen-Übungsplatz, the troop training area, at Heuberg. Steiner had allotted Hans with his

Dutch ancestry to Westland, the regiment of foreign volunteers, mainly Dutchmen – a ragbag of civilian policemen and convicts rounded up from the jails in Amsterdam and Rotterdam. The war had moulded them into inveterate killers. Wehrgeologen officers had been attached to other Wiking regiments and soon after their arrival at Heuberg they were addressed by a senior geologist from Kontinentale AG, the state oil company founded in March 1941 to manage oil and synthetic fuel production in Germany and occupied territories. He gave a briefing on the oilfields of the Caucasus. Maikop was the first target, the refineries in Grozny the second. The Caspian, and Baku, was the ultimate prize.

Wiking began its crossing of German-occupied Poland at blistering speed, reaching Grosse Wartenberg and then Wielun, on the eastern side of the Drawa River. Only once in Konskie, a town to the south-west of Radom, did the division take a breather. Wiking then moved on, through Skarzysko-Kamienna, Ostrowiec and Swietokrzyski before skirting the Vistula at Baranov. On the eve of the invasion Wiking wheeled north-east to the city of Lublin.

In the early hours of June 22 Wiking's panzers trundled through Lublin and into the district of Majdanek, passing the concentration camp that already had achieved notoriety as a death camp. At dawn Wiking paused momentarily at Zamosc, a German military strongpoint before continuing to Belzec, just five miles from the Ukrainian border. Once a sleepy hamlet, SS engineers in Belzec had constructed a death camp for Ukrainian and Polish Jews and its unfortunates were to become the victims of tests for new nerve gases manufactured by I. G. Farben, the German chemical company.

At the rear of the huge convoy of tanks and troops the Wehrgeologen unit stopped and started. Wiking began an advance on Lemberg and its population of 50,000 Ukrainians and Poles. Five German divisions approached the city from the west, encountering sporadic Red Army opposition. With the German bombardment at an end, cheering women and children lined the roads, offering traditional Ukrainian gifts of bread and salt and showering Wiking soldiers with flowers. Dead Soviet troops littered what was left of hedgerows and the 43-ton panzer tanks rolled over the shattered bodies. Every street in this historic city became clogged. The renowned opera house built in 1900 when under Austrian rule remained standing, but had been largely wrecked by German shelling. Priceless paintings had been stripped from its walls, snatched by Soviet troops fleeing east. In Ploshcha Rynok, the market-square with its unique and colourfully painted eighteenth-century fire station was surprisingly intact. Himmler's Einsatzgrüppen quickly turned Lemberg into a killing ground. Slaughter, however, had already been visited upon the unfortunate inhabitants of Lemberg, the retreating Russian NKVD settling past scores.

Steiner ordered the Wehrgeologen ahead to evaluate the condition of Lemberg's infrastructure before Wiking entered the city; Hans was in command. Alert to snipers, he drove past the jail where he witnessed a large crowd of screaming civilians. Stopping the vehicle he ran up the steps. A terrible stench emanated from the jail; inside the stink became overpowering. The door to the cells was open as Hans, pistol in hand, put his handkerchief to his face and gingerly descended the dimly lit staircase. Suddenly he came face to face with a German sergeant, a camera in his hands. In the gloom Hans demanded his identity and the soldier uttered he was Oberfeldwebel Hans Demleitner of 1st Mountain, whose job included providing a photographic record for the division. Demleitner had received word about an atrocity, saying no more before racing up the steps. Hans was destined to come across Demleitner again, eight months later.

In the bowels of the jail Hans saw the cells. The first was closed, but through the grill he saw the bodies, distorted by concentrated machine-gun fire. Carnage filled the other cells. At the end of one corridor he saw a woman lying on a heavily blood-stained table, grotesquely sliced open from her chin to her crutch and crudely sown up again. Something else caught his eye – a foetus, fully formed, with its throat sliced open. He ran out into the sunshine and vomited.

With Lemberg taken and left to the Einsatzgrüppen, Wiking and the 1st Mountain moved towards Tarnopol, famous for its Dominican churches and located some 70 miles east. Wiking passed through the farming community of Zborow, where on July 11, 1941, some 600 Soviet PoWs were executed by the Waffen-SS. At Tarnopol the Red Army had tank superiority, but it was no match for the ebullient and confident German military machine. Wiking sacked the city and set afire the large Jewish synagogue before standing aside for the Einsatzgrüppen as a seven-day pogrom began. No Jew was left alive. An Einsatzgrüppen report filed to Berlin on July 16 reported that 10 German PoWs were found murdered in the jail – seven Luftwaffe pilots and three members of the 1st Mountain. In retaliation, 180 Jews were rounded up and ritually executed in the jail. Hand grenades were thrown into nearby occupied houses and the Ukrainians mercilessly mown down as they tried to escape.

During July city after city fell as the tanks rolled deeper into the Ukraine and huge numbers of the Red Army were taken prisoner. Fresh German soldiers were moved to forward positions. For Hans there was no time for reflection as he witnessed daily atrocities, some by the very men he ate and drank with. Cowardice was not tolerated in the SS, nor were opinions. Wiking enhanced its reputation, with the Westland regiment regularly in the thick of the fighting but taking large casualties.

As the month drew to a close the Russians no longer ran but defended with a greater ferocity. Wiking pummeled Berdichev, 50 miles south of Zhitomir. The division wheeled south-east to Byela Tserkov, the route to the Dnieper River. By August, Cherkassy, on the low left-bank floodplain was overrun. Given the rate of the advance, the Caucasus moved ever closer. The Wehrgeologen group attached to Wiking, with the exception of Hans, joined the LAH for the push on Rostov-on-Don, the gateway to the oilfield wealth of the Soviet Union. Hans had his own orders, direct from Schumann.

Further down the Dnieper, Kremenchug fell, a soft victory. The loss of the town worried Moscow as it provided the Germans with a valuable bridgehead to Kharkov, 240 miles east. Russian sappers, as part of Stalin's 'scorched earth' policy, destroyed the dam at Zaporozhe, one of the largest in the world and completed under Russia's first five-year plan. A huge area was flooded. Wiking continued its push to Dnepropetrovsk, founded by Prince Gregory Potemkin in 1776 and called Ekaterinoslav in Czarist times. The city enjoyed a rich hinterland of mineral wealth that supplied its huge iron and steel industry. Nearby lay the major coalfields of the Donbas, the iron mines of Krivoy Rog and the Nikopol manganese mines.

With Dnepropetrovsk in sight Hans was summoned for a meeting with Steiner. At first light and during a pause in the attack a light personnel carrier manoeuvered its way through the side streets. An ambush by a pocket of Russian soldiers proved no match for the eight-man squad.

The large modern building was conspicuous in the street, standing out against the older architecture and located some distance from the main square. Hans and the squad hugged the shadows outside the Institute of Physical Chemistry, its main door hanging open. Westland went in and took up positions in the large hall, but there was no sign of activity.

The Dnepropetrovsk facility was the first Soviet nuclear institute to be taken in *Operation Barbarossa*. On inspection it was deserted, but in the garden 20 civilians were discovered hiding in a cellar. In poor Russian, the sergeant in charge of the Westland unit yelled for everyone to return to the main building for questioning.

It soon transpired that despite the imminent German attack some staff had conscientiously turned up for work, bringing their families into the laboratories for safety. Their main fear was the NKVD. The previous day a NKVD officer had ordered the scientists to prepare for evacuation to Kharkov, the institute was to be ransacked, leaving nothing for the Germans. Its research into nuclear fission could be replicated in more secure locations. That was a ruse. To the NKVD the staff were expendable. Only the actions of a quick-thinking chemist who had been tipped off saved everyone. He rounded up everyone into the cellar and left the door of the institute open to give the impression to the NKVD that the staff had joined in the general exodus from Dnepropetrovsk. The plan worked. The NKVD entered the building, carrying containers and explosives. However, heavy German shelling began again and they fled, falsely reporting to Moscow that the staff had been executed and the building raised to the ground.

A scientist escorted Hans around the institute, ending up in the laboratory that had conducted isotope separation experiments. Outside in the street the city's citizens ran for their lives. Westland expected to encounter Soviet troops at any moment. Surprisingly none came, only Wiking, mopping up resistance and shooting anyone on the streets. Two transport vehicles arrived at the institute but Dnepropetrovsk yielded material of little use to the Kaiser Wilhelm and the Heereswaffenamt, although Hans carefully recorded the apparatus and documents. Two centrifuges were disassembled.

166

There were several jars of uranium oxide but no signs of heavy water.

Radio contact with Steiner was established as soon as Westland had secured the institute and Hans requested that the staff and families be transported back up the line. Steiner promised to contact Schumann for clarification. As the afternoon wore on the Germans began occupying the city. Steiner had yet to return the call. With the trucks packed, the Westland sergeant and his men were restless and nervy – not wanting to be caught out in the institute during the night. Steiner was contacted again but was unreachable; he was in conference with other divisional command-ers, said his adjutant, who offered no help apart from ordering the trucks to leave immediately. Hans and Westland remained; the Russian civilians feared the worst.

The radiophone crackled and the sergeant passed the handset to Hans. It was Steiner. Contact with Berlin had been intermittent all day, he said, and Schumann was proving elusive. Only some sectors of Dnepropetrovsk were secure and the NKVD remained active, the commander of Wiking explained. The staff should be let go and would have to fend for themselves. Hans returned the handset, the ser-geant turned his back and listened to his own more urgent orders.

Moments later Hans found himself manhandled into the personnel carrier. Inside, the civilians were pushed at gunpoint back into the cellar and the door closed. The sergeant pulled two stick grenades from his belt and tossed them in. The deaths were another notch for Westland. As the personnel carrier negotiated its way south to where the division had made camp, Hans tackled the sergeant on the muffled explosion he had heard. The Dutchman grinned, but on the face of the man from the Kaiser Wilhelm there was only complete and utter resignation to his situation.

Berlin Radio reported on October 25, 1941, that the great industrial city of Kharkov to the north-east of Dnepropetrovsk had fallen to von Reichenau's 6th Army. Hitler sent premature congratulations to the Field Marshal as in the streets of Kharkov the battle raged unabated. On the first day of the attack von Reichenau's Army lost 3,500 men, a foretaste of the huge loss of life to follow. Enigma machines chattered to Berlin, intercepted by the British at Bletchley Park, the code-breaking facility north of London. One transmission reported that the 257th Infantry was advancing towards Kreasnopawleka, a village east of Izjum and a day's march to the outskirts of Kharkov, while the 9th had set up camp at Pawlowa, accompanied by the 298th. In the thick of the fighting was the 168th. Given the massive volume of military traffic, German tanks were unable to move in the city's outskirts. Large numbers of Russian PoWs were being marched to Gorbowski, in the south, and the Luftwaffe showered leaflets over the dormitory suburbs of Morefa and Alexejewe, demanding an immediate Soviet surrender.

Kharkov was done for. German casualties totalled 120,000. The Soviet losses were much larger, but no one could estimate the true number. Two days before the surrender Bletchley Park decoded an even more extraordinary story – the NKVD was desperately trying to move great swathes of Kharkov's industrial might eastwards. A tank manufacturing plant was completely disassembled, as were centres that manufactured any type of weapon. This sacking of Kharkov, a major railway hub for the Soviet Union, was one of the largest logistical movements of the war. Some 800 Soviet trucks had been sighted by German reconnaissance at Walniki, one of the main rail stations for Kharkov, loading cargoes onto trains to Kuibyshev and Kazan. At Kupjansk, another terminus, eight steam trains were backed up with an estimated 3,000 trucks parked close to the tracks. A further 150 trucks were reported at Senjkowo, 200 at Sswatowo, 120 at Liman, 300 at Sslawjansk and 250 at Sentjanowka.

In Army Group Centre Das Reich had captured Smolensk and Kiev, and Moscow was well within its sights – just 55 miles away. Vyazma fell on October 13 and Mozhaisk the following day. Stalin had prepared the Muscovites to expect the biggest fight in Russian history, determined that the capital would be defended whatever the human cost. Obergruppenführer Wilhelm Bittrich had recently been appointed as Das Reich's new commanding officer and he spearheaded a force of 4,500 tanks. Hitler was ecstatic at the progress.

Men from Der Führer, a regiment of Das Reich, had already provided the escort for the chemist from the Kaiser Wilhelm to the University of Kiev on September 19, but the physics laboratories were already aflame having been set ablaze by Red Army engineering units. In Berlin, Schumann asked Bittrich to provide a much larger force from Der Führer to fly south in order to secure the Physical Technical Institute in Kharkov.

With the war raging so bitterly in and around the city, Schumann feared that the institute would be lost and he was desperate that the Heereswaffenamt should take possession of the cyclotron, the first of its kind in the Soviet Union and in Europe. Furthermore, the Germans were very much aware of the application put forward to General Timoshenko, Russia's Defense Commissar, by three Kharkov physicists in 1938 to construct an atomic bomb.

Good fortune was a scarce commodity in the battle for Kharkov and it ran out completely for the Kaiser Wilhelm chemist. Soviet KV tanks obliterated the two armoured personnel carriers and their Der Führer occupants. They hadn't even got close to the institute. It was 24 hours later when Schumann heard the news and in desperation he ordered the scientist Fritz Houtermanns to the front.

Bletchley Park intercepted a Berlin transmission – two Ju-52 aircraft had left Gatow for Kharkov with accompanying civilians. On-board one were Fritz Houtermanns and Erich Schumann, the latter to directly lead the mission to ascertain Kharkov's nuclear wealth. Before he took off, Schumann placed calls to both Hans and Steiner in Dnepropetrovsk, urgency in his voice.

In Kharkov the battle ebbed and flowed, but few espied Colonel Ilya Starinov of the Red Army mining group supervising the destruction of the city. Commanding the 5th and 27th Railway Brigades, Starinov had been ordered to tear Kharkov apart. With the assistance of Nikita Khrushchev, the chairman of Kharkov's Front Military Council, he identified the key targets. The task was immense and Starinov requested 300 tons of explosives as well as radio-controlled and delayed-action mines from Moscow. The request was rebuffed as the capital was already beginning to mine its own installations. After much pleading from Khrushchev one-third of the requested items were flown into Kharkov.

Completely by chance, Starinov discovered that 22 of the 300 Spaniards who came back with him from action in the Spanish Civil War were working in the Kharkov tractor factory – Domingo Ungrier, the expert saboteur, among them. The city's Communist Party steadfastly refused to allow the Spaniards to join Starinov's wrecking crew, but after Khrushchev threatened the firing squad it hastily reversed its decision.

Starinov unleashed in Kharkov one of the biggest sabotage operations in history. He and his men placed decoy mines, easily found and luring the Germans into a false sense of security. The Katyusha missile factory was mined, as were the four airfields with delayed-action explosives buried alongside the runways.

Khrushchev had one special task for Starinov, the destruction of Number 17 Dzerzhinsky Street, the office of the Communist Party. The future premier of the USSR was convinced the Germans would establish their headquarters in this plush pre-Revolutionary building surrounded by splendid oak trees. On October 20 Starinov and others sneaked into the gardens and broke into the basement. A huge decoy mine was placed in the boiler room under a pile of coal, but under the flooring the saboteurs dug a deep shaft, difficult to find even if German sappers pulled up floorboards. A 350kg radio-controlled charge of TNT was carefully laid in the shaft and sealed. On October 24 Khrushchev and what remained of his staff evacuated the villa, leaving it in a condition that suggested its occupants had hurriedly left.

The German tanks and troops edging closer to the city centre had no inkling of what lay in store for them. Major General Georg von Braun, in command of 168th Infantry, was in no mood for chivalry and he ordered the execution of hundreds of civilians, their bodies left hanging from the balconies of their homes. Khrushchev had been correct in his assessment. Safe in the nearby city of Voronezh, Starinov played his hand. Within moments of sending the radio signal the house was devastated, collapsing into a crater. Von Braun and his senior officers died in the explosion.

At Kharkov's airfields Starinov's mines caused utter mayhem, the Luftwaffe unable to taxi aircraft off the runways as delayed-action mines exploded all around. Throughout the city charges brought down 46 bridges, causing massive German and Soviet casualties. The Germans panicked, lining up civilians and demanding to know where the mines were buried before shooting them out of hand. Captured Soviet troops were herded into areas of potential danger. More Germans were killed or wounded by the Soviet mines than in the occupation of the city. Stalin was pleased and Starinov was rewarded with another medal.

In Dnepropetrovsk, Steiner briefed Hans on the operation ordered by Schumann.

A squad of 20 men from Westland, accompanied by the Wehrgeologen major, had to fly immediately to Kharkov. The nuclear facility must be taken intact with as little damage as possible.

That night, October 26, Bletchley Park intercepted a cypher from Kharkov to Berlin reporting that none of the captured airfields in the city were considered secure. Aircraft were marooned on the runways, making easy targets.

As the transport made ready for take off in Dnepropetrovsk the pilot received a last-minute order to delay as the only operational airfield in Kharkov was under aerial attack. In the front of the plane Hans sat next to the sergeant, the same soldier who had executed the institute staff in Dnepropetrovsk. Few words were exchanged. One hour later the plane was airborne. Approaching Kharkov the pilot had no difficulty in locating the airfield – Soviet fighters had turned it into a mass of burning metal and fuel.

Within moments of landing the Westland squad and Hans raced for their lives to the waiting trucks provided by 168th Infantry. Hans met up with Dietrich Kraiss, a senior officer who had taken instruction from the Heereswaffenamt. Kharkov was a bloody mess, said Kraiss, refuting the continuous Berlin Radio broadcast that the Soviets had surrendered. The institute, he told the major, was near the centre of the city but even if Westland managed to hold it, it may be days before the main body of his troops could relieve them. No quarter was being given in the battle and the SS did not live long if captured. Atrocities were rife on both sides.

Kraiss provided Westland with two armoured personnel carriers; new Sd Kfz 251 half-tracks APCs, weighing three tons and armed with two fixed machine guns and a mounted flame-thrower. Hans had brought with him from Dnepropetrovsk two large sealable drums to hold any uranium that might be found and had already spoken to his squad about the risk of radioactivity. The decision was made to attack the institute before sun up, usually the time when there was a lull in the bombardment and both sides recovered their dead and injured.

The icy wind cut right through him as Hans apprehensively rechecked the firing mechanism on his 9mm Schmeisser machine gun. Bitter experience had quickly taught him that in the Ukraine it was kill or be killed. As the APCs moved out of camp they passed a slow-moving convoy of trucks, full of corpses. The death rate was so high that field ambulances were unable to cope and bodies were piled unceremoniously in lorries for disposal in large pits. Few were returned to Germany for a decent burial.

Hans rated his chance of survival as zero and his mind drifted back to Berlin, to his conversation with Franz and Helmut on the *Red Orchestra* – all now completely irrelevant. Kharkov was an inferno. The APCs passed pockets of the 168th in forward positions. Fortune smiled on Hans and they encountered no resistance. Turning into the square where the Kharkov Physical Technical Institute was located, they were met by the sight of civilians frantically loading up trucks under the watchful eye of uniformed NKVD. Within moments, and much to Hans' dismay, the flame-throwers spewed out their lethal fuel that devoured the lorries and their contents. Westland summarily finished off the survivors.

Inside the institute the sight of the APCs had caused panic. The remaining scientists pleaded for their lives. The first part of Schumann's mission had been accomplished, but holding out now was another matter. Twice the NKVD counterattacked, each time repelled. Only by the following evening did units of the 168th secure the sector, providing Hans with the opportunity to inspect the burnt-out trucks, but nothing remained. Contact had been made with Schumann who instructed that nothing should be moved until he and Houtermanns arrived with an SS engineering team.

Schumann was jubilant as Hans escorted him around, inspecting the half-completed cyclotron and the isotope centrifuges. Large quantities of uranium oxide were discovered and the apparatus was disassembled for transportation to the University of Munich. Houtermanns, wearing the uniform of an SS colonel, aggressively interrogated the scientists, many of whom refused to co-operate with their former colleague. Hans felt powerless as they were ordered into the garden and shot. Satisfied with their work Schumann and Houtermanns left Kharkov for Kiev. Westland and Hans returned to Dnepropetrovsk and, much to his surprise, Steiner, on Schumann's recommendation, granted Hans home leave. He gratefully grabbed a lift on the first available transport to Gatow.

His room in Harnack House was very much as he had left it. Unanswered mail lay on a side table, mainly letters from his parents. Hans recognized the flowing handwriting on one envelope with a Berlin postmark. The letter couldn't have been more brief. *'I miss you, love Maria,'* he read. There was no address. For the first time since he was a boy, tears welled until tiredness overwhelmed him. Tomorrow he would call Franz and Helmut.

CHAPTER 21

The Red Orchestra *mission*

Hans rang Helmut several times before he gave up. Franz sounded distant and uncommunicative, but he agreed to the suggestion that they meet for a stroll along the banks of one of the Dahlem lakes.

'Helmut has disappeared,' said Franz, quietly, as they sat on a bench watching the mature oak trees shedding their leaves in the wind.

'The Gestapo intensified its search for the *Red Orchestra* throughout Germany in the knowledge that *Operation Barbarossa* had been badly compromised. One day Helmut failed to show in Meinekestrasse. He was always careful; something must have happened. I've resisted calling his office at the Air Ministry and I think we should fear the worst.

'Tell me about yourself. I must say you look splendid in your SS uniform. We missed you. Initially I suspected you might have betrayed us, but Helmut scolded me for even suggesting such a thing. He used the pretext of an official visit to the Kaiser Wilhelm where a friendly chat with the porter at Harnack House confirmed that you had left for the Eastern Front.'

'Never, never, in my life have I betrayed a friend,' Hans retorted angrily. 'Your secret was always safe with me, although recently it has been difficult to share your view about the Russians. The Nazis act like barbarians, but the Bolsheviks are little better.' In the pale winter sunshine Hans recounted to his friend recent events in the Ukraine, describing the horrors of Lemberg as well as the butchered woman and foetus he witnessed in the cellars. Franz grinned when Hans recalled Schumann's suggestion that the Iron Cross, 2nd Class, might be in the offing for the capture of the institute in Kharkov.

'I'm sorry I harboured any doubts – but these are dangerous times and no one is safe. How long is your leave?'

'I can't say. Steiner didn't commit himself and Schumann hasn't yet been in touch – I don't even know if he's back from Kiev. No doubt I'll find out tomorrow at my debriefing with the Heereswaffenamt, but I'm pretty certain that I'll be ordered back for the push on Rostov-on-Don. My ultimate mission is to locate the uranium oxide deposits at Lermontev. The mines are not far from Voroshilovsk.'

In the park the shadows lengthened and the chill cut through Hans' greatcoat. He walked with Franz to the nearby railway station at Thielplatz.

'Is your notebook safe, the one you told us about?' enquired Franz, nervously scanning the deserted platform.

'Yes, I believe so. It is where I left it – on the bookcase in my room,' responded Hans.

'Excellent. Have your debriefing tomorrow, but I must see you in the evening. Please be careful – the Gestapo has undercover agents in the Kaiser Wilhelm. Are you free to move around?'

'I haven't been stopped yet. Where shall we meet?'

'I think we are better off in a crowd. Catch the train from here to the Unter den Linden, but change at least twice to ensure you haven't been followed, and meet me outside the Hotel Adlon at six o'clock. Bring the notebook with you.'

Next morning at the Heereswaffenamt Hans asked about the two chemists from the Kaiser Wilhelm who were part of the operation to locate Russia's nuclear institutes and laboratories. He wasn't surprised to learn they had perished.

Returning to Dahlem he walked to the main entrance of the Kaiser Wilhelm Institute for Physics only to find his way blocked by SS guards asking for papers. His name no longer appeared on the current list of employees and he was denied entrance. In his room at Harnack House he recovered the letter from Maria that he had crumpled up and thrown in the waste bin. Hans carefully flattened it out and caught a whiff of the scent that Maria must have daubed on the writing paper. He began to reminisce on some of the great times they had enjoyed together in Munich, laughing out aloud at the episode in the coffeehouse on the shores of Walchensee the day that Hitler, Himmler and von Schirach unexpectedly came for lunch.

On his shelf Hans found the notebook that Franz was so excited about, which had been gathering dust since June. The formulae that had seemed so logical when Heisenberg, von Weizsäcker, Hahn and others had explained them in the conference room at Harnack House to an audience of Kaiser Wilhelm staff and bored Government officials no longer meant much to him. Skimming through each page he recalled many of the meetings and names of the people he had met when he was researching possible uranium sites in the Soviet Union and Eastern Europe. He slipped the notebook into his Army briefcase and walked to Thielplatz.

On the train Hans felt self-conscious in his SS uniform, aware of the furtive side-glances from fellow passengers. Alighting in the Unter den Linden he hovered around the Hotel Adlon observing the doorman clad in his long red jacket, welcoming the high-ranking guests stepping from their military staff cars.

Franz had seen Hans lingering on the street, his office in Wilhelmstrasse was only a short distance away. Their eyes met and Hans followed his friend down the Unter den Linden towards the State Opera House and a tiny square adjacent to it where he ducked into the entrance of a dimly lit bar. Hans quickly entered but Franz remained outside, checking if anyone emerged from the shadows.

The bar was full and thick with cigarette smoke. The sight of SS officers intermingling with civilians was not unusual in this part of Berlin and the proprietor guided them towards a table in a quiet corner. Franz warily eyed the door.

'Have you brought your notebook?' asked Franz, finally satisfied that they could not be overheard.

Hans unclasped the briefcase tucked behind his knees and placed the notebook under the palm of his hand, slowly steering it towards Franz. Both men casually discussed the war as Franz looked through the pages, occasionally raising a point.

'Well, it's quite something,' said Franz returning it to Hans and picking up his beer.

'This notebook is immensely valuable to the *Red Orchestra* but the operation I have in mind is fraught with personal danger,' he whispered through his teeth. 'We want you to try to get your notebook into Russian hands.'

'Pardon?'

'It is vital that you engineer a situation enabling this notebook to be analysed by Russian scientists. They need to learn what is being developed at the Kaiser Wilhelm and the Heereswaffenamt, and, more importantly, they should hear it directly from you. Some of these names you have jotted in the notebook, are they Russian?'

'You mean Ioffe and Kapitsa?'

'Yes. Who is Ioffe?'

'He is the head of one of the main institutes in Leningrad, arguably Russia's leading nuclear physicist.'

'And Kapitsa?'

'I know little about him apart from the fact that he spent some years working in Cambridge, England, in the Rutherford Laboratory. Heisenberg often mentioned his work in his lectures at Harnack House. The nuclear physics world is a small global community and each year, before the war, the eminent Danish physicist Niels Bohr ran summer seminars in Copenhagen. Even the Russians attended.'

'Ioffe, or Kapitsa, must see your notebook,' stated Franz firmly.

'If you think it so important why can't I just pass it over to you? Surely with your contacts you must be able to arrange its transfer to the Soviets?'

'Since the Gestapo began its wave of arrests Moscow appears reluctant to continue working with us, as if we can no longer be trusted. I'm convinced my controller would consider your notebook a Nazi fabrication. Is Moscow the target if this bomb is ever built?'

'I overheard a conversation at the Heereswaffenamt during which some officers joked that the bomb would be tested on both London and Moscow.'

'I'm afraid the only way that the Russians are going to seriously believe what is going on is for you to deliver both yourself and your notebook into their hands,' said Franz quietly.

'You really are mad,' said Hans. 'In Kharkov, Russian snipers relished the sight of an SS officer. Do you really think my life would be spared if I walked towards the enemy, hands in the air and waving a white handkerchief.'

'There must be a way. It is imperative that Ioffe reads the notebook.'

'But I'm back at the Front in the next day or so, in the Rostov area. What opportunities will I have?'

'That's down to you, but I have something that may be of help,' replied Franz, extracting two folded sheets of paper from the inside pocket of his suit.

Hans looked quizzically at the two diagrams.

'What are these?'

174

'Take a closer look.'

'One is a drawing of the small prototype reactor in the underground laboratory of the Kaiser Wilhelm. I've seen it. This other drawing, is this what I think it is?'

'Yes. It's the first design for the German atomic bomb. Ugly isn't it, almost too spherical and barely resembling a conventional device.'

'Where did these drawings come from, the Kaiser Wilhelm?'

'I can't tell you. All I can say is that in your absence the Heereswaffenamt has pushed the Kaiser Wilhelm very hard to get this far. Now perhaps you see the importance of what you have to do. The Soviets must be told about the bomb. Your notebook and these drawings provide conclusive evidence. Germany must be defeated. Britain is on its knees, as is Russia, but we must have hope. Tuck the diagrams into the notebook.'

'So, it's down to me to defect to the Russians, there is no other way and you can't help?'

'If there was we haven't thought of it.'

'You keep on saying we, who are *we* exactly? Don't I have a right to ask as you want me to risk my life?'

'For your own protection I can't say any more.'

'Are you suggesting to me that Britain has some involvement with this mad scheme of yours?'

'Enough. We have spent too long here. Let us drink to the memory of Helmut,' said Franz, raising his glass.

'My friend, why have you asked me to commit suicide?' whispered Hans through his teeth.

Both men disappeared into the Berlin night, Hans first. Franz followed later, anxious to meet his controller and confirm that one of the craziest ideas of the war had just gone operational.

Hans needed time to think. He walked through the Brandenburg Gate and into the Chausee. Searchlights in the Tiergarten pierced the sky in wait for the RAF's Stirling and Halifax bombers. Into the blackness Hans strode, angry now. Berliners scurried past on the Charlottenberg Bridge, anxious to reach an air raid shelter. In Stuttgarter Platz he caught a train back to Thielplatz in Dahlem.

The Stirlings came that night. From his window Hans saw searchlights lock onto one aircraft, caught like a fly in a web, its pilot frantically trying to weave his way out of the blinding beam of light. Hit, the aircraft went into a tailspin… another crew would not be returning to base. He read again his new orders from Schumann. Hans was instructed to be at Gatow airfield in the morning; the move into the Caucasus had begun but this time he was to be attached to the LAH, destination Rostov, astride the mighty Don. At some point in the advance he would detour with a small force to Lermontev, in an area called 'Five Hills' – potentially the richest source of uranium oxide in Russia.

The Ju-52 climbed laboriously away from Gatow, circling over Berlin and enabling Hans to view the damage of the previous night's raid. He agreed with Franz – if Hitler ever had his super weapon, Germany would be unstoppable. From what he had heard from his friends in the Heereswaffenamt, the physicists at the Kaiser Wilhelm Institute for Physics were shortly to personally present their plans to Hitler and Goering. From his briefcase Hans took out the notebook and examined again the drawings provided by Franz. The schematic of the reactor and the bomb were perfectly annotated, so perfect that they could only have come from someone intimately involved in the project.

With the plane climbing higher in the first part of what would be a long and exhausting flight to Mariupol in the Ukraine, Hans doubted whether he could fulfil the *Red Orchestra* mission. He was also upset that in the past two days he had unsuccessfully tried to contact his parents in Munich. According to reports, the RAF had bombed the city and the lines were down.

Hans was destined never to return to Berlin for the remainder of the war.

CHAPTER 22

The race for heavy water

'*We have learnt through Norwegian Secret Intelligence that the Germans in Norway are interested in obtaining heavy water,*' reported a SIS agent on February 6, 1940. Confirmation was provided on March 7: '*Norsk Hydro's production of heavy water is 1.5 kilos per day, which is being sent to Germany for use by the Wehrmacht,*' it was communicated to London.

Encyclopaedia Britannica describes heavy water as: '*water composed of deuterium, the hydrogen isotope with a mass double that of ordinary hydrogen and oxygen. Ordinary water is obtained from most natural sources and contains one deuterium atom for every 6,760 ordinary hydrogen atoms. If water is electrolysed the gas produced at the cathode is mostly hydrogen, and the residual water is enriched in deuterium content. Continued electrolysis of hundreds of litres of water until only a few millilitres remain yields practically pure deuterium oxide.*'

In 1939 a limited volume of heavy water was produced by ICI's Billingham plant in County Durham, England. Even smaller amounts were available in America. As nuclear physicists established that heavy water was a moderator of neutrons in a controlled chain reaction, demand outstripped supply. The world's only commercially available source was in Ryukan, central Norway, produced in the Vermork hydro plant that was operated by Norsk Hydro.

On the Western Front, France in September 1939 remained in the grip of the 'Phoney War', occasionally enduring shelling from the huge German guns mounted on railway bogies in the Saar-Moselle region to the south-east of the Luxembourg-France border. In Paris, Professor Joliot-Curie continued his research on heavy water, French supplies of which were fast diminishing. A member of Joliot-Curie's team, Dr von Halban heard from Norwegian sources that Norsk Hydro had a total stock of 180 kilograms. The French Minister of Armaments, Monsieur Dautry, offered to purchase it. Actual negotiations were left to his fellow Cabinet colleague Lieutenant Allier, a member of the French Secret Service and a former director of Banque de Paris et des Pays-Bas, which owned the majority of the shares of Norsk Hydro. Allier flew to Oslo in February 1940. To his dismay he was informed that the Germans had thwarted him, having already placed an additional order for 2,000 litres.

The persuasive Allier managed to reverse the deal and immediately made plans to transport the heavy water to Paris, signing for the consignment on behalf of the French Government. No money changed hands. Instead, after the war, the entire stock would be replaced or purchased for cash. In return the Norwegians swore Allier to guarantee that no part of the stock would be sold to any third party. Frantic that the heavy water might end up in the hands of the Allies, the German Abwehr attempted to sabotage the new French source, but was unsuccessful. The consignment of heavy water arrived safely in Paris – but Joliot-Curie surprisingly declined all responsibility for the precious cargo, entrusting it instead to von Halban. Allier ordered the construction of an air raid shelter in Paris, strong enough to withstand a 1,000-lb bomb.

With the 'Phoney War' at an end, the Wehrmacht closed in on Paris. By June 5, 1940, the Germans crossed the Ailette Canal near Rheims, and by June 9 Soissons was occupied. Two days later the battle for Paris neared its peak as the Seine was reached. Further east, a salient at Chateau-Thierry meant that the city was encircled and the French offered its capital as an 'open city' in order to avoid aerial destruction. German paratroopers crossed the Seine at Romilly and France sued for peace – the armistice was signed on June 22.

Days earlier, an anxious von Halban took matters into his own hands, commandeering a lorry to transport the heavy water to a private house in Clermont-Ferrand in the Auvergne. The Abwehr was in hot pursuit. British Intelligence and Allier moved fast and the Earl of Suffolk, in his role as senior scientific advisor to the French, organized an operation to take the containers to England. Von Halban, his colleague Dr Kowarski and Joliot-Curie were to be spirited away to Bordeaux during the night of June 16, where they would await transportation to England by a Royal Navy destroyer.

In Clermont-Ferrand Joliot-Curie threw another spanner in the works by insisting on remaining behind, citing 'moral and administrative responsibilities'. The Abwehr still hadn't given up and chased the containers to the port, but it was too late. Arriving safely in London von Halban and Kowarski were debriefed by MI5 in Savoy Hill House, in central London, where they handed over documentation and reports relating to their experiments in Paris.

The Air Ministry took responsibility for the deuterium oxide, delivering the stock, consisting of a mixture of 27 square and round small metal containers, to Wormwood Scrubs, the jail in west London that had been commandeered by MI5 and the Home Office. Abwehr agents in Britain were alerted and tasked with ascertaining the consignment's new location. Windsor Castle, a Royal residence, was chosen as a safer alternative. The castle's librarian, O. J. Morshead, now became the official custodian of the world's largest supply of heavy water. According to an Air Ministry minute the choice of Windsor Castle 'was the safest place we can think of'. Some containers were later moved to a secret address in Cambridge, to be used by von Halban and Kowarski who were now employed at the Cavendish Laboratory.

RAF squadron leader Cackett had already had a strange telephone call on the morning of November 8. He now received an even more complicated written instruction.

'With reference to the conversation this morning regarding the tins containing fluid which we desire to have removed to the Cavendish Laboratory, Cambridge, we should be much obliged if you would kindly arrange removal on the following lines:

'Three round tins, bearing the numbers 3, 20 and 25, and three square tins (unnumbered) to be collected from Wormwood Scrubs prison and taken to Windsor Castle.

'The above three square tins and the round tin No. 20 are to be left at Windsor Castle in the care of Mr Morshead and a further 16 tins, numbered 4–17 inclusive, and Nos 23 and 24, are to be collected from him.

'The above 16 tins from Windsor Castle and the two previously collected from Wormwood Scrubs are to be taken to the Cavendish Laboratory in Cambridge.

'The attached receipts are to be signed by the person receiving the four tins deposited at Windsor Castle and the other by the individual receiving the 18 tins at the Cavendish Laboratory.

'Those concerned at Wormwood Scrubs and Windsor Castle have been advised to expect RAF personnel to call for the tins within the next few days and it would be appreciated if you could arrange for them to be collected and delivered to the Laboratory on Monday next, the 11th instant. The tins, the total weight of which is about 4 cwt [hundredweight] should be handled with care, but are in no way dangerous and will not necessitate the presence of an armed guard.'

As an afterthought, 'an armed guard is desirable' had been added. A representative of MI5 would collect all the receipts.

Cambridge could be a bombing target, believed von Halban, but MI5 disagreed. What was worse, the British made him financially responsible for every container, round and square. The frustrated von Halban couldn't believe the British attitude, especially after risking his life to ensure that the heavy water came to England. Angry, he wrote to the Ministry of Aircraft Production to explain how valuable the consignment was: 'Heavy water of 99.6% purity costs 1.5 Norwegian Crowns per gram (pre-war value) to the factory and is sold for scientific purposes at 2.5 Crowns, and for commercial purposes at 5 Crowns. Heavy water of 99.95% purity costs for scientific purposes 10 Crowns per gram and the cost to the factory seemed to be near this value, but I am not sure about this. In any case, this shows that our stock of 181.2 kilograms of 99.6% purity is worth 450,000 Norwegian Crowns, which is about £20,000; and our stock of 4.3 kilograms of 99.95% purity is worth 43,000 Crowns, which is about £2,000.'

After interminable civil servant squabbling, the Treasury eventually indemnified von Halban against the event of any of the material being lost through enemy action; the heavy water to be vested 'in the Custodian of Enemy Property' with a value of £22,000.

* * *

Germany had declared war on Norway on April 27, 1940. By June 4, Haakon and his Government were evacuated with the last Allied troops, Quisling replacing the King. Heereswaffenamt representatives flew to Ryukan to view the Norsk Hydro plant and demand greater output as Werner Heisenberg had stressed the importance of constant supplies for the German nuclear experiments to continue. Deuterium oxide, he told the Heereswaffenamt, was the only serious moderator material that could rapidly remove energy from neutrons by slowing them while absorbing as few neutrons as possible. The physicists at the Kaiser Wilhelm had also experimented with helium, but rejected it.

Plans were drawn up for a series of catalytic exchange ovens to be constructed in Germany to help in the process of producing heavy water. By July 1942 the extension to Vermork was completed, as was the new facility at Leuna, located 10 miles due west of Leipzig in the valley of the Saale River. Total German production of deuterium oxide reached a rate of 220 litres a month. One physicist realised the value of utilising the one percent of heavy water in the huge numbers of spent batteries used by U-boats. These batteries were transported to Ryukan.

Norwegian Intelligence continued to alert the British on production levels and Sir John Anderson realised that Norsk Hydro's plant had to be destroyed. An air strike was ruled out because of the location and the high terrain; instead, an airborne Commando group of 34 sappers from the 9th and 261 Field Park Companies of the Royal Engineers (Airborne) was given the mission.

Operation Freshman, however, would end in catastrophe.

Two aircraft, each towing a glider, piloted by Staff Sergeant Strathdee and Staff Sergeant Doig, took off from Skippen airfield in Scotland at 7pm on November 19, 1942. The towlines were cast off successfully, but the gliders were way off target. They crashed in the Stavanger area, on the Norwegian coast. One glider came down at Helleland, near Egersund, killing four sappers; the other at Florli on the Lysefjord, killing nine. At 3am the next morning Fenrik Arne Lima, a civil servant from Helleland, received an urgent telephone call from Lensman Hovland, telling him of the crash and the need to rescue the survivors before the Germans reached them. Lima, with five others, stopped to collect Doctor Benestad, but he was unwell. His wife, Magne, with her limited medical experience, joined in the rescue.

On reaching the crashed glider Lima found 13 men alive – although one died almost immediately in his arms. The survivors thought about walking to the Swedish border in a desperate attempt to get back to England, but before they could do anything a German patrol arrived. Some Commandos wanted to stand and fight but they decided to surrender because of their injured colleagues. They were escorted to a military camp at Slettebo, near Egersund, which at the time was under construction. The lorry halted at the main gate at the same time as a group of local construction workers began their morning shift. An officer ordered the Norwegians to go home. With no witnesses left the Commandos were lined up in the road and shot one by one, including the injured. Their bodies were driven to Ogna, a nearby settlement, and buried in the sand next to a minefield to dissuade any local interest.

Survivors of the second glider that crashed at Florli fared equally badly, quickly rounded up at the crash scene by the local Wehrmacht under the command of Colonel Probst. The Gestapo arrived, an officer announcing that the British were his responsibility and they must be treated as saboteurs. The survivors and injured were taken to cells in Stavanger.

The Wehrmacht continued to insist that the British were PoWs, but the Gestapo refused to listen. Further instructions were wired to respective commanding officers in Oslo – Probst to General von Falkenhorst and the Gestapo officer to General Rediess. Falkenhorst reluctantly agreed to an immediate court-martial, resulting in the death penalty. Kirkeby Jacobsen, a Norwegian partisan who later escaped to England, told the British that he saw all the prisoners, some badly wounded, in the cells just hours before execution.

After the German capitulation in Norway in May 1945, the British ruthlessly hunted down the perpetrators of the slayings. Captain Glynne-Jones, from the Office of the Judge Advocate General, gathered evidence. Von Falkenhorst, Rediess and the local Gestapo chief in Stavanger were indicted for war crimes. Major-General von Behren, in command of Fortress Stavanger at that time, confirmed that the 12th Company of 355th Infantry, under SS supervision, carried out the Slettebo executions.

The bodies of the Commandos from the Florli glider were disinterred and there was evidence that the men had been poisoned before being shot. Members of the two firing squads were sought throughout Europe by the British War Crimes team. Hans Rauter was found at an address in Scheveringen, Holland. Rudolf Koch-Erpach and Helmut Felmy, both members of the SS, were discovered in a PoW hospital in Dachau, near Munich. The Americans found and handed over Gefreiter Bohle. Kurt de Brower was located in an evacuation camp in England, as was Gustav Benz, a 32-year-old sergeant, found at PoW Camp No. 18 in Newcastle. General von Falkenhorst, who had managed to escape to Germany, was picked up and transferred to England for interrogation. Colonel Probst was arrested in Germany. Everyone connected with the executions was found. There is no record of what happened to General Rediess of the Gestapo. Many captured SS and Gestapo officers never made it into a courtroom – immediate and more final measures were deemed more appropriate.

After the failure of *Operation Freshman* further subversive attempts interrupted heavy water supplies. Another Commando raid took place in February 1943, as nine British-trained Norwegians parachuted into Norway and wrecked 300 heavy water cells at the plant. In November that year 155 Flying Fortresses of the US Eighth Airforce bombed the facility, putting it temporarily out of action. Only limited production restarted some months later.

In February 1944 the Reich Bureau of Standards demanded that all stocks of heavy water in Norway, totalling 680 litres, be shipped to Germany. Partisans sank the *Hydro*, the ferry on Lake Tinnsjo that was used in the operation, and the drums of heavy water sank into the depths. Norway no longer featured in the race for the atomic bomb. In Britain, physicists had concluded three years earlier that heavy water was no longer critical to the building of a super weapon.

CHAPTER 23

Van der Velde inspects Krivaya Kosa

The German advance into the southern Ukraine and Russia was relentless. The town of Taganrog fell on October 22, 1941. Rostov-on-Don, the gateway to the Caucasus and Stalin's oilfields was a mere 30 miles distant. Marshal Walter von Reichenau, the commander of Army Group South, was now faced with his biggest challenge. Intelligence had suggested that Rostov would be taken quickly so he allocated the task to the LAH, the SS division regarded as the weakest of the four Waffen-SS divisions on the Eastern Front.

On his return from Berlin Hans had been transferred from Wiking to the LAH, attached to a large unit of the Wehrgeologen. The Abwehr had reported that the Soviets were prepared to sacrifice Russia's entire crude oil output in the Caucasus rather than let it fall into German hands.

Grateful to von Reichenau for being extended the opportunity of leading the attack on Rostov, the LAH didn't disappoint. By the third week in November the division had established a forward command post in Rostov's jail. However, the occupation of Rostov would last just seven days and it would be marked by disaster.

Thanks to Colonel Ilya Starinov conditions for the occupying force were as terrifying in Rostov as they were in Kharkov. Delayed-action mines took out bridges while in the main street buildings collapsed. The Germans were particularly wary of the docks and the dingy Shanghai sector, where Russian snipers lurked. Starinov's engineering group destroyed the railway station, preventing supplies from Mariupol and Taganrog. Even worse, the huge metal bridge spanning the Don, the route to the Caucasus, toppled into the river after explosives removed the main supporting spars. In the air Soviet Ilyushin fighters constantly harried the Stukas of the Stuka Geschwader 1 squadron.

The morale of the LAH collapsed. On November 28 the Soviet 57th Army, commanded by General Remisov, launched fierce counter-attacks from the south-west. To the north the 9th Army broke through German defences, cutting off thousands of troops. The Wehrgeologen retreated to Taganrog, escaping by the skin of their teeth. In Rostov the civilians came out into the snow to welcome the victorious Red Army who scoured the streets systematically executing LAH stragglers. In seven days the division lost 5,000 men, with large numbers taken prisoner.

Hitler raged on hearing the breaking news of the first major defeat of *Operation Barbarossa*. He cabled von Reichenau to immediately retake the city, whatever the cost in lives. Events in Shakhty, a town north-east of Rostov, were no better as the Red Army, clothed in winter furs, drove back Wiking, with the Westland and Nordland regiments sustaining heavy casualties. Wiking, trained to attack and never retreat, reluctantly withdrew to the Tuzlow River after a number of its units helped out in the LAH retreat. It consolidated 18 miles west in Uspenskaja, a Cossack village on the Mius River.

Hitler had reluctantly accepted that the push into the Caucasus was on hold. The Red Army appeared content to let the Germans and their Rumanian and Italian allies suffer in the frozen dugouts. Hans and his Wehrgeologen colleagues survived as best they could in flimsy tents exposed to the rigours of the harsh and flat landscape of southern Russia. Not once since the retreat from Rostov had he thought about the notebook in his briefcase. To relieve the daily tedium, Hans drove up and down what was now called the 'Mius Line' in a battered Opel Kapitan that had been used as a staff car by another officer before he was killed by a sniper. Every night he protected the engine from the cold with several layers of tarpaulin.

In January the skies began to clear. One morning Hans drove down the line to Nikolaevka, the largest settlement on the river, where most of the divisions were encamped. Negotiating his way through the village he was brought to a halt as the road ahead was blocked. A noisy altercation was in progress between the driver of a kubalwagen inconvenienced by Russian PoWs being marched to a holding centre. Hans immediately recognised its passenger as the master sergeant from the 1st Mountain Division who had photographed the massacre in Lemberg jail. Suddenly the kubalwagen's driver placed his gun against the temple of the leading PoW and fired. The German guards laughed as the ice turned crimson with spurting blood. Revolted, Hans started his engine to move away, only to be seen by the sergeant. Their eyes met and Sergeant Demleitner waved a hand in greeting. Hans didn't reciprocate and drove on towards the little promontory with its ferry that transported both vehicles and men over to the flat Taganrog peninsula and Lakedemonovka, a traditional Cossack village with its simple one-story dwellings. Hans scanned the landscape through his binoculars. For miles all he could see were thousands of tents and tanks under camouflage netting.

The Opel proved immensely useful over the next few weeks, with Hans driving his Wehrgeologen colleagues into Taganrog to watch a film and newsreels in the cinema, or more often than not to visit a brothel. Every fortnight the visit to the delousing centre brought its own pleasure, a tepid bath and sometimes a change of clothes. Weekly briefings of senior officers in Taganrog sometimes required his attendance. No one disagreed that as soon as the temperatures rose and the tanks could properly function, Rostov must be recaptured. Von Reichenau's recall was no surprise. The official dispatch relayed to the troops in Taganrog on January 17, 1942, reported that he had died of a heart attack on-board his flight to Berlin to provide a first-hand report of conditions to Hitler. Many loyal officers were of the belief that something more sinister had befallen their former commander.

At one briefing in Taganrog the commanding officer from the Rumanian 5th Cavalry demanded action and retribution for the increasing number of attacks by Ukrainian partisans on the Mariupol to Taganrog road that were depressing the morale of his troops. The Soviets, he explained, were masters in the use of delayed-action mines and many of his soldiers had been killed or wounded. In a disturbing new development, Russian sappers, led by the now-legendary Colonel Ilya Starinov, were crossing the frozen Taganrog Bay in sleighs from Yeysk to inflict both damage and casualties.

Despite the risk Hans decided to explore the north shore of Taganrog Bay for himself, setting off south, through Nikolaevka and past the ferry, to Matveevski and the Mius estuary, where he joined the road to Mariupol. With his tyres barely gripping the compacted ice he drove on, safe in the knowledge from the briefings that the Russians only raided at night and that German sappers swept the road for mines as soon as it was light. He passed the roadblock at Veselo Voznesensk and entered Obruivski. The countryside was even bleaker than on the Mius.

Low on the horizon was Krivaya Kosa; the sand spit stretching like a curled finger into Taganrog Bay, its beacon clearly visible. Hans drove towards the village and German sentries in a watchtower warily tracked the approaching Opel. After stopping the car in the main street Hans waved reassuringly to the sentries. Surveying the frozen expanse of Taganrog Bay with his binoculars he could hardly believe that men could actually travel over the ice and remain in a condition that allowed them to mount a raid.

A yell from an officer standing in the doorway of a house brought him back to reality.

'What are you doing here?' shouted the lieutenant from the 13th Panzer division.

'I'm sorry. I should have alerted you about my visit. I'm from the Wehrgeologen and our unit is based with the LAH to the north of Taganrog. I'm scouting around the area looking for mineral deposits,' Hans replied hurriedly.

'Don't you know how dangerous this road is?'

'You're referring to this Colonel Starinov and his raiders? Yes, in Taganrog we hardly talk of anyone else. Why can't we launch raids on Yeysk, where they come from?'

'We have tried,' came the surly reply, 'but only madmen walk on sheet ice in blizzards.'

'Are they hitting the coast of Taganrog Bay every night?'

'That seems to be the case. The problem is we don't know where. Surprisingly they haven't yet ventured into Krivaya Kosa. You may be aware that some of your LAH colleagues are here giving our Rumanian friends some training, would you like to meet them?'

'No, thanks. I must go, it's quite a trip back and I don't want to be on the road at night. A final question though, do these Russians ever take prisoners?' enquired Hans very casually.

'That's an odd question. It is a policy of the Soviet sappers never to take prisoners. They spare no one. Why do you ask?'

'Just curious. Good to meet you.' Hans climbed back into the Opel and drove slowly back past the watchtower. Returning to his billet the lieutenant turned over in his mind whether he should report the strange encounter with this major from the Wehrgeologen.

Someone called from inside, a middle-aged woman from the village who fraternised with the enemy in return for cigarettes. She was a more rewarding distraction.

The next day, after cadging some fuel, Hans drove up the Mius north to Uspenskaja, where Wiking had encamped. Conditions were just as wretched. The division was a pale shadow of its former self and Steiner, in the middle of a medal presentation, waved as Hans parked his car. Steiner had aged years, thought Hans, shaking his hand before being introduced to Obersturmführer Fritz Hahl, the new holder of the Iron Cross, 2nd Class. Westland had been badly mauled at Shakhty and the regiment desperately needed replacements.

Hahl escorted Hans around the camp, pointing out the moribund tanks that were useless in the extreme cold. Men huddled around fires in an attempt to keep warm. Hans asked about the sergeant who had accompanied him in Dnepropetrovsk and Kharkov, only to be told that he had been taken prisoner and was probably dead. Hardly rough justice mused Hans as he was taken to a forward outpost to view the closeness of the Red Army positions.

'Do they raid?' ventured Hans, trying hard to make out the well-hidden enemy.

'Only at night. During the day they simply observe us.'

'Do they take prisoners?'

'Yes, several of my men have been taken; usually for intelligence.' Hahl looked puzzled at Hans' line of questioning.

'I just wondered if their interrogation methods were any different to ours. Obersturmführer Hahl, I need to return to my unit. Let's hope the weather improves. Good luck.'

As Hans left Wiking licking its wounds he glanced back in the direction of the Russian positions. In recent days he had contemplated the possibility of carrying out his *Red Orchestra* mission.

* * *

The date was February 22 and in Krivaya Kosa Maria Leonidovna Prokopenko dressed her daughter, Simonova, warmly for school. The wintry conditions were the worst that she had ever experienced in all the years she had lived in the village. Soldiers from 5th Cavalry and 13th Panzer had occupied the ancient village since October. The fearful sight of panzers moving unopposed into Krivaya Kosa in the advance on Taganrog had caused panic among the inhabitants. A small occupation force had set up its headquarters in Budenovsk at the head of the kosa. In Krivaya Kosa soldiers were billeted with the owners of some of the larger houses. In the tiny khattas, the numerous fishermen huts that occupied the crumbling coastline, the villagers coped as best they could.

Pillboxes were constructed in the main street and minefields laid. In a two-story house on the shoreline a powerful searchlight was installed. The elderly fishermen who daily ventured out onto the bay to break the ice and cast their lines were subject to a strict curfew. The beacon at the end of the kosa, the longest sand spit on the northern shoreline, served as a landmark during the day for German aircraft flying into a landing strip outside Taganrog. Temperatures had plunged in February. With food and fuel scarce, life was very hard for the troops and even more miserable for the villagers.

'Bastards' was the politest word that Maria Prokopenko used as she swore at the Germans under her breath. More choice expletives she reserved for the Rumanians, an undisciplined rabble that openly groped the women and young girls. They patrolled the streets of Krivaya Kosa with their snarling German Shepherd dogs, entering homes on any pretext to steal food. For the few young Russian men in the village, such behaviour was unacceptable; but it was foolhardy to mess with the 5th Cavalry, the so-called elite of the Rumanian Army, who readily handed out savage beatings.

In overall command of Krivaya Kosa and nearby villages was Colonel Friedrich Schmidt, based in Budenovsk. Schmidt, a rotund, typical Nazi, enjoyed his task of providing vital protection for the convoys from Mariupol to Taganrog. Moody and often violent, Schmidt coerced local women into his bed with promises that were rarely kept. Junior officers saw fit to copy their senior officer and houses were set aside in Krivaya Kosa for such recreation.

Schmidt dispensed death sentences for even the smallest of crimes. Two young men from Krivaya Kosa were misguided in believing that friendship with the Rumanians gave them a license to violate German curfews. Execution by firing squad took place one morning in January 1942, their bodies left in the snow as a deterrent to others.

Maria Prokopenko had four soldiers billeted in her home – three German, one Rumanian. The Germans were relatively friendly, sharing their rations with the family, but the Rumanian was regularly drunk and ate elsewhere with his countrymen. Sleeping arrangements were difficult, as the soldiers took the straw beds, leaving Maria and Simonova the slate floor. Thick clothes did little to prevent the raw cold from seeping into their bodies.

In the past desperate months one German, a sergeant, couldn't have been kinder to Maria. He related tales of his own family in Schleswig Holstein, a farming community similar in many ways to Krivaya Kosa. Simonova had celebrated her eighth birthday and the German had found some sweets for the young girl. What passed as breakfast was divided equally, but Maria gave her share to her daughter. For centuries dried fat was a constituent of the staple diet of poor Ukrainians. It was underbelly of pork soaked in salt, sometimes garlic – an acquired taste, but the insurgents soon came to rely on the food. Sugar was limited. However, the resourceful sergeant had found some supplies, making life in the household more bearable. He had even tried to ascertain what had happened to Maria's husband, a regular in the Red Army. But Maria feared the worst. With the retreat of the Red Army across the

Ukraine the Germans were unable to process the vast numbers taken prisoner.

For fuel, Maria used dried cow dung gathered during the summer and stored in the garden where in the winter it became rock hard and brittle. When permitted she and other women scrounged lifts on German lorries that made daily runs into Mariupol, noted for its steel industry. Now under German occupation the steel output was transported to munitions factories in the Ruhr. Ash from the coke used in the smelting process lay in great spoil heaps that could be picked over for unburned fuel. Maria filled a sack and struggled under its weight as she walked to the lorry for the return journey.

Gossip had intensified amongst the villagers in Krivaya Kosa after shadowy figures had been observed entering the khattas. The raid on February 16 had taken the villagers and the garrison completely by surprise. Little damage had been done but several Rumanians had been killed. Oddly, prisoners were taken, a Rumanian and a member of the LAH. They had been transported over the ice to Yeysk. The guards in the watchtower were now more alert than usual.

Simonova hugged her mother as she left for school on that bitterly cold morning of February 22. Even during the occupation the villagers were determined to keep the school operational. The teacher, like all the other able-bodied men, had left for the Front as soon as Germany invaded. Some elders had offered their services and did their best for the handful of children. Simonova halted on the corner of the street, waiting for her 15-year-old cousin, Maria Danilova, who lived next door, to join her. The girls trudged through the heavy snow. Passing the watchtower they waved to the young German guards, who waved back.

Zoya Samsonovich's khatta had been used by generations of fishermen. In more recent times it had served a different, more urgent purpose. Aged 20 and good-looking, Zoya was married to Gavrila, one of the best fishermen but now a partisan operating for Maria Belova, an undercover Red Army agent, and Colonel Ilya Starinov in Yeysk. The Wehrmacht had standing instructions to turn any partisan over to the SS headquarters in Mariupol. In Krivaya Kosa the partisans monitored the convoys on the Mariupol to Taganrog road.

That morning Zoya peered out of her window and saw the girls on their way to the schoolhouse. She looked up at the Germans standing by the open windows of their watchtower before she put on her green coat. About to leave the khatta she suddenly remembered that some days earlier an undercover Russian sapper had borrowed the coat. Concerned that a guard might remember seeing the coat on a man, not a woman, she burned it in the tiny grate. No one noticed the strange smell coming from Zoya's chimney as it was mixed with the nauseous stink of dried animal dung.

Nicandr Sklerov, the chief partisan, was too committed to the cause to care much about his own safety. There had been an incident during his recent rendezvous with Vitali Levitsky, one of Starinov's men, who often hid for days collecting intelligence in the village before walking out on the ice to await collection by a sanya from the sapper control centre in Yeysk. They had been talking in a khatta when a guard approached. Levitsky drew his sapper's knife, but the Rumanian cavalryman walked on by. It had been Sklerov's information that had led to the raid on February 16, as he had identified possible captives in a house some streets away from the watchtower.

As the day wore on fresh falls of snow turned the village into a winter wonderland. Only the guards in the pillboxes and in the watchtower brought a cruel reality to Krivaya Kosa. Three partisans arranged to meet at the home of Ivan Turchaninov, a 'safe house'. Gavrila and Grigori Nikitenko were already there when Sklerov arrived. He informed his comrades that another raid was planned for the early hours of the following morning, February 23, to coincide with Red Army Day – an annual celebration of the Soviet military. It would be a show of strength involving more than 100 sappers from Yeysk. Fortifications would be blown up, including the watchtower, said Sklerov, who had provided Levitsky with an accurate sketch of the village. Two sappers were already hidden in the village, their job to destroy the telephone cables to Budenovsk and Mariupol at the appropriate time.

The three then discussed another matter that needed to be taken care of, permanently.

They were convinced that a traitor was passing intelligence to Colonel Schmidt. They suspected a schoolteacher in Budenovsk, a man held in high regard in the community who combined teaching with the important position as head of the fish processing plant. In recent weeks the schoolteacher had asked the children if strangers had been seen in the surrounding villages.

Sklerov agreed to act as executioner.

Suddenly the drone of an aircraft could be heard in the distance, the German mail plane on its daily run from Mariupol to Taganrog. Sklerov listened carefully. There was another sound, this time from a twin-engine Yak-9 Soviet fighter, followed by gunfire. Levitsky had informed him that today would be the pilot's last delivery. The stricken plane banked away from the ice of Taganrog Bay, the pilot gambling on landing in a field. He almost made it, but a wingtip hit the ground and the plane flipped over. Only the co-pilot was able to drag himself from the flames.

Anna Borisovna Podolskaya didn't go to school that day. Her house was used as a billet for two Rumanian officers. She had been petrified when they arrived in October, banging on the door. Her mother immediately complied with the order, fearfully noticing the look one officer gave her daughter. For the first week the atmosphere was charged and soon the sexual demands began, resulting in physical violence when they were refused. The only course of action was to complain to Nikolay Duschenko, the Russian starosta, chief of administration for the village and personally selected by Colonel Schmidt. Despite his despised position, Duschenko had proved helpful to the villagers.

A concerned neighbour took Anna's mother into Budenovsk in his pony and trap to see the starosta, who was instantly recognizable in his shapka, a furry hat, and an ankle-length Soviet military greatcoat with a large white patch stitched to one arm.

She broke down in front of Duschenko and blurted out the tale of abuse. Unknown to her, at home the two Rumanians had again picked on Anna and this time damaged her much-loved guitar in the ensuing scuffle. Brutalized, Anna wrote a despairing note for her mother. She quietly left by the rear door, carrying her guitar with its broken strings, and trudged out of the village. Her face a flood of tears and seared by the biting wind, she attempted to walk to Taganrog where she had relations.

German lorries rattled past. Not one offered the young girl a lift. A convoy of Rumanians passed, their drivers hooting. It had been a tedious day. Two Rumanians used Anna for target practice, one bullet missed, but the other struck home, passing through the guitar and into her body. They laughed as Anna crumpled, falling to her knees before collapsing onto the road. The following lorry veered away from the body but couldn't miss the guitar, smashing it beyond repair. Decades later the slaying of Anna Borisovna would be sadly commemorated.

Later that evening and moving stealthily between the khattas to avoid the curfew, the partisans gathered again in another 'safe house', this time belonging to Dunya Pamazan and her husband. Until recently this house was occupied by Rumanians on the ground floor, but right under their noses two sappers from Yeysk had lodged in the attic. Levitsky had offered the Pamazan family evacuation to Yeysk but 'Baba', as the old lady was affectionately known, declined. With the Rumanians now billeted elsewhere the Pamazan home, out of view of the watchtower, offered a perfect meeting place.

The partisans again went over the details of the raid that was scheduled for 2am the following day – February 23. Sklerov crept away to Budenovsk to take care of business.

As Krivaya Kosa slept, its citizens were oblivious to 125 Russian sappers leaving their holding point one mile out on the ice, far enough away so as not to be seen by the German searchlight, and now walking silently towards the sandbar. There was quiet, too, in Budenovsk as Sklerov crouched outside the schoolhouse. Forcing a window open he moved stealthily through the darkened classroom to the schoolteacher's room. Sklerov heard a movement, the door opening too quickly for him to properly aim his silenced pistol. The bullet only wounded the victim who raced outside. Sklerov gave chase, but it was hopeless. It was imperative that he should be back in his khatta in Krivaya Kosa before the mayhem really started.

The schoolteacher had been the traitor. He had run to the home of a friend where his arm was bandaged. The next day he disappeared in Mariupol, joining the tens of thousands of displaced Ukrainians, and was never seen again.

Gunfire could be heard as Sklerov ran back to Krivaya Kosa. At the brickworks on the edge of the village Sklerov saw the telephone lines were down. More careful now, he made his way through the back alleys behind the houses in the main street. He stopped and crouched as he saw a saloon car, whose make he didn't know but it had to be German, that was parked outside the very house from which the German sergeant and the Rumanian had been taken prisoner just days earlier.

An SS officer was tearing off the tarpaulin protecting the engine from the cold, before racing back inside only to emerge with a briefcase in his hand. Someone else joined him, lurching out through the doorway, gun in hand. The engine over-revved, the car wheels spinning on the icy road. Sklerov expected the vehicle to head north away from the village to the safety of Budenovsk but, to his amazement, it went south towards the shoreline. At the lifeboat station the car careered left, past the Prokopenko house towards the school and watchtower, seemingly out of control.

Curiosity took over from caution for Nicandr Sklerov. Racing through the khattas he witnessed the raid in the early hours of February 23, 1942. For decades after the war he would be sworn to secrecy on the capture of Major Hans van der Velde.

CHAPTER 24

Encountering the giant with huge hands

Beria attempted to curtail the interrogation of Major Hans van der Velde but Stalin would have none of it. On one occasion so overwhelmed was Beria with anger that he walked over to the prisoner and slapped the German officer's face. The scientists sat around the table were embarrassed by his behaviour. As the hours passed tea was provided, followed by Georgian brandy and vodka – but not for Hans. Nor was he allowed water. Pipe and cigarette smoke hung like a heavy pall around the room. At times Stalin drifted off, only to be woken by Beria, who rubbed the sweat off his pince-nez glasses before engaging in another tirade.

'Fiction, everything you have told us today is pure fiction,' snarled Beria at the now very weary Hans.

'I don't doubt for one single moment that part of your notebook is genuine. It would have to be, wouldn't it, given that there are many scientists in this world who are fully aware of the properties of uranium?

'But are we discussing German or British fiction here, or don't you know? Perhaps you, too, have been taken in? The British are masters in deviousness – better than we are in many respects. And the Germans? They pride themselves on their deception techniques.

'In some of the scientific documents we have obtained in Britain there are formulae that are constructed in such a manner so as to deliberately mislead. Oh yes, we have been taken in, despite my advice to my NKVD colleagues not to believe everything we gather from our agents,' said Beria with a piercing glare at General Victor Kravchenko and Lt General Pavel Fitin.

'Every formula in your notebook – how long would it take us to work them through and what different result would we come to?' This time he pointedly turned to the glum Abram Ioffe and his prodigy, Igor Kurchatov.

'However, you are German not British and probably a member of the Abwehr using the cover as an employee of the Kaiser Wilhelm. What disturbs me is your motive. Why give us one of Hitler's deadliest secrets? Something is wrong here, very wrong.'

He picked up the notebook in the middle of the conference table and extracted the two diagrams.

'These two loose diagrams – one purports to be a reactor, the other an actual design for an atomic weapon. Who drew them?'

'I have no idea, truthfully. All I can say is that my friend, Franz, unexpectedly handed them to me in Berlin when I was on leave, just before we left the bar in the Unter den Linden,' replied Hans.

'This Franz, was this his real name? And the *Rote Kapelle*, the *Red Orchestra* you keep on mentioning, no such organization exists.'

'Why would I invent it? Franz told me that the Soviet Comintern established this secret group in 1932 and that the Gestapo had infiltrated it. Some of its members had been hung, others beheaded. Why would he not have told me the truth?'

'Ah, the truth,' retorted Beria, 'do Abwehr agents have any conception of the word? We believed Ribbentrop. He lied to us. The Nazis never were an ally, and now the SS and the Einsatzgrüppen carry out their pogroms on our people. What men would do such things?'

Hans placed his head in his hands, reliving the dreadful events in Lemberg and Tarnopol – he couldn't answer.

'You tell us you worked at the Kaiser Wilhelm Institute for Physics with access to the Heereswaffenamt, but you do not know the author of these two drawings from your notebook?'

'Franz did entrust me with a name, not the author, but a contact.'

'Please share it with us.'

'It is someone that Franz said I should mention to establish my bona fides if I needed to.'

'My SS friend, don't keep us in suspense. Would you like some water?'

The translator gave Hans a glass but the water did little to slake his thirst.

'Martin Gershfeld,' said Hans softly, 'Franz met him in Hamburg.'

Beria looked stunned, as did Stalin.

'And what did Franz share with you about Martin Gershfeld?' enquired Beria, regaining his composure.

'Absolutely nothing. Perhaps you can tell me who Gershfeld is?'

Beria had sat down and he lit a cigarette. Fitin looked uncomfortable.

Georgii Flerov saw this as an opportunity to ask questions.

'Major, I am a real physicist unlike yourself. I have a doctorate and it is probably fair to say that my practical experience is far superior to yours. The realisation of a nuclear bomb is more a question of combining technology with chemistry. No one has solved the problem of how to implement such an explosion, releasing the energy locked in the uranium and its transfer in the blast wave. If we did have a solution, in my estimate, the power unleashed in one uranium bomb would be equivalent to three years of RAF bombing over Germany. Quite a force, wouldn't you agree?'

'If you say so,' Hans nodded.

'The bomb drawn on your diagram is round and has two spheres filled with U-235. Do you know what happens next with these two spheres?' continued Flerov.

'Not really. As you said, I have no doctorate. I'm really a printer from Munich with a physics degree. Heisenberg once referred to bomb design in one of the seminars I attended at Harnack House.'

'Let me enlighten you, then. An explosive device is required which in a split second ensures that both spheres collide to create a nuclear reaction. This is the most critical element in such a bomb and, as far as I know, this is a difficulty yet to be fully understood. Who in the German nuclear project has the expertise to construct such a trigger?'

Stalin interjected. 'Interesting question, Comrade Flerov. I am keen to hear the answer.'

Hans prevaricated. In his infrequent visits to the underground laboratory he had only seen what he believed to be a prototype reactor, nothing else.

'I can only assume that the diagrams came from within the Kaiser Wilhelm, there is nowhere else. Heisenberg, von Weizsäcker and Wirtz must be involved in the design,' he blurted out.

'Come now, Major,' jested Flerov, 'be honest with us. You have already admitted that your responsibility at the Kaiser Wilhelm had become broader. As one of your responsibilities included the regular supply of metallic uranium to the laboratories you would surely be in possession of the name of every location in the programme?'

'Yes, that is true. After several months Bewilogua increased my role to include liaison between the Auer factory in Oranienburg and the universities and institutes.'

Everyone in Stalin's conference room looked transfixed at Flerov, the physicist from Leningrad who had been conscripted into the Soviet air force. He looked immaculate in his uniform, with his inky-black hair meticulously combed. Raising his eyes to the ceiling Flerov slowly brought them down to fix on Hans.

'Is there a location outside Berlin, so secret that even Heisenberg is not privy to it, that is run directly by Goering, or perhaps Himmler?'

'My notebook detailed Leipzig, Hamburg, Heidelberg, Munich, Kiel, Göttingen and Lichterfelde. There are smaller laboratories in Celle, Freiburg and Strasbourg. Then there are the institutes in Vienna.'

Flerov paused, considering the answer. At a seminar convened by the Russian Academy of Sciences in Kazan on December 20, 1941, he had presented a paper on nuclear fission and past co-operation with other countries. For a number of years Leningrad's Radium Institute exchanged research with the Radium Institute of the Vienna Academy of Science and the physics department in Vienna's university. The work of Austrian professors Gustav Ortner, Georg Stetter and Josef Mattauch was well known in Russian scientific circles.

'Didn't you miss out one, potentially the most secret of them all?' prompted Flerov. 'What German city is on a railway line, less than two hours from the uranium mines at Joachimsthal in the Erzebirge Mountains and on the very limit of the new long-range British bombers? Major van der Velde, I am not referring to Leipzig, or Chemnitz.'

Hans averted his eyes from Flerov's stare. Stalin lit another cigarette and sipped his brandy.

'Major van der Velde,' I repeat, 'enlighten us with its name please.'

'Dresden. It is Dresden.'

'Thank you Major.'

Not for the first time during this long day General Kravchenko wanted to leave. Now he might be in trouble. His staff had informed him that the troublesome physicist had been digging around for weeks for intelligence on Dresden. In the NKVD operational files were photographs of a half-constructed laboratory hidden away in one of the many woods that surrounded the city.

'Comrade Flerov,' demanded Stalin, 'have you been withholding information from us?'

'Forgive me, Comrade Stalin, it is unfortunately remiss of the NKVD not to have acquainted you with recent developments. For myself, in 1938 I was in friendly correspondence with a German chemist who worked for Professor Claus Clusius in the University of Munich. He had first contacted me in Leningrad after someone, I haven't found out who, had related to him my own experiments on nuclear fission. His last letter was received just weeks before the German invasion, but he mentioned that he and others from around the country had been transferred to Dresden to work on a project he couldn't disclose. He didn't know when he would next be able to write. I replied to his letter but I never heard from him again.'

'Comrade Kravchenko, is what Comrade Flerov says true?' asked a visibly irritated Stalin.

'I regret not sharing this intelligence, but the evidence was too thin until recently,' replied Kravchenko. 'Goering no longer has any enthusiasm for the nuclear project, believing instead in the more advanced rocket programme. Hitler has ordered Himmler to organize a top-secret group to replicate much of the Kaiser Wilhelm's nuclear research. Too many scientists, in Himmler's opinion, were not committed to the building of an atomic bomb. It is not clear to us yet if Heisenberg, von Weizsäcker or Diebner, the head of the Kaiser Wilhelm, has any knowledge of this development.'

Stalin turned on Lt General Fitin. 'Comrade, your department has established a special group to monitor nuclear intelligence. Were you aware of Dresden?'

Fitin, too, had been concerned at how the questioning of the SS officer had turned to more sensitive matters. Van der Velde's mention of Gershfeld had shocked the Counter-Intelligence chief. Gershfeld was the most effective NKVD recruiter in Germany, personally enlisting many *Red Orchestra* agents, but in 1939 he had fallen under suspicion and had been purged under the orders of Stalin. A year later Moscow reactivated Gershfeld, but since the invasion contact had been severed. The NKVD may have lost its top agent in Germany. However, it appeared to Fitin that van der Velde might be telling the truth, unless Gershfeld had been turned.

'Comrade Stalin, I confess I am at a disadvantage,' said Fitin hesitantly. 'There is much rivalry between the 4th Department run by Comrade Kravchenko and my own 5th Department and intelligence is rarely shared. We have regularly asked the 4th Department to keep us informed of its own efforts in nuclear intelligence gathering but it ignores us.'

'Answer my question, Comrade.'

'I can say categorically that my department did not know the significance of Dresden. We have received reports about new construction in and around the city but we had no idea that nuclear fission is one of the purposes. That is the truth.'

'That word again,' muttered Stalin. 'Comrade Flerov, I think you should continue.'

'Thank you Comrade Stalin.'

'Major, is this trigger being designed in Dresden?'

'I do not know. All I was ever asked to do was arrange a consignment of uranium oxide from Joachimsthal directly to an address outside the city.'

'On whose order? – Professor Schumann?'

'No. I received a letter from the Reichsforschungsrat, the National Research Council. I didn't need to question its instruction.'

'Does that imply that somewhere in Dresden there is a facility to manufacture metallic uranium?'

'It does.'

'Dresden was never mentioned in your notebook, why?'

'Simply because I had very little to do with it, there was no need and I certainly never visited the location.'

'How often did you organize these consignments?'

'Usually once a month.'

'I put the question again, Major. Is the nuclear trigger being developed in Dresden?'

'I did no more than arrange uranium oxide. I swear I do not know.'

Flerov, sensing that his disclosure had shocked most people in the conference room, including the German, didn't need an answer. He flicked through the pages of the notebook and momentarily studied the diagrams on the two loose sheets of paper. In his opinion the notebook was disturbingly genuine. Inwardly Flerov felt vindicated. For months he had written many letters from the Front, including several to Stalin saying that it was imperative that Russia restart its own nuclear efforts. In another sense, however, he was disappointed. He had believed that such an unconventional weapon would be similar to his own design that he had drawn up in his spare time at Yoshkar-Ola where he was stationed. His schematics were of a ball composed of U-235, shot through a barrel of five to ten metres in length to achieve the necessary velocity. The problem was that the acceleration of the bomb into the barrel at 3,000 metres per second could cause the barrel to disintegrate due to Mach waves. From the diagram it appeared that the Germans were well ahead, their spherical device was not much larger than a conventional bomb.

'Comrade Flerov, are you finished for the moment?'

'For the time being Comrade Stalin.'

'Lavrenty?'

Beria shook his head brusquely, fuming that his people hadn't briefed him about the potential terror of Dresden.

'Velde,' said Stalin, 'explain how you engineered your capture at Krivaya Kosa. I'm sure you have a fascinating story to tell us.'

* * *

The greyness of the winter afternoon had turned into dusk as Hans drove back to camp from visiting Wiking in its encampment on the upper reaches of the Mius, the chains on the tyres of the Opel crunching into the compacted snow. He had observed the long rows of panzers under their camouflage, the war machines that had flattened the Ukraine in endless victories. Some had their engines idling to prevent the oil from solidifying in the sumps. For the first time Wiking had tasted defeat and even the arrogance of the Westland, which Hans had witnessed at first hand, had dissipated.

That night Hans couldn't sleep. Wearing his greatcoat for warmth, the biting winds that whipped across the desolate plains that bordered both Russia and the Ukraine howled around his tent as his mind churned with the vestige of a plan that would need him to be transferred back to Wiking.

Events were to take a different turn.

The next day, February 20, at an officer briefing in Taganrog a colonel from 13th Panzer complained again at the alarming number of Soviet attacks on the Mariupol to Taganrog road. Berlin had demanded action. Rewards were now posted in all occupied Cossack villages for information about the sappers from Yeysk, also warning of the death penalty for harbouring partisans.

The colonel informed the assembled officers that the Soviets might have changed tactics as on February 16 two prisoners had been taken in Krivaya Kosa and transported back over the ice to Yeysk.

An informer in Budenovsk, a schoolteacher, had provided interesting intelligence. Moscow had ordered that across all fronts Red Army Day – February 23 – should be celebrated by a show of strength. In the villages of Budenovsk and Krivaya Kosa, strangers had been observed. There was speculation that they might be a forward group of sappers and the garrison was on full alert.

Hans sensed an opportunity, but the risk was so much higher than merely handing himself over to a Soviet forward position near Wiking on the Mius. As an officer in the Wehrgeologen he could legitimately travel around the Krivaya Kosa area for a few days on the pretence of searching for mineral resources. His LAH commanding officer was aware of the special status of the Heereswaffenamt representative and permission was granted. But Hans encountered an unexpected snag. A lieutenant, a Wehrgeologen colleague, wanted to accompany him. Word had spread that the major had been given a seven-day pass. Conrad, a petroleum engineer, was an amateur archaeologist and knew that the southern part of the Ukraine featured kurgans – ancient burial mounds more than 5,000 years old. Some of the best and totally unexplored examples of these deep shafts built by the nomadic Kurgan tribes were near Krivaya Kosa, and he didn't want to miss the opportunity of seeing them for himself.

For the mission Hans had in mind the last thing he needed was a companion. Conrad was a grave complication, but Hans agreed that his colleague could be an assistant so as not to cause suspicion.

On the morning of June 22 they set off. Conrad wanted to see kurgans, but Hans was venturing into the unknown, probably leaving the River Mius forever and fearing death as the most likely outcome.

Hans drove the Opel slowly south through the vast Army encampment, where tens of thousands of men were freezing and near starvation. Occasionally he glanced apprehensively into the back of the car where his briefcase lay tucked under two sleeping bags.

The trip took longer than before. At Veselo Voznesensk the Russian sappers had been active, their mines leaving large craters in the road. A tank lay incapacitated, covered with snow and abandoned, its tracks blown away. Conrad whooped with joy on spotting a huge kurgan in the distance. A little later the Opel entered Obruivski, a hamlet of six run-down houses, now the billets for Rumanian soldiers who had driven the elderly residents out to find alternative accommodation. Nearing Krivaya Kosa the car skidded on the icy road and collided with a tree. Unable to reverse both men were left with no option but to walk the final half-mile.

They reached the watchtower, its occupants suspicious of the two unfamiliar faces tramping through the snow carrying their kit and a briefcase. Hans, more circumspect than the last time he was in the village, formally presented his ID and orders to the same tight-lipped lieutenant from 13th Panzer that he had met previously. Surprised to see the major again the lieutenant scrutinised the credentials, suggesting they must be mad to explore for minerals in such a hellhole. However, he agreed to send out a truck to rescue the Opel. Conrad enquired about accommodation and a huge grin spread across the lieutenant's face.

The dried blood had extensively stained the floor in the house where, on February 16, Soviet sappers had shot dead its occupants, bar the two unfortunates who were captured. In the garden the frozen and contorted bodies remained piled under a sheet, awaiting a burial detail to transport them to Budenovsk. Hans shuddered at the sight, but tiredness overwhelmed him and he stretched out on the palliasse that passed as a bed, fearful of the events that may lie ahead. There had to be a strong probability that Krivaya Kosa would be chosen as a target for Red Army Day, given that prisoners had been taken on the reconnaissance raid.

The Opel arrived.

As Hans fell into a deep sleep Conrad inspected the vehicle, managing to lever away the battered wheel arch from the tyre before starting up the engine. Leaving Hans to his slumber he got in and cautiously threaded his way between the snow-drifts in the village to the Taganrog road, only to return as a blizzard began.

Later both men walked into the village centre to the billet where the lieutenant had said that an evening meal would be provided. It was warm inside and the food basic but very welcome. The beer flowed freely, a heady sweet-tasting dark brown Ukrainian brew. To be sociable, Hans joined in the conviviality and the singing. The snow was still falling, but gently now as the two Wehrgeologen officers bade their farewells near midnight. From the watchtower the resentful and sober guards were alert.

Back in their house Conrad laid down and snored loudly, lost in a drunken stupor. Hans piled every available log on the fire and sat in the rocking chair, staring into the flames and pondering Franz's parting words before they went their own ways into the blackness of Berlin. 'No one will ever know if you have succeeded in your mission,' Franz had said gently with a hand on Hans' shoulder, 'and even if you are fortunate you will never be allowed to return to Germany to tell your story.' Many times Hans had thought of that sinister implication.

Hans picked up the briefcase and extracted the black notebook, realising for the first time that his name didn't appear anywhere in it. He carefully wrote in the inside cover: *'Major Hans van der Velde, Wehrgeologen, and special representative of the Kaiser Wilhelm Institute for Physics and the Heereswaffenamt'*, dating it *'February 23, 1942, Krivaya Kosa, Ukraine.'*

With the flickering shadows from the fire bouncing off the walls of the tiny Cossack house, Hans was determined to read all 80 pages, beginning with the early notes he had made in the Kaiser Wilhelm library during his first week at the institute. He remembered one of the first conversations he had had with Dr Ludwig Bewilogua, the head of administration, who barely ever left the Kältelaboratorium, the 'cold' laboratory where the hydrogen experiments were conducted. Bewilogua had advised him to be fastidious in his note taking.

He unfolded the two diagrams given to him by Franz and strolled to the window. The village resembled a silent winter wonderland, a far cry from the ear-splitting bombardment of Kharkov or the screams of the wretched citizens of Lemberg. He imagined the street as it used to be, with Ukrainian peasants going about their business, farming and fishing. In the summer the sun would tan their faces, the cold bleaching their features in the extreme winter. Once this house, Hans surmised, with its gabled windows and sloping roof painted in traditional green, was a home resonating with laughter and joy.

The snow had stopped. Krivaya Kosa was temporarily at peace with the world. Back by the fire the strong Ukrainian alcohol took its inevitable toll.

The sound of gunfire from the watchtower reverberated around the village. In the grate the cinders glowed. Conrad, too, was awake. It was too far to run in the deep snow. Grabbing the briefcase, but forgetting his greatcoat, Hans raced for the car, as did Conrad with pistol in hand. Hans yelled at Conrad to stay behind but he followed him. It was too late now. Hans whipped the tarpaulin off the Opel and to his relief the engine fired first time.

With wheels spinning the vehicle and its occupants careered down the street. Hans turned left at the lifeboat station and headed towards the watchtower. The gunfire had ceased, the searchlight smashed and its guards lay half-slumped. Instinct told him to switch on the headlights. As he did so he spotted bodies in the snow and the outlines of what resembled white-clad ghosts emerging from the trees, machine guns in their hands.

To save their lives Hans cannoned the Opel into a snowdrift, the engine whirring. Conrad raced towards the house where they had earlier eaten, its door wide open now, but it was an unequal race for life. The sappers in their camouflage ruthlessly cut him down, his convulsing body caught in the beam of the car headlamps. The kurgan in Obruivski, with its buried treasure, would never now be excavated.

Terrified, Hans remained glued to his seat, hands on the steering wheel, expecting bullets to smash into the car and end his life. It had been suicide – even worse, he had effectively murdered his colleague. But the bullets never came, only shouts in Russian and Spanish. Whispering a prayer Hans opened his door and gingerly stepped out, hands in the air. Yards away a giant of a man, with eyes barely visible through his hood and scarves, ran towards him, aiming his gun at the SS officer's head. Within seconds two massive hands threw Hans face down into the snow.

The Russian wedged a foot hard on the back of his neck. Gasping for air Hans yelled out in a mixture of German and poor Russian that he had vital information and needed to speak to Abram Ioffe, a scientist from Leningrad. After some moments Hans was pulled to his feet and dragged towards the shoreline where sanyas, the sleighs pulled by horses clad in white camouflage, waited. Hans cursed that he had left behind his greatcoat in his haste to start the car.

Unceremoniously he was thrown aboard and given a blanket. The horses began their pull, their hot breath parting the cold air. Hans witnessed the frantic activity around him as other sanyas filled up with excited sappers. The watchtower was aflame, sparks flying high into the dark sky. Hans began to shiver uncontrollably but his heart thumped as he saw his briefcase by the side of the sapper who inexplicably had spared his life. Thoughts now were on survival. Within minutes the horses, their hooves spiked to maintain grip, were well into their stride. For a few seconds the radio cackled and Hans' captor talked excitedly into his headset.

The snow began to fall as the sanyas made their way back to Yeysk.

* * *

The 24th anniversary of the Red Army was being celebrated in London and in other Embassies around the world in a less-deadly fashion. Ivan Maisky, the Russian Ambassador, and his wife hosted a party, a glorious affair with six hundred guests. Winston Churchill couldn't attend but he had written a short note to Maisky offering both congratulations and apologies, delivered personally by his wife Clemmie.

These were difficult days for Churchill. The North Africa campaign was at its height and the Royal Navy had been in battle in the English Channel against the combined might of the *Scharnhorst, Gneisenau* and *Prinz Eugen*. Churchill had reshuffled his War Cabinet. Sir John Anderson's duties now included 'home-front policy'. Clement Atlee became Deputy Prime Minister while Sir Stafford Cripps, the former Ambassador to the USSR, joined the War Cabinet as its twelfth member.

Some War Cabinet Ministers did turn up for the Embassy party, including Sir Stafford and Lady Cripps. The NKVD officers Vladimir Barkovsky, Pavel Yerzin and Anatoli Gorsky moved freely among the elite of British society, as did their opposite numbers from GRU. The invitation list had been put together with the greatest of care, with Maisky inviting many of his own intelligence sources. Several 'confidential contacts' attended, engaging in small talk with their Soviet case officers. The party included endless toasts of friendship between two allies.

Barkovsky would have no idea that much earlier during Red Army Day – February 23, 1942 – the 'atomic' notebook had been found in the possession of an SS officer in Krivaya Kosa. Only four years later after his recall to Moscow was he briefed on the strange episode that had taken place in the village on Taganrog Bay and the interrogation that had followed in the Kremlin. He tried to view the 'atomic' notebook, but his request was denied.

CHAPTER 25

Sonya *spins her web*

While the Russian Ambassador in London entertained the great and the good at the Russian Embassy on Red Army Day, around the country *Tube Alloys* had taken on an increased urgency, expanding outside the university laboratories in Birmingham, Oxford, Cambridge, Liverpool and London. ICI and Metropolitan-Vickers were central to the programme, while a considerable number of contracts were awarded to other industrial companies such as Mond Nickel, Percy Lund Humphries, Sharples Centrifuge Company, Morgan Crucible, Edwards High Vacuum and Sun Engraving. Centrifuges were manufactured, as were nickel and copper membranes for uranium separation. In Rugby, British Thompson Houston utilized their entire scientific team for *Tube Alloys*. Specialists from other industries were enrolled such as Michael Clapham, a publisher and an expert on printing techniques who advised on techniques to manufacture fine gauze and mesh.

The Clarendon hummed with activity, fulfilling not only the *Tube Alloys* and radar commitments but also its secret Admiralty contracts with scientists spread over three other locations. At Jesus College, a team under Nicholas Kurti, aided by the American Shull Arms, researched the difficult problem of metal corrosion in the manufacture of an atomic bomb. Frequent visitors included Peierls and Fuchs from the University of Birmingham. The YP Laboratory occupying the staff theatre at the ICI Metals plant in Witton, Birmingham, had been equipped with the membrane testing apparatus that, if successful, would be incorporated into industrial-size uranium separation machines. Professor Franz Simon and Kurti had designed them in Oxford. In July 1942 Simon earmarked a bright young physicist he had interviewed who had recently graduated from Cambridge. After a five-week induction at the Clarendon Robert Berman was seconded to ICI and put on the payroll. Nobody had fixed up accommodation for him as he alighted from his first class carriage in Birmingham on August 29 and collected his bicycle from the guard's compartment. Berman cycled for hours around Sutton Coldfield attempting to find some living quarters. In desperation he resorted to knocking on doors, finally finding a family who agreed to give him a bed. The following morning he showed up at the YP Laboratory.

Initially, there were just four members of staff handling the testing – Berman and three female assistants. Within weeks, the staff had grown. Kurti and another Clarendon project head, Heinrich Kuhn, took it in turns to travel to Birmingham to review progress. It was standard procedure that after each test Berman phoned Simon with the results, but the Clarendon's chief scientist never put in an appearance. War duties, however, brought progress at the YP Laboratory almost to a shuddering halt. Like all other young and able-bodied men Berman was required for the

Home Guard service. The physicist proved proficient at handling a Lee Enfield rifle and he marched with his platoon in and around the streets of Birmingham. To lessen the boredom the platoon engaged in shooting contests at one penny a shot. Simon was incensed but could do nothing about securing Berman's release. Remedy was left to Wallace Akers, the head of *Tube Alloys*, who used his clout with the military authorities to get Berman excused.

The Clarendon's final site was in Wales, codenamed *P6* and referred to as 'Valley'. There had been problems at the Clarendon with the size and weight of the prototype separation models. The two-stage model and two further 10-stage separation machines weighed five tons and could only perform if they were bolted to a solid floor and received a plentiful water supply. Simon felt that the high-tension room in the Clarendon was the obvious location for them and engineers from the Ministry of Supply were called in. It was necessary to remove the first floor before a large crane was positioned outside the main wall of the Clarendon to lift the cumbersome models into position to stand on 15 inches of reinforced concrete covered with a layer of asphalt. Water was available through a two-inch pipe, with radioactive waste pumped away into a drain that flowed into the main Oxford sewers. Contamination wasn't considered a problem.

Back in London Perrin wasn't happy about developments within the Clarendon as cranes manhandling large equipment created unwanted local interest and gossip. An alternative location in Wales was offered, and Perrin seized the opportunity. The Ministry of Supply owned a large disused factory in Rhydymwyn, near Mold, close to a plentiful water source. Nickel powder, essential for the membranes of the separation models, was also locally available. Furthermore, Perrin could keep away prying eyes with armed military police patrolling the newly constructed high-security fencing.

Within weeks *P6* doubled its size. Some 200 Army engineers and technicians, many attached to ICI, joined the project and every available large house in the surrounding villages was requisitioned as a hostel. In charge of the separation models was Stephen Barrett, a captain in the Royal Engineers; Arms and Kurti also supervised from time to time. Metropolitan-Vickers and Edwards High Vacuum manufactured the large centrifuges. Imperial College's separation prototype, the 'Jitterbug', underwent testing at *P6*, supervised by the physicist Wilfred Mann, the double agent who worked for MI5 and the NKVD. Few outside *P6* were aware that the models would provide the blueprint for an industrial-size uranium separation plant.

With its tight security *P6* soon became an alternative location to Shell-Mex House in London for top-secret discussions. Perrin and Lt Commander Eric Welsh of MI6 often convened meetings in the main administration building. The history of the atomic bomb has generally glossed over the role of *P6*, but what was conducted behind its high fences up to 1943 was just as valuable to the Americans, who were developing other methods of separation. The following year a team from *P6*, including Barrett, was invited to Oak Ridge, Tennessee, to view the faster electro-magnetic process; but no Americans were ever entertained in Wales. From its inception *P6*'s research was shared with the United States and, thanks to Mann and another scientist, shared additionally with the Soviet Union. *P6* finally closed in 1945, its machines transported elsewhere.

In the Clarendon itself research into nuclear fission continued unabated. But with its open doors and with scientists and university students co-mingling in the corridors, the locale was never the ideal location for the concealment of secret research. Lord Cherwell, the now titled Professor Lindemann, often dined at Christchurch College and brought guests back to the Clarendon to openly view its shrouded work. Oxford's fire brigade raced to a laboratory one evening when a long-running experiment failed and a fire erupted that threatened to engulf the building. Several physicists dining in Brasenose College raced to the scene, much to the amusement of the firemen who witnessed the spectacle of scientists in evening dress rescuing what they could. With just rudimentary security in the Clarendon *Tube Alloys* staff took it in turn each night to sleep on a metal camp bed in one of the laboratories to guard against predators. The radar group headed by Arthur Cooke, Prebis Bleaney and Richard Hull copied that procedure. In addition staff were included in the obligatory fire watch that entailed sitting on the roof with a bucket of sand in case of an air attack. At times the pressure told on the scientists. For example, Arthur Brown, labelled the 'wild man', would upend chairs and tables and in a fit would smash expensive equipment in his laboratory when experiments went awry, much to the concern of his colleagues.

Cherwell ran the Clarendon like a personal fiefdom and he placed his chauffeur, Topp, in charge of the lab boys who fetched and carried for the physicists and chemists. Topp performed countless other essential tasks for Churchill's advisor, such as tending the chickens in the Clarendon's garden. Every Sunday morning he would deliver the eggs to Cherwell's home. Eggs, a rare wartime commodity, became the subject of many a heated conversation in the staff canteen. Cherwell usually displayed arrogance and aloofness to the junior staff. Late one Saturday a tired female lab assistant panicked as she encountered one of the rare occasions on which the Clarendon's front door was locked. Walking down the main steps in the foyer was Cherwell wearing his familiar bowler hat. She asked for his help but Cherwell ignored her, striding away without saying a word. The girl eventually located Dr Keeley, a key holder who was in charge of the laboratories.

Enemy bombing hadn't affected Oxford; the only bomb to fall was a stray near the railway station. Academic life continued much the same as it had always done, the restaurants full and the pubs busy with students, some now studying for the two-year wartime degrees. Rents soared as accommodation became scarce with affluent Londoners fleeing London. Some Government organisations had evacuated to Oxford in 1940, including MI5 who took possession of Blenheim Palace – the historic birthplace of Winston Churchill.

The British Secret Service had first requisitioned Wormwood Scrubs, the jail in West London, but relocation of both staff and MI5's voluminous records became a priority as the Blitz intensified. The choice of Oxford was a popular decision amongst the MI5 staff. On the day of evacuation they had assembled in the prison yard, each with a suitcase, to be given a stern lecture on maintaining secrecy in a city like Oxford. Waiting outside for them were 10 red double-decker buses.

On arrival in Oxford those officers with the better connections found the most agreeable accommodation while the lower grades made do with sharing redundant student rooms at Keble College. In Blenheim priceless tapestries and antiques were covered with dustsheets. At lunchtimes MI5 personnel strolled through the grounds. Gaiety had turned to sorrow on November 14, 1940, however, when staff gathered on the lawns to witness a red glow in the sky – Coventry had been firebombed, the blaze discernible for many miles distant.

MI5 couldn't conceal the use of the red double-deckers to daily ferry the staff from their local lodgings to Blenheim and the sight of the buses became a standing joke in Oxford. Security at Blenheim Palace was also lax, despite the pretence. As a joke an MI5 officer replaced the photograph in his ID pass with one of Adolf Hitler, gleefully marching through the main exit waving his credentials under the nose of Special Branch without being apprehended. That stunt caused quite a rumpus and the officer was severely censored.

In the cavernous basements were metal filing cabinets containing personal records on millions of individuals. A junior officer who often joked with her friends that the only reason she was offered a position in MI5 was because her father was an Army general, began a relationship with a local man who never told her what he did, apart from saying it was war work. Taking advantage of her position she persuaded a filing clerk to run a check on her boyfriend. To her sheer astonishment she found that he was a physicist on *Tube Alloys* at the Clarendon. They married five years later.

* * *

Oxford had been a target for the GRU since the early 1930s. Soviet Military Intelligence had extensively penetrated establishments such as the prestigious Clarendon Club, which attracted the most politically aware and ambitious of undergraduates. Its membership was not just restricted to Oxford. There was a strong presence from Cambridge, including Donald Maclean and other fellow students such as Andrew Cohen, who would contribute both to the debates and the extensive drinking that followed.

Upon the defection of Burgess and Maclean in May 1951, Cohen, who had had a glittering career in the Colonial Office and was knighted for his services as

Governor General of Uganda, would be interrogated by MI5. The British Secret Service also employed within the membership of the Clarendon Club, recruiting Left-wing students who could be trained as potential double agents.

With MI5 now evacuated to Oxford and the Clarendon so heavily involved in secret wartime research work, GRU headquarters took the decision to post one of their best operatives to the city. Both the GRU and NKVD employed different methods of corresponding with Moscow with regard to stolen material. The GRU usually transmitted to Moscow by radio while the NKVD preferred contact through the diplomatic bag, except in urgent circumstances. The person GRU chose had exceptional skills in radio transmission that had already been proven in China, Poland and Switzerland.

Ruth was the daughter of the eminent German economist and statistician Professor René Kuczynski, who had settled in Britain in 1933 and whose advice was regularly sought by politicians of the day. No one had any inkling that the professor regularly imparted confidential details of Britain's economic policy to a Soviet controller. Jürgen, Ruth's brother, was equally expert in the subtleties of espionage and his methods often included blackmailing young homosexual men. Jürgen would arrange a set-up in London, even on occasions in a country house owned by the Russian Embassy in Sussex, and unsuspecting male guests would be encouraged to have sexual relations with trusted male prostitutes. Faced with embarrassing photographs such men were encouraged to take the civil service exams once they had graduated – and so began their careers as Russian agents. After a glittering academic career in Germany, completing his PhD in 1925, Jürgen became a research fellow at the Brookings School in the US and he founded the research department of the American Federation of Labour. On returning to Germany he became a journalist and editor, but increasingly he was under threat from the NSDAP, the National Socialists. Given his membership of the German Communist Party, the KDP, Jürgen left for Britain in 1936 where he was offered a lectureship at the London School of Economics, an appointment that proved ideal for talent-spotting students.

Unlike her brother, Ruth Kuczynski wasn't an academic. She had joined the KDP in May 1926 and was at the forefront of Communist demonstrations in Berlin and in other German cities. Worried for her safety she and her husband, Rolf, travelled to Manchuria in China in 1934, a haven for many European and American Communists. Just weeks after Ruth and her husband arrived the Japanese invaded, but Ruth and Rolf decided to remain in their rented apartment in Mukden. Some new friends introduced Ruth to Dr Richard Sorge, a long-standing GRU operative who recruited her into the organization and provided training in the art of covert radio transmission. Sorge provided her with a radio 'handle' – *Sonya*; a cover name she would use throughout her spying career. After Moscow sent Sorge to Tokyo, Ruth became an integral element in the GRU network. The Japanese later uncovered Sorge, executing him in November 1944.

In late 1935 Europe was embroiled in political turmoil. Germany had officially quit the League of Nations and up to 50 countries had applied economic sanctions to Italy after Mussolini's invasion of Abyssinia. The GRU called Ruth to Moscow to prepare for a posting to Warsaw – a vital centre for Soviet Intelligence. Rolf had stayed in China. Ruth's training took six weeks and it was only after she had taken up the posting that she discovered she had been awarded the Order of the Red Banner, one of Russia's highest military awards, for her work in China.

For the next two years Ruth built up the GRU cells throughout Poland before she was again recalled to Moscow. With the League of Nations in Geneva incapable of dealing with the ambitions of Hitler and Mussolini, the GRU needed Ruth in Switzerland where it could monitor developments. She rented a house in Caux, near Lake Geneva, but before she settled in Ruth visited England to see her family. By this time Jürgen and her father were well aware of her GRU activities.

Len Beurton, an Englishman who had fought in the Spanish Civil War and was a committed comrade, entered Ruth's life in early 1939. She trained him, among others, in radio transmission. By the outbreak of war Ruth Kuczynski controlled an espionage web that covered several European capitals.

It was clear that her marriage to Rolf was at an end and the GRU suggested that a union with Len might be a convenient cover for her next posting – the most important to date.

Ruth agreed and married Len, taking the Beurton surname. She applied for a British passport and to Moscow's delight she was quickly granted one. In December 1940 she and her three young children set sail from Portugal to Liverpool, leaving Len in Switzerland to continue his own activities. He would join her in Oxford later. A former vicarage at Glympton, near the city, was her first home and from there she travelled to London to introduce herself to a GRU officer at the London Embassy, Captain Nikolay Aptekar, codename *Sergei*. For the first six months she was given no agents to manage. Instead she was ordered to establish herself and her family in the local community. In April 1941 the family moved to a house in Kidlington. However, this wasn't really to Moscow's liking – it needed her to be in the city.

The end of terrace house, No. 50 Middleway, seemed perfect for Ruth's needs. Middleway is a pretty street of small properties squeezed between the Woodstock and Banbury roads in Summertown in north Oxford. With Summertown and nearby Headington the choice of more than fifty Germans who fled the Nazis during the 1930s – mainly Jewish doctors, artists, musicians, writers and scientists – a German housewife would not look out of place. The house was poorly maintained; inside it was dark and dingy. A regular visitor to the house remembered it as rather shambolic and unkempt.

However, on her first transmission to Moscow Ruth discovered that the house had a major flaw – radio reception was poor. Living in an adjacent larger and taller house were Neville Laski, a judge, and his wife, Marganeta, who had moved from London. Laski's brother, Harold, was a prominent figure in the Labour Party who favoured greater co-operation with the Soviet Union. Ruth became acquainted with her neighbours and persuaded them she was an amateur radio enthusiast. They allowed her to extend the aerial from her radio transmitter up their chimneystack.

Using the surname of Beurton, Ruth quickly introduced herself to the local German community. She chattered with wives at bus stops, and sometimes went cycling with them. On other occasions they pushed their prams side by side. The cake factory in Middleway always attracted a queue at the end of the week and Ruth would join in, patiently waiting to buy leftovers at two shillings per bag. Conversations were always in English, never German, as the émigrés thought it necessary to integrate into the British way of life as much as possible.

Len was by now also proving his worth for the GRU in Oxford. Perversely, however, he felt patriotic enough to want to enlist in the Royal Air Force, but was refused on medical grounds. Later he applied to fight with the Coldstream Guards, but he ended up spending many months kicking his heels in a training camp in the west of England getting to grips with driving a tank.

The GRU network in Oxford since Ruth's arrival in England in 1940 had expanded considerably and in July 1942 she was given her biggest task to date. Simon Kremer, the GRU case officer for Klaus Fuchs, was eager to return to Russia to fight in the counter-attack against the Germans. His colleagues and Ivan Maisky, the Ambassador, would sorely miss him. The NKVD officer Vladimir Barkovsky described Kremer as *'very intelligent, kind and very attentive to detail. Given we worked for different intelligence organisations, our relationship wasn't that strong but he was always friendly towards me. There were few people in the Embassy in those days, and he was always very courteous to others. I don't remember any occasion when he raised his voice.'*

At first Lt General Ilyichev, the Moscow head of GRU, wanted Fuchs to maintain direct contact with the Embassy. However, Ruth was finally given the responsibility. Knowing that his former charge was in very capable hands Kremer departed to Moscow to take over as commanding officer of the 8th Guards Mobile Brigade. He was destined to become a major general and a war hero for his exploits in Poland while in charge of the Soviet 10th Army. After the war he would be an adviser to Stalin at meetings with visiting heads of state and act as English translator when necessary.

Fuchs enjoyed the social whirl of Oxford compared to the industrial grime of Birmingham. He loved his freedom as a bachelor and was known for his excellent dancing at the parties he was often invited to. Equally, Fuchs quickly warmed to Ruth who shared the same mother tongue and philosophy. He regularly arranged trips from the University of Birmingham to the Clarendon to meet with the scientists involved with *Tube Alloys*. But despite his brilliance as an experimental physicist, Fuchs' arrogance did not overly endear him to the Clarendon staff. Fuchs and Ruth usually met at a chosen rendezvous in the evenings as he would stay over and catch a return train in the morning. On other occasions he would use 'dead letter drops' where material would be left for collection. At the start of the relationship Fuchs proved reluctant to impart to Ruth the details of his Clarendon meetings or the conversations at the cocktail parties hosted by Simon and others, but he soon changed his mind.

Managing Fuchs brought the GRU even greater opportunities. As Fuchs attended *Tube Alloys* committees chaired by Michael Perrin in Shell-Mex House he was privy to Britain's atomic bomb project in every strategic location. Ruth handed the more extensive reports to Captain Aptekar in London, but more urgent information was directly transmitted via the aerial on Judge Laski's roof. From when he first began spying for the Russians in 1941 to when he departed for America in November 1943 Fuchs supplied the GRU with 570 pages of information on the atomic bomb.

In America, matters involving the atomic bomb were moving quickly. Sir John Anderson, the UK Chancellor of the Exchequer and the prime mover of nuclear co-operation between Britain and America, flew to Washington in August 1943. The trip resulted in Roosevelt and Churchill establishing the Combined Policy Committee at a meeting in Quebec on August 19. At the same time Professor John Cockcroft, who in 1932 with Ernest Walton had built the first atom particle accelerator and was the head of the Air Defence Research and Development establishment in Christchurch, Hampshire, was pulled away from radar to focus almost exclusively on *Tube Alloys*.

With Britain's plans to construct its own atomic bomb now temporarily postponed and with America building the nuclear facilities at Los Alamos, Oak Ridge and Hanford, Anderson had insisted that the British effort should not be wasted. Reluctantly, General Groves, the newly installed head of the *Manhattan Engineering District*, the US codename for their atomic bomb project, agreed to the British request that a number of its scientists should work in America. Lord Cherwell, Wallace Akers and Michael Perrin, his deputy, met to decide what names to put forward to Groves, who reserved the right of refusal. Advised by two of the key scientists, Mark Oliphant and James Chadwick, a list was finally agreed. Surprisingly the American Shull Arms was refused entry. Word quickly spread in the scientific community as to who was on the list. Fuchs provided the names to Ruth, who then transmitted them to a grateful Moscow on September 4.

Fuchs was one of 15 scientists on-board a passenger liner that set sail for America in November 1943, marking the beginning of serious nuclear collaboration between the United States and Britain. Before his departure he had been briefed by Ruth ever the consummate professional, about future Soviet contact in New York.

The initial choice was the adept Arthur Aleksandrovich Adams, the chief GRU 'illegal' in the US. Formerly a senior director in Moscow's automotive and aviation industries, Adams, codenamed *Achilles*, had moved to the United States in 1938 to help manage the GRU networks. A naturalised Russian immigrant, Julius Heiman, ran a front trading company that imported Russian jewels, which financed this operation. However, the departure of the 15 scientists to America was one of the key factors in Stalin's decision to commit all atomic espionage to the NKVD. Moscow cabled Colonel Anatoli Yatskov, the Soviet Vice-Consul in New York who used two covers, *Aleksei* and *John*. Yatskov, a key member of *Operation Enormoz*, the special NKVD unit set up to steal atomic secrets, had already established a network that included contacts in two nuclear laboratories.

During the voyage across the Atlantic the scientists bantered with each other and enjoyed the bar. At one stage they annoyed the ship's captain by rigging up a theodolite to calculate where they might be landing on America's East Coast, a location that deliberately hadn't been imparted to the passengers. Otto Frisch, the Austrian physicist, provided musical entertainment with his superb piano renditions. As the liner ploughed through the choppy seas, surprisingly unescorted and at grave risk from German U-boats, Fuchs joined in the singing.

Thanks to Groves the departure could have been delayed from leaving port by a last minute order that only British scientists would be allowed entry to the US. Fuchs, Peierls, Kuhn, Kurti, Simon and others were naturalised, but Frisch lacked citizenship. The necessary paperwork arrived literally as Frisch placed his suitcase on his bunk.

A bus awaited the party on landing at Newport News, the busy supply and embarkation port in south-eastern Virginia. They then boarded a train for Washington. After a short stopover, another train took the group to New York where Groves met them. Rooms had been reserved at the Barbizon Plaza in Central Park, its FBI telephone operators primed to report all calls to Edgar Hoover's special team that monitored the activities of every foreign scientist on American soil.

Fuchs made no phone calls – Ruth had warned him about the FBI surveillance. A date had already been made for him to meet his new controller.

Within days the majority of the scientists were established as the British Atomic Energy Diffusion team working on gaseous uranium separation processes with the Kellex Corporation in a New York skyscraper. For some reason the identification cards given to the British gave them access to every floor, including every laboratory. This decision angered their new American colleagues who enjoyed only limted access. One team member, Heinrich Kuhn, decided to move out of the Barbizon to a smaller and more discrete hotel.

Fuchs, given the codenames *Charles* and *Rest*, was to begin his second period of spying for the Russians. Within months Yatskov would begin to receive top-secret papers on the gaseous diffusion process, referred to as the *MSN Papers*, mostly co-written by Fuchs and Peierls. When copies reached Igor Kurchatov in his private room in the Kremlin, where he viewed and assessed all stolen nuclear intelligence, he was astonished at their content. Yatskov was asked to probe further.

The group soon lost Kuhn, who fell ill with severe tonsillitis and then succumbed to a kidney problem. After discussion with Simon it was agreed that he should return to Britain for treatment, but this time not in luxury. Instead he had to endure the hard metal seat in the converted bomb bay of a Liberator aircraft. In his bag he carried fresh fruit for his children and an aluminium comb, both luxuries in Britain.

Already three members of the British team had moved to Los Alamos – Otto Frisch, Ernest Titterton and Niels Bohr, with his son Aage. They arrived in December 1943. In January, James Chadwick, the head of the British team, moved in. Groves had already agreed that Oliphant would move most of his team from Birmingham to Berkeley in California and to Oak Ridge, Tennessee, but in the design laboratories of Los Alamos Groves insisted that he would accept only 10 British experts. Chadwick sent a cypher telegram from Washington to Anderson at the War Cabinet offices on February 3, confirming that Groves had agreed the names, bar one – Norman Feather from the Cavendish – a decision that was later rescinded. Fuchs was on the list, but he would remain in New York until the second week in August 1944.

With Fuchs gone Ruth still remained a vital component in the Soviet penetration of Britain's atomic research. One scientist provided highly sensitive material for the course of the war. He was a reluctant contributor and had met both Ruth and Len Beurton but he preferred to use an intermediary.

In May 1945, a matter of days before Ruth moved to the 'The Firs', a rambling house in the village of Great Rollright on the Oxfordshire-Warwickshire border, there was a knock on the door of No. 50 Middleway. The Beurtons had made many friends in Oxford – such was their way. That day one was to ask a major favour. Len, dour as usual and on leave from his tank regiment in Germany, answered the door. Dressed in his undone battle-dress he greeted the wife of one scientist he hadn't seen for some time. Under her arm she held a small box, consisting mainly of tins of processed meat. He gave an assurance that he would try to deliver the package to an address in Germany. The woman also passed to Len a letter for the relative. In it she had included the paragraph:

'I have just heard that Len Beurton is now stationed near you. I have given to him a food parcel, which I hope will reach you soon. He is a rather special person deeply serious and very shy. I am grateful to him, as I have been on many occasions. His wife is the daughter of Professor Kuczynski.'

CHAPTER 26

Exile to Taboshar

Stalin was tired. It was very late in the day and Poskrebyshev, his private secretary, had continuously interrupted with notes saying that several Politburo members and Red Army generals needed to speak to him and Molotov, the Russian Foreign Minister, on urgent matters – and they were growing impatient. Poskrebyshev was being pumped for details on why Stalin had even been engaged in the interrogation of an SS officer. Lazar Kaganovich, the hard-liner Oil Minister who hated waiting at the best of times, stormed back to his office after loudly demanding of Poskrebyshev that he be the first to see Stalin when this bizarre examination taking place in Stalin's personal conference room was at an end.

The incessant bickering between Georgii Flerov and Abram Ioffe had irritated Russia's Premier. Flerov's loyalty and honesty was never in question, but the fact that he portrayed greater courtesy towards the prisoner than to the most celebrated physicist in the country was unforgivable. The two scientists had clashed when Ioffe expressed doubt as to whether the Germans were ahead of the Soviets in both the theory and the development of an atomic bomb. Sergei Kaftanov, Stalin's scientific advisor, shared the same opinion. Flerov seethed, as did Stepan Balezin, Kaftanov's deputy who had evaluated the contents of the 'atomic' notebook and the two diagrams found in the possession of Major Hans van der Velde in Krivaya Kosa. They feared that Kaftanov, yet again, would prevaricate and advise Stalin to stall on a resumption of the Soviet nuclear programme.

After van der Velde had related how he had engineered his capture, Stalin had picked up the telephone and spoke quietly into the receiver. Shortly afterwards Poskrebyshev had entered the room and handed a file to him. The folder marked *Athenaeum* was full to over-flowing. Poskrebyshev, on Stalin's instruction, had kept it locked away in his office, hidden from the prying eyes of Beria. The first entry in the file, a radio transmission from the London Ambassador Ivan Maisky, was dated late April 1938. It referred to the expected resignation of Stanley Baldwin as the British Prime Minister and an anticipated softening of attitude towards the Soviet Union upon the likely appointment of Neville Chamberlain. There were numerous carbon copies of original documents in the *Athenaeum* file – secret notes circulated by a member of the British War Cabinet to his colleagues and later passed to the Russian Embassy for dispatch to Moscow in the diplomatic bag.

Rifling through the file Stalin quickly found what he was searching for – a transmission from London dated January 1942, with accompanying photographs of a document headed *'Personal, Most Secret, Eyes Only'* and addressed to Winston Churchill. Maisky had sent the photographs in the diplomatic bag after he had transmitted an urgent summary.

Around the conference table whispered private conversations had fallen away into silence. Beria, inquisitive as usual, asked Stalin what was the nature of the file, only to receive a stony glare in return.

Satisfied, Stalin closed the file and returned it to the hovering Poskrebyshev with the instruction that his guests would not have to wait much longer.

Stalin had now perked up. He lit his pipe and called for more brandy for everyone, even water for the prisoner who was slumped in his chair, totally spent. Stalin turned towards Beria.

'Comrade, you earlier denied the existence of the *Rote Kapelle*, the *Red Orchestra*,' he said with a disapproving tone in his voice. 'Why?'

'Intelligence matters should never be openly discussed, Comrade, and certainly not in front of a bastard German.'

'I agree, but this bastard is going nowhere. I convened this interrogation not merely to listen to an SS officer elucidate details of his life, his scientific and military career, and his capture. It is important that we heard how the German atomic bomb is progressing and how we should proceed with our own work.'

Beria didn't react.

With a wave of his hand Stalin gestured to the translator to leave the room – his job was done.

'Comrades,' said Stalin, 'our people owe a great debt to the *Red Orchestra*. Its members were brave men and women who believed that Fascism needed to be conquered and only we were prepared to do so. The British and the Americans have their own agendas and are not to be trusted. Churchill might proclaim that he is a friend of Russia but he lies. In private he holds a pathological hatred for Communism and will do anything to undermine us, as does America. Only in 1933 did America agree to establish diplomatic relations with us. Churchill and Roosevelt need us to rid Europe of the Fascists, but once victory has been secured they will unite and attempt to break us. With America in the war why haven't these two leaders announced the date of a Second Front to ease the pressures in the East? The reason is obvious. They want to see us beaten and then they will do a deal with Germany.

'The *Red Orchestra* have given their lives to our cause. Our SS friend here has told us about their deaths at the hands of the Gestapo. They occupied important positions within the German Civil Service, the Abwehr, even the Gestapo itself. In recent months the organization has been deeply penetrated by informers and few members now remain alive. Those who have evaded capture have gone underground. So, Comrade Beria, let us not deny its existence to our scientists here today who have no access to intelligence matters.'

Stalin stood up and walked around the table.

'Comrades, we need to come to a decision,' he said, picking up the notebook and walking over to van der Velde to stand behind him.

'Why waste any time over this bastard, as Comrade Beria rightly refers to him?

I threatened him with execution, and his body thrown onto the frozen Moscow River for his flesh and bones to be devoured by our starving dogs. That may still be his fate.

'However, what if the story he has unfolded today is genuine?'

'Comrade Stalin,' retorted Beria, cynically. 'There is something very wrong here. I genuinely believe this notebook is a cleverly produced document inspired by either German or British Intelligence. My opinions are never incorrect.'

'That is true, Comrade. But there is always a first time. Our top scientists seem totally divided on the nuclear issue. Comrade Ioffe persuades me to invest our resources in other wartime scientific efforts, but Comrade Flerov sends me strongly-worded letters that we are imperilled by the Fascists if we continue to do nothing. What am I to do?'

Stalin left van der Velde and positioned himself behind Kaftanov.

'Comrade, you are my closest scientific advisor. I value *your* opinion. You have studied my detailed weekly summaries from our intelligence services on the development of the British atomic bomb which they call *Tube Alloys*. I have also received from my own sources in London confirmation that America is to co-operate with Britain and will lead the project. Intelligence from Berlin is limited now, following the break up of the *Red Orchestra*, so little is known of what is happening at the Kaiser Wilhelm, and we have heard today the belated news of a secret facility in Dresden. After what you have heard from our prisoner, what would you advise? Should we recall our physicists and chemists from the Front and move them to Kazan to resume work on the bomb?'

Kaftanov breathed in deeply before replying.

'Comrade Stalin, I would advise caution. Nothing that I have read in recent months confirms that Britain and America will be successful in their efforts, despite the resources that may be poured into the project. Producing uranium and plutonium on an industrial scale may even be beyond them. The war with Hitler may be long over before the technology has been developed. Given the expertise of Comrades Kurchatov, Flerov and many others we will be in an advantageous position once the war has been won. At the moment they have other valuable uses. Comrade Kurchatov, for example, with his brother, Boris, is developing special materials for the Russian Navy to demagnetise the hulls of vessels so the placing of mines against them is impossible. Other scientists in Kazan, in our laboratories, are working on our rocket programme that will give our missiles a much longer range.

'There is one problem that I would like to see corrected, however. I think it was a mistake for the NKVD to channel all nuclear matters through *Operation Enormoz*. The GRU cells in Britain and America have been very effective. I think that all our agents should be alerted. Furthermore, I think it would be foolish to believe all the reports our agents send to us. It is difficult to assess whether we have been fed misleading information. I would also like to see greater cooperation

213

between the major NKVD departments.'

'Do you believe the reports from your agents in London and Washington?' Stalin sneered, suddenly facing Fitin and Kravchenko.

'Comrade Stalin,' retorted Fitin, 'I have every confidence that in the 5th Department the material from our agents is reliable.'

'And you, Comrade Kravchenko?'

Kravchenko glowered at Flerov, an annoying physicist who meddled in intelligence matters. The head of the NKVD's 4th Department knew he was already in trouble. He had not informed Fitin or, indeed, any other department within the NKVD about Dresden. Stalin, too, had been unaware of the danger that Dresden may possibly pose to the Soviet Union, but he lacked the final confirmation from an agent, a senior officer within the Abwehr. The construction of the nuclear laboratory in Dresden had been placed under the personal supervision of Himmler and few in Berlin were aware of its existence. He could see that Flerov, like Stalin, was keen to hear him answer.

'I respectfully suggest a private audience with you, Comrade Stalin. There are issues we urgently need to address,' Kravchenko finally replied, shuffling in his chair.

Hans was only barely aware of what was going on around him. Despite the water offered by Stalin his mouth and throat remained dry and his body ached. He had felt Stalin's breath on his neck. The *Red Orchestra* mission had been crazy from the outset, a death warrant. He cursed ever meeting Franz and Helmut, his two drinking friends from the bar in Meinekestrasse, and now bitterly regretted not tearing up the two schematic drawings he had been given. Not for the first time Hans had contemplated how the news of his capture would be fed back to the Heereswaffenamt, if there had been anyone left alive in the village to witness it. The death of Conrad, his fellow Wehrgeologen officer, troubled him deeply; it had been unnecessary and all for the sake of finding a kurgan. Hans prayed for a miracle, vowing that if he somehow miraculously survived he would visit Conrad's widow and confess the real circumstances of her husband's death.

'Comrade Kravchenko,' responded Stalin. 'Do I infer that your reticence is a refusal to answer my question?'

Kravchenko shrugged his large shoulders, and bowed his head. He had not the slightest intention in sharing his department's secrets with others around the table. He would brief Stalin personally.

'Enough!' exclaimed Stalin. 'There is nothing more to be gained here today Comrade Balezin, you will undertake a thorough evaluation of this notebook assisted by Comrade Kurchatov.

'And our prisoner? Comrade Beria, if we find that this bastard has been economical with the truth you will then have my permission to dispose of him in any way you choose.' Stalin handed the notebook to Balezin and left, clearly displeased at Kravchenko's provocation. Molotov, who had barely spoken a word all day, meekly followed.

Fitin and Kravchenko hurried away for urgent discussion. Despite the hour they needed to prepare for what would be a challenging session with Stalin the following day. Kaftanov had scurried after Stalin. Ioffe and Kurchatov left together to catch the midnight train to Kazan, but not before Balezin had called them back. He needed a private word with Kurchatov, the likely head of the Russian nuclear project if it went ahead. There were matters to arrange. Flerov hung around, waiting for Balezin to finish. Later they strolled together across Red Square, crossing the Moscow River to the private apartments near the British Embassy where only senior members of Government lived, mainly with their mistresses. In the basement of the large building there was a bar, open throughout the night, which Balezin had often frequented after long sessions at the GKO. Over large glasses of vodka they recalled the events of the quite remarkable day. Flerov had reason to propose a toast – perhaps now Russia's pre-war nuclear fission efforts, of which he had been such a major part in Leningrad, would not be wasted, despite Kaftanov's reservations. Stalin had not been in an accommodating frame of mind. Flerov's second toast was to the courage of Major Hans van der Velde.

The light in Hans' cell burned incessantly for two days before, mercifully, one night it was switched off and sleep came. In the dimly lit corridor outside members of Stalin's personal bodyguard maintained their 24-hour vigil, keeping away curious NKVD colleagues who had heard about the Lubyanka's most unusual prisoner. Each morning Hans was escorted to the open sewer to empty his toilet bucket, passing other cells whose solid doors concealed other luckless occupants. One morning he came face to face with a Red Army general, his face puffy and tunic stained with blood, being pulled into the lift. A guard joked with Hans that turnover was high, not just for Red Army officers but also for captured Abwehr agents who endured torture and medical experimentation before execution.

Hans' days were filled with emptiness, the constant smell of faeces and terror. One day, Beria barged past the guards and into Hans' cell to gleefully introduce Colonel Engelsov Lapshin, in charge of the NKVD's toxic laboratory located two floors above the cells in the Lubyanka, and Dr Mayranovsky, its chief scientist. Hans' heart sank when Mayranovsky fixed upon what might be his latest human guinea pig, questioning him about his medical history. An orderly was summoned to take blood samples. Beria sat on Hans' metal bed and in English happily described some of Dr Mayranovsky's chilling experiments.

Summer descended onto the Russian capital and the cell became a furnace. Even the guards became bored and they gave Hans their copies of *Pravda* to read. With his now rudimentary knowledge of Russian Hans read that the second German offensive on the Caucasus, codenamed *Plan Blue*, had begun. Army Group South now accounted for half of the combined Wehrmacht and SS strength against the

USSR, and the capture of the Maikop, Krasnodar, Grozny and Baku oilfields were a major priority for the German High Command. By the end of July the Germans had retaken Rostov-on-Don, but Soviet sappers were exacting terrible revenge by mining many of the buildings in the retreat. North of Rostov the German Army was making a push on Stalingrad. *Pravda* reported in an August 1942 edition the details of Churchill's visit to the Kremlin, with Stalin castigating the British and Americans for not opening up a second front that would relieve the pressure in the east.

There were several visits from the odious Dr Mayranovsky, disappointed that he hadn't yet been handed his victim. At times Hans panicked, believing that he was gradually being poisoned.

Igor Kurchatov appeared weekly, bringing bread and pickled herring. He gently probed for further elaboration on the notebook's contents. Hans observed that the notebook was now scruffy and worn through use. The two men conversed in German, sometimes English, and got on well. Once, Kurchatov brought several pre-war German magazines – hardly newsworthy but welcome none the less. He also had some maps of Europe and Russia and asked Hans to locate all the uranium oxide sources that he had carefully pinpointed for the Heereswaffenamt.

September marked a major improvement in Hans' conditions. The guards were more communicative, even helping him with his Russian. Kurchatov introduced a colleague, Vitali Khlopin, a radiochemist and director of the Radium Institute in Leningrad.

The first real evidence that Hans' life might be spared came from the most unlikely source. He had been reading when the bolts were pushed back on his cell door and Beria entered.

'You continue to enjoy our hospitality,' uttered Beria, contemptuously, observing the copy of *Pravda* on the bed.

'We feed you well and even provide Russian newspapers, what luxuries. I understand you are even mastering our fine language. Has it occurred to you that the only reason you are still alive is that you continue to enjoy the personal protection of Comrade Stalin?'

Hans daren't respond. He had guessed that he had some special status.

'So, you prefer not to talk – probably part of your training. Was it the Abwehr or Britain's SIS you worked for? Of course, you never told us, did you?'

'I had nothing to do with either. I worked solely for the Kaiser Wilhelm and the Heereswaffenamt,' replied Hans flatly.

'Yes, yes, spare me any more of your fairy tales. I've already had to endure that tedious account of your life. I am still trying to figure out why Comrade Stalin believed you, it's most unlike him. Have you any idea how many of our innocent citizens he has personally signed away to the GULAG, hard labour camps not too dissimilar to your own concentration camps?

'No? Let me enlighten you. One of my departments here in the Lubyanka keeps meticulous records for me, just in case one day I may need to use them as insurance you understand. Since 1938 the total runs into many millions, and more than half are now dead. Impressive, don't you think?

'So, why does he waste his time on an SS bastard – can you help me with an answer?'

Hans buried his head in his hands, hoping Beria would go away.

But Beria hadn't finished.

'I hear Kurchatov spends hours with you, discussing what Stalin now always calls the 'atomic' notebook, that document which you conveniently planted with us. I don't trust scientists; they waste time and argue. Dr Mayranovsky called me today and he's itching to get his hands on you. He has developed a new truth drug and tested it on one of our Red Army officers who proved to be a coward in battle. His men were massacred by a panzer attack, so he ran rather than sacrifice his miserable life. I witnessed the pain on his face seconds after Dr Mayranovsky administered the drug. There is an antidote but it has to be given within five minutes or the heart stops. Alas, however, Comrade Stalin has not yet tired of you.'

Hans would not see Beria again until July 1945.

Khlopin, like Kurchatov, Hans found friendly. The chemist from Leningrad had been the natural choice of chairman when the USSR Academy of Sciences, on July 30, 1940, had established its Uranium Committee that included Ioffe, Kapitsa, Kurchatov and 11 other prominent chemists, physicists, mineralogists and geologists.

Uranium oxide was scarce in the USSR but there had been indications that large reserves existed. Pre-war annual production was a pitiful one ton a year, whereas Canada produced 400 tons. In March 1940 Khlopin and Vernadsky, the founder of Leningrad's Radium Institute, had written a lengthy report to Stepanov, the secretary of the Geological and Geographical Sciences Division of the Academy of Sciences, outlining the dire problem. At a full session of Academicians on June 25 their paper was overwhelmingly supported.

Accompanied by Academician Fersman, the renowned mineralogist, and Professor Komlev, the chemist, Khlopin travelled by train in October to the Uzbekistan capital of Tashkent. Their report to the Uranium Committee was encouraging but still disappointing – Fersman estimated that within two years Central Asia could produce, at best, just 10 tons of uranium.

Geologists from the Radium Institute had in the late 1930s identified 70 potential sites for exploration as uranium was usually found in the presence of radium. Khlopin now dispatched exploration teams to Kazakhstan, Uzbekistan and Tajikistan, vast areas of Soviet territory closed to both Russian citizens and foreigners – Kazakhstan, on its own, as large as Western Europe. He set off again with Fersman and in late October 1940 they told the Uranium Committee that potential production in Central Asia could be 250–300 tons annually, but expansion to 600 tons was feasible if a large labour force was available.

Three areas were very promising – the Taboshar site in northern Tajikistan, and the Kazakhstan prospects of Mailu-Su and Uigur-Sai. Exploration crews were soon increased to 14 in the region. More than 8,000 radio-metering tests were conducted and six radiochemical laboratories established. By early 1942 the number of crews had risen to 80 and production of uranium ore had totalled 4,000 tons. Probable reserves were now estimated at 18,390 tons. Plant 18 in Taboshar was the largest mine, and the most notorious. The oxide from this mine was destined to produce the plutonium for Stalin's first bomb in August 1949, but at a huge human cost.

The chemists from the Radium Institute managed all uranium prospecting, and had been at the forefront of fission research. Hahn and Strassman from the Kaiser Wilhelm in Berlin had grabbed the world's newspaper headlines with their fission discovery, but two Radium scientists, Mysoksky and Zdanov, were in the process of declaring their own successful fission results to the Russian Academy of Sciences. Their colleagues, Petrzhak, Flerov, Perfolov, Khlopin, Pasvik and Volkov, soon added to the large store of Soviet knowledge on the properties and potential of U-235 isotopes.

German PoWs now added to the labour supply from the GULAG hard labour system for Plant 18, Mailu-Su and Uigar-Sai, while geologists from the Radium ventured deeper into the deserts of Central Asia. In Kazakhstan Professor Starik and a team travelled to Akchatau, to the north of Lake Balkash, Maytass and north Gaushad – locations that subsequently proved to be rich in uranium.

Thousands of displaced souls dug for uranium oxide with shovels and buckets, under the watchful eye of the NKVD who provided the security for all mining camps. No body protection was provided, not even gloves. Radiation sickness caused thousands of deaths, but as one prisoner collapsed others were brought in by train such was the inexhaustible supply of labour. Accommodation was primitive. No one would escape and, even if they had been successful, the extremes and vastness of Central Asia would soon overwhelm them.

Kurchatov visited the SS prisoner in the Lubyanka for the last time in October 1942, eight months after Hans' capture, with some unexpected news. Days earlier, on September 28, at an audience with Stalin he had been informed that the Russian atomic bomb project was to be a major priority. Beria had become ever more vocal in his opposition since the 'atomic' notebook had been found, but eventually he had been placated by Stalin who informed him that despite the project being under the official control of Molotov, the Foreign Minister, the head of state security would have the greater authority.

Fingering his beard, Kurchatov passed to Hans some sausage that was most welcome. He was unusually quiet and sat on the bed.

Kurchatov finally imparted to Hans the real reason behind his visit. Stalin had wished to utilize van der Velde's talents in the Soviet nuclear programme, but far away from Moscow. Kurchatov asked Hans whether in his research at the Kaiser Wilhelm he had ever heard of Taboshar. Hans replied that he hadn't and questioned its location and significance.

Kurchatov declined to answer, wished Hans farewell and ordered him not to ever mention the events at Krivaya Kosa and Moscow to anyone. He was merely a German PoW captured in a Soviet reconnaissance action in the Southern Ukraine – there was no 'atomic' notebook.

In one sense Hans was elated, he had evaded Beria and the medical torture of Mayranovsky – but on the other hand he was deeply perplexed as to the location of Taboshar and its purpose. He ate his sausage.

As Kurchatov returned to his office in the Lubyanka to read the latest atomic intelligence stolen from Britain and America, he felt a twinge of conscience. The German officer had been more than helpful in recent months, describing every detail of Germany's process to manufacture uranium metal. Extreme exposure to radiation at Taboshar ensured that life expectancy was short and extremely painful. Stalin had given Major van der Velde a death sentence.

CHAPTER 27

Final German, Austrian and Japanese atomic efforts

Doubts had begun to circulate within the Heereswaffenamt by December 1941 whether an atomic bomb was feasible. Hitler and his generals, despite the first setbacks of *Operation Barbarossa*, still held to their beliefs that the war with Russia would be over by the following summer. At the Kaiser Wilhelm and in other laboratories throughout the country, however, the scientists anticipated that their goal would be achieved. Three months earlier, in September, Werner Heisenberg and Carl Friedrich von Weizsäcker had travelled to Nazi-occupied Denmark in an unsuccessful attempt to solicit the help of the eminent physicist Niels Bohr. The rebuff only stiffened Heisenberg's resolve.

At a three-day conference in Berlin in February 1942 the Heereswaffenamt heard a review of current progress from Heisenberg and von Weizsäcker. Heisenberg stressed the urgent requirement to build an atomic pile to produce plutonium. There followed a heated debate within the Reichsforschungsrat, the Reich Research Council that now had the ultimate responsibility for nuclear research. In Steglitz, a suburb of Berlin, the Minister for Research and Education Bernhard Rust met with the scientists to hear their grievances about the lack of funding. Heisenberg couldn't believe the decision taken by Hitler to place the nuclear project under Rust, an arrogant, often abusive civil servant who strutted around in his SS uniform.

The Heereswaffenamt could do nothing but keep a watching brief over the Kaiser Wilhelm Institute for Physics. Rust, surprisingly, came up with fresh funds. Heisenberg developed plans for a nuclear-powered submarine and von Weizsäcker and others upgraded their designs for the reactor and the bomb itself. There was an impasse, however, after Rust insisted on a schedule leading up to when the bomb would be ready for its test despite being told by the scientists that completion may be years away.

Albert Speer, the Minister for Armaments, visited the Kaiser Wilhelm in March to assess the situation for himself. Speer listened carefully to the arguments from both sides but pointed out that with Germany now at war with both America and Britain there needed to be military and scientific priorities. Hitler's favourite Minister downgraded and shelved a number of projects, but the bomb was not one of them. He urged the scientists to progress their work. Focus turned to the physics laboratory in the University of Leipzig, which had constructed a prototype reactor designed by Heisenberg. Codenamed *L-IV*, it comprised 140 kg of heavy water and 750 kg of uranium metal powder. In April there was excitement when the reactor demonstrated neutron generation of up to 13 per cent. The results were sent to Speer who sent Heisenberg his congratulations. According to Heisenberg's calculations the reactor could go critical using 5,079 kg [five tons] of heavy water and 10,160 kg [ten tons] of metallic uranium.

Disaster struck in June, however, when fire devastated the Leipzig laboratory and Germany's first prototype reactor was completely destroyed. On hearing the catastrophic news of the fire Speer convened an urgent meeting at the Kaiser Wilhelm and Heisenberg was ordered to construct another reactor, much larger this time and in Berlin.

The invasion of the Soviet Union, which should have reached a victorious conclusion before the onset of winter 1941, was now at the beginning of its second year. Fighting on two fronts was stretching every resource that Speer had at his disposal. Despite the agreement to proceed with the reactor Heisenberg met with indifference from the Reichsforschungsrat when he applied for the necessary heavy water and uranium metal. Reactor experimentation, however, continued in the underground laboratory in the Kaiser Wilhelm. Weeks of inaction drifted into months and doubts mounted about the location of the reactor as Allied raids increased in intensity over Berlin.

Walter Gerlach, a professor at the University of Munich and a member of the Reichsforschungsrat, had support for his suggestion that a new laboratory and the reactor should be accommodated outside Berlin, in an area where even the most agile of Allied aircraft would find it difficult to penetrate. He had in mind Haigerloch, located in the narrow limestone valley of the Eyach River in southern Germany. Speer approved the proposal and a wine and beer cellar underneath the Bavarian town's historic church was chosen as the site. In the Kaiser Wilhelm work carried on as usual as the Reichsforschungsrat handled the move, but the rental agreement of 100 Reichsmarks per month was only agreed with the landlord of the Schwanen Inn on September 1, 1944.

Amid tight security Heisenberg, von Weizsäcker and 12 other scientists from the Kaiser Wilhelm Institute for Physics moved into a former textile factory in Hechingen, not far from Haigerloch, and converted the premises into a laboratory. Uranium and heavy water were transported by truck from Berlin and the experimental B8 reactor was now constructed, built as a concrete cylinder deep in the cellar. Once in operation normal water occupied the space between the reactor's outer concrete shell and the inner shell made of aluminium that contained a vessel made of magnesium. The space between the two vessels was filled with graphite weighing 10 tons, with 664 rectangular blocks of uranium attached to the circular graphite lid that was bolted onto the reactor. Heavy water was gradually pumped into the inner vessel, triggering a chain reaction.

Work on the bomb had not ceased in Berlin despite the move south to Haigerloch and Hechingen. Kurt Diebner, ever the committed Nazi, remained at the Heereswaffenamt's experimental station in Gatow where, in the radiation laboratory, he was never reconciled with the growing view among his colleagues that the super weapon could not be built in time to reverse the tide of the war.

As bombing intensified over Berlin there was a wholesale evacuation of the

Dahlem institutes to the comparative safety of southern Germany. Otto Hahn and his chemists moved to Tailfingen in southern Württemberg. In January 1945 Gerlach, Diebner and Karl Wirtz accompanied a convoy of trucks from Berlin with heavy water and uranium to Stadtilm, a village near Erfurt. However, due to the poor facilities in Stadtilm the stocks were eventually taken to Haigerloch.

The US 8th Airforce had been pounding Vienna since late 1944, creating panic in the Austrian capital that had led to part evacuation of a number of research institutes, including the Neutron Institute that carried out work on isotope separation and experimented on neutron beams throughout the war. The institute's leading physicist, Stetter, in January 1945 issued the order that vital equipment and the research library be moved some 50 miles outside Vienna to the village of Mautern. Engineers had already partly constructed a high voltage installation in Mautern, capable of producing 900kV and that could power neutron beams, but the work was never completed as essential parts manufactured in Hamburg were never delivered due to RAF bombing.

With Vienna under threat from the Red Army in April 1945, the Neutron Institute and Vienna University's Radium and Physics Institutes were completely emptied. Fleets of trucks transported materials and equipment to Tumersbach, near Salzburg, and documents to Schwallenbach in the province of Wachau. The scientists dispersed, aware that their contribution to Hitler's atomic bomb was at an end and that the Russian NKGB was trying to capture them.

In Moscow Igor Kurchatov was keen that Vienna's laboratories should be captured intact and included one of his top uranium separation specialists, Igor Golovin, in the NKGB group. Many of the Austrian nuclear team were quickly rounded up, with Professor Ortmann, Dr Wambacher, Dr Hernegger, Dr Bruckl and Dr Benit soon undergoing intensive interrogation. NKGB units drove to the villages of Treibach, Foorlach and Seebach bei Willach in the Klagenfurt region, to guard the mines that had produced uranium for the Vienna experiments. Major Barannikov, deputy commander of the 37th Border Guards, the elite regiment of the NKGB, cabled Lavrenty Beria on what had been found in the three Vienna laboratories between April 25 and May 10. Golovin offered his own assessment to Kurchatov.

In the eastern theatre of war Japan had already pared back its research into the development of a U-235 bomb, instigated initially by the Army Aviation Technology Research Institute in October 1940. The military, under Lt Colonel Suzuki, had approached Professor Ryokichi Sagane, the head of the physics faculty at Tokyo's Imperial University, the most prestigious in the country, to undertake a study. However, his 20-page report didn't convince Suzuki's fellow officers who were enjoying such unexpected success in the Pacific.

The Imperial Navy strongly believed that Japan should have its bomb and funded their own project at Kyoto Imperial University, codenamed the *F Project* – the *F* referring to fission – under Professor Bunsaku Arakatsu. Uranium was separated in

Kyoto using the centrifugal process. There were 10 meetings in all on the *F Project* between July 1942 and March 1943. The project then waned, only to be resurrected when Professor Tadayoshi Hikosaka from the Dai-Ni High School in Sendai convinced the Navy in November 1944 that plutonium was a more potent fissile material than U-235. The *F Project* was active up to July 1945.

Of greater concern to the Americans was the nuclear programme tasked in 1942 to the Japan Institute of Physical and Chemical Research, known as Riken. This was the largest private scientific research establishment in Tokyo and the project's leader, Yoshio Nishina, had based his designs for an atomic bomb on stolen British and American nuclear reports. By May 1943 Lt General Yasuda reported to the Japanese High Command that Nishina could build the bomb, codenamed *Ni Project* using the first two letters of Nishina's name. However, only 15 scientists were assigned to Nishina and work soon fell behind schedule. Within months half of the group had been re-deployed to radar development.

Uranium for both the *F* and *Ni* projects mainly came from mines in the Fukushima Prefecture, but Japanese mineralogists had located other smaller supplies in Korea and Malaysia. A uranium separation facility employing thermal diffusion was constructed in March 1944, but was destroyed by a massive US air raid on April 13, 1945. In the weeks after the Japanese surrender the US conducted an assessment of Japan's atomic capability, concluding that its final level of research was equivalent to that achieved by 1942 in the United States. Total Japanese spending on both projects was the Yen equivalent of US$650,000, a limited sum compared to the $2 billion expenditure of America.

A major worry to the British and Americans was Dresden, the German city out of regular reconnaissance range. Rumours had reached London about the plethora of laboratories hidden deep in the woods. Dresden had become a research centre for chemical warfare and large stocks of nerve gases had been manufactured – its anthrax stocks were enough to wipe out city populations. During *Operation Barbarossa* a number of senior German officers advised Hitler on the merits of the use of anthrax and other toxic gases but, fortunately, they were never used.

Yet Dresden, forever remembered for the raids in February 1945, was the location of another, even more deadly, secret.

The only item on the agenda at the Chiefs of Staff meeting in an underground bunker in London on July 5, 1944, was *Operation Thunderclap*, the codename for an aerial attack on Germany of unprecedented devastation. *'The time might well come in the not too distant future when an all-out attack on German civilian morale by every means at our disposal might be decisive,'* was one of the minutes of the meeting that had debated the breaking of morale of both the German armed forces and the civilian population. *'This may take the form of defeat by the opposing Army in the field and also by realisation of such overwhelming air superiority as to make their personal destruction appear almost inevitable. What is required is an attack of unprecedented magnitude, directed against a nerve centre of Germany whose destruction would obtain rapid publicity throughout the country. It is obvious that the maximum result is the administrative centre of Berlin,'* posed the document, which had been drawn up under the highest level of security.

The Chiefs of Staff studied photographs of the German Blitzkrieg on Rotterdam in 1940, which had led to 30,000 deaths, comparing them to the expected destructive levels if such a raid had taken place over central London or Berlin. Using London as an example, the Ministry of Home Security had estimated that to extract 90 per cent devastation over an area of 2 $^1/_2$ square miles, some 2,000 aircraft dropping 5,000 tons of 500-lb bombs would be necessary.

In such an area, reported the Ministry, during the hours of darkness there may well be 100,000 people, trebling or quadrupling in number during the day. In the case of Westminster, in London, there were five times as many people during the day as at night. It was pointed out at the meeting that in Berlin the ratio could be much higher. In the event of a daylight raid by the US 8th Airforce, some 220,000 casualties could be expected, of which half, or 110,000, would be killed. If the RAF followed up with an evening attack a firestorm would result, lasting for days.

To accompany such a blanket raid over Berlin, hitting specific targets throughout the country would increase the level of devastation. The SS would be a key target – its headquarters in Oranienburg and Bad Sarrow, the officer training school in Bad Tölz near Munich and the NCO centres in Lauenburg and Radolfzell would be razed to the ground. SS guard barracks at two concentration camps, Dachau and Buchenwald, would be attacked by Mosquitoes. Tacticians agreed that morale amongst the SS would collapse. Other targets were the SS training camp for foreign volunteers at Sennheim and the Nazi Party colony at Salzburg. At the same time the Special Operations Executive [SOE] would organize havoc and pandemonium on the ground. The Chiefs of Staff left the planning to the Air Ministry and the SOE, with the hope that 'Braddock', the new and highly effective incendiary, would be tested in the raids.

Berlin and the SS would burn.

The German capital was not the eventual target for an operation of such magnitude, however, nor was it Hamburg or Cologne despite the incessant attacks on these cities – instead it was Dresden, right on the furthest range of British and American bombers. But by early 1945 the morale of the German nation and the activities of the SS were no longer the main objectives of an operation that would flatten the city.

Dresden had been 'softened-up' by the Americans in a raid on October 7, 1944. It was a low-key operation, followed by a similar attack on January 16, 1945. These were merely a portent of what was to follow. Poor weather conditions on February 13 prevented the B-17s, the 'Flying Fortresses', from taking off from their airfields in Britain, but the RAF did fly. Flying in heavy cloud for most of the flight over Germany the skies cleared over Dresden and 796 Lancasters and nine Mosquitoes released 1,500 tons of high explosive and 1,200 tons of incendiaries in two waves.

An uncontrollable fireball tore through the city, sucking out its life. The next day brought better weather and 311 B-17s unleashed a further 770 tons of bombs. The Americans came again on February 15. With the Luftwaffe unable to mount any real threat the Allies suffered minimal losses – the RAF lost six Lancasters and the Americans suffered similar small casualties. The bombing and the resultant firestorm caused more than 50,000 deaths in Dresden, many more than the earlier firestorm over Hamburg.

In May 1945 two NKGB missions flew from Moscow to Dresden, the city now under the control of the Red Army but not far from the agreed demarcation line between the Russian and American forces. The Laboratory No. 2 group included the physicists Georgii Flerov, Mikhail Pevzner and Aleksandr Krasin. Flerov was aghast at the level of devastation. The chemists from the Radium Institute in Leningrad comprised the second NKGB unit and they quickly cabled Moscow that the chemical warfare facility had remarkably survived the raids and was almost unscathed. In carefully constructed underground bunkers the chemists found large stocks of anthrax. Most of the employees had already surrendered to the Red Army and were placed under guard. In a matter of weeks the facility was dismantled and flown to Schucheye, south of Stalingrad, where it was to form the core of Russia's chemical warfare industry during the forthcoming Cold War and develop into an immense centre. The NKGB gave the chemists from Dresden a stark choice as to their future – either a labour camp in the GULAG or a position at Schucheye. Everyone chose the latter.

For Flerov and his two colleagues, the task was more difficult. He wrote a letter to Igor Kurchatov on a scrappy piece of paper, the writing barely legible, on May 21: *'Today, or tomorrow,'* he wrote, *'we are leaving in the direction known to you. I am taking with me Dubovskii's apparatus but I feel that its sensitivity is too low. If, in situ, it becomes clear that there are suitable objects for study, and the whole matter hinges on the sensitivity of the apparatus, I will send you a telegram.'*

Kurchatov decided that Flerov needed more help and two more physicists, Stolyarov and Davidenko, who were part of an NKGB mission to the Kaiser Wilhelm in Berlin, flew in to help. Cases of equipment from Laboratory No. 2 also arrived in Dresden.

A despondent Flerov wrote again to Kurchatov on May 29: *'We are still here in Dresden and we have decided to direct our efforts along a different path.'*

Flerov described to Kurchatov the chaos he had witnessed in the Dresden zone. Three centres had been opened on the demarcation line as part of the repatriation programme, but the Russian authorities and the NKGB were unable to cope with the sheer numbers involved. Each day up to 15,000 displaced German civilians were arriving and 50,000 released Russian troops that had been in nearby German PoW camps. On top of these numbers were tens of thousands of German troops. Flerov had been informed by the NKGB that under the repatriation programme some two million people would be transported east within weeks.

'We visited some of the repatriation points and camps, talking to prisoners of war and civilians, but unfortunately people from different locations have been mixed in a bizarre manner that is most unhelpful to us. It is important that the NKGB organize a systematic filtration system of all these persons who are arriving, based on the principle of where they have come from. It is vital to our mission that in every camp we need sufficient people to handle the interrogation if we are to find anyone who has come from the locality we are looking for.

'What do the theoreticians say on the influence of atom shell ionisation?

'I think that as a result of such searches we may find what we need – a person who was in the vicinity, by chance, when many runaways were roaming the forests. If we are successful, we will have the final confirmation. Speed is of the essence as everybody will soon be dispersed in the Soviet Union and even an enthusiastic person, such as myself, will never then find them.

'In order to clarify precisely what they were testing here it is necessary to test for artificial, not natural, radioactivity. Unfortunately a long time has passed.'

Flerov asked Kurchatov for yet more equipment, including an A1 Geiger-Muller radioactivity counter. He even suggested in his letter that he should return to Moscow to build some apparatus to bring to Dresden.

'We will be connected with Dresden for some time,' finished the physicist and, as an afterthought, he asked Kurchatov to visit his wife and son.

Nothing remained of Germany's most secret nuclear laboratory after the firestorm. The Lancasters and the B-17s had done their work, the Braddock incendiaries setting the forest alight and destroying a facility much feared by the British and Americans. Throughout the war MI6 maintained an intelligence network in Berlin with strong links into the Kaiser Wilhelm, but of the advanced work of the physicists and chemists in Dresden it had limited knowledge. Even with the end of the war in sight drastic measures needed to be taken. Not only did the raids end German efforts to build its nuclear bomb, they put paid to the facility falling into the hands of the Soviets.

Flerov found the shattered nuclear centre, but the uranium had vaporised. In his notes he recorded that his radioactivity meters indicated that *'something had been located here'*. Some weeks later Flerov was recalled to Moscow by Kurchatov, but not before the NKGB group had rounded up many of the German and Austrian scientists and engineers who worked at the facility, including a team of chemists from the University of Munich, specialists in uranium isotope separation. A group of them, some 33 in number, were transported to Russia to work on Stalin's atomic bomb in an isolated and well-guarded location in Georgia.

CHAPTER 28

The race to capture scientists and materials

As the German U-boat slipped silently out of its northern port in late March 1945 the crew was in sombre mood, their final mission of the war so secret that only the captain knew the final destination.

Just hours before departure trucks had arrived from the Institute for Physical Chemistry in Hamburg and from other locations at the forefront of the German nuclear programme. This would be the first of such consignments to leave for Tokyo Bay in Japan. On the bridge the captain had no clue as to the explosive properties of the metallic uranium so carefully stored in 10 sealed containers. He and his crew had watched with growing apprehension as SS engineers moved around the U-boat strategically placing explosive charges. Under no circumstance must the vessel fall into enemy hands.

Their chances of escaping detection by the British Navy and RAF in the North Sea were marginal at best. Even if the U-boat got that far navigation in the heavily patrolled waters west of Ireland would be difficult. The South Atlantic and the rounding of the treacherous waters of Cape Horn would provide an even greater challenge. German supply vessels on station in ports throughout South America had been alerted.

From the quayside the scientist from the Heereswaffenamt, the German Weapons Office, dwelt on what might have been as he watched the U-boat enveloped by the growing darkness. For him, and Germany, the nuclear dream was over – indeed, some of his colleagues doubted whether it had ever really got going. Japan, Germany's ally, had requested the uranium, still clinging to its belief that the American supremacy in the Pacific could be overcome. The scientist had been part of the project in the early years and felt bitter about how it had been managed – only in late 1944 had the Heereswaffenamt regained some element of control, but by then it was too late.

The sound of a car horn brought the scientist back to his senses, the driver eager to get away as the U-boat pens were attacked nightly. The return journey to Gatow would be dangerous and might take some days as RAF Mosquitoes strafed the roads, unopposed.

Of the U-boats that attempted the trip to Japan almost all were intercepted. One, *U-234*, with its precious cargo of uranium oxide, surrendered to the US Navy near Newfoundland – an event the Americans turned into a major propaganda coup for the newspapers.

Another U-boat slipped through the net – but its destination was not Japan.

This U-boat had more than just metal containers of uranium on-board. Its inventory included highly-detailed documents on the configuration of a nuclear reactor, supplied by the Heereswaffenamt, and a number of dismantled centrifuges used for isotope separation. The captain's orders were to head for a sheltered inlet several hundred miles south of Buenos Aires, in Argentina, where the cargo was unloaded. Explosives later sunk the U-boat.

* * *

The Kaiser Wilhelm institutes and sensitive Government buildings were being systematically ransacked by the SS in a desperate attempt to spirit Berlin's wartime secrets and documents to safe storage. Czechoslovakia was a favoured destination, with Prague remaining under SS and Gestapo control. A convoy of 11 trucks reached the Czech capital on May 2, 1945, to be met by an 18-man SS technical detail from the Geheime Technische Geselschaft, under the command of General Heinrich Klein. He personally verified that the manifest included the Molotov-Ribbentrop Pact, the original of the document that had cemented the alliance between Germany and the Soviet Union and that had been so violently broken in June 1941. Other boxes contained records from Himmler's office – numerous files referring to the elimination of Jews in Europe.

Another Berlin consignment was expected the next day.

The two Junkers 52 transports and the single Messerschmitt 109 escort were amongst the last aircraft to take off from the Gatow airfield. Initially the crews were briefed that Madrid, the main routing for cargoes for Argentina, was the destination. However, bad weather and enemy attacks over Berlin delayed the departure and those orders were amended, with Prague the new destination.

Loaded aboard were crates containing the scientific secrets of the Kaiser Wilhelm institutes. Some crates were unsealed because of the haste of the operation. The Kaiser Wilhelm Institute for Biology had crated up their files on the medical experiments conducted by the infamous SS doctors both before and during the war. Josef Mengele's barbaric work in Auschwitz was also included. Each week from the Polish death camp he would send samples from his human guinea pigs for analysis. Meticulous notes on Germany's chemical warfare programme relating back to the Great War were packed and made ready for transport in the Kaiser Wilhelm Institute for Chemistry. In the Kaiser Wilhelm Institute for Physics some safes were emptied – but in the rush much was overlooked, especially the extensive library on nuclear fission. Some metallic uranium was also crated and placed aboard the Junkers.

Undetected, the three aircraft flew low and penetrated the Czech border. However, Soviet fighters picked them up and the ME-109 was hit and crashed. An anxious Klein and his SS unit waited at the airfield. The Junkers circled twice before their pilots felt comfortable that they could land on the bumpy airstrip. During the night both aircraft were emptied, then dismantled and buried in pits dug out by commandeered tractors. Ever the perfectionist, Klein did not want to leave behind any evidence.

By morning Klein's men had loaded the 400 crates from the two Berlin deliveries onto trucks. Klein had told no one of the final destination, only his driver knew and the SS sergeant, Hans Lauber, who acted as bodyguard to the general. The convoy moved off to the south of Prague, to the heavily wooded area of Stelhovic, two hours drive away. The trucks were unloaded in a large clearing. A platform was constructed with quick-setting cement and several large drums were heated up to melt the tar that the men had brought with them. As each crate was properly sealed Klein checked his manifest.

The smell of the molten tar wafted through the woods and a curious young Czech girl hid in the undergrowth some distance away, observing the activity. It was only when shots rang out that she ran home, terrified, and told her mother what she had seen. The mother scolded her child and banned her from ever mentioning the event she had witnessed in the woods. After the war she would settle down in Bavaria in southern Germany, abiding to the wishes of her mother, afraid that the long arm of the Nazis could still harm her.

For what seemed like hours she had watched Klein and his unit struggle to manhandle the heavy crates into a tunnel dug out of the rock by SS engineers some weeks earlier. With the last crates inside the tunnel, Lauber, Klein and his driver turned their machine guns on their SS colleagues. Those that weren't killed in the volley of fire were clinically finished off. The tunnel entrance was sealed – Klein would forever hold onto one of the Third Reich's last secrets.

It was only a matter of weeks before Prague finally fell to the Red Army. Cut off from any escape the three SS men were captured and soon interrogated by the NKGB who had heard the rumours about secret consignments from Berlin that included part of the gold reserves of the Reichsbank, the German central bank. The NKGB scoured Prague but nothing was found. Klein never broke under interrogation, despite the torture; nor did his two trusted colleagues. German PoWs imprisoned throughout the USSR were repatriated between 1952–1955 but the Russians and the Czechs insisted on holding onto their members of the SS technical group. Klein remained in Valdice jail until 1968, when the Czech Government agreed to exchange him for a payment of DM250,000 from Odessa, the organisation that helped fleeing Nazis after the war. He would be the last SS officer to return to Germany from Eastern Europe.

The Berlin consignments of May 2–3, 1945, remain buried in Stelhovic, despite numerous Russian and Czech attempts to locate the tunnel.

* * *

By the first week of April 1945 the Third Reich was in its death throes. American and British forces sat to the west of Berlin, on the Elbe, ordered by General Eisenhower to stop the advance. The Red Army relentlessly carried on its advance taking every street in the city's outskirts in hand-to-hand fighting. General Rokossovsky's Army to the north was barely 20 miles away from the city centre. From the south General Konev prepared for the final push.

The Russians had assembled two and a half million men, six thousand tanks and seven thousand aircraft for the taking of Berlin. Hitler, from his bunker in the garden of the New Chancellery in Voss Strasse, issued desperate orders – Germany was to burn by its own hand, nothing of value was to be left to the Soviets. Horrified, Albert Speer immediately rescinded that command.

Hitler celebrated his 56th birthday on April 20 in the bunker as Konev reached the River Spree. Hermann Goering wanted to take command but was threatened with arrest. Himmler spoke of conditional surrender. American and Russian forces 'officially' met at Torgau, on the Elbe south of Potsdam, on April 27, a symbolic meeting for the newspapers and newsreels. There was better news in the bunker when Germany's 12th Army, commanded by General Wenck, momentarily held up the Soviet advance.

SS execution squads roamed throughout the devastated city, shooting anyone they accused of cowardice. The scientists who remained in the capital feared for their lives after learning that they were SS targets.

The final battle for Berlin ended on April 30 with two Russian sergeants, Yegorov and Kontary, raising the Red Flag over the shattered Reichstag. In the bunker Hitler and Eva Braun committed suicide.

Winston Churchill broadcast to the British nation and its Commonwealth on May 8 that the war in Europe had ended. Prague, the last European capital to be freed, was liberated from the SS the next day.

With one war won and the Cold War about to begin the race was now on to share the spoils – the fantastic scientific wealth that Germany had accumulated over the past ten years.

Stalin hosted urgent meetings in the Kremlin. He commissioned Igor Kurchatov to head a scientific task force, under the command of the NKGB and GRU, to search for German scientists and materials such as uranium from the Belgian Congo that had been taken when Belgium was overrun. The first aircraft took off from Moscow on May 2, its destination Berlin. On-board was Lt General Avraami Zavenyagin, the deputy head of the NKGB, and Makhnev, his assistant. There were four other passengers, each one looking resplendent in their new uniforms with the rank of colonel – Isaak Kikoin, Yuli Khariton, Lev Artsymovich and Lev Nemenov, all physicists from Laboratory No. 2. Kurchatov had decided to remain behind in Moscow. A second plane later departed with the physicists Victor Davidenko and David Simonenko. The following day a large group of Soviet rocket specialists led by Yakov Zeldovich, one of Kurchatov's closest colleagues, set off to locate Hitler's new and untested generation of rockets whose warheads might contain nuclear devices. The final group that Kurchatov had assembled was destined to locate the bombed nuclear facility in Dresden.

Surprisingly, the Kaiser Wilhelm institutes in Dahlem had escaped relatively unscathed from the massive aerial bombardment and artillery shelling. Soviet soldiers billeted in the institutes ransacked the large compound, smashing apparatus and lighting bonfires in the corridors. Eventually a NKGB unit took control to await the arrival of Zavenyagin and Kikoin. Other sites put under strict guard included the laboratory of Baron Manfred von Ardenne in Lichterfelde, the University of Berlin in the Unter den Linden and the Technische Hochschule in Berliner Strasse, all wartime locations for work on nuclear fission.

Waiting to greet Zavenyagin at the Kaiser Wilhelm Institute for Physics was Dr Ludwig Bewilogua. Zavenyagin, a gruff, no-nonsense officer, demanded to be shown the nuclear archive and Bewilogua was keen to help. Bewilogua, with a sense of loyalty to his science, had ignored the SS command to burn the contents.

Kikoin rifled through the papers and to his utter astonishment he found the complete records of Germany's atomic bomb project, from 1939 to early 1945 when the last scientists had embarked on the trip south with heavy water and uranium. There was also a file with some limited details of the Dresden facility. The NKGB team located two containers of heavy water, labelled *Norsk Hydro*, small quantities of metallic uranium and a few kilograms of uranium oxide. Anything of interest was dismantled and transported back to Moscow, along with the entire contents of the library.

Another NKGB unit raced to the Auer factory in Oranienburg, the largest manufacturer of metallic uranium in Germany that had been heavily bombed on the personal orders of General Groves, head of the *Manhattan Project* in Washington. One of the company's chief scientists, Nicholas Riehl, was arrested. In Lichterfelde, Baron von Ardenne had also been found.

Bewilogua informed Zavenyagin that most of the Kaiser Wilhelm's uranium supply was probably in Allied hands, in Hechingen and Haigerloch. Intriguingly, however, he provided the record of a consignment in storage in Grünau, 50 miles southeast of Berlin. The next day Zavenyagin and Kikoin found the half-destroyed factory used to manufacture paint and gas masks. A search yielded nothing and the chief engineer was uncooperative. Another member of staff, a girl from the accounts department, directed the Soviets to another building with two industrial-size chimneys.

Shooting off the padlock, the NKGB found themselves in a large empty room with furnaces at either end. Traces of uranium oxide lay scattered on the concrete floor. In a corner a metal ladder led into a cellar. Kikoin climbed down into what had been an underground laboratory. His spirits rose when he discovered a glass jar labelled *Special Metal*. He found other jars containing more uranium oxide and thorium. One of the secret underground uranium laboratories in Berlin had now been located but the large consignment had gone.

Returning to the main building, the girl again proved useful. A waybill for

February 1945 had recorded a delivery of several tons of uranium oxide to the factory from Rohestoffgeselschaft, a firm tasked with transporting essential materials to industrial sites in Berlin and elsewhere. Another waybill confirmed an instruction in April that Rohestoffgeselschaft had insisted that all stocks be immediately transferred to the Hoffman and Moltzen company based in Parchim, a three-hour drive away in north-west Germany.

Khariton transferred from his NKGB group to join Kikoin in the chase. Together they drove to Parchim and presented their credentials to General Khrulev, head of the Russian division who had taken the town that had surrendered without a fight. Troops were provided to search for the uranium. For three days they scoured factories and buildings, never waivering in their determination to find the Grünau consignment. Back in their sleeping quarters in Neuhagen, just outside Berlin, the scientists re-examined every waybill. Someone suggested that there may be records at the Grünau railway station, but the team found it in ruins. This led them to believe that the uranium had never left Grünau.

The waybills located Rohestoffgeselschaft at 26–28 Tirpizufer, Berlin. A visit confirmed what they dreaded. It, too, was a ruin. However, an employee offered a glimmer of hope, informing the Russians that trucks had recently delivered to a number of addresses.

Kikoin and the team drove to each one and, in a stroke of luck, a card index identified a paint factory on the banks of the River Spree. Fortunately the seven-story building was intact and in operation, staffed mainly by women. A search yielded another card index, this time with delivery consignment numbers. One in particular excited the scientists – *U 43 00 480*. There was every possibility that the *U* referred to uranium. The staff were uncommunicative, apart from a male clerk who confirmed that a large consignment of uranium oxide was located 30 miles east of Berlin, near Vogelsdorf, held with other materials in a warehouse. Elated, the Russians were soon in hot pursuit – only to discover empty wooden packing cases containing just traces of uranium. Yet another disappointment was cabled to Kurchatov in Laboratory No. 2 and the NKGB headquarters in the Lubyanka.

They took a few days off to relax and were invited to the headquarters of Marshal Zhukov in Karlhorst to celebrate the victory over Germany. Wine and beer flowed freely and Zhukov was in an ebullient mood.

Inadvertently, it was another NKGB group engaged on a different mission that set in motion a train of events that would lead to the discovery of a huge quantity of uranium.

A captured senior Rohestoffgeselschaft employee, arrested in Potsdam, had confessed to arranging the shipment of the Belgian Congo ore into Germany in 1940. Kikoin interrogated the man but the manager refused to answer any questions relating to Grünau and Parchim. When Kikoin showed him the waybill for *U 43 00 480* he clammed up. Exasperated, Kikoin left him to the interrogation methods of the NKGB. The following day Kikoin returned and this time the bloodied prisoner couldn't have been more helpful. The consignment – *U 43 00 480* – didn't go to Parchim. That was a red herring put out by the German drivers. Instead, the trucks had driven to Neustadt.

Excitement was immediately tempered with dismay as the employee explained to the Russians that there were many locations with that name in Germany and he didn't know which one held the uranium. Worse was to come. Kikoin realised that only 10 of the 20 Neustadts were in the Russian zone. Over the next week the NKGB group drove or flew to nine of them, looking for leather and paint factories in particular, the favoured guise for the secret uranium facilities. Nothing was found and their hopes now rested on Neustadt am Glewe, a village set right on the border of the British and Soviet zones.

In full sight of the British Army, a Red Army officer directed the team to a leather factory already commandeered and in operation for the Russian military. Nearby was a large warehouse where they came across a pile of small barrels containing lead oxide, a tanning agent. Kikoin demanded to see the manager, an old man who had diligently kept the factory functioning even in the last days of the war. He confirmed that a directive had been received from Hoffman and Moltzen just weeks earlier to say that a special consignment would be arriving for storage.

After so many setbacks Kikoin felt cautiously optimistic as he followed the old man to another warehouse containing a large pile of barrels covered by tarpaulin. Kikoin broke open one and whooped with joy as uranium oxide tumbled through his fingers – 100 tons, right under the noses of the British: *U43 00 480* had been located. Kikoin called Zavenyagin now back in Moscow, who first thought that Kikoin was pulling his leg. Zavenyagin personally delivered the news of the coup to Stalin.

Many barrels were in no condition to withstand transportation, first to Berlin by truck and then by air to Moscow, so Kikoin and Khariton decided that the consignment needed repackaging. A group of German women charged with the task declined, afraid that the material was hazardous. Khariton removed his NKGB colonel's tunic and plunged his hands into the yellow powder to convince the women that the substance was safe. Within two days the barrels were en route to Laboratory No. 2, the contents to be used in the manufacture of more than half of the metallic uranium needed for the building of Russia's first nuclear reactor.

Another discovered waybill confirmed the existence of a further 12 tons in another village near Neustadt, but, to Kikoin's horror, he discovered that the Soviet Navy had grabbed the uranium oxide believing it to be lead oxide and useful for painting naval vessels. That too, was sent to Moscow.

Returning to the Kaiser Wilhelm, Kikoin and his colleagues carefully examined much of the documentary material and participated in interrogations of captured scientists. Time was of the essence now, given that all the Dahlem institutes would soon be incorporated into the American sector of Berlin. Karl Friedrich Bonhöeffer, a physicist, had given himself up to the Russians. For the duration of the war Bonhöeffer had been a British agent and had remained in Berlin when most of the nuclear fission group had moved south to Hechingen and Haigerloch. He had thwarted the Gestapo, especially after the abortive assassination attempt on Hitler on July 20, 1944, which led to the arrest of Admiral Canaris, the head of the Abwehr, fellow Abwehr officers and known dissidents. Bonhöeffer had known several of the conspirators. The SS at Flossenburg concentration camp executed Canaris in April 1945, but only after they had exacted horrendous torture on their victim.

Putting the lives of his family and himself in great danger, Bonhöeffer steadfastly refused to be coerced into working for the Soviet nuclear programme. Eventually an NKGB officer arrived at Bonhöeffer's Berlin apartment, accompanied by a lorry and an order to transport the family to Obninsk, some 60 miles south-west of Moscow and the new home for a number of German isotope specialists.

Bonhöeffer struggled with the Soviet soldiers as they evicted the family. Then, for some unknown reason, the officer apologised for their actions and the soldiers left. They didn't return. In 1947 Bonhöeffer became the director of one of the Kaiser Wilhelm institutes, temporarily merged by the Americans with other facilities into the German Research Colleges of Berlin-Dahlem.

Throughout the American and British zones the capture of officers involved in all top-secret aspects of the German war machine was a number one priority. British Army intelligence and MI6 formed 'G Intelligence' to help with the task, headquartered at Herford. The unit was commanded by Brigadier Keenleyside, a first-rate soldier and an excellent jazz pianist, who reported to MI6, which had based itself at nearby Bad Salzuflen. One operation masterminded by 'G Intelligence' ran until 1953. In the months after the war hundreds of senior Russian officers defected and MI6 housed some of them with their defeated German Army equivalents to discuss opposing tactics on the Eastern Front from 1941–1945. Lessons needed to be learnt now that the enemy was the USSR. The results of these face-to-face war games were codenamed the *Daffodil Papers*.

Locating the key German nuclear scientists fell to the more specialised *Alsos Mission*. In November 1944 this joint American and British team had entered the University in Strasbourg, where papers relating to the German uranium project, including the activities of the Heereswaffenamt experimental station in Gatow, were found. Included in the haul were details of the move to Hechingen and Haigerloch by the Kaiser Wilhelm's physicists, left by von Weizsäcker who had spent little time in the university where he was a professor.

Spearheaded by US Major Bob Pash and the Dutch-American physicist Samuel Goudsmit, the *Alsos Mission* included several MI6 operatives – Lt Commander Eric Welsh, Major David Gattiker, Wing Commander Rupert Cecil and Lt Colonel Percy Rothwell. Sir Charles Hambro, head of the SOE from 1942–1943, and Michael Perrin, deputy head of *Tube Alloys*, completed the British contingent.

Moroccan troops under French control had burst into the Hechingen laboratory on April 21, unaware of its true significance. Von Weizsäcker and his colleagues were terrified that they would be shot. Two days later the *Alsos Mission* arrived. At Haigerloch the last experiment on the nuclear reactor had produced a sevenfold increase in neutrons. With advance news that the *Alsos Mission* was soon to arrive Karl Wirtz, the heavy water expert, hid all 664 uranium blocks and the heavy water, but these were later retrieved in the basement of a neighbouring mill. All the uranium was sent to Hanford, the US plutonium plant near Seattle. None went to Britain.

Werner Heisenberg had fled before the troops arrived, cycling to his home in the woods at Urfeld in the German Alps, worried for the safety of his family. Arriving in the chalet, which overlooked Walchensee and whose neighbour was Baldur von Schirach, the head of the Hitler Youth, Heisenberg barricaded his wife and children in the basement as gunfire reverberated around the village. The local SS were not giving up the village to American troops without a fight. Heisenberg was a prime target for the SS, and his home was surrounded, but remarkably the Americans saved him and his family.

The British decided to bring 10 key nuclear physicists to England for interrogation, a decision that angered the Americans who wished to dispatch the group to Alaska, far away from prying eyes and any possible Russian, or even French, contact.

Farm Hall, a stately home in the village of Godmanchester near Cambridge that had been commandeered in wartime by MI5, was chosen as the venue for the interrogation. Every room was bugged; listening devices were even placed in the garden. Via Rheims, Paris and Huy in Belgium, the scientists landed in England on July 3 at RAF Tempsford, the station used by the Lysanders that flew SOE agents into occupied Europe. On the aircraft were Bagge, Diebner, Gerlach, Hahn, Harteck, Heisenberg, Korsching, von Laue, von Weizsäcker and Wirtz. British Army listeners, led by Major Rittner and Captain Brodie, recorded every conversation as the Germans were allowed free association. Each week a summary was prepared for General Groves, head of the *Manhattan Project* in America, Lt Commander Eric Welsh and Michael Perrin.

The dropping of the atomic bombs on Japan completely threw the German scientists at Farm Hall – they had been totally unaware of how advanced the Americans and British had been in building the super weapon. Diebner broke down when he heard the reports, retiring to his room and insisting that the Germans should have built the bomb first. News of the detainment of the scientists leaked out, but the British Government only admitted to holding two. On several occasions MI6 drove Hahn and Heisenberg to London for more in-depth discussion with Welsh, Perrin and others. Von Weizsäcker, trying to downgrade his involvement in Germany's nuclear efforts, was excluded. After six months, and with nothing more to be gained, the scientists were returned to Germany after promising never to be involved in nuclear research at a practical level. The Americans had demanded further incarceration, convinced that the scientists would become Russian kidnap victims.

Heisenberg was permitted a visit to England in 1947, where he spent several days in Oxford seeing Simon and other German-born physicists at the Clarendon. Simon wrote down the salient points of their conversation for Michael Perrin, still located in Shell-Mex House. *'Heisenberg insisted that the scientists knew about everything, including the fast neutron reaction and the possibility of using plutonium, but all their actions were determined by their aim to mislead Hitler and the 'high-ups' about the possibilities of a bomb. He said that if he had gone to Hitler at the beginning of the war and told him what he knew, then he was quite sure that Germany could have developed the atomic bomb just like the Allies!'*

Simon was damming in his conclusion: *'Naturally I could not tell him about some of our sources of information from which we know for certain that his story does not correspond with the facts. I therefore took the line that his interpretation did not seem to me quite consistent with the general attitude of the great majority of German scientists before the war. At the end of our lengthy discussion on this point he admitted that this was not without justification; the German scientists had not behaved very well, except for a few, for instance Hahn and Laue, and more or less himself.'*

* * *

Equally important to the Allies were the German rocket men, the scientists and the technicians who built the V-1 and V-2s.

Captain Harvey reached Kochel, the village at the top of Kochelsee, in Bavaria, at the head of a US tank convoy in the last week of April 1945. Tanks positioned by the tiny chapel between Schlehdorf and Grössweil had poured fire onto a Waffen-SS unit, guided by a reconnaissance aircraft. Two civilians frantically boarding up the shop windows of the chemist shop in nearby Urfeld were killed.

Kochel held one of the Third Reich's greatest military secrets, the experimental rocket centre, complete with wind tunnels.

Berlin had insisted that the prototypes at Kochel be destroyed before the Americans arrived. The head of the experimental facility and the works chief of the nearby Lake Walchensee power station were instructed to report to SS headquarters at Bad Tölz, 12 miles away to receive their orders. Scared to disobey both men left for Bad Tölz, but with a different plan of action in their minds.

For several days they stalled the SS before deciding that someone had to reach the Americans, now just an hour away. Harvey and an advance group now sped to the rocket facility in the village where the SS guards surrendered without the need for force. The gates of the plant were closed, sealing in all remaining staff. During the day staff had buried documents, films, photographs and apparatus in the woods.

Some 180 scientists and technicians had worked in Werner von Braun's experimental rocket laboratory in Kochel, which comprised two tall brick buildings joined by wind tunnels for velocity experiments. At the entrance stood an SS-guard barracks and a dilapidated building housing 200 Russian PoWs used for slave labour. Von Braun lived offsite, preferring the Grauer Bar, a pretty hotel outside Kochel on the road to Walchensee. Germany's chief rocket scientist wasn't in the village as Captain Harvey's tanks ringed the whole area in a show of strength – he was elsewhere and already in American hands.

Rumours had abounded in Kochel in September 1943 as the Dike Construction Research Institute began building work in the parish district of Herrenkreuth. PoWs had cleared trees, barracks were erected and huge holes excavated and lined with concrete under the direction of engineers. News soon leaked out. In the Postwirt bierkeller, Lopp, a Prussian labourer, was plied with beer by some villagers and admitted that the institute was merely a cover for a new rocket facility.

Trainloads of equipment were transported to the site and secrecy was again compromised. This time a site foreman arrived at the local railway station to find a discarded sign, crudely painted with the words '*Rockets – Peenemünde Testing Station*', lying on the platform.

Germany had built rockets since the 1920s, but in 1929 the military had grown weary of the failed trials. Under General Walter Dornberger, a highly respected engineer, matters soon changed. In 1930 he sanctioned further testing, with the brilliant von Braun joining the programme. In Kummersdorf, near Berlin, two rockets reached a height of 2,200 metres. Peenemünde became the main test site in 1936, with well-equipped laboratories and a trial centre. The inspirational von Braun, as technical director, told new employees that one day a German rocket would fly to the moon.

Within two years the world's first supersonic wind tunnel was ready, with small trial models tested at up to two and a half times the speed of sound. Work began on a prototype V-2 [Retaliation Weapon 2]. Flushed with early success, von Braun powered ahead on the design of the Waterfall Rocket, claimed to be capable of winning any war in the air. One large missile, carrying smaller rockets, would be shot at high flying hostile aircraft. These rockets, each equipped with an infra-red homing device, would pursue the warm exhausts of any aircraft. Hermann Goering, the head of the Luftwaffe, was impressed by the rocket's potential and urged further development; although early trials were constantly postponed. The first trial took place at the end of 1944, but it had design flaws.

A second supersonic wind tunnel at Peenemünde opened in 1941 and work began on two sub-sonic relief tunnels. Speeds of 3.3 times the speed of sound were now attained. In 1942, with the progressive development of fuel injection, von Braun experimented on rockets capable of 4.4 times the speed of sound. Germany's top rocket man believed that speeds of seven to 10 times the speed of sound were achievable.

Such growth in the programme required great volumes of electricity and output to

Peenemünde was inadequate. Lake Spitzing, south-east of Munich, was suggested as an alternative centre and plans were submitted to dam the lake to feed a new hydroelectric station in Fischbachau. Senior Nazi party officials scuppered the idea, as they owned holiday homes in the area. Attention then focused on Kochel, with its plentiful power supply generated by the existing power station on Walchensee.

Some 600 RAF aircraft broke through Peenemünde's protective artillery barrage on a raid in August 1943, setting the plant ablaze. However, the wind tunnels remained unscathed. That attack finally prompted the move to Kochel. Day and night 300 rail wagons travelled south, accompanied by 150 Peenemünde personnel. Germany's experimental rocket research was interrupted for only seven months after the RAF raid and Kochel's two wind tunnels became fully operational in April 1944. Every spare room in Kochel was commandeered. Dr Wegener, the senior engineer, lived in the loft at the Stein Villa on the Schelmbichl. The Stöger Hotel by the railway station overflowed with rocket engineers sharing rooms. Villagers were worried about an aerial attack on the same scale as that experienced at Peenemünde.

There was no address for the facility, which was referred to as WVA. Each day a motorcycle courier collected mail from a post office box number in Munich. The British, desperate to locate the new experimental station, received intelligence about the Munich post box but had no more detail.

Despite the importance of their work the scientists endured meagre food rations, only partially relieved by the offer to till a vegetable allotment at the Grauer Bar Hotel. During the winter months trees were felled outside the laboratories for firewood. In the Russian PoW block the inmates suffered terrible deprivation – many were shot out of hand by the SS guards for the slightest misdemeanour.

Problems were encountered during the trials of the models of the V-2 rockets, designed to fly at 4.5 times the speed of sound. As they approached such speed they overheated, the outer skin of their tips exceeding their tensile strength and causing the rocket to rip open. Research continued on the Waterfall Rocket and the StovePipe – an armour-piercing missile. Goering clung to his belief that the Waterfall Rocket might turn the direction of the war as it had the capability of downing every Allied aircraft that flew into Germany or German-held territory.

The V-1 rocket had already inflicted heavy casualties in Britain. Propelled by a pulse jet engine, with a range of 200 miles and a speed of 300 miles an hour, it killed 6,190 civilians and seriously wounded 17,980 others before the war was out. By September 1944 the first of the 12-ton V-2s, fuelled by liquid oxygen and alcohol, were launched from sites in the Netherlands and Belgium. No other rocket could fly as fast, with the V-2 reaching speeds of 3,500 miles per hour. In the last three months of the war the 900-kilogram explosive warhead of the V-2 was irradiated at the Griefwalt facility in eastern Germany, to increase its explosive power while aluminium powder was added to the fuel to produce greater speed.

The Kochel scientists had developed a two-stage V-2 rocket by the end of 1944, successfully tested in the wind tunnels in January 1945. Known as the A9/A10 the rocket had a calculated range that would include the eastern seaboard of America. Once in production, Washington and New York would be in range of the world's first inter-continental ballistic rocket.

Upon capture of the Kochel site by the Americans, all the qualified employees were transported to Landshut, 50 miles north-east of Munich, and quartered behind barbed wire to await the arrival of engineering teams from the US, Britain and France. By October 1945 some 20 had been selected for employment contracts in America, with another 12 specifically assigned to the US Marine Corps to build similar supersonic wind tunnels. The remainder waited anxiously for news of possible American positions.

Frustrated at the delay a mathematician in Landshut managed to make contact with the French who immediately offered him and other colleagues work. Within the hour they had gathered up their belongings and stole a lorry. Giving chase, US guards brought them back at gunpoint. It was on January 11, 1946, that nine men from the wind tunnel group in Kochel finally travelled on a 'liberty ship' to a far from friendly reception in the United States.

In Peenemünde, overrun by the Red Army, the Russians found the intact records of the German rocket programme, including the Waterfall Rocket and the planned inter-continental ballistic missile. Only pure luck provided the Americans with the discovery of one of the main V-2 construction sites.

On April 11 the US 3rd Armoured Division had taken the town of Nordhausen in the Hartz Mountains, reporting to headquarters that a nearby camp, Doramittelbau, needed further investigation. At first sight it appeared to be a concentration camp.

Arthur Stroh, an officer in one of the first US artillery units to cross the Remagen Bridge, the only crossing of the Rhine left standing by fleeing Nazis, was en route to Leipzig. Over the radio he received an urgent order to proceed instead to Doramittelbau with his unit. Not knowing what they would find Stroh and his men, equipped with 105-mm Howitzers, warily approached the camp. They were greeted by emaciated men wearing dirty, ragged blue pyjamas, telling of a 'fantastic underground factory'. Driving through the gates he saw pile after pile of decaying bodies in the large square – his unit later counted 5,000 around the camp. Stroh radioed his headquarters for urgent instructions.

In October 1944 Albert Speer had instructed that Camp Dora be converted into a gigantic underground V-2 production facility using labour from the Buchenwald concentration camp. Extensive underground rail facilities linked two huge parallel tunnels, a progressive assembly line. Smaller channels measuring 40 feet high and 37 feet wide interconnected with them. In this underground industrial nightmare the SS beat, starved and murdered 25,000 labourers. Up to 3,000 at a time slept in one single shaft with no ventilation. Few saw daylight again once taken underground.

There were no washing or toilet facilities, just rows of iron bunk beds. Many prisoners drank their own urine, slowly going mad. The SS shot them as they lay on the ground, their bodies dragged out by other inmates into the square.

Near Camp Dora's entrance stood the gibbet, 20 feet high and 40 feet long, big enough for simultaneous executions. Using a discarded cement bag as underwear or shaping a spoon out of a piece of aluminium was enough to merit a death sentence. The offender would be gagged with a chunk of wood, hauled off the ground by a rope over the gibbet and left to choke to death.

Stroh was shocked at the sight of the inmates, most of whom were barely alive. One walked slowly towards the American, stretching out a hand in pitiful greeting. He was Dr Odschourn, a Dutchman and the camp doctor. Sipping weak tea, the doctor told Stroh that German engineers and technicians, some 4,000 in total, had abandoned them just days earlier. The SS had taken several thousand inmates on a death march towards the German lines. Von Braun was often in the camp but he and his group hadn't been seen for weeks.

Without entering the underground complex Stroh walked around the camp. In a hut he witnessed one man in a foetal position. He later wrote: *'I came across what looked like a skeleton. I asked him gently who he was – but he spoke quite incoherently. However, he did manage to tell me that he was a Frenchman. I guided him gently back to the administration block and saw that one of my men looked after him.'* Stroh returned to speak further with Dr Odschourn and share his K rations. The doctor, he ascertained, had been arrested by the SS in Holland and held in Ravensbruck before transfer to Camp Dora to provide some measure of medical cover for 60,000 slave prisoners. Typhus and typhoid were rife throughout the camp.

After a sleepless night Stroh drove into Nordhausen to confront its Burgermeister. Chaos greeted Stroh as he arrived at the town hall. Local women had fled to the protection of the mayor after the SS had fed them stories that American troops would rape them.

'I told the Burgermeister to appear at the entrance to Camp Dora at 08.00 the following morning, with pails, brushes and plenty of energy,' recalled Stroh. On his way back to the camp he requisitioned a tractor and a large cartload of hay – giving the farmer a receipt and telling him to collect his money from the US Army. Stroh drove the tractor back to the camp himself. At least the straw could replace a few of the vermin-ridden sacks that the inmates had been sleeping on.

That evening the American Army captured a German field hospital at Sondershausen and offered it to Stroh who, with his driver, went off to find it. In Stroh's absence Dr Odschourn organized the townspeople from Nordhausen who were forced to file past the piles of corpses sacrificed in the rush to build rockets less than three miles from their town.

Finding the field hospital was no simple task, several times Stroh and his driver came under fire. Checking the grid references given to them, they finally realised that

Sonderhausen was in fact Sangershausen, east of Nordhausen. They located the field hospital, which was under the command of a 45-year-old German officer, Dr Zimmerman, who spoke impeccable English. It moved off in convoy, with Stroh in his Jeep at the rear. The road back to Nordhausen was clogged with DPs, displaced persons. American vehicles barrelled along at breakneck speed in the opposite direction.

Stopping at Nordhausen, Stroh ordered the mayor to rustle up food for the German medical team that hadn't eaten in days. Dr Zimmerman shared Stroh's Jeep on the road to Camp Dora that night, dutifully swearing that none of his men would attempt to escape. As soon as they arrived the operating theatre was in continual use.

Camp Dora was quickly overwhelmed by DPs and the US Army quartermaster struggled to find adequate supplies of basic food, served in the large soup containers used by the SS to feed the inmates. More US military personnel arrived and news came through on the radio that, within three days, Nordhausen and the surrounding area were to be part of the Russian zone of occupation. That announcement frightened the DPs and hundreds dispersed into the countryside, preferring to take their chances. American engineers worked around the clock to remove all the V-2 rockets from the underground tunnels.

Stroh befriended three Polish women Army officers who had escaped German capture only to be caught up in the chaos that was beginning to completely overwhelm Europe. They too disappeared, Stroh never hearing of them again.

With just hours to go before the deadline Camp Dora was deserted, every DP gone. The former inmates had been moved to American holding stations to continue with their recuperation. Only Stroh, his men, and the engineers remained. Eventually time ran out and they had to withdraw. It had not been possible to remove the last two V-2s before Russian troops marched through the gates. Stroh imagined Stalin's reaction to the gift left behind. *'I think I will call one FDR, the other Winston,'* Stroh imagined Stalin's comment.

On the road to Berlin with his unit, the memory of Camp Dora bored deep in Stroh's mind, yet for the next 50 years he was sworn by US secrecy rulings never to disclose the most sensitive aspect of the American discovery. He kept in touch with an inmate, David Salz, a survivor of Auschwitz transferred to Camp Dora in early 1945. In 1965 Stroh again met Dr Odschourn who in later life sketched some of the atrocities he had witnessed.

Von Braun and Rudolf Arnold, his deputy, had regularly travelled from Kochel to Camp Dora, as had General Dornberger who had drawn up the plans for the V-2 production facilities for Speer. From his conversations with Salz, Dr Odschourn and others, Stroh had incontrovertible evidence that Germany's primary rocket men were complicit in the mass slaughter of the civilians and the Russian PoWs, an episode the US authorities were keen to cover up as the scientists joined its own rocket programme. Arnold, in particular, was a beast, agreeing with the SS that labour was expendable. He often watched the executions on the gibbet.

Of the rockets found by the Americans in Kochel and Camp Dora, the development markings went from No. 1 to No. 10. One, two and three were in preliminary stages, and the supersonic V-2 and its derivative was number four. Numbers 8, 9 and 10 were middle-range rockets, with a reach of about 360 miles. The V-2 killed 2,754 civilians in Britain, seriously injuring 6,523 others.

The British had been deeply worried that a V-rocket could eventually deliver an atomic bomb. Werner Heisenberg in his visit to Professor Simon in Oxford in 1947 explained that he and his team at the Kaiser Wilhelm believed that an atomic bomb could be made 'the size of a pineapple'. A five-page letter delivered to both British and American authorities by 13 key British scientists working in Los Alamos confirmed similar thinking just days after the two bombs had been dropped on Hiroshima and Nagasaki. *'The Memorandum from British Scientists at the Los Alamos Laboratory in New Mexico'*, initiated by Niels Bohr, was kept secret for decades.

'The undersigned British scientists have been connected with the development of the atomic bomb in all the aspects studied at Los Alamos. Several of us took part in the test of the first bomb, and one of us has thoroughly inspected the damage caused at Hiroshima and Nagasaki. Many of us have been associated for a long time with the work on the bomb, since its early stages, and have considered for a long time the implications of this completely new weapon. We have recently had many discussions with our American colleagues, and practically all of us, American and British, are in agreement as to the gravity of the problems involved in controlling the use of atomic bombs, and as to the general lines along which their solution must be sought. We feel it is our duty to bring our knowledge and ideas on this subject to the attention of those responsible for British policy.

'A single bomb of the present type can completely cripple the life and resources of a city the size of Bristol or Coventry. It is clear that in a single operation, a score or two of such bombs, successfully delivered, could remove a large fraction of the industrial and military potential of a country like ours. There exist possibilities of making atomic bombs that will completely outclass the present type.

'There is no specific defence against atomic bombs,' the scientists warned darkly. *'The prospects of preventing their delivery, or intercepting a large fraction of them, seem extremely remote, particularly since they could be delivered in a variety of ways, for example by rockets of the V-2 type.'*

Klaus Fuchs was a signatory to the document calling for supervision of atomic weapons, its raw materials and the creation of an international organisation to monitor future development.

Dr Lehnert, a senior engineer from Kochel who after the war worked for the Americans, knew precisely the eventual role of the V-rockets. He was of the belief that Heisenberg deliberately misled Hitler into believing that an atomic bomb could not developed before the end of the war in Europe. Some years after the war, he wrote: *'Within a reasonable space of time atom bombs would have been dispatched into the eastern part of the United States, destroying Washington and the other major cities. A monument should be erected to Heisenberg in Urfeld, where Heisenberg lived until his death, and a very short distance from Kochel because he had saved the populace of Europe and America from an unforeseeable tragedy.'*

Lt Commander Eric Welsh, the MI6 officer in charge of *Tube Alloys*, did not share that 'heroic' opinion of Heisenberg. He had received conclusive intelligence during the war confirming Heisenberg's great enthusiasm in attempting to build an atomic bomb.

* * *

An Eastern European wearing the uniform of a British officer was very much part of the effort to track down German scientists in addition to bringing high-ranking Nazi officers to justice. Jan Ludvik Hoch, a young man of 17, had managed to work his way across Europe to England in 1940. Born of poor parents in Slatina-Selo, Czechoslovakia, he was determined to escape from poverty and anti-Jewish sentiment. Fluent in several languages, he was part of the invasion of Europe in 1944 – but with his name changed to Robert Maxwell.

In Berlin, in the weeks and months after the surrender, the intelligence networks proliferated as each side relentlessly fought over the remnants of Nazi Germany. Karlhorst would grow into an unparalleled centre for Soviet espionage. Three intelligence branches were established – Smersh, the military Counter-Intelligence organisation run by General Ivan Serov; the foreign branch of the NKGB managed by General Aleksandr Korotkov; and Department F, the special wing of the NKGB that, under the command of General Michael Maklarsky, interrogated captured German and East European officers. Department F was particularly notorious for the interrogation of Allied PoW officers held captive by the Germans during the war. Those officers with an intelligence connection were transported to Moscow and imprisoned in Vladimir jail. They were never released. After interrogation they were either executed or sent east to the mining labour camps.

Part of the US presence in Berlin included BOB, the Berlin Operations Base, with its primary aim of gathering intelligence on the Soviet nuclear programme and details of the uranium mines in East Germany and other Eastern Bloc countries. Britain, soon to be abandoned by the Americans in nuclear co-operation, needed to outflank both Americans and the Soviets and expanded its operations.

Maxwell, in military intelligence, served several masters. He worked for Airey Neave in the Special Operations Executive, for Naval Intelligence and MI6. In Berlin Maxwell participated in the interrogation of senior Nazi officers and Abwehr employees over the location of hidden caches of German documents, including atomic files. Under the diplomatic cover of head of the Berlin Press Service,

Maxwell reported into the third department of MI6 that was responsible for the Eastern Bloc. As war with the Soviet Union looked inevitable at that time due to the mutual intransigence of Stalin and Truman, this department established a special unit known as the Russia Orbit Group. Maxwell was one of its officers. The *Leotey Plan* was developed. Named after a French general, *Leotey* was the codename to be used by the BBC on the radio as an advance signal to undercover agents to begin sabotage operations in Eastern European capitals and Moscow. In the BBC itself a topsecret communications centre was linked to the *Leotey Plan*, referred to as *PROP2*.

In his Moscow file Maxwell is described as a 'walk-in'. Using officially sanctioned co-operation between Britain and Russia as an excuse he walked into Karlhorst and asked a favour of a surprised NKGB officer. Maxwell was desperate to know if his parents, Michael and Anna, and other family members had survived the SS pogroms. Colonel Joseph Cohen, head of the British desk in the Lubyanka, authorised an investigation, but some weeks later when Maxwell visited Karlhorst again he was given the bad news. Most of Maxwell's immediate family was dead, with no known graves.

That heralded the beginning of a relationship that would last until Maxwell's death on November 5, 1991. The Russians were keen to hear the details of the MI6 interrogation of the notorious Waffen-SS officer, Colonel Otto Skorzeny, who had rescued Mussolini from confinement in 1943. Intensely loyal to Hitler, Skorzeny had personally rounded up those suspected of the July 1944 plot to kill Hitler. He also master-minded the bizarre operation that same year to infiltrate hundreds of English-speaking Germans, dressed in US uniforms, behind enemy lines. Maxwell also handed over transcripts of interrogations of other top Nazis.

Not everyone in Karlhorst or in the Lubyanka was convinced that Maxwell was genuine and background checks were conducted in the Ukraine, Czechoslovakia and Britain. Such distrust did not stop at Maxwell. Beria distributed a missive to all NKGB directorates throughout the USSR, the Peoples' Commissars of State Security and, surprisingly, the heads of river transport entities. It was headed *'Directive of the NKGB USSR on strengthening the struggle against British Intelligence which has become more active in its sabotage activity against the USSR since the end of the war.'* Beria alluded to stolen MI5 and MI6 documents in his possession, confirming his suspicions that professional intelligence officers were included in official missions and were travelling on the railways, on the rivers and talking to Russian journalists. Britain's plan, wrote Beria in his memo, was to build a comprehensive database of Russia's economic and military strength. Beria believed that the British had increased their recruitment of agents by using Poles, Czechs, Greeks, Norwegians and Yugoslavs in particular. He insisted that by January 1, 1946, a memorandum must be prepared that would address the serious problem of British espionage, followed by monthly reports. Arrests must be made, he said, informer networks checked and, above all, agents needed to be acquired.

who could penetrate British cells active in the USSR.

Maxwell passed the NKGB checks and was given the codename *Tolmatch*, the Russian equivalent of translator. His initial contact was Maklarsky but that arrangement was soon amended. Moscow decided that Korotkov should be the case officer, reporting directly to Major General Dmitry Utekhin, in charge of the department responsible for the recruitment of double agents. On occasions Maxwell met with Serov, who would years later become the director of the KGB between 1954–1958 and head of the GRU between 1958–1962. The East Germans also saw Maxwell's potential and a strong bond developed between him and Andrei Grauer, the senior advisor to the Ministry of Security in the GDR, the intelligence department that grew into the Stasi.

In the early post-war years Maxwell's contacts and language skills proved vital to MI6. Carey Foster, the head of security at the Foreign Office, implemented an operation to parachute British-trained Ukrainians back into their country in an attempt to destabilise the Soviet regime. Maxwell helped Carey Foster vet the Ukrainians, many with dubious and murderous pasts as wartime German collaborators. Some operatives had been members of 'Galicia', the SS division formed of Ukrainians who committed mayhem and terror not just in the Ukraine. The MI6 operation was deemed a failure, not helped by being compromised to the Russians courtesy of Maxwell. Carey Foster cut his losses and closed it down.

* * *

In Britain the newly elected Labour Government under Clement Atlee had the problem of what to do with Rudolf Hess. His interrogations were considered so sensitive that British Intelligence warned against any disclosure. The details of the meeting at the Reich Chancellery when von Weizsäcker briefed the deputy Fuhrer on progress in Germany's atomic bomb project would remain outside the public domain.

Hess became prisoner No. 7 at Spandau after conviction at Nuremberg, with six former colleagues – Baldur von Schirach [No. 1], Grand Admiral Karl Dönitz [No. 2], Baron Konstantin von Neurath [No. 3], Grand Admiral Erich Räder [No. 4], Albert Speer [No. 5] and Dr Walter Funk [No. 6]. Von Neurath was released in 1954 and Rader a year later, because of ill health. Dönitz completed a 10-year sentence in 1956. Funk, the former head of the Reichsbank, was released in 1957 due to illness, having served 11 years of a life sentence. After completing 20-year sentences, Speer and von Schirach left in 1966. Only prisoner No. 7 remained, despite numerous pleas for release, many from Hitler's nuclear scientists, including Hahn and Heisenberg. He would die in Spandau in 1987.

CHAPTER 29

Potsdam and Problem No. 1

Truman's advisors closely observed the lack of expression on Stalin's face as the Soviet dictator heard the news that the United States had successfully tested a super weapon in the desert of New Mexico. The Potsdam Conference was the first Allied meeting since the war had been won in Europe. It began on July 17, 1945, as Truman, Churchill and Stalin flew into a war-ravaged Berlin to discuss how Japan could be beaten. Already large numbers of Red Army divisions had assembled in the ports on Russia's eastern coastline, accompanied by squadrons of heavy bombers to await the signal to attack. Truman, however, had no intention of letting Russia into the war against Japan – that would be a solely American victory. For Churchill there would no reward for winning the war against Hitler. He did not stay until the final day, August 2 – he had lost the General Election and the faith of the British electorate.

In America opinion was split into two camps on the use of the atomic bomb. Not surprisingly the military wanted to use the devastating and new weapon in its armoury. Some scientists had different views.

Truman had waved aside the opinions of several eminent nuclear physicists from the Metallurgical Laboratory in Chicago, one of the secret atomic facilities. In what subsequently became known as the *Franck Report*, James Franck, Glenn Seaborg and Leo Szilard argued against its use, suggesting instead that just making Japan aware of the bomb's potential would be sufficient. They wrote: *'It is doubtful whether the first available bombs, of comparatively low efficiency and small size, will be sufficient to break the will or ability of Japan to resist, especially given the fact that the major cities like Tokyo, Nagoya, Osaka and Kobe will already be largely reduced to ashes by the slower process of ordinary aerial bombing. Russia, and even allied countries which bear less mistrust of our ways and intentions, as well as neutral countries, will be deeply shocked.'*

On June 16 Robert Oppenheimer, Arthur Compton, Ernest Lawrence and the Italian, Enrico Fermi, met under the auspices of the Scientific Panel of the Interim Committee on Nuclear Power. *'You asked us to comment on the initial use of the new weapon,'* they told the generals. *'We recognise our obligation to our nation to use the weapons to help save American lives in the Japanese war.'* However, they forcefully recommended that Russia, France and China be advised of America's progress in the manufacture of an atomic bomb, suggesting co-operation Resignedly, Oppenheimer, as the Panel's chairman, signed the recommendation that the bomb be used, with the rider: *'With regard to these general aspects of the use of atomic energy, it is clear that we, as scientific men, have no proprietary rights. It is true that we are among the few citizens who have had occasion to give thoughtful consideration to these problems during the past few years. We have, however, no claim to special competence in solving the political, social and military problems that are presented by the advent of atomic power.'*

One last-minute suggestion was put forward – the use of a deadly nerve gas. America had built up a formidable arsenal, enough to wipe out the population of every city in Japan. The idea was discussed but, perversely, the use of gas with such lethal potential was deemed distasteful by the US military – somehow worse than any nuclear explosive.

On his return to Moscow from Potsdam, Stalin was in no mood to hear any more excuses on why the Soviet nuclear project was so far behind America. Time was of the essence. He summoned Igor Kurchatov to the Kremlin for what would subsequently become a heated discussion. Poskrebyshev took down the minutes. Beria had been invited and he wasted no time in blaming the scientists, deeply critical of Kurchatov and his methods. Beria advocated stricter discipline in Laboratory No. 2 and in other facilities throughout the USSR that weren't under direct NKGB control. Punishment was key, believed Beria, for any scientist or engineer that shirked hard work. Execution had to be the final sanction, as an example to others.

Kurchatov listened to Beria. He detested him, but with good reason he feared the man. To worsen matters Stalin, in December 1944, had removed the last vestige of responsibility for the project from a relieved Molotov and handed total control to Beria. Within days of the appointment NKGB officers had swarmed all over Laboratory No. 2, questioning everyone. Some members of staff had already disappeared and it was only through the intervention of Stalin, following urgent prompting by Kurchatov, that they had been returned – although somewhat worse for their experience in an NKGB interrogation centre on the outskirts of Moscow.

Intelligence from Washington, from a source in the White House, had confirmed that the New Mexico test had indeed happened, but Truman's aide knew no more. That didn't matter. Stalin now had on his desk a more detailed report from one of the Los Alamos scientists who had been so key in the test – a member of the NKGB cell in which Robert Oppenheimer was a member.

Kurchatov had already studied the document and had decided to use this meeting to be totally frank with Stalin. Every aspect of the Soviet nuclear project was bedevilled with problems, he said. Technology was limited, even primitive, compared to American and British efforts. The scientists were disillusioned and the initial euphoria after the restarting of the nuclear programme in 1942 had dissipated. That view, argued Kurchatov, was shared by some of his colleagues.

Stalin flew into a rage when Kurchatov suggested that with present resources it would be an age before an atomic bomb of any significant power could be built in Russia. He asked Poskrebyshev to get his diaries for 1944 and 1945. The dutiful Poskrebyshev did so and Stalin asked him to total up the number of meetings he had had with Kurchatov.

While Poskrebyshev did as he was told Beria excused himself as he had another matter that needed his attention. Beria was also in charge of Russia's oil industry and plans had been submitted to build two new refineries in the Volga region. As he left Stalin's room he smirked at Kurchatov. Kurchatov could only sit and watch Poskrebyshev carefully going through the diaries.

As the minutes slowly ticked by Stalin read the urgent cyphers transmitted to him from Fedor Gusev, the London Ambassador who had taken over from Ivan Maisky. The War Cabinet source, so vital to Stalin during the past five years, had confirmed that Truman had given his blessing to the dropping of two bombs on Japan. The first would be dropped on Hiroshima on August 6, now just two days away; the second planned for a few days later if Japan didn't immediately surrender. Gusev had been asked to ascertain if London had received any indication on how many atomic bombs were being assembled. Since Potsdam Stalin had feared the worst – Moscow would be a target after Japan.

Poskrebyshev finished his count and passed the number to Stalin – in 1944 there were 140 meetings in the Kremlin. So far in 1945 there had been 90. Stalin passed the piece of paper over to Kurchatov, who merely shrugged his shoulders. But Stalin wasn't about to let Kurchatov off the hook. The atomic bomb had been one of Stalin's priorities ever since the interrogation of Major van der Velde. He asked Kurchatov if the scientists had any idea at all of a date for the bomb's completion, but Kurchatov would not be provoked.

Stalin returned to Gusev's transmissions. There was no American intention to unleash a nuclear holocaust on Moscow but, disturbingly, Washington increasingly was reluctant to impart too much detail to London on its nuclear plans. He closed the *Athenaeum* file and he asked Kurchatov if he could recall a meeting earlier in the year when the scientist had pleaded for additional funding. Kurchatov could only smile – more in hope than expectancy. This time, however, he would be surprised.

'When a child does not cry, its mother does not understand what it needs. Ask for anything you need,' said the Soviet Premier, softly. Those words Poskrebyshev copied verbatim in his notes.

On August 20, 1945 – 11 days after America had dropped the second atomic bomb, *Fat Man*, on Nagasaki – the GKO, the State Defence Committee, met in urgent session. Stalin immediately rejected the first draft of the order as no target date had been specified. After much discussion he reluctantly accepted that delivery would be no later than August 1950. Two days later Stalin signed the official document committing Russia to its accelerated schedule to build the atomic bomb.

A nine-man committee was established, reporting to Beria. Surprisingly, only two scientists were represented – Kurchatov and Peter Kapitsa. Stalin also ordered Lt General Pavel Sudoplatov, an officer in the NKGB he could rely upon, to set up a new group – Department S – to effectively co-ordinate all nuclear intelligence. Department S was also tasked by Stalin to re-evaluate the atomic intelligence that had been obtained, a decision that wasn't welcomed by Lt General Pavel Fitin and his officers in the 5th Department. Against Beria's advice, Stalin took the unprecedented step of agreeing to a request from Kurchatov that Khariton, Zeldovich, Kikoin and Khlopin should be allowed to read all items of intelligence and not just selected material. Colonel Vasili Makhnev became the co-ordinator, distributing such documents accordingly, but he insisted that each scientist be given a safe and stressed the harsh penalties for careless security.

Kurchatov called these scientists together at Ostoshenka 51, a building used by Department S, to inform them of the GKO's decision. The scientists had never felt comfortable with meeting in the Lubyanka, with its sinister and threatening environment; this very elegant palladian-style building in downtown Moscow offered a far more suitable alternative. The timetable agreed by Stalin was discussed, which was considered feasible, but there was concern given that no capacity currently existed in the country to produce metallic uranium and plutonium on an industrial scale. As the meeting stretched far into the evening they viewed Makhnev's bundle of intelligence received in the latest diplomatic bag from Washington. The latest photographs of the huge sites at Los Alamos, Oak Ridge and Hanford were greeted with dismay. Kurchatov agreed that the Soviet Union could never compete on this scale, but the volume of nuclear intelligence gained in both America and Britain had given them one major advantage. The maximum scientific effort and expenditure could be utilized on building a replica of America's plutonium bomb, the type used over Nagasaki. However, insisted Kurchatov, the scientists should also move forward with their own design – a bomb they considered far superior.

A maid brought in vodka and Kurchatov proposed a toast to August 1950. Khlopin enquired about the codename for the bomb.

Kurchatov laughed aloud, as did the others, when he told them. Stalin had decided the name, he had replied, it was *Problem No. 1*.

* * *

Peter Kapitsa had spent 13 years living in Cambridge, enjoying the first class research facilities of the world-renowned Cavendish Laboratory. He had visited Moscow in April 1935 but on the direct order of Stalin his exit visa was revoked. London was furious and the Foreign Office tried very hard to get Kapitsa back. On a number of occasions during the war the British had suggested to Russia a limited temporary exchange of scientists – Kapitsa was always the first choice. Stalin, however, would never countenance any proposal involving the swapping of such an important physicist.

Accepting the inevitable Kapitsa had contacted his wife, who had remained in Cambridge, to send him much of his library and scientific papers. His reputation in Russia as a scientific genius then grew. For his work in developing a new technique in the manufacture of liquid oxygen, Kapitsa had been awarded the Hero of Socialist Labour in April 1945, following two Stalin Prizes in 1941 and 1943. *Pravda* lauded Kapitsa in its editorial of May 19 and Georgii Malenkov, the Secretary of the Central Committee of the Communist Party, explained to Stalin that Kapitsa's method would be beneficial throughout Russian industry.

Beria had been against Stalin's proposal to include Kapitsa on the committee dealing with *Problem No. 1*. He loathed Kapitsa and the feeling was mutual. The relationship became so tense that Kapitsa wrote to Stalin on October 3, complaining of Beria's high-handed attitude towards him. A special scrambler had been installed in Kapitsa's office at the Institute of Physical Problems, located on Kaluzhskoye Shosse, linked directly to Beria's office – but it never rang. Instead, Beria called Kapitsa's secretary to arrange meetings, a favourite Beria ploy.

Kapitsa had other enemies in the Politburo and in the scientific community. They viewed him as a maverick that had spent too long in England. Some doubted his loyalty – the NKGB had long suspected that he worked for British Intelligence. Kapitsa had been involved in a poorly conceived wartime NKVD attempt to lure the Danish physicist Niels Bohr, an old friend, to Moscow. The NKVD had instructed Kapitsa to write to Bohr in Denmark, suggesting he visit, but Bohr and his son had already fled to England via Sweden. The letter finally made its way to the Russian Embassy in London where Bohr collected it in person.

When the committee on *Problem No. 1* met, Kapitsa was the most vocal. When his opinions weren't accepted he sometimes dared to suggest that the project be scaled back, even abandoned. It wasn't just Beria who felt the sharpness of Kapitsa's tone. In another argument Kapitsa told a senior Minister, to guffaws of laughter around him, *'You are not the Minister of Heavy Machine Building but the Minister for Heavy Thinking.'* Kapitsa had two powerful allies on the committee – Malenkov and Mikhail Pervukhin, the Deputy Prime Minister, but even they were beginning to tire of the celebrated physicist.

In a fit of anger Kapitsa wrote another letter to Stalin, arguably the most damming. *'Comrade Beria will have a quieter life…'* it began. The decision by the committee to establish two new universities in Moscow to train nuclear physicists was the last straw for Kapitsa, as once again he had been side-lined from the discussion.

Kapitsa bombarded Beria with telephone calls, but the calls were never connected or returned. By this time he had lost the support of both Malenkov and Pervukhin. Some committee members complained to Stalin, whose patience was now at breaking point. Beria hoped that Stalin would issue an order for Kapitsa's arrest. However, Stalin had given Kapitsa one more chance to solve his differences with the committee.

That wasn't to happen.

On November 25, 1945, Kapitsa quit Russia's atomic bomb project for good. He had written one final letter to Stalin accusing Beria of slander, even murder, and didn't wait for a response. The committee collectively breathed a huge sigh of relief. Beria was overjoyed and gleefully called Kapitsa not just to offer his condolences, but to give him a leaving gift. It was an exquisite shotgun, handmade in Tula, a museum piece but in working order. However, Beria couldn't bring himself to present the gun to Kapitsa personally. He asked Lt General Sudoplatov to hand it over to the physicist.

If Kapitsa believed that without him *Problem No. 1* would collapse he was sorely mistaken. Kurchatov, now Russia's chief physicist, was more than capable of single-handedly carrying through the project to completion.

On September 28, 1942, Stalin had signed the official directive instructing Abram Ioffe at the Russian Academy of Sciences to restart the nuclear programme that had been interrupted by the German invasion. A cable had summoned Kurchatov from Kazan to Moscow to present himself to the GKO. Stalin ordered Kurchatov to prepare a paper for distribution within weeks. Kurchatov did so and almost without question every one of his proposals were accepted. He returned to Kazan on December 2 to tell his excited wife about his appointment. More discussion followed, but on January 18, 1943, Kurchatov, then aged 39, left Kazan for good with the clearest of mandates from Stalin to build an organisation from scratch and directly report to Pervukhin. On February 11, 1943, Kurchatov was officially appointed scientific director.

Within two months the GKO had signed an order to build Laboratory No. 2, the centre for all nuclear research. The remnants of the cyclotron from Leningrad's Radium Institute, that had been left in boxes after evacuation to Kazan, were transported to Moscow for reassembly. Staff were given contracts of employment and ordered to design a prototype nuclear reactor constructed of graphite and fuelled with uranium. Progress, however, proved painfully slow and only in early September 1944 did the reconstructed cyclotron produce deuterons. Kurchatov wrote to Beria about the delays on September 29, requesting extra funding and staff, but the request was ignored. Further attempts followed and only a letter to Stalin in May 1945 saw some stirring in the Kremlin. The First Main Directorate [PGU] was set up under three men – Pervukhin, Lt General Zavenyagin, the deputy head of the NKGB, and Kurchatov who had now been awarded senior Ministerial rank. This Directorate was to last only to the Potsdam conference.

With the troublesome Kapitsa now removed from Stalin's special committee Kurchatov fully exercised his new powers granted under *Problem No. 1*. Efforts were redoubled on the construction of the reactor at Laboratory No. 2. Around the country uranium separation plants were commissioned, using both diffusion and electromagnetic processes similar to those tested in Britain and America, and the construction of a heavy water facility began at Chirchiksky in Uzbekistan. Plans were drawn up for a nuclear centre outside Moscow, KB-11, where scientists could perfect designs for the bomb itself. Scientists and top engineers were given better accommodation and food, and their children were rewarded with education at the best schools and universities in the country.

Khariton, Zeldovich, Kikoin and Khlopin became Kurchatov's key managers. But there were two other scientists who would become just as vital. One would win international fame, the other, a woman, would never receive the recognition she so manifestly deserved.

School in Rostov-on-Don had hardly figured for Flerov after his parents separated, but he had ambition. He needed a job and in 1929 he moved to Leningrad. In the Red Putilovets factory he worked as an electrician but he studied in the evenings and at weekends when he wasn't on shift. Eventually Flerov was enrolled into the Kalinin Polytechnic Institute, graduating with an honours degree in experimental physics in 1938. Kurchatov saw Flerov's potential and employed him as an assistant in his laboratory in the Leningrad Physical Technical Institute.

Flerov very quickly made his mark in Russia's premier institute, with his boundless energy and enthusiasm for trying to prove the impossible. His reward was a Stalin scholarship to study for a higher degree. While the scientists in Berlin's Kaiser Wilhelm Institute for Chemistry won international plaudits for their work on nuclear fission in 1938, Flerov and his more experienced colleague, Konstantin Petrzhak, demonstrated in 1940 how it would be possible to achieve a sustainable nuclear chain reaction. Although the scientific elite in Russia admired Flerov's work, this experimentalist was unknown in Europe and America at that time.

His colleagues considered him stubborn and difficult to work with. At times Flerov had the temerity to question, even admonish, senior members of staff. After the German invasion in June 1941 Flerov's world had fallen apart as he and Petrzhak were conscripted. Although Flerov performed his duties well as a technician in a front-line airforce squadron at Yoshkar-Ola, inwardly he seethed. He passionately believed that while he kept aircraft in the air, nuclear scientists outside the Soviet Union were building a bomb. To add further insult to injury he learned that the Leningrad institutes had been relocated to Kazan, so ending all nuclear research in the USSR.

Fearing a potential German nuclear strike on Moscow, Flerov wrote to Ioffe and Kurchatov in Kazan, pleading to be allowed to leave the military and restart his work that had been truncated in Leningrad. That prediction galvanised Ioffe and in December 1941 Flerov received a permit to travel to Kazan to address an audience of the best physicists in the country and to elaborate on his fears. If any country was to develop a super weapon, it must be Russia, Flerov urged. An elated Flerov returned to Yoshkar-Ola, only to be disappointed when his release request was again rejected. He had hoped that Kurchatov's plea to Stalin on his behalf would be sufficient.

From Yoshkar-Ola Flerov tried in vain to keep abreast of developments in Kazan, but Ioffe showed nothing but contempt for his ideas. In desperation, Flerov bombarded Kurchatov with letters, badly written, incoherent and misconceived, often on scraps of paper. One letter dated February 17, 1942, demanded that a short article he had written be published in *Doklady Akademii Nauk*, a confidential report distributed to academicians in the Academy of Sciences of the USSR. The article was returned, rejected.

Sergei Kaftanov, Stalin's scientific advisor, was also in receipt of Flerov's letters. They were derogatory in content, stressing that while his former scientific colleagues in Kazan continued to ignore him, scientists in Berlin were increasing their lead on the explosive properties of uranium. Not a single letter to Kaftanov was answered and Flerov was beside himself with fury. Disappointed at Kaftanov's inertia, Stepan Balezin, his senior assistant who also studied in Leningrad under Kurchatov, gladly kept in touch with Flerov. Balezin solicited his opinion on scientific issues that came in front of the GKO, including the 'atomic' notebook found in the possession of Major Hans van der Velde. It had been Balezin's suggestion that Flerov be ordered to Moscow in March 1942 to attend the extraordinary meeting in Stalin's conference room to discuss the notebook's contents.

Occasionally Balezin had hinted to Flerov that he should write to Stalin and ignore the indifferent Kaftanov. Flerov wrote to the Russian leader asking Poskrebyshev to type up the notes, correct the spelling and append the latest nuclear intelligence stolen from western capitals before the letter was handed to Stalin. Flerov accused Ioffe of a criminal act against the state and concluded: *'The question of nuclear fission is most probably being worked on abroad. Solving the problem would lead to the creation of a nuclear bomb equivalent to between 20–30 thousand tons of explosives, sufficient to completely devastate either Berlin or Moscow, depending on whose hands this bomb will be in.'*

Kaftanov, also heavily castigated in the letter, was summoned by Stalin and curtly asked to comment. Stalin was advised not to respond.

Uncertain if Stalin ever received the letter, Flerov wrote another, directly to Stalin this time and hand-written. Again, he didn't mince his words: *'Ten months have passed since the beginning of this war and all this time I have felt as if I have been bashing my head against a brick wall. Academician Ioffe believes that our research into the uranium question should be postponed until the end of the war, but this is a great mistake. Let us not voluntarily cede the position we have. We all want to do everything we can to destroy the Fascists.*

'Why am I raising such a storm? I am in the military now, but I want out to conduct experiments on uranium. I bombard everyone with letters containing negative opinions about some of our leading Academicians and I do it from the most selfish personal motives. To resolve the matter, invite all our leading physicists to a conference that I will address for 90 minutes. Invite Ioffe, Fersman, Khlopin, Kapitsa, Landau, Alikhanov, Artsimovich, Frenkel, Kurchatov, Khariton, Zeldovich, Migdal, Gurevich and, of course, my colleague Petrzhak.

'Your presence would be very desirable, Josef Vissarionovich. This is the only

way to prove I am right. In response to my five letters and telegrams to Kaftanov I have not received a single reply. There is a wall of silence at the Academy of Sciences that I hope you will help me to breach.

'This is my last letter. I will write no more and wait until the uranium problem is solved abroad...'

Stalin had had enough. He bypassed Kaftanov, Ioffe and Kurchatov and instructed Poskrebyshev to arrange the release forms for Flerov to be excused military duties. Within days Flerov was on a train to Kazan to begin his significant contribution to the building of Stalin's bomb. By March 1945 Flerov would be head of Section 7 at Laboratory No. 2.

However, it was Zinaida Vasilyevna Ershova who provided the vital breakthrough for *Problem No. 1*.

She enjoyed the nickname of the 'Russian Marie Curie' and was Russia's most notable expert on metallic uranium and plutonium manufacture. Born in 1904, after graduating from Moscow State University, she was instrumental in commissioning a radium laboratory in the capital in 1930. Paris beckoned and Ershova spent time working with the renowned radium specialist Irene Joliot-Curie.

Returning to Moscow after a year, Ershova became the director of the radium laboratory at Giredmet, the Institute for Rare Metals. In 1943 Kurchatov tasked her to manufacture some samples of the purest metallic uranium. After many attempts, in the summer of 1944 Ershova duly obliged and she produced an ingot weighing one kilogram. A delighted Kurchatov insisted that Ershova herself present the ingot to Beria, which she did, surrounded by her applauding colleagues. Thanks to Ershova, Russia had now acquired the skills to refine uranium oxide to such a level that could be used to fuel a nuclear reactor.

Stalin, on hearing the news, agreed to the immediate funding of a radiochemistry laboratory, codenamed *NII-9*, close to Laboratory No. 2. Ershova and her team were soon *in situ* as Kurchatov asked his able chemist to use her skills for the biggest task yet. It was essential for the Russian nuclear programme to refine the technology to isolate plutonium from irradiated blocks of uranium. In America the industrial-scale plutonium site at Hanford was already under construction.

It was to take Ershova three years to perfect her process, hampered by the inevitable arrest of several members of her team by the NKGB on Beria's orders on trumped-up charges. She weighed her first perfect plutonium sample – a tiny 73 micrograms – in December 1947. Within weeks Ershova had produced 300 milligrams. The technology was then transferred to Chelyabinsk, the large-scale plutonium plant being constructed in the Urals.

Kurchatov now had a surprise for Stalin. He was confident that he could deliver the atomic bomb a year ahead of schedule – in August 1949.

Potsdam had been the catalyst for Stalin. Within a year Kurchatov had put the necessary building blocks in place to accelerate the nuclear project. On June 21,

1946, Kurchatov had presented a plan to Stalin to build two bombs, RDS-1, the plutonium copy of the Nagasaki bomb, and RDS-2, a U-235 bomb constructed to purely Russian design and technology. Plans were also advanced to build an H-bomb, a thermonuclear weapon of even greater power. Even before Russia had conducted its first nuclear test in 1949, on April 6, 1948, the preliminary calculations for an H-bomb were approved. By June 10 that year Stalin had agreed the funding for RDS 3, 4, 5 and RDS 6, the H-bomb, being designed by a special group headed by Igor Tamm with Andrei Sakharov and Vitali Ginsberg.

Georgii Flerov and Zinaida Ershova helped take Russia into the thermonuclear age but, to Ershova's immense disappointment, the ablest female scientist of her generation was forever denied membership of the exclusive Russian Academy of Sciences.

CHAPTER 30

From Taboshar to Alma-Ata, and a return to Moscow

After Kurchatov had bade van der Velde farewell in the Lubyanka, the cell door closed on Hans and no one visited him for days. His guards became disinterested as the incarceration of the SS officer continued. He had been a prisoner for nine months since his capture in Krivaya Kosa on February 23, 1942. Hans enquired of his guards if they knew the whereabouts of Taboshar but they shrugged their shoulders, having no idea. Some days later he finally discovered that Taboshar was a penal community in north-east Tajikistan, known as Plant 18.

Thanks to his guards, Kurchatov and a lesser extent Khlopin, Hans had learned the rudiments of the Russian language during his captivity. Often he wondered if the LAH or Wiking had reached the uranium mines at Lermontev, his ultimate destination in the northern Caucasus. Copies of *Pravda* had vividly portrayed the great battle of Stalingrad when Red Army offensives north and south of the city had smashed through German positions in November 1942, resulting in the annihilation of the German Sixth Army. Hans' guards had joined in the jubilation throughout the Lubyanka. Army Group South was in retreat, falling back to the Red Army that was now vastly superior in numbers and hell-bent on revenge.

Realisation that he was to begin the journey to Taboshar came when Hans was handed a worn jacket and trousers that still had the lingering smell of their previous owner. That same day his two guards escorted him out of the Lubyanka and drove him through the Moscow streets to Kazansky railway station where he joined a swirling sea of German PoWs and enforced Soviet labourers. NKVD guards with dogs watched over their charges, who sat on the cold platforms, legs crossed. Trains exited the station with their human cargoes, tiny metal grills the only ventilation in each goods wagon.

Suddenly it was Hans' turn and his guards forced him to his feet. Both departed, leaving him to the mercy of the NKVD. In a strange way he would miss their company. Inside the wagon the atmosphere was stifling. He sat on the filthy straw that littered the floor. The other occupants also looked helpless, as indeed they were. Hans asked one in Russian if he was going to Taboshar, but the man just stared blankly back.

Conditions aboard the train as it wound its way through the mountain ranges and valleys were dreadful. The straw soon became soaked with urine and faeces and several people were sick with fear of the unknown. Hans discovered he was the only German. Some of the other prisoners tried to engage him in conversation but he decided it may be safer to remain silent, curious as to why he hadn't been placed with the German PoWs – there had been hundreds on the platform at Kazansky. He worried about falling asleep and having his throat slit. He rehearsed his story of being captured on the retreat from Rostov to Taganrog in case he did meet another German prisoner.

The train rattled east to Samara before turning south-east. Stops were frequent, the NKVD opening the sliding doors. Those foolhardy enough to attempt an escape were shot down. The fresh air was welcome, despite the biting cold. Dead bodies from the wagons were unceremoniously thrown to the side of the railway tracks. Hans recognised many as Wehrmacht.

As the train slowly approached Kuibyshev, Hans manoeuvred himself towards one of the grills and peered at the huge industrial city that had taken on a new significance since the German invasion. Stalin's choice as the new Russian capital in the event that Moscow was overrun, the city had grown to several times its pre-war size, almost overwhelmed by dismantled factories transported east as Ukrainian and Russian cities capitulated like collapsing dominoes. Assembly lines in Kuibyshev now churned out hundreds of aircraft a week for the Soviet air force.

Orenburg, a shantytown of dilapidated wooden dwellings, their roofs heavy with fresh falls of snow, was the last stop in Russia before the train crossed into Kazakhstan. The wagon doors were opened. Despite the early hour the station heaved with people who were forced onto the already packed train. Some hours later the train wound its way through a long pine-filled valley, en route to Aktyubinsk, and crossed the Gory Mugodzhary mountain range. From Aktyubinsk the train took two days before it reached Kyzylorda, the gateway into Uzbekistan. Hans lost count of the dead he had seen tossed into the ditches beside the track each time the train was reprovisioned. In his wagon starvation and the cold had taken its toll, especially among the older prisoners. A rollcall was taken on the platform at Kyzylorda before the train set off for its final destination – the Moslem city of Tashkent.

A convoy of lorries awaited to transport the prisoners to a local transit camp where identity papers were checked. When done the NKVD ordered everyone back on the trucks for the long and dangerous trip south towards Almalyk on the Tajikistan border, on a road that was merely a track. Taboshar was a further two hours away. Arc lights could be seen in the distance after a nightmare journey that saw one truck fall into a ravine. The convoy had briefly paused but carried on, any search for survivors both impossible and fruitless. Hans realised that this was really the end of the road. There could be no way back from Taboshar.

NKVD guards dressed in heavy greatcoats, with dogs by their sides, yelled at everyone to dismount for rollcall and Hans observed long grey shapes in the distance, the accommodation blocks. The wind tore into the prisoners, standing to attention and hardly clothed for the harrowing conditions. Surprisingly, Hans' name was called out and he was given an armband. He was to be a camp supervisor at Plant 18.

Allocated to their blocks, the prisoners were allowed some hours of rest before sunrise. Hans and the other new supervisors were marched to the vast open cast mine and to his horror he now knew the worst – Plant 18 was a uranium mine. He had witnessed similar conditions in Joachimsthal. The workers were covered in yellow dust and attacked exposed rock formations with pickaxes and shovels. A human train passed the material in buckets to be deposited in heaps.

Work began at 8am and continued until 4pm, before dusk fell. Fully aware of the dangers of inhaling the noxious dust, Hans tied a cloth over his nose and mouth but few others bothered. Primarily his job of supervisor was to take daily samples of the oxide, place them in phials and report to the site manager. At least Kurchatov had spared him the task of actually labouring, so Hans felt grateful.

At intervals these samples were transported over 500 miles to two new laboratories in Alma-Ata, the capital of Kazakhstan, for analysis. The city lay in the foothills of the Trans-Alay Alatau, close to the western border of China, and renowned for its well-tended apple orchards. Within weeks Hans proved himself and was provided with better accommodation, a wooden bunk was certainly better than sharing a cold floor with a dozen others. The NKVD guards generally left him alone.

Dust from the mining penetrated every building, permeating the water supply and what passed as food. Contamination usually led to irradiation of the trachea and Hans estimated that the incidences of lung cancer must be very high. Each day a burial detail threw emaciated bodies into large pits and covered them with spoil from the excavations. No records were kept of their deaths.

Staying healthy for as long as he could was Hans' primary concern, but he knew that he must soon succumb to the poisonous radiation. Not for the first time since the events of Krivaya Kosa luck took a hand. A geologist from Leningrad's Radium Institute asked Hans if he would like to accompany him on a visit to the laboratories in Alma-Ata, an offer that was quickly accepted. The camp commandant didn't object as he had been in receipt of a cable from Moscow saying that van der Velde should be given extra privileges and, anyway, no one escaped from Central Asia – there was nowhere to run to. Elated at his temporary freedom Hans carefully packed the uranium phials for the arduous two-day train journey through the Jalal Abad mountains.

Two weeks later both men returned to Taboshar and Hans was shocked at the increasing level of radiation sickness, especially among the German PoWs. Their sunken eyes and pallid faces clearly showed that uranium oxide dust had pervaded their bodies. Desperate, Hans volunteered for further trips to Alma-Ata.

On these journeys Hans carefully avoided discussing his past with his companion, describing his role at the Kaiser Wilhelm as a purely administrative one before inevitable conscription. In Alma-Ata, as the geologist discussed the results of the samples with his Radium Institute colleagues, Hans willingly offered any assistance he could to the hard-pressed radio-chemists.

It was on his third trip that he summoned up the courage to enquire if his talents couldn't be better employed as a laboratory assistant in Alma-Ata, as the samples were piling up in the laboratories. The request was submitted to the NKVD. With his return to Taboshar imminent, Hans was taken under guard to Alma-Ata's NKVD headquarters. He almost whooped with joy as the NKVD colonel informed him that Moscow had surprisingly granted the request. The geologist returned to Taboshar alone.

The facilities in Alma-Ata expanded as production of uranium oxide gained in priority. It was at the end of 1943 that Kurchatov and Khlopin visited the Kazakhstan capital to discuss progress. Hans heard about the visit but never saw them. In the following months other scientists and military officers from Moscow made the trip and Hans often observed such delegations being given guided tours around the laboratories.

Reliable war news was scarce, but the reports that the Allies had invaded mainland Europe in June 1944 was greeted with great excitement. Alma-Ata's sole newspaper devoted almost an entire edition in July to *Operation Bagration*, named after a Soviet general who fought against Napoleon. Upwards of 124 Red Army divisions vowed to destroy Hitler's Army Group Centre in Byelorussia to mark the third anniversary of the German invasion. As Minsk, Byelorussia's historic capital, fell to the Soviets the retreating Wehrmacht and SS shot thousands of Russian citizens in retaliation. By the middle of July the Germans were in disarray as the Red Army had several Ukrainian cities in its sights, including Lemberg, where Hans had witnessed the result of the NKVD massacre of Jews and Poles.

Hans had proved a popular addition to the laboratory staff. If his colleagues were aware of his background and the strange circumstances of his capture at Krivaya Kosa, they never said so. There were occasions when he accompanied exploration teams into the field as some 50 groups were now in Central Asia at any one time, using new devices and testing organic solutions that would make production safer and faster. The mine at Mailu-Su had grown to the size of Plant 18 and tractors were now employed in moving the uranium, but labourers remained unprotected. In 1944 alone, 5,000 prisoners at Plant 18 had perished.

Germany's eventual defeat in May 1945 led to celebrations that continued for days but Hans felt it prudent not to be involved, preferring the solitude of his room. Months before the Soviet victory in Berlin he knew that he would end his days in Kazakhstan. The local NKGB no longer treated him as a potential escapee, allowing him out on his own into the rapidly growing city. Factories had sprung up and railway lines constructed linking Alma-Ata to the rest of the USSR. Often he prayed in Alma-Ata's Ascension Cathedral, the construction made completely from local timber. He spoke Russian fluently now, thanks to a chemist in the laboratory, a woman who was lonely in the evenings and at night, yearning for a husband left behind in Leningrad.

The news of the dropping of atomic bombs on Hiroshima and Nagasaki prompted a subdued atmosphere amongst the staff and the scientists were called into endless committee meetings to discuss the implications. In the background, Hans continued his sampling and found solace with his female companion and in cheap Kazakh vodka. The head of his section read out aloud an instruction from Kurchatov that uranium production had to double and that the number of field crews would be increased. Production started at two new locations on the western fringes of Uzbekistan, south of the Aral Sea in Respublika Karakalpakistan. Large numbers of German PoWs provided the main component of the labour force in other mines in Leninabad and Khodzhet.

With the war over, many of the Radium Institute's chemists and geologists drifted back to Leningrad or to Moscow, to be replaced by younger men and women, former soldiers who had been enrolled into Kurchatov's nuclear programme. Hans' lover left for Leningrad. Without her, life in Alma-Ata became pretty unbearable so he volunteered for further field trips.

Yet again another lifeline arrived, courtesy of Kurchatov. Hans was wanted in Moscow within the month but first there was a mission that needed to be accomplished. He had to provide Kurchatov with a first-hand report on the working conditions in Taboshar and Mailu-Su, which would necessitate a visit.

Given the urgency of the mission Hans was given a permit to fly to both mines. The Taboshar mine had quadrupled in size to a manmade hole of immense proportions. A road wound down into its core with countless lorries and tractors bringing the oxide to the surface. Thousands of labourers, young and old, toiled with axes and spades under the ever-watchful glare of the NKGB.

For the best part of a day Hans walked among them, listening to the many languages. He was staggered to find one part of the mine given over to men wearing British and French uniforms, but the guards ordered him away. Hans enquired of his guide why Allied soldiers were in Taboshar, only to be told that they had been rescued by the Red Army from overrun German-held camps. Comrade Stalin had ordained they be used as forced labour because Russia's relationship with its Allies had deteriorated over arguments about the control of Berlin. They were dispensable human fodder, Stalin had decreed. Hans witnessed similar numbers at Mailu-Su, in even worse conditions. Only one Allied PoW would ever experience freedom from the camps in Central Asia, a Frenchman, who emerged some 45 years later. In Britain, respective Governments censored any reports that many British PoWs had been transported east and not west on their release by the Red Army.

Hans completed his report, concluding that the combined total of deaths in the two camps through radiation sickness and cancer had reached a staggering 30,000 from 1942 to 1945. In reality, however, that was a very low estimate. The records at Taboshar were incomplete, only in 1945 did the NKGB bother to produce a register. There were no memorials to the dead, no headstones.

On his return to Alma-Ata Hans bade farewell to his colleagues. There was even a party for him, for which he was most grateful and a little emotional.

Alma-Ata, Taboshar and Mailu-Su were behind him now. With his hand-written account in his bag to be delivered personally to Kurchatov, Hans boarded the converted Tupolev bomber that lumbered slowly off the concrete runway. Also in his bag was a memento, taken from the laboratory – a sealed phial containing a uranium sample from Taboshar. He was returning to Moscow, but this time not as a prisoner in the Lubyanka.

Hans had survived.

CHAPTER 31

The scale of American penetration

In a remote section of the Alamogordo airbase, 120 miles south-east of Albuquerque, the world's first atomic explosion had been detonated on the morning of July 16, 1945, with a force equivalent to 20,000 tons of TNT. Heavy rain accompanied by lightning had heightened the drama.

The final assembly of the nuclear device on the McDonald Ranch had begun on the night of July 12 when an Army staff car delivered the plutonium core. Philip Morrison, the theoretical physicist and former student of Robert Oppenheimer at the University of Columbia, had sat in the back seat gently holding the precious cargo. In charge of the core assembly was Robert Bacher, who in less stressful days taught students at Cornell. There was a near panic during the assembly process when one section wedged tight, going no farther. The scientists pushed and pulled, with brute force finally winning the contest, much to everyone's relief. The completed assembly was finally mounted on a steel tower at Alamogordo.

Bad weather prevented aerial observation and delayed the scheduling. In the control centre General Leslie Groves, head of the *Manhattan Project,* Vannevar Bush, James Conant, Robert Oppenheimer and 20 others waited anxiously. Groves had recently been informed that expenditure to date had reached a massive $2 billion. Out in the desert Keith Bainbridge of the Massachusetts Institute of Technology was in charge of detonation, accompanied by Lt Bush, head of the Military Police detachment. Bainbridge checked the tower one final time.

At 3am General Groves and Oppenheimer consulted with the meteorologists, agreeing that the test could not be postponed by inclement weather. Zero hour moved from 4am to 5.30am. With 20 minutes to go, Samuel Allison of Chicago University made periodic time announcements and at minus 45 seconds the count locked into automatic, now out of his control. A soldier next to a trip switch could have stopped the explosion, but now it was too late.

A sustained roar and a heavy pressure wave followed the blinding flash, flattening two men outside the control centre who had failed to take cover. The boiling yellow and crimson mushroom cloud surged to over 40,000 feet. Where the tower had stood, nothing remained. It had been vapourized and in its place was a huge sloping crater.

Bogdan George Kistiakowsky, the Ukrainian-born and Harvard-trained scientist that had been vital to the success of the Trinity Test, was ecstatic, jumping up and down, embracing Oppenheimer. As chief of the explosives division at Los Alamos he had supervised the manufacture of the charges for the testing of the plutonium device.

The following day Truman flew into Berlin for the conference in Potsdam, where he passed Churchill a note – '*Babies satisfactorily born,*' it read. Churchill smiled, he already knew that Trinity had given birth to a new age.

It was at a meeting in London on September 18, 1944, that Churchill and Roosevelt had agreed on a swift conclusion to the war with Japan. The short *aide-memoir* of the decision confirmed their intentions: *'When a bomb is finally available it might, perhaps after mature consideration, be used against the Japanese who should be warned that this bombardment will be repeated until they surrender,'* it read.

During the Potsdam conference, on July 28, Truman, Stalin and Churchill issued a final ultimatum to Japan, threatening blanket firebombing of every major city.

When the surrender demands were rejected, two atomic bombs were made ready.

* * *

A highly confidential document from the American Embassy was passed to Sir John Anderson at the Privy Council Office in Great George Street, London. *'My dear Sir John,'* started the accompanying letter, which was captioned *'US Confidential – British Secret'* and dated January 13, 1943. *'We are pleased to enclose for your information a list of the new divisions and panels, showing the chiefs of each and the areas of responsibility of the individual divisions.'* Anderson authorised copies for the War Cabinet, the Scientific Advisory Committee and the North American Supply Committee Scientific sub-committee.

Identified were the titles and addresses of the heads of 18 reorganized scientific departments reporting directly to Vannevar Bush in the Office of Scientific Research and Development in Washington. At the top of the four-page list was the Division of Ballistic Research, naming Dr L H Adams, Geophysical Laboratory, 2801 Upton Street, NW, Washington DC. The Division for Special Projectiles was next, headed by Dr J T Tate, 172 Fulton Street, New York. On the fourth page Dr G B Kistiakowsky was shown to be the chief of the Division of Explosives, located at the US Bureau of Mines, 4800 Forbes Street, Pittsburgh, Pennsylvania.

Somewhere in Anderson's distribution process a copy was delivered to Moscow via the diplomatic bag – a prized acquisition for the NKVD.

With family in the Ukraine, Kistiakowsky became an easy target and NKVD agents enlisted Ukrainians living in the United States to help recruit the new head of explosives for the US military. Moscow Centre was angry that Kistiakowsky was proving uncooperative, urging greater effort in turning him, including the threat of harm to his relatives in the Ukraine. In a transmission from the New York Consulate on December 16, 1944, updating the Lubyanka on the activities of Julius and Ethel Rosenberg, the American spies who provided atomic bomb intelligence to the Russians, the cypher clerk mentioned further attempts to enlist Kistiakowsky. Rebuffed again, still the NKVD chiefs didn't give up. More meetings took place. However, Kistiakowsky never reported these approaches to Groves.

The penetration of America's scientific secrets had been underway for years.

Since 1940 instructions had been made to agents in England, the United States and Canada to use the abbreviation 'XY' on all scientific and technical intelligence to help speed up the distribution process in Moscow. Lt General Pavel Fitin, codename *Victor* and head of the NKVD's 5th Directorate, on January 27, 1941, cabled Gaik Badalovich Ovakimian, *Gennady*, the deputy NKVD *rezident* in New York. Ovakimian had been in the US since 1933, operating under the Amtorg Trading Corporation, the US-registered company used as a cover for Russian espionage. The cable was short, referring solely to the issue of U-235. Even the Chinese, said Fitin, had learned of the US work in separating the uranium isotope and Fitin quoted the Shanghai newspaper, the *North China Daily News*, which had run a headline story that Columbia University in New York had produced minute quantities of the fission material.

Another Fitin missive, dated March 27, 1942, was transmitted to Vasili Mikhailovich Zarubin, *Maksim*, Ovakimian's replacement. The instruction couldn't have been clearer.

'The situation firmly demands the mobilisation of all possibilities we have within the scope of tasks given in letter No 4 [1941] and other guidelines, in particular on the chemistry of toxic substances, protection from toxic substances, issues in bacteriology and the problem of uranium-235.

'We think it is necessary to inform you about a number of people who must be immediately involved in our work. Among them will be those people we already gave you in our letters in 1941.'

Enclosed in Fitin's cypher were names of key physicists, chemists and mathematicians, some of who were covert members of the US Communist Party, the CPUSA. Every major scientific centre in the country was now under threat of Soviet penetration.

Moscow has gone to considerable lengths to cover up its links with Robert Oppenheimer, the chief scientist in the *Manhattan Project,* and veteran KGB officers such as Vladimir Barkovsky remain touchy to this day on the extent of the physicist's co-operation. The son of a German immigrant who made his money by importing textiles, Oppenheimer had quit Los Alamos at the end of the war and moved to Princeton as director for the Institute of Advanced Study, a position he held almost up to his death in February 1967.

US senator Joe McCarthy captured the headlines in 1950 with his charge that Communists had infiltrated Government, but he could never substantiate such claims. Only after live television exposed his brutal interrogative technique as the Senate chairman of the House Committee on Un-American Activities to investigate Communist penetration did his reputation wane. McCarthyism had swept across America, increasingly involving scientists who had a secret association with the CPUSA. Oppenheimer became a target in 1953, although the previous year he had resigned his post as chairman of the influential general advisory committee of the Atomic Energy Commission (AEC). He did, however, retain security clearance on the programme that had just successfully tested the H-bomb in the Pacific. Concerned senior Army officers refused to deal with Oppenheimer and demanded that his clearance be withdrawn.

Such suspicions were not new. Edgar Hoover, the Director of the FBI, had long suspected Oppenheimer's possible connivance with the Soviets. He authorised an interrogation that took place on March 8, 1947, when Oppenheimer was directly accused of compromising the American nuclear bomb programme. Knowing full well that he was being followed, Oppenheimer asked a colleague to alert his Soviet controller that he was under surveillance. During April 1947 Moscow mounted an operation that would smuggle Oppenheimer out of America on board a Russian freighter. The defection of America's top nuclear physicist would have created shock waves throughout the West and his immeasurable expertise could have speeded up the building of Russia's bomb. However, the NKGB had other consid-erations to take into account – the sudden disappearance of Oppenheimer would have had disastrous effects on Soviet intelligence operations throughout America. After Oppenheimer's colleague again reported that the FBI interrogation would intensify the NKGB reluctantly conveyed to Oppenheimer that the escape plan was ready. For several weeks Oppenheimer prevaricated but eventually decided to remain and tough it out, believing that there was no real evidence of any guilt that could be directly attributed to him.

In late 1953, given the increasing level of military hostility towards Oppenheimer, the AEC had no option but to convene its own investigation. A three-man security board consisting of nuclear scientists was established, and from April 12 until May 6, 1954, Oppenheimer was interrogated. It is doubtful whether the board were given access to the FBI files. Edward Teller, the Budapest-born scientist responsible for the building of the H-bomb, was one of a number of former Los Alamos colleagues summoned to testify. His attestation created quite a stir, suggesting that Oppenheimer shouldn't be trusted. Teller had not forgiven Oppenheimer for ceasing development of the H-bomb in 1945 upon the capitulation of Japan. The project was only restarted after Russia tested its first atomic device at Semipalatinsk, Kazakhstan, in August 1949, and the assumption that the spy Klaus Fuchs had passed the H-bomb concept to his Soviet controllers. Oppenheimer was evasive in the questioning from the three members of the AEC board, denying close contact with the CPUSA or any meetings with Russian Intelligence officers. However, he did confess to an affair with Jean Tatlock, a fervent Communist who committed suicide during the war – but for those that knew Oppenheimer this revelation was far from startling. Oppenheimer wasn't the first scientist to have an affair with a Communist.

It was difficult for Oppenheimer to conceal that Katherine, his wife, had strong Communist views as her previous husband, Joseph Dallet, had been a member of the CPUSA. He had been killed while fighting in the Spanish Civil War. Katherine was the driving force behind her husband in betraying his country. In the 1930s, as a student at the University of Wisconsin she had flirted with Communism, and during her long association with the CPUSA she was acquainted with several scientists on the *Manhattan Project* who were investigated by the FBI. One was Professor Clarence Hiskey from Chicago who was also a secret member of the All-America Anti-Imperialist League. Hiskey worked in the physics laboratories of the University of Chicago and was co-opted into military service to work on the SAM [Substitute Alloy Metal] project, a deliberately misleading term for uranium. He maintained a notebook and regularly shared its contents with the renowned GRU agent Arthur Adams, codename *Achilles*. On one occasion Hiskey and Adams made a trip to Cleveland where Hiskey introduced him to a friend, another chemical engineer involved on the bomb. The new contact subsequently became *Camp*.

Security clearance for the scientists, engineers and other technical staff on the *Manhattan Project* – which encompassed Los Alamos and other locations, such as the reactor facilities in Oak Ridge in Tennessee and the Hanford plutonium plant in Washington State – had proved onerous given the huge numbers involved. General Groves, in overall command, had insisted that the Counter Intelligence Corps of the US Army, rather than the FBI, be given the responsibility. Oppenheimer was vetted and unanimously given clearance. Edgar Hoover, the FBI chief, mounted his own operation and agents eavesdropped on *Manhattan Project* scientists.

There was no real incriminating evidence but the AEC security board recommended by two-to-one that Oppenheimer's clearance be cancelled. That decision was subsequently ratified by the full membership of the AEC with only one dissention, Professor Henry DeWolf Smyth. Years later, however, this renowned scientist from Los Alamos revealed that he had harboured suspicions of Oppenheimer's guilt.

The result of the hearings shocked Oppenheimer's former colleagues, and the Federation of American Scientists took up his celebrated case. They rallied around the well-liked and charismatic Oppenheimer. One still recalls the strong persona that Oppenheimer so successfully projected towards his staff. 'Everybody worshipped him,' he explained. In the key 'Cowpuncher' meetings – a committee set up by Oppenheimer in May 1945 to discuss the final preparations for the atomic weapons – he demanded the very highest level of professionalism.

After the bombs had been dropped on Hiroshima and Nagasaki Oppenheimer developed an almost mystical personality. One of his closest friends, Haakon Chevalier, the Norwegian writer, committed Communist and languages professor at the University of California, described Oppenheimer as 'the man who would be God'. The physicist certainly enjoyed living up to that image in public.

Despite his persistent denial of contact with any Soviet Intelligence officer, in the Lubyanka archives there is a two-page KGB document written in October 1944 that confirms Oppenheimer's involvement. Marked top-secret, the memo to Lavrenty Beria was sent by Lt General Vsevolod Merkulov, his first deputy who became Minister of State Security in April 1943 with personal control for the management of NKVD agents in America. Penetration into America's key scientific centres was a major priority for Merkulov and he delighted in the success of his agents.

The document reads:

'*To the People's Commissar of Internal Affairs of the USSR [and] General Commissar of State Security*

'Comrade Beria LP.

'*In accordance with your instructions of 29th September 1944, the NKGB continues its work on obtaining more comprehensive information on the state of progress on the uranium problem and its development abroad.*

'*In 1942, one of the leaders of scientific work on uranium in the USA, Professor Oppenheimer, a secret agent in Comrade Browder's network, informed us about the beginning of the work.*

'*At the request of Comrade Kheifets, confirmed by Comrade Browder, he provided assistance in gaining access to this research of several reliable sources we have, including a relative of Comrade Browder.*

'*Due to complications in the operational situation in the USA, the dissolution of the Comintern, and taking into account the clarifications of Comrades Zarubin and Kheifets in the case of Mironov, it seems expedient to break immediately the contacts of the leadership and the activists of the Communist Party of the US with scientists and specialists participating in the work on uranium.*'

Recent events in the US had worried Merkulov. The NKGB for some time had been concerned about the activities of the CPUSA and its outspoken president, Earl Browder. The FBI watched Browder like a hawk and had already contrived a jail sentence over passport irregularities in 1940. Browder had been a successful talent spotter for a number of years. Operating under the codenames *Helmsman* and *Rulevoy*, the head of the CPUSA targeted physicists, chemists and engineers. Imprisoned for vociferously opposing America's entry into the Great War, he had travelled widely, including trips to China with his first wife Katie Harris, an NKVD agent.

Thanks to Browder's efforts several scientists involved in the *Manhattan Project* had secretly joined the CPUSA. In the radio traffic from the US to Moscow, 'Countryman' or 'Countrywoman' denoted CPUSA members. 'Gymnast' referred to membership of the US Young Communist League. Browder had engineered Oppenheimer's first meeting in 1941 with the NKVD officer Gregory Kheifets, who was based in the Consulate in San Francisco. Kheifets, codenamed *Tharon*, had a fruitful meeting. Stalin's decision in 1943 to end the Comintern, now that America and Britain were allies was a good excuse to order members of the CPUSA to cease any further contact with Oppenheimer and other nuclear scientists.

The situation had also taken a bizarre and possibly disastrous turn. An NKVD officer in New York, Lt Colonel Vasili Mironov, wrote a letter to the FBI denouncing several of his fellow officers as intelligence agents, including Vasili Zarubin, the

Second Secretary at the Washington Embassy. Furthermore, Mironov had contacted Moscow Centre denouncing Zarubin as a double agent working for the Germans. The Russians had hastily removed Mironov back to Moscow where he was declared insane and executed.

Taking advice from Zarubin and Kheifets, Merkulov decided that new operating instructions were needed, but given the delicacy of the NKGB's involvement with Oppenheimer he thought it best that Beria be consulted. Not long afterwards Kheifets was recalled to Moscow for several months of debriefing and a dressing down from Beria who was annoyed that the recruitment of nuclear scientists from Berkeley and Los Alamos had slowed. Stalin eventually purged Kheifets in one of his many attempts to rid Soviet Intelligence of its Jewish officers. Katie Harris suffered the same fate.

Although Oppenheimer died an embittered man, in 1963 he had been rehabilitated and presented with the AEC's Enrico Fermi award by the US President Lyndon Johnson. The espionage speculation, however, never went away and there was always a chance that the 'smoking gun' would be uncovered in Moscow.

Oppenheimer had joined the CPUSA in 1937 in a highly secret cell formed by Browder, with each member under NKVD control. This cell provided Moscow with wartime atomic intelligence obtained at the very highest level, and included the legendary *Perseus*. From the outset Oppenheimer insisted on paying his membership and records in Moscow show that these dues totalled $1,800, or $300 a year. The codename *Chester* was often used as Oppenheimer lived in South Chester Avenue, Pasadena.

There is another document in Moscow confirming Oppenheimer's membership of the CPUSA, located in the files of Department S, the special group set up by Stalin to co-ordinate atomic espionage and headed by Lt General Pavel Sudoplatov. The document is 12 pages in total and is dated January 7, 1946. It is titled *'The status of development of the problem of using atomic energy in capitalist countries'* and Beria was among the key people it was distributed to.

Officers within Department S had assembled a complete dossier listing every key scientist in America, Britain, Canada and France – with short biographies – who were instrumental in their respective nuclear programmes. In addition, every nuclear facility had been identified, with its location and purpose noted. Fourth in the listing of American scientists is Robert Oppenheimer with the underlined note *'Secret member of the US Communist Party'*. Oppenheimer was also aware that his Berkeley colleague, Bernard Peters, was under the wing of the NKVD. Peters, the German-born physicist had been drafted into the *Manhattan Project*, and attended underground meetings of the German Communist Party.

The CPUSA cell in which Oppenheimer was a member included a number of scientists from the *Manhattan Project*. His brother Frank was one, working in Berkeley, Oak Ridge and Los Alamos. Others included the Los Alamos physicians

David Hawkins and Edward Condon, the former head of the radiation laboratory at the Massachusetts Institute of Technology and the *Manhattan Project*'s initial deputy co-ordinator.

Condon was an invaluable contact for the NKVD. He had clashed frequently with General Groves over a number of issues at Los Alamos, including staff accommodation. Matters quickly came to a head and Condon left Los Alamos but continued in an advisory capacity from the Berkeley campus in the University of California. In June 1945 Condon was part of a small group of US scientists invited to Moscow as guests of the Russian Academy of Sciences to celebrate a major anniversary. At the last minute Groves decided against the visit and the trip was cancelled.

However, Groves was in no position to prevent Condon's new position in 1945, that of director of the US National Bureau of Standards, America's premier physics institute. Condon excelled in the role and Moscow was pleased. He, like Oppenheimer, was never far from FBI surveillance, but he was prepared to take the necessary risks. The FBI intercepted a delivery to Moscow of 270 books on nuclear physics in 1947 organized by Condon with the help of Dmitry Vinogradov, a Russian acquaintance and NKGB 'illegal'. Unwittingly, Condon was now used as a disinformation channel by the FBI after it turned Vinogradov. The Russian controller for Vinogradov was Andrei Shevchenko, codename *Arseni*, whose real name was Andrei Ivanovich Raina. This agent had arrived in New York in June 1942 to take up a position in the Soviet Purchasing Commission and in 1943 was attached to the Bell Aircraft Corporation's plant at Niagara Falls as the Russian purchasing representative. Raina, highly-regarded and ambitious, was recalled to Moscow in 1946 and in 1947 became chief of the Science and Technical Intelligence department, responsible for the Soviet worldwide scientific espionage.

Condon, like Oppenheimer, had been a subject of intense interest to the FBI in 1947 but no evidence came to light. There were subsequent leaks to several politicians who believed that there was a case for the head of the US Bureau of Standards to answer. Public furore grew and Condon was subsequently investigated by the House Committee on Un-American Activities. Embarrassed by the flood of support for Condon, President Truman openly declared support for the beleaguered physicist.

Two close friends of Oppenheimer were members of the GRU scientific cell run by Arthur Adams. Benjamin and Zelda Miller worked in the nuclear laboratories of the University of Chicago and unbeknown to them they became the focus of a furious row in Moscow between the GRU and the NKVD. In 1943 Stalin had tasked the NKVD with full responsibility for atomic espionage but the GRU resisted passing over control. Finally it was agreed that Adams continue as the Millers' case officer.

Venona, established by the US Army's Signals Security Agency to decypher 2,900 intercepted Soviet diplomatic telegrams transmitted to Moscow between 1940 to 1948 from the Consulates in New York and San Francisco and the Embassy in Washington, was one of America's biggest post-war secrets. On April 16, 1948, the first message was decoded. Many more followed, identifying traffic referring to the

Amtorg Trading Corporation, World Tourists, the Soviet Purchasing Commission and Tass – all fronts for Russian Intelligence. Other decodes identified the NKVD, GRU, Naval GRU and the Soviet Foreign Ministry. By 1952 the American Intelligence services had evidence that 209 GRU and NKVD agents had operated in the United States during the war – and those were only the ones they knew about from *Venona*. Oppenheimer had been mentioned in *Venona*, through the codenames of *Chester*, *Reservation Director* and *Loan Note*, but none referred to his real intelligence role.

All Soviet radio transmissions had run the risk of interception by the Signals Security Agency based at Arlington Hall in Northern Virginia, especially after scorched but readable codebooks relating to radio traffic had been discovered in June 1941 in the Russian Consulate in Petsamo, Finland. Initially the Army declined to share its decoding skills with the Navy and Airforce. It was only in 1952 that the director of the CIA, General Bedell Smith, was informed. From 1943 to 1946 US Army operators had intercepted 400 messages transmitted just from San Francisco to Moscow – many of the 172 telegrams decoded related to events at Los Alamos.

Cryptanalysts Meredith Gardner and Gene Grabeel, a Virginia schoolteacher, worked on the programme until it closed in 1980. The use of the term *Venona* did not begin until 1961; in earlier years codenames used included *Gardner material, Bride* and *Drug*. The British collaborated extensively. As *Venona* grew the FBI couldn't cope with the extra surveillance necessary to investigate and monitor every suspect.

Prosecutions were few. In court, the prosecution would have squirmed in their seats if a defending lawyer had got wind of the fact that Roosevelt had personally agreed with the Russian Ambassador that Soviet diplomats in wartime be granted permission to use US Army facilities in the Pentagon to transmit messages to Moscow. NKVD agents availed themselves of this very kind offer extended by an ally. Roosevelt even promised that the Americans would not interfere or listen to any of the transmissions.

Venona itself was penetrated. Fluent in Russian and born in Egypt of Russian parents William Weisband was hired by the Signals Security Agency in 1942 for gainful employment in the Soviet department. His codename in the very *Venona* traffic he was intercepting was *Zveno*, the Russian word for 'link'. Later arrested for espionage, Weisband denied all charges of spying and was never prosecuted.

The transmission from New York on December 2, 1944, was dynamite – if only Arlington Hall could have read it at the time. Names of prominent scientists working for the Russians and involved in the *Manhattan Project* were included, all in code.

* * *

The majority of the 15 British scientists that had arrived by liner in December 1943 quickly earned the respect of their new American colleagues. The *MSN Papers*, the product of the work on gaseous diffusion conducted by Fuchs and Peierls, were highly valued by scientists from the Kellex Corporation, their American counterparts. Even today these papers remain classified on both sides of the Atlantic, but most of the set are in Moscow's atomic archives.

Apart from the work in Canada, much of the independent British wartime nuclear research was now suspended. America was now in the driver's seat with Britain the junior partner. Despite initiating the design of a nuclear weapon, British scientists had feared that their pioneering efforts would be ignored.

However, in Los Alamos, *Camp Y*, the group from Britain expanded to 17 scientists.

Some would be made welcome at *Camp X*, the uranium separation plant at Oak Ridge, near Chattanooga, Tennessee. *Camp X* was a huge site, 300 square miles, with 70,000 engineers and labourers constructing electromagnetic and diffusion plants as well as a graphite unit. On a trip back to England Mark Oliphant, held in high esteem by the Americans, reported that the electromagnetic method for separating uranium offered greater advantages in the short term as it was cheaper and more efficient. He suggested that in Britain gaseous diffusion research should be discontinued.

General Groves imposed strict limitations on the movement of the British scientists. At Oak Ridge none had permits for X-10, the site of the nuclear reactor, or K-25, the gaseous diffusion facility. At Y-12, the electromagnetic separation plant on Poplar Creek, some visits were allowed. Bohr was only able to view K-25 from the perimeter. At K-27, another facility under construction, entry was also forbidden. Even to this day the British are barred from the K-25 site, now a weapons component plant, where in 1944–1945 the gaseous diffusion membranes were fabricated and the uranium separated for the Hiroshima bomb. In the Lubyanka archives are carefully drawn diagrams of many of the facilities at Oak Ridge, including the nuclear reactor itself provided by a senior American scientist.

Kearton, the ICI scientist and a member of the New York team, reported to London details of a disturbing evening spent with Professor Harold Urey, the Columbia physicist who acted as liaison scientist. Over drinks at Urey's club on March 25, 1944, Kearton was informed that it was difficult to see how co-operation with Kellex on the gaseous diffusion project could continue, as any further experimental work would be of little use to the *Manhattan Project*. In a litany of complaints Urey had related to Kearton that Groves had privately accused the British of forever relying on the Americans to provide the lead. The Americans were annoyed that the British, despite their ambitious plans outlined in the *Maud Report*, had not invested in any large-scale plants, or even any pilot separation facilities in the United Kingdom apart from *P6* in Wales. There had been disquiet, too, on the slower than expected progress in the Montreal Laboratory and the construction of a nuclear reactor in Canada. Kearton concluded to London: *'Groves was becoming more strongly isolationist in sentiment and he seemed to be more in the saddle than ever. He has dominated the Washington committees to whom he reported.'*

Groves' views couldn't have been further from reality. Every British scientist proved his worth. Fuchs and Peierls provided two-thirds of the combined team at Los Alamos that handled the hydrodynamics in T Division, making the implosion development possible. Frisch, head of the critical assembly group in G Division, would be long remembered for the *Dragon* experiments, a series of tests determining the quantity of U-235 necessary for the Hiroshima bomb. Sir Geoffrey Taylor correctly predicted the size and extent of the mushroom cloud while Penney, who was part of the survey team that went to Japan, calculated the actual strength of the explosion. All members of the British mission at Los Alamos took part in the Trinity Test, either as observers or as participants.

The inclusion of Bohr in the mission was not favoured by Churchill. The Danish underground had smuggled Bohr, the Nobel Prize winner in 1922 for physics, out to Sweden in September 1943 and he was flown to Britain in an RAF Mosquito. He almost died on the trip, unable to operate his oxygen mask in the unpressurised bomb bay. In his short time in England before embarking to the US he had stayed in Michael Perrin's country cottage in the Fair Mile outside Henley-on-Thames where he whiled away his time whittling chunks of wood into ornaments, one of his many talents. Churchill disliked Bohr intensely, concerned that Bohr's long-standing friendships with German and Russian scientists could compromise *Tube Alloys*. Furthermore, Bohr's unauthorized trip to the White House several months later to meet Roosevelt had further angered the British Prime Minister who had not been given prior warning of the visit.

The president of the Royal Society, Sir Henry Dale, had written to Lord Cherwell hoping that Churchill would take a more positive attitude to Bohr despite his *'mild philosophical vagueness of expression and his inarticulate whisper'*. Churchill wasn't impressed by Dale's well-intentioned intervention and in a letter to Lord Halifax, Britain's Ambassador in Washington, he wrote: *'It seems to me that Bohr ought to be confined, or at any rate made to see he is very near the edge of mortal crimes. I did not like the man when you showed him to me, with his hair all over his head, at Downing Street. Let me have by return your views about this man. I do not like it at all.'*

At the end of the war, when Bohr returned to Copenhagen, Department S sent two officers to Denmark to ascertain exactly how much Bohr knew about the British and American work. Dr Nikolai Terletski, a physicist seconded to Department S, asked the technical questions, accompanied by Colonel Lev Vasilevsky, the former NKVD chief in Mexico City. Meetings with Bohr took place over November 14–16, 1945, but proved a disappointment, especially the session at the Russian Embassy. Bohr went through the motions, under the instructions of MI6. A kidnap plan was later hatched by Department S, but then abandoned.

The greatest secrecy in the United States was reserved for the Hanford site acquired in February 1943. Hanford had large supplies of electricity and water and offered a mild and dry climate. Its remoteness also helped if radiation leaked. Construction began the following month under the management of the Army Corps of Engineers and E I DuPont de Nemours Corp. Some 50,000 workers were hired. Over the next three years more than 1,000 buildings and the town of Richland were created. Nine reactors were to be built between 1944 and 1963. B reactor was the first to go critical, in September 1944; D and F reactors followed in 1945, as did the T plant, the plutonium reprocessing facility. Groves imposed strict press censorship and staff were not allowed to keep private diaries or engineering notes. Locals were encouraged to believe Hanford was a germ warfare plant or a fuel facility for secret high-powered aircraft. No foreign scientist was permitted to visit Hanford, under the express orders of Groves. Accelerated production schedules meant that little attention was given to waste and by-products. Only in the early 1960s did the Government admit that large amounts of radioactive iodine had been released in the atmosphere, contaminating rivers and pasture for hundreds of square miles.

By early July 1945 the Americans had produced enough Pu-239 and U-235 from Hanford and Oak Ridge respectively to manufacture three atom bombs, but Groves and the FBI knew full well that the entire *Manhattan Project* must be compromised given the huge numbers of personnel involved. That conclusion was well founded. In 1940 the number of NKVD officers in the United States had reached 18, growing to 40 by 1944. The FBI would only discover many years later that the Soviets had established a permanent meeting place right under their noses in Santa Fe, a short distance from Los Alamos, effectively a 'post box' for collection by couriers. GRU numbers had also grown under the command of Colonel Melkishev operating under the guise of Vice Consul in New York. Using the cover names of *Feodor, Mikhailov* and *Malin*, he personally ran a GRU cell at Oak Ridge until the Americans threw him out of the country in 1945.

The first intelligence shock was of seismic proportions, but emanated from Canada, not America. In September 1945 the GRU cypher officer Lt Igor Gouzenko, based in the Ottawa Embassy, defected and was on the run for his life with his family. He had received the fright of his life when he personally decoded a cable from Moscow to find that GRU headquarters had named him as a possible double agent. Moscow soon realised their mistake in sending the cable but, by this time, Gouzenko had admitted to the Royal Canadian Mountain Police the extent of Soviet espionage in Canada as well as the US. He named Dr Alan Nunn-May, the British scientist then working in Montreal, as a GRU source, recruited by Jan Chernyak, codename *Jan*, specifically charged by Moscow to infiltrate the Cavendish Laboratory at Cambridge.

Nearly all the Cavendish staff involved with *Tube Alloys* had departed for Montreal in December 1942. In Canada Nunn-May was assigned Senior Lt Pavel Angelov, *Baxter*, as his controller. Colonel Nikolai Zabotin, the military attaché at the Ottawa Embassy, ran the entire GRU network. Aware that a Russian 'We

Tricks' or murder squad would try to find Gouzenko, the Canadians hid him and his family from sight. Gouzenko fingered several spy rings, including nuclear intelligence from the Montreal Laboratory. Professor Isidor Halperin, *Bacon*, was a huge loss to the Russians as was Durnford-Smith, *Badeau*, a radioactivity specialist. Overlooked by British Intelligence, much to its regret, was Halperin's address book containing the names of Klaus Fuchs, who had been interned in Canada at the onset of war, and Fuch's sister, Kristel, married to Robert Heinemann, an active member of the CPUSA. If that address book had been scrutinised Fuchs could have been uncovered some years earlier than he was.

The Konsomol, or association of young Communists, was Gouzenko's training ground before attending the School of Engineering in Moscow. Recruited into the GRU he was posted to Canada in 1943. Gouzenko's defection led to 39 suspects being identified. The Kellock-Taschereau Royal Commission of Inquiry confirmed the extraordinary level of Russian infiltration in Montreal and the nuclear research centre in Ottawa. Also compromised was the British pilot atomic pile under construction at Chalk River, north-west of Pembroke, codename *NRX*.

New identities were provided for Gouzenko and his family. In September 1946 they were moved to a house on a highly restricted area of *Camp X* in Whitby, officially known as the Oshawa Wireless Station, a vital listening post under joint Canadian and British control. Later the family moved to Mississauga. Moscow raged. Zabotin was recalled to Moscow, tried and executed. Russia's Ambassador to Canada, Georgi Zaroubin, was recalled – there is no record of his fate.

Edgar Hoover wrote to Matthew Connelly, the private secretary to Truman at the White House on the matter, on September 12, 1945.

'The RCMP has advised that they have obtained positive information that the Soviets have an extensive espionage network in Canada. The Soviets have made the obtaining of complete information regarding the atomic bomb the number one project of Soviet espionage and such data must be obtained before the end of this year. The RCMP report that there is considerable loose talk in the office of the Soviet military attaché in Ottawa regarding the 'next war' which the Soviet Union will have with the Anglo-American nations.

'With regard to the atomic bomb project, Dr Allen Nunn-May, a British scientist assigned to the McGill University laboratory in Canada, has been identified as a paid Soviet spy of long standing. May spent some time at the Metallurgical Laboratory in Chicago, working on the separation process for uranium and is well informed as to the methods of setting up uranium piles or lattices.

'The FBI has furnished this information to General Groves. It has also been definitely determined by the RCMP that Dr May, in the first part of July 1945, advised the office of the military attaché in Ottawa that the US Navy was using radar-controlled projectiles against Japanese suicide planes and that the tubes and batteries within the projectile were furnished with a special plastic protective

device against the firing, which the Americans have not furnished to the British.
'The Canadian situation is being closely followed and any additional information
will be brought to the attention of the President and yourself.
'With assurances of my highest esteem and best regards.
Sincerely yours. J Edgar Hoover.'

Nunn-May had already returned to England as Reader in Physics at Kings College, London. He was arrested on February 5, 1946, some five months after Gouzenko's defection, and taken to the fourth floor of Shell-Mex House to be interrogated by Leonard Burt, Deputy Commissioner of the Metropolitan Police and former Head of Special Branch, and by Major Spooner of MI5. Nunn-May did not confess and was interrogated again on February 20, this time at Savile Row police station. He was subsequently jailed for treachery, escaping the death sentence that many thought he deserved before acquiring a teaching position in Ghana.

The defection in 1945 of the 'Blonde Spy Queen' to the FBI, as she was later called in the press, confirmed that the Russians had penetrated right to the heart of American Government. Elizabeth Bentley provided details of agents in the Pentagon, the Treasury, the OSS, the forerunner of the CIA, and the White House. While she was in hiding, fearing for her life, the FBI systematically rounded up the networks, a disaster that set Soviet Intelligence back a generation.

Vassar-educated from up-state New York, Bentley had joined the Harlem section of the CPUSA while working in an administrative position at Columbia University. Early promise led to the role of agit-prop, the propagandist director in the organisation. Working at the cash-starved Home Relief Bureau and living in Greenwich Village, she became a 'Steeled Bolshevik', fully committed to the cause. Bentley's espionage career grew after meeting Joseph Eckhart, an NKVD agent, a Lithuanian who purchased American aircraft on behalf of the Russian Government for shipment to Spanish loyalists via Mexico during the Spanish Civil War.

After Eckhart was recalled to Moscow in 1938 Bentley, codenamed *Smart Girl* and *Myrna*, became involved with the Russian-born Jacob Golos, the head of World Tourists, who ran a clutch of agents in New York and Washington. They became lovers. Golos, a heavy smoker, suffered several heart attacks so Bentley took over the management of the networks. Following the death of Golos Bentley fell out with the NKVD and exposed 80 agents upon her defection. None were convicted as the Americans did not want to risk disclosing the *Venona* operation.

Colonel Vladimir Barkovsky, as assistant *rezident* in Washington, was subsequently tasked in 1949 with re-establishing the networks that had been so devastated in New York, Washington and Baltimore. His network also included scientists working in the universities, as well as a prime source at the Lawrence Livermore laboratory in California. He often worked closely with William Fisher, otherwise known as Colonel Rudolf Abel who used the codename *Mark*. Using the cover of a Brooklyn artist Abel was finally discovered by the FBI after nine years of espi onage. He was exchanged for Gary Powers, the pilot of the U-2 spy plane shot down in 1960 over Russia.

To this day Barkovsky seethes at any mention of Golos, codenamed *Sound* and *Zvuk*, and the freedom he allowed to Bentley. Born into a Jewish family in the Ukraine, Golos, aka Jacob Rasin, had been committed to a Siberian labour camp after his parents had emigrated to the United States. Golos had escaped to China in 1917 and travelled to San Francisco, where he received medical training. Returning to Russia in the early 1920s Golos became an intelligence recruit. Back in the US he joined the CPUSA, editing its New York newspaper *Novy Mir*. In 1927 party funds were used to set up World Tourists, ostensibly to promote both trade and tourism between the US and the USSR, in reality a cover for the NKVD. The FBI, concerned about World Tourists, managed to close it down on a registration technicality – but Golos went on to establish the US Service and Shipping Corporation, another front.

Bentley had provided the FBI with the names of the operatives in her networks. Most damaging were her disclosures of the agents active in the White House run by Nathan Gregory Silvermaster, codename *Robert* or *Pal*, and his wife Helen, *Dora*. The Silvermaster's had run 35 agents, operating mainly in Washington. Harry Dexter White, *Jurist*, assistant to US Treasury Secretary Henry Morgenthau, provided details on the funding of the atomic bomb project. He was a well-placed agent, reporting in August 1944 that Roosevelt was confident of victory in the forthcoming presidential election. Another report to Moscow that month included details of a visit to the Normandy beachhead with Morgenthau for discussions with American and British commanders, initiated by Roosevelt. *Jurist* lived in dread of disclosure. Interrogated but not prosecuted, he died unexpectedly in 1948. Another White House aide supplying intelligence was Samuel Roseman. In the US State Department Alger Hiss, *Ales*, had been active for some years. Unknowingly Roosevelt was identified as *Kapitan* in radio transmissions from the Washington Embassy. Details of overseas trips, including one to China, made by the Deputy President Henry Wallace were conveyed to Moscow. Silvermaster had extended his reach to beyond Washington. For a short while he was in contact with Edward Condon, the physicist.

Security was also compromised at the OSS. Maurice Halperin, *Hare*, provided details of US State Department cables. Other agents included Duncan Chaplin Lee, *Koch*, the assistant to 'Wild' Bill Donovan, the head of OSS; Donald Niven Wheeler, *Izra*; and Helen Tenney, *Muse*. Donovan was given the code *Radio Announcer* when his name was mentioned in radio transmissions.

Another Washington ring, operated by Victor Perlo, *Raider*, was equally active. Perlo was an economist in a number of Government agencies, including the War Production Board and the Treasury Department. He was a prodigious supplier of highly-classified secrets and reported to Bentley. His ring members included

Plumb, *Ted* and *Mayor*. A well-known CBS correspondent, *Yun*, was also a regular purveyor.

First Gouzenko, next Bentley; but the Americans were thunderstruck when in October 1949 *Venona* finally uncovered Fuchs who, in turn, had identified Harry Gold as his courier. Gold, *Gus*, or sometimes *Goose* in *Venona* traffic, was arrested in May 1950. At one stage the authorities believed that *Gus* referred to Arthur Phineas Weber, an employee of the Kellex Corporation in New York who had worked closely with the British scientists in 1944. The arrest of Gold, run first by NKVD officer Anatoli Yatskov and then by Filip Sarychev, led to further arrests. US Intelligence agent Robert Lamphere, intrigued by the frequent use of *Calibre* in *Venona* traffic from New York, now knew the codename belonged to David Greenglass, an enlisted man at Los Alamos during the war. In October 1943, the 9812th Special Engineer Detachment [SED] began to supply technical personnel to the laboratory. By the end of 1943, 475 SEDs were onsite, rising to 1,823 two years later – many were young scientists and engineers fresh out of university.

Gold was well paid by his Soviet controller, often $1,000 a delivery. When Yatskov bade farewell to Gold in December 1946 after being recalled to Moscow, he handed over a bonus of $300 and one last mission – a strange assignment that would involve travelling to France.

A CIA file revealed more: *'Gold was to meet a Frenchman at a subway stop in Paris. The man was to approach Gold and give him certain info that Gold would then take to England and hand over to a subsequent contact. Gold has advised that he believed that this European assignment had to do with collecting atomic information and that it would maybe involve more than one European trip. Gold has also advised that on at least two occasions Yatskov told him he'd introduce Gold to a young woman whose husband was in the US Army and would perform the function of doing leg work between Yatskov and Gold. Gold recalled that she lived in upper Manhattan, in the neighborhood of Lexington Avenue, and she may have been Russian born or of Russian descent, although Gold never did meet her.'*

The Russians were desperate to spirit David Greenglass out of the US, given that he could unveil to the FBI the details of a Los Alamos cell. An exit plan was devised that involved using the military attaché of the Polish Consulate in New York. Ludwig Zagorsky, an officer in Polish Intelligence, had since 1944 been a member of the NKVD and was hugely experienced in covert operations. Everyone in the Russian Embassy in Washington and the Consulates in New York and San Francisco were under intense FBI surveillance given the *Venona* decodings. Therefore it was left to Zagorsky to collect Greenglass and drive him across the border into Mexico where an armed special squad from the Embassy in Mexico City would collect him and arrange immediate transportation to Moscow. However the plan went awry and the FBI caught up with Greenglass on June 15, 1950. He quickly confessed to passing nuclear secrets to the Russians, including the details of the bomb's firing mechanism. With his own cover now blown the FBI threw Zagorsky out of the country and for the rest of his life, until his death in Germany in 1984, he was prohibited entry into the US.

Greenglass now implicated Julius Rosenberg, his brother-in-law. For some days the FBI carefully watched Rosenberg and Ethel, his wife, and on July 17 both were arrested. In *Venona* Rosenberg was *Antenna* and *Liberal,* and was first mentioned in traffic on September 21, 1944. Two *Venona* messages implicated Ethel.

From September 1940 to February 1945 Rosenberg had worked in the US Army Signal Corps as a radio engineer before running his own business, G and R Engineering Company, in Monroe Street, New York City. The previous occupier of this apartment was David Keppel, whose father was a former Dean of Columbia University and President of the Carnegie Foundation. Keppel worked as a geologist at Gulf Oil Corporation and the FBI believed that there existed a possibility *'that he may have had some connection with Rosenberg that was not entirely innocent'.*

The CIA recorded the depth of the Russian atomic espionage network in a document dated December 26, 1950.

'Dr Klaus Fuchs' espionage confession in England has led to the identification and arrest of various persons in the United States engaged in atomic espionage on behalf of the Soviets. The FBI and CIA are still pursuing various leads in order to track down certain foreign contacts of Fuchs and to obtain documentation and evidence of assistance in the conviction of those individuals presently under arrest.

'Fuchs passed his information to Dr Harry Gold who was directly in touch with Soviet Intelligence officers and acted as a cut-out to them. Another of Gold's agents was an individual named David Greenglass who also furnished atomic intelligence reports. Greenglass' sister is the wife of one Julius Rosenberg. Greenglass also furnished information to Rosenberg. The relationship between Gold and Rosenberg is not entirely clear. Apparently Rosenberg, after recruiting his brother-in-law, gave him part of a box top, retaining the other half for himself. Gold later presented himself to Greenglass with the piece of box top from Rosenberg for identification.

'Greenglass has stated that when Fuchs was arrested Rosenberg advised him to leave the country. On the arrest of Harry Gold, Rosenberg pointed out to Greenglass that Gold had been in touch with him. He insisted that Greenglass leave the country and furnished him with money and certain instructions for re-contacting Soviet Intelligence. Greenglass did not leave the country, was arrested by the FBI and confessed. Rosenberg was also arrested but has not confessed to date.'

Also unmasked were the past clandestine activities of NKVD agents Anatoli Yatskov and Semyon Semyonov in New York. *'Gold has advised that from 1940 to the departure of Semyon Semyonov, whom he knew as* Sak, *Semenov [Semyonov] had been his superior in the Soviet espionage apparatus for which he worked. After the departure of Semyonov from the US he was taken over by Yakovlev [Yatskov], whom he knew as* John, *who continued to run him until 1946,'* says a CIA report

277

dated June 9, 1951. Semyonov was awarded the Order of the Red Banner in October 1949 for his efforts on atomic intelligence.

Theodore Hall, at 19 the youngest scientist to be employed at Los Alamos, was one of four young Harvard men hired personally by Robert Oppenheimer. Hall was an easy recruit, reporting to Lona Cohen, one of Russia's best. At Harvard, Hall's room-mate was Saville Sax, identified as *Star* in *Venona*, who died young. Meredith Gardner, the cryptanalyst, identified *Mlad* and *Youngster* as Hall in late 1949. At that time Hall still worked for the KGB, meeting Vladimir Barkovsky, then established in New York. Never prosecuted, the British surprisingly allowed Hall to enter England in 1961 to live in Cambridge, working at the Cavendish. A *Venona* transmission on November 12, 1944, referred to the recruitment of Hall.

Late one night in March 1943 a scientist from the radiation laboratory at the University of California in Berkeley had visited the home of Steve Nelson, a courier for the Russians and a leading party member, whose real name was Steve Mesarosh. Investigated as *The* Scientist X *Case* by the Committee on Un-American Activities in August 1949, an FBI officer gave evidence. *'After Nelson had greeted* Scientist X *the latter stated that he had some information that he thought Nelson could use. He read to Nelson a complicated formula that Nelson copied down.* Scientist X *gave as his reason for asking Nelson to copy it down the fact that the formula was in the hand-writing of some other person and that he,* Scientist X, *had to return the formula to the University of California radiation laboratories in the morning. The radiation labora-tories were engaged in vital work in the development of the atomic bomb.'*

In an open park by the St Francis Hospital in San Francisco, the FBI had observed a package being passed to Peter Ivanov, the Soviet Vice-Consul in San Francisco. Several days later Vasili Zarubin was also observed entering Nelson's home. *Scientist X* was identified and interrogated by the committee in secret session, but he denied all charges. Charges had been made that Dr Joseph Weinberg of Berkeley had passed atomic secrets to Nelson in San Francisco. Special FBI agents Murray, Zindle and Rathman from the *Manhattan Project* operated surveillance on Weinberg and had seen Nelson talking to other Berkeley scientists, including Frank Oppenheimer. The Russian Consulate in San Francisco became a major intelligence-collecting centre for Berkeley and Los Alamos. Many scientists were just as useful to the Russians after the war.

Some were fearful of discovery and fled as the FBI net closed in. In Oak Ridge Oscar Seborer had been part of a large SED detachment and later he became an accomplished atomic weapons expert and rocket specialist. He and his brother Jack disappeared on a trip to Europe in June 1951 and turned up in Moscow. Oscar was accommodated in an apartment block reserved for foreigners, where he lives still. He was awarded the 'Order of Lenin'. Jack became a confidant and drinking buddy of the defector Donald Maclean. In a similar Moscow apartment resides *DelMar*, the chemist from Oak Ridge who was so codenamed by his GRU controller after the *De*

Mar horse racing track in San Diego. *DelMar* worked on the electronic uranium isotope separators at the Y-12 facility in Oak Ridge. These were called 'race tracks' by the scientists because the uranium beams ran in circles.

In the case of Tsien Hsue-shen, the Chinese-born rocket expert and an American pioneer of jet-propulsion, the FBI believed it had incriminating evidence, but not enough, however, to prosecute. At the California Institute of Technology in the 1930s he had perfected his skills under the legendary eye of Professor Theodore von Karman. In the last days of the war Hsue-shen was a member of the *Lusty Project*, a group of American rocket experts who arrived in Kochel, the German experimental rocket centre. The FBI interrogated him in 1950 on an accusation of scientific espionage for the Soviet Union. He and his family left Los Angeles in September 1955, bound for China where in the years to come he would become the father of its ballistic-missile programme. As a young man the NKVD had recruited Hsue-shen and he was a member of the same scientific cell that included Robert Oppenheimer. For a short period Vladimir Barkovsky was one of his handlers in 1949, who ranked Hsue-shen very highly amongst an elite group of scientists supplying details of American technology.

* * *

Robert Oppenheimer had convened a crucial meeting at Berkeley in the summer of 1942 to hear a presentation from Edward Teller. The very select audience included Hans Bethe, the German scientist, and Robert Serber, a key member of the design team that would produce the Hiroshima bomb. Teller spoke on the possibility of a fusion bomb, thermonuclear, which he called SUPER – a weapon with even greater explosive intensity than a fission device. Teller was convinced that SUPER was viable.

He later related in 1996 in Dubna, Russia's scientific capital, to an attentive audience of Soviet and American nuclear scientists a conversation he had with Oppenheimer on August 15, 1945, after the Japanese surrender. 'Oppenheimer came to my office,' he said, 'and told me in a friendly but very determined way that the war was over and to stop work on the hydrogen bomb. To my mind this was very unwelcome news, but I could do nothing about it. The general opinion of people involved in atomic explosives after the nuclear raids on Japan was enough is enough, and possibly even too much.'

Teller thought it futile to argue and quit Los Alamos to teach and further his research in Chicago. The prospects for SUPER were discussed again at a four-day debate in Los Alamos in April 1946. Again the decision went against Teller. America did not want an H-bomb. Only after Russia exploded its first atomic bomb in August 1949 did SUPER top the agenda and Teller return to Los Alamos.

'I was afraid of the possibility of the Soviet Union getting ahead of the United

States in the military application of science,' Teller continued in his Dubna speech. 'After World War II the democracies demobilised, but Stalin's empire did not. With my Hungarian origin and an interest in the Soviet Union that I have never lost, I considered more power in the hands of Moscow as a real threat. I might add that events in the Soviet Union got an emotional emphasis when Stalin jailed my good friend the excellent Lev Landau. I had known him in Leipzig and Copenhagen. I was pushed to the conclusion that Stalin's Communism was not much better than the Nazi dictatorship of Hitler. I felt strongly that scientific and technical developments must go ahead at full speed. Political considerations should not interfere and should not slow down our work, particularly if one is working for a Government as sharply different from any dictatorship as the Government of the United States.'

Truman agreed to the H-bomb programme in January 1950 but errors in key calculations led to a setback. Norris Bradbury, the Los Alamos director, prevented further development until some experiments planned for the spring of 1951 were conducted.

These were worrying days for Teller, who often clashed with both his colleagues and the authorities. 'A few hours after the test, but before the results were in, Ernest Lawrence and I went for a swim in the lagoon at the Eniwetok Atoll in the Pacific. I told Ernest, who later ran the Lawrence Livermore laboratory in California, that I was worried about the results. Ernest bet me $5 that the answers would be positive. Early next morning I received news that the experiment had been a success but I was cautioned about telling anyone for a few hours. When, the same morning, Ernest sat in a car to be driven to a plane leaving the test site, I ran and caught him in his car and happily gave him my $5. I think that was the greatest security violation I have ever committed.'

In Princeton the General Advisory Commission [GAC], chaired by Oppenheimer and which reported to the Atomic Energy Commission, met in urgent session to consider the results of Teller's experiments. Teller had primed Oppenheimer the day before. Bradbury was again negative on the H-bomb project, as was his deputy David Froman. Also against was Carson Mark, the Canadian who had been part of the wartime British team at Los Alamos, now the head of the physics department. Frustrated and annoyed, Teller was allowed only to address the GAC for 20 minutes. However, to his complete surprise Oppenheimer gave Teller his full support, and *Mike*, the codename for SUPER, went forward.

Despite all his involvement Teller declined to witness America's first H-bomb test in the Pacific on November 1, 1952, preferring to remain at Lawrence Livermore. Despite the security blackout Teller was kept abreast of the test – 'Fortunately my friend David Griggs, an expert in seismology, told me that the shock from the nuclear explosion could be readily observed on the Berkeley seismograph located not many miles from Livermore. So at the appointed time I was staring at the little green dot whose motion would indicate the arrival in Berkeley of the earthquake wave. The time of the explosion came and went. Of course I saw nothing because the shock would take 15 to 20 minutes to travel under the Pacific Ocean. Indeed, with the proper delay, I saw the green dot exercise a dance. All our predictions turned out to be correct. Los Alamos had strict security rules and I had no code to communicate. So I sent a wire to Elizabeth Graves, wife of the physicist in charge, saying 'It's a boy!' I was highly pleased to hear that this was the first notice of success received in Los Alamos. The participants in the Pacific station had to get the proper clearance together with the proper coding and decoding, so my method of communication beat the official one by several hours – I was very pleased by that.'

Klaus Fuchs, who had supplied the NKGB with the results of the Trinity Test in 1945, had been invited to attend the Los Alamos meeting on SUPER in April 1946. He had already given Moscow mathematical calculations regarding the formation of lithium and tritium as well as a schematic diagram of a fusion process unit. Two months later he would pass to his controller a sensational 19-page report he had written in Los Alamos for US and British consumption entitled *'Analysis of Penney's data for the blast at Hiroshima and Nagasaki'*. This was a comparison made by the British scientist on the TNT equivalent for both explosions, estimated by others at 15,000 tons of TNT and 90,000 tons respectively. Fuchs' critique agreed with the Hiroshima figure, but he argued that 50,000 tons was nearer the mark for Nagasaki.

That same year the McMahon Act in the US put paid to further collaboration with the British, such was the animosity towards them forcibly expressed by General Groves and others. The Americans deemed it prudent to allow only three areas of co-operation – the Declassification conference, the holding of three joint conferences on health and safety relating to radiation protection, and the setting up of a unit that would detect remote explosions if Russia ever developed its own nuclear capability. To say the British scientific community was miffed would be an understatement given it had made the entire running in *Tube Alloys* during the early years of the war. Some dispensation was allowed, however, and four scientists from Los Alamos were given CIA clearance to continue a liaison. One formed a strong friendship with Lt Commander Eric Welsh and Michael Perrin, and assisted in the defection to the West of a Russian physicist.

Washington was the venue for Declassification to assess the large volume of highly secret documents that had been part of the joint atomic bomb project. Declassification began on December 1, 1947, at the Atomic Energy Commission. Perrin's office in London had cabled in advance that the three-man British delegation needed two private rooms and the use of a large safe and a screwdriver. The safe had to be delivered with its door open so the group could use the screwdriver to set its own combination. MI5 and the CIA later reflected on the wisdom of Britain's choice of delegates. Donald Maclean as Britain's Washington representa-

281

tive at the Atomic Energy Commission had been an obvious choice. So too was Rudolf Peierls from the University of Birmingham, who had with Otto Frisch in 1940 produced the *Frisch-Peierls Memorandum* outlining to an initially sceptical British Government that only a small amount of U-235 was necessary to manufacture a nuclear weapon. The third member was Klaus Fuchs. Of the three, Moscow controlled two. In addition, the FBI later had grave doubts about Peierls. After the arrest of Fuchs in 1950 the FBI wanted to interrogate Peierls but were unable to as he was a British citizen.

With the Declassification process completed Fuchs visited the Metallugical Laboratory in Chicago as well as other nuclear centres to renew past Los Alamos acquaintances. He saw Hans Bethe, Victor Weisskopf, Philip Morrison, Richard Feynman, Walter Zinn and George Placzek, the Canadian who had stayed on at Los Alamos at the end of the war to become the first post-war division leader of the theoretical division. On his return to Harwell in Britain Fuchs gathered his new material for Aleksandr Feklisov, his Soviet NKGB case officer from the Embassy.

In March 1948 Moscow received its largest ever package from Fuchs. Included were the projected dimensions of both American and British H-bombs and an extensive description of the fusion reaction of deuterium and tritium atoms. Also in the package was a description of the implosion principle, patented by Fuchs and the Hungarian scientist John von Neumann at Los Alamos in 1946. The Armaments Research Establishment, the secret weapons establishment at Fort Halstead near Sevenoaks, England, became a veritable gold mine for Fuchs. He had established a strong working relationship with Bill Penney who in 1947 had been tasked to build Britain's H-bomb. Penney selected 35 of his top scientific staff to begin work, isolating them from other employees but, unfortunately, not from Fuchs.

Such a monumental intelligence acquisition from Fuchs was reported to Stalin, Molotov, Beria and Boris Vannikov, who had taken over from Beria some of the responsibility in running the Soviet nuclear effort. Kurchatov immediately flew to Arzamas, the secret Russian nuclear weapon design centre, to brief Khariton, Zeldovich, Frank-Kamenetsky and Tamm on the Fuchs material. More clarification was needed and Feklisov received an urgent coded cable in London on May 28, 1948, to ascertain whether the H-bomb remained just a theory or under development. Feklisov met with Fuchs in London and asked for the names of the scientists working on the H-bomb and their locations. Another physicist, an American, had in 1947 provided more H-bomb research to the Soviets. He also provided information on using a uranium bomb as a fuse with deuterium, tritium and lithium to trigger a thermonuclear explosion.

With additional documents from London, Stalin and the Council of Ministers were now prompted to proceed with Russia's own H-bomb. On June 10, 1948 Stalin agreed to proceed at full speed.

In the White House in the same year Admiral Roscoe Hillenkoetter, the first head of the CIA, reported to Truman that the Russians would probably only develop a uranium bomb by the mid-1950s. Since June 1949 the British Embassy in Washington had been alive with rumours that a scientist would shortly be uncovered for passing nuclear secrets to the Russians and that Peierls and Fuchs were on the shortlist. In Los Alamos there was near panic, its director insisting on a full report of the activities of the 29 British scientists and politicians, including their wives, and two Canadians that had worked in or visited the facility during wartime and in the years thereafter.

In October 1949 the FBI was in a position to officially inform Kim Philby, the newly arrived member of MI6 who was the British liaison officer for both the FBI and CIA, that Fuchs was the traitor. *Venona* had decoded two Soviet cyphers sent from Moscow to New York in February 1944 confirming Fuchs as having the code-names of *Rest* and *Charles*. Philby cabled London, but now had a major dilemma on his hands. As a matter of urgency he met his controller Anatoli Gromov, otherwise known as Colonel Anatoli Gorsky, whom he had dealt with in London during the war. In Moscow the intelligence chiefs debated long and hard about spiriting Fuchs away but decided against it. The physicist had enjoyed a spying career spanning nearly nine years, twice the average for other contacts. They decided to let Fuchs fend for himself as Philby had informed them on the inevitability that *Venona* would soon uncover further names.

Understandably the Americans were furious that the naturalised British scientist might have compromised the secrets of Los Alamos. Within months their worst fears were realised as Fuchs confessed to a spying career that began in the physics laboratory in the University of Birmingham in 1941.

At Fuchs' trial William Skarden, the chief MI5 investigator, stated that the first interrogation was on December 21, 1949. That statement was untrue. Several months earlier the interrogation of Fuchs in Harwell had begun, in complete secret. Skarden was worried that Fuchs would abscond and he needed more time to drag the full truth from the Harwell scientist.

In the autumn, Fuchs had been in Oxford on a visit to the Clarendon from Harwell. Fuchs wasn't at his best, paler than usual and extremely nervous. He was always a thin, somewhat weedy man, continually threatened with tuberculosis. One of the Clarendon physicists had organized a drinks party at his apartment in Headington.

In the warmth of the evening and with a gentle breeze blowing through the room from the open windows Fuchs was certainly off colour, avoiding all attempts to draw him into conversation. The hostess wandered up to him. 'Klaus,' she said. 'You look terrible, are you ill?' Fuchs glared at her, then averted his eyes and remained unsociable, confirming the view of his friends and colleagues that he was unwell.

Harwell's premier nuclear physicist wasn't ill, far from it. He was desperately worried about a probable death sentence. None of his friends present that evening in Headington were aware that Fuchs, long admired in both the British and American scientific communities, was already being interrogated by MI5. In July Fuchs had contemplated immediate resignation from Harwell, discussing his intention with Wing Commander Henry Arnold, head of security and a former Great War pilot. The Americans were already convinced that either Fuchs, Peierls or indeed both were guilty of scientific espionage.

As the sun set that warm autumn evening in Oxford Fuchs sweated, hardly listening to the conversation around him. Staring out of the window his mind was in turmoil. Skarden had probed only gently so far, discussing Fuchs' life in Germany and his father, who he hadn't seen since before the war. Fuchs knew his interrogator was skilled and must shortly step up the level of questioning. So far he had managed to be evasive, refusing to provide any incriminating answers. Outside the Headington apartment MI5 'watchers' kept a careful eye on their charge. Fuchs dwelt on what evidence may have been found. He had met a contact of fellow traitor Dr Alan Nunn-May years earlier and sought advice on whether to accept payment. Expenses of £100 were offered and accepted, but the money was never deposited in a bank account. He knew there were files on his activities as a Communist agitator in Germany. In the closing days of the war he had begged his Russian controller to instruct the NKGB to find his file, relating to his Communist activities in Germany, in the Gestapo Field Office in Kiel before the Americans did. Only in 1949 were these files being opened for the first time in a US Army storage centre, and the file on Fuchs was revealed.

Sir John Cockcroft, head of Harwell, called Fuchs into his office on January 10, 1950. He told him that he had to resign his position at Harwell with immediate effect.

Fuchs remained firmly convinced as to the legality of sharing both his work and the work of his colleagues with Russia. In his statement at the trial he said that he only passed over his own papers and reports. That may have been the case at the beginning of his spying career in 1941 but he betrayed much more as time went on, including the substance of many of the meetings he had attended in Birmingham, Oxford, London, New York and Los Alamos. In Britain Feklisov had instructed Fuchs to cultivate Penney and, before his arrest, Fuchs had handed Feklisov details of Windscale, the plutonium facility in Cumberland, and Capenhurst in Cheshire, the gaseous diffusion plant. While Fuchs served his jail sentence MI5 and selected scientists visited him for further debriefings. By the time of his release for good behaviour in 1959 Fuchs had provided a more definitive statement on his spying career.

Michael Perrin, the deputy controller for Britain's post-war nuclear efforts, knew that Fuchs had only partially admitted the extent of his treachery. He had been in Skarden's office at the War Office on January 30 when Fuchs admitted to just four specific periods of spying, including New York. British Intelligence has never shifted from its position that Fuchs provided a comprehensive confession. Before the trial Perrin visited Washington to brief the Pentagon and the Atomic Energy Commission on the interrogations. A CIA-cleared physicist from Los Alamos was handed the confession for scientific evaluation. General Henry 'Hap' Arnold, the head of the US Army Air Corps during the war, sat in on the Perrin briefing, as did Kim Philby as the senior MI6 representative in the US. The Americans thanked Perrin for sight of Fuchs' statement but they believed that Perrin had been economical with the truth, especially on Fuchs' spying activities in the United States after the war on his trips from Harwell. Later that evening Philby was in good humour as the Embassy held a drinks party in honour of Perrin's visit.

In his confession Fuchs wrote that it was highly probable that the FBI knew that he had passed classified material on at least one occasion to Yatskov in New York. An FBI note dated September 26, 1949, confirmed that view, citing *Rest*, one of the codenames for Fuchs. *'On June 15, 1944,* Rest *furnished to a representative of Soviet Intelligence, Part 111 of a document now identified as MSN-12. A document is on file with the Atomic Energy Commission and is entitled 'Fluctuations and the Efficiency of a Diffusion Plant'; Part 111 refers to 'The Effect of Fluctuations in the Flow of N2'. The designation MSN stands for documents prepared by British scientists who were in New York City working on Atomic Energy Research. The author of this document is K Fuchs, who is actually Emil Julius Klaus Fuchs. He is a top ranking British atomic scientist.'*

Ruth Beurton, *Sonya*, the Oxford-based GRU controller, left England in a hurry as the news of Fuch's arrest made newspaper headlines, leaving on February 27, 1950, for East Berlin. They would meet again 30 years later, this time in Dresden, Fuchs' new home after leaving jail. Len, Ruth's husband, also fled.

Two MI5 officers had visited Ruth and Len in 1947, in their house in Great Rollright, a village outside Oxford. The couple had been nervous for some time after a warning that Allen Foote, a member of their GRU cell in pre-war Switzerland, had defected to the British. No search of the house was made. If there had, Ruth's radio transmitter would have been detected. The expected arrest never happened, nor were there further visits from MI5. Ruth and Len curtailed their trips to London and temporarily ceased contact with their agents. Despite unease at GRU headquarters, *Sonya* later continued transmitting.

Unbeknown to one of the greatest female intelligence officers in Russian history, the British were fully aware of her activities as well as those of Len. Eavesdroppers electronically listened to her transmissions. Even worse, the Russian network in Oxford had been penetrated and the threat of prosecution, even the death sentence, was enough to turn several British nationals to work for MI5. This time selected information, often incorrect, was fed to *Sonya*.

The Americans never admitted the extent of Russian penetration into their midst. Some scientists and engineers quietly left their positions, without arrest or trial. At Oak Ridge one head of department was uncovered by the FBI and promptly resigned. His name and treachery is often mentioned in hushed tones in the complex that has now developed into a large rocket design facility.

The case against Joseph Rotblat would never be proven. As a member of the British team in Los Alamos he had suddenly lost his security clearance and returned to Liverpool. He had been acquainted with an English woman, Elizabeth Grant, who lived at 550 East Alameda St, Santa Fe. She was in the US receiving treatment for deafness. Grant was in fact a member of a Russian 'illegal' cell and Rotblat stayed with her for three weeks. The NKGB had wired up her apartment to record every conversation about Los Alamos. In 1950 Rotblat became professor of physics at St Bart's medical school in London. Always against the proliferation of nuclear arms Rotblat was a founding member of the Pugwash Movement and was one of the authors of the Bertrand Russell-Albert Einstein Manifesto in 1955.

During wartime nuclear intelligence from America, Britain and Canada had poured into Moscow. After 1945, the flow didn't stop, it increased. Lt General Pavel Mezhik, the Russian equivalent of General Groves, generally had first sight of the material in his role as deputy head of the Soviet Atomic Administration, responsible for personnel and secrecy. Much of this intelligence was stored in his over-flowing office. Mezhik, like Beria, loved to terrorise fellow officers and scientists. He often attended and occasionally took part in executions. In October 1941, with German tanks moving ever closer to Moscow and plans put in place for a wholesale Government evacuation to Kuibyshev, Beria had instructed Mezhik to remain to head an underground NKVD operation in the capital if it was overrun. A colleague described Mezhik as 'an honest guy but with no brains'. Mezhik's friendship with Khrushchev did not prevent his arrest in 1953 in Kiev and at his trial he confessed to no crime, stating that he was 'a true Communist and not an enemy of the people'. He was shot alongside Beria.

With the discovery of Fuchs the Soviet operations were at great risk in both Britain and America. In Harwell FBI agents joined MI5 in interviewing everyone who had spent time in Los Alamos, Oak Ridge or with the British mission at the Kellex Corporation in New York. Bruno Pontecorvo, the Harwell physicist whose codenames were *Mayor* and *Mer*, usually met his NKGB controller in Rome when he returned to his home country for holidays. On April 1, 1950, he and his wife and children boarded a plane for Copenhagen. From Denmark they boarded a train for Stockholm and then the following day flew to Helsinki where NKGB agents in a posse of Embassy cars met the party. The sealed train to Russia carried the Pontecorvo's to Moscow; they arrived in the capital on April 10. Whilst the family went to a 'safe house', Pontecorvo was driven to the Lubyanka for an appointment with Beria. The meeting did not last long. Beria quizzed him about Britain's development of the H-bomb and was annoyed when the physicist said he had not been directly involved with the project. On April 25 the family moved to Dubna, to the new Institute for Nuclear Studies of the Academy of Science in the USSR where they were met by Academician Igor Tamm, the scientific leader of work on the development of the Soviet hydrogen bomb. Tamm, on the orders of Beria, put Pontecorvo on the team but ensured that he was not privy to highly sensitive work.

As news of Pontecorvo's defection broke, J E Jackson, the head of Harwell's scientific administration who had also been the first employee in the *Tube Alloys* organisation during the war, was heard to say: *'Oh no, not Bruno too!'* Any Russian connection was deemed deeply suspicious. The Russian-born scientist Boris Davison, who had been working in Los Alamos from October 1945 as a member of the British team and was now at Harwell, resigned. For some time he had been worried about blackmail attempts as he had family in the Soviet Union.

Only nine months after the Americans had tested its 10 megaton H-bomb Russia exploded its own thermonuclear weapon in August 1953 at Semipalatinsk. On October 30, 1961, the USSR would test the largest known device with an explosive force of 58 megatons, each megaton the equivalent of one million tons of TNT. Not content with stealing the secrets of America's wartime bombs, Russia had now stolen the design for the H-bomb.

* * *

In the history room at the Lubyanka in Moscow the stone plaque on which the names are inscribed of past KGB officers who have achieved the highest intelligence honours has had two recent additions – Vladimir Barkovsky and Lona Cohen, better known in Britain as Helen Kroger, who, with her husband, ran a cell that stole naval secrets in the early 1960s. Both Barkovsky and Cohen were vital in securing nuclear secrets during the war. Lona Cohen, active in the US in the 1940s, was a controller for Robert and Katherine Oppenheimer, Theodore Hall and other key agents.

The atomic exhibits include a number of cables from Colonel Vasili Zarubin. His report dated March 1942 had provided the final confirmation to Stalin, Molotov and Beria that America was building its bomb. *'The US Government on its entry into the war, with the Pentagon, has decided on the manufacture and use of atomic weapons. It is called the* Manhattan Project *and a top secret laboratory will be established in Los Alamos, New Mexico. Despite the secrecy we will gather intelligence from Los Alamos. Maksim.'*

Next to this report is an April 1942 communication from London, from *Vadim*, alias Colonel Anatoli Gorsky: *'In a number of countries, work has been carried out on the nuclear fission process using uranium for military applications. In 1939 in France, the United Kingdom, the United States and in Germany extensive efforts were undertaken for uranium usage in new explosives. In England the well-known physicist, George Thomson, heads the uranium committee. The following is an extensive report obtained by the NKVD from intelligence sources...'.*

Days later Gorsky sent another telegram. *'Comrade Stalin – Top Secret No.6,'* it read. The news was just as disturbing. *'We now have more data about Germany. The Kaiser Wilhelm is developing top secret nuclear weapons. Top ranking*

Wehrmacht generals have said that this should guarantee the Reich's victory.' Gorsky had been given this information from one of his MI5 sources.

In March 1943 *Vadim* had transmitted a three-line report. When Kurchatov read it he immediately dictated a note to Mikhail Pervukhin, the deputy chairman of the GKO, the wartime state defence committee: *'Churchill has been informed that the atomic bomb can be manufactured before the end of the war. The US President has agreed to a wide transference of technology and science in this particular area.'*

Six photographs are included in the *Operation Enormoz* exhibit in the history room, the specific operation launched by Stalin to steal atomic secrets – five are of Leonard Kvashnikov, Anatoli Yatskov, Vasili Zarubin, Semyon Semyonov and Vladimir Barkovsky. Many others haven't been included, but that is not to negate their effectiveness. Elizabeta Yurieva Zarubin, codenamed *Helen* and *Vardo*, was Vasili's partner and ran her own network that included agents in a number of US Government agencies. She had also been a contact for Robert Oppenheimer before handing over to Lona Cohen. Her daughter, Zoya, was an expert linguist and translated scientific material for Igor Kurchatov. Eventually Elizabeta would be put on trial and jailed, but later reinstated back into the KGB. Significantly there is no photograph of Anatoli Gorsky, who made a huge contribution to the Soviet bomb managing John Cairncross and Donald Maclean. The sixth photograph is of Klaus Fuchs, his picture pinned next to some reports he sent between 1947 and 1949. One details the Windscale plutonium plant in England and a schematic diagram of an H-bomb.

There is no exhibit for the departments run by Lt General Pavel Sudoplatov, despite the success of the secretive Department S which was closed down in May 1947. General Naum Eitingon, codenamed *Tom* and *Pierre*, was Sudoplatov's senior deputy, who in August 1940 had masterminded the assassination of Trotsky in Mexico City and later had been responsible for the re-evaluation of much of the NKVD stolen nuclear intelligence. Other deputies to Sudoplatov had included Lt Generals Lev Vasilevsky, *Yuri*, and Amayak Kubolov, *Zakar*. Vasilevsky provided the liaison between the NKGB and Kubolov managed the employment of German scientists and engineers in Russia.

Codenamed *Andrei*, Sudoplatov held several positions simultaneously. Before the outbreak of war with Germany he ran Russian Intelligence in Germany and his agents helped establish the *Red Orchestra* under the control of the elegant and beautiful Colonel Zoya Ribkina. He was also chief of the Special Tasks Group and German Airborne Operations, involved in espionage. Other commands included chief of the International Directorate of the NKVD between 1939 and 1942, and the head of the 4th Guerrilla War Directorate from 1942 to 1946.

Sudoplatov was jailed in 1953, accused of being an active participant in the Beria plot to seize power on the death of Stalin and referred to as 'Enemy of the People No 8'. In 1958 he was found guilty at a secret trial and Sudoplatov continued his sentence in Vladimir jail. He was finally released in 1968. Emma, Sudoplatov's wife, half German and Jewish, was a colonel in the NKVD and KGB, active in the Ukraine, Rotterdam and Paris before the war. Later she returned to Moscow, working in the universities in addition to lecturing at the KGB training school.

The past would come back to haunt the family in 1989 when Sudoplatov was attacked in the Russian media for controlling departments 'that had liquidated undesirables'. He was subsequently cleared in 1991 but there was now another charge. The Ukraine state prosecutor accused Sudoplatov of ordering the liquidation of Ukrainians before the war. Sudoplatov did arrange the execution of members of the OUN, a pro-Nazi group that reported to the Abwehr. In 1938 Konovalets, the OUN's leader that had met Hitler twice in Berlin, was assassinated. Another bullet had ended the life of SS Hauptstürmfuhrer Roman Shukhevich in 1946, the last head of the OUN, an organisation with 10,000 members active in the Western Ukraine and which remained loyal to Hitler even after his death.

The volume of atomic material stolen by the Russians was staggering, the greatest intelligence theft in history. The NKVD and its successor, the NKGB, only counted pages, unlike the GRU who counted pages and individual documents. Up to 1943 the GRU received 853 pages in 142 documents. Fuchs, a GRU agent before he crossed the Atlantic in December 1943, accounted for the bulk of the pages – 570, of which Ruth Beurton collected 370 when she ran him for a year from her home in Oxford. When Fuchs was in the United States, run by Yatskov, his pages were included in the NKVD figure. Given the huge NKVD and NKGB number of 15,000 pages stolen on nuclear matters, Fuch's treachery would have formed only a small proportion. Another estimate is far, far higher. An atomic historian, Alekseyev, for the first time has access to Stalin's atomic files in the Kremlin. The archive is vast and unsorted. From what he has seen so far, he estimates there are over 13,000 documents in the files.

If the theft of the atomic bomb was the pinnacle for Russian Intelligence, another acquisition comes very close. In Moscow's archives lies an American plan that would have plunged the world into a war to end all wars. The first operational detail was stolen on June 26, 1948, and was confirmed with more material on July 26. Under the US codename *Chevalier*, for a period of 30 days beginning in April 1949 bombers based in Britain, West Germany and Japan would unleash 133 atomic bombs on 70 cities and towns in the USSR. Eight such bombs would obliterate Moscow. If Russia had any fight left, *Chevalier* would turn into a war that America estimated would last no longer than two years, codenamed *Fleetwood*. Unimaginable firepower would then be amassed against the Soviet Union with the dropping of a further 200 atomic bombs and 250,000 tons of high explosive. Such terrifying intelligence had confirmed to Stalin that the West needed to eradicate Communism. More than ever now, Russia had to develop a nuclear deterrent.

Stalin had every reason to be proud of his intelligence services, especially the Scientific and Technical Intelligence department, the group of NKVD and NKGB agents who plundered every major secret of both Britain and America. The acquisition of the *Chevalier* and *Fleetwood* plans was testament to their skills. Copies had been urgently passed to a Russian Embassy case officer in London for immediate photographing before their return. The agent worked for the British Secret Service.

Who was the physicist in Oppenheimer's secret CPUSA cell with the codename of *Perseus*, the king of ancient Macedon who waged war on the Greeks before being stopped at Delphi? In the early 1990s when the *Perseus* hunters attempted to identify the now-legendary agent, the KGB fabricated a story about a US physicist named 'Arthur Fielding', who worked in the Chicago nuclear laboratories during the war. Supposedly this scientist passed over top-level atomic intelligence; but it was pure disinformation. There was no 'Arthur Fielding'. Colonel Vladimir Barkovsky disclosed the identity of *Perseus* in a highly classified note written to the head of the FSB, the successor to the KGB, in 1994. In the United States there was again speculation about Oppenheimer's possible clandestine involvement with Russian Intelligence and the veteran Barkovsky was asked to prepare an internal briefing paper. Not only did he describe how Oppenheimer had been recruited and his invaluable assistance in providing contacts in every major nuclear centre in the United States, Barkovsky identified the scientist who was the most prodigious wartime agent for the Soviets. This Oppenheimer prodigy worked initially at Berkeley before moving to Los Alamos, and he participated in one of the air reconnaissance sorties over Hiroshima just days after the explosion. Several scientists were asked to prepare reports on their visit but his found its way to Moscow in just three weeks. This report was included in a large volume of other documents that had been passed to his controller since Oppenheimer had suggested his recruitment. With the war won this physicist didn't let up and material from Los Alamos and the Lawrence Livermore laboratory was handed to a series of Soviet controllers, of which Barkovsky was one.

CHAPTER 32

Building Stalin's bomb

There is only one Russian alive now who witnessed the testing of Stalin's plutonium bomb in August 1949 from one of the two main observation posts. The other 17 have passed away. Of the three key architects of Stalin's bomb, Igor Kurchatov died at the age of 58, in 1960. Yuli Khariton, its chief designer, lived well into old age, dying in 1996 aged 92. Despite his frailty, Khariton delivered a lecture in June that year, without the aid of notes and completely blind. Yakov Zeldovich lived until 1987, aged 83.

It is a harrowing 270-mile drive on the M8 road north-east out of Moscow to the city of Yaroslavl – notable for its Kremlin, the second largest after the one in Moscow. The road has acquired the unenviable reputation as 'the road of death' due to the high accident rate along its route. In the city's university, Dr Yakov Dokuchayev still teaches chemistry to an attentive class – but none have any idea about his war record and vital contribution to the test at Semipalatinsk. Dokuchayev was 29 in 1949, a surprise and last minute choice to view the explosion at first hand.

The village of Presnovka in north-west Kazakhstan lies close to the border with Russia, a short distance from the city of Petropavlovsk. Dokuchayev was born here in 1920. Considered a bright pupil at school he enrolled at the University of Kazan to study organic chemistry. Humorous and immensely proud of his war record, Dokuchayev clearly remembers July 15, 1941, the date of his call-up for the Red Army, just weeks after Germany invaded the Ukraine. Unlike other student colleagues who were conscripted and sent straight to the Front, he was trained as a tank commander in Chelyabinsk, the manufacturing centre for the KV heavy tank that was the work horse of the Red Army.

The first KV model, manufactured in 1940, weighed 52 tons. With a crew of six it managed a top speed of 21 miles per hour. When Dokuchayev arrived in Chelyabinsk, the KV had been extensively upgraded to increase its speed. After graduation as a lieutenant he finally caught up with the war at Velikye Luki, 250 miles west of Moscow, in Tverskaya oblast.

In October 1942 Dokuchayev was in command of the newer T-34 tank, which was capable of a top speed of 34 miles per hour. A member of the 38th Tank Regiment in General Galitski's 3rd Army, he fired his first shots in anger as the Russians attempted to surround the large German garrison. Opposition in the nearby village of Fedkovo was knocked out but Soviet losses were high. Dokuchayev's tank, however, emerged unscathed.

The massive assault on Velikye Luki, a mediaeval town with narrow streets, began on December 14, a bitterly cold day – although no shots were actually fired. Hundreds of Soviet tanks from the 38th and 34th Regiments surrounded Velikye

Luki to prevent a breakout and Galitski demanded the immediate surrender of General von Zatz, the German commander. Galitski sent two officers into the town with the ultimatum, which von Zatz rejected out of hand, relishing the opportunity to match his Panzers against the T-34s. Hurriedly, Marshal Zhukov, commander-in-chief of the Soviet forces, arrived to assess the situation. Galitski preferred a full frontal attack, but Zhukov ordered continued encirclement and to wait for a German counter-attack. Zhukov departed to Stalingrad, but he returned on Christmas Day and this time ordered an assault. Galitski was the prevaricator now and stressed that reinforcements were necessary. More ground troops were called up to the line, notably the Estonian 8th Rifle Corps under the command of General Pern.

The ferocious barrage started on December 31, with three Soviet infantry divisions in action behind the T-34s. Early the next morning Dokuchayev heard over his tank radio, in an official Soviet statement, that the Germans had surrendered. That news was mere propaganda. All around him a tank battle of epic proportions raged with Velikye Luki a blazing inferno. Each day it ebbed and flowed, but on January 17 the T-34 had won. Von Zatz capitulated but insisted on surrendering only to General Pern, the Estonian, and not Galitski. At the official surrender in Galitski's tent, von Zatz and Pern exchanged conversation and banter in German that angered the Russian officers present.

Thirty years after the war Dokuchayev visited the Soviet war cemetery where he was dismayed to learn that there were only 4,500 individual graves. Large communal graves had been dug to bury most of the 65,000 Soviet dead.

Regrouping after Velikye Luki, Dokuchayev's tank regiment had been retired behind the lines. Dokuchayev visited a field hospital as the noise of constant shelling had shattered an eardrum. With just partial hearing the doctors considered that Dokuchayev could no longer command a tank and he was posted to Chuguyev, near Kharkov, to join Battle Brigade No. 10 as an instructor. That was to be the end of his short war at the front. He finally left the Army in October 1945, looking forward to demobilisation and returning to Kazan to finish his war-interrupted university education. He declined the Army's offer of promotion to captain.

Several weeks later, in the university, Dokuchayev was mystified by a large crowd of students and lecturers reading a strange GKO declaration that had appeared on the notice board of the chemistry faculty. It was signed by Stalin. Technicians were needed for unspecified 'dirty work', it proclaimed. There was a new priority, the State Defence Committee announced, vital to the USSR. Volunteers would be trained at the University of Leningrad. The same notice had been displayed in the universities of Kharkov, Moscow, Leningrad and Gorki. Never one to shirk a challenge, Dokuchayev applied.

Each university could select three candidates for consideration and Dokuchayev submitted his application to the university's Communist Party. He was called for an interview and joined the short-list from Kazan. Within a short period of time

Dokuchayev found himself in Leningrad in a group of 25 hand-picked students from the five universities. Looking around him at his new fresh-faced colleagues he mused that he was the only one to have survived one of the bloodiest tank battles of the war. All swore an oath to secrecy.

A specific role awaited the former tank commander. He was to be trained to measure radiation under the guidance of Professor Konstantin Petrzhak, the renowned scientist at Leningrad's Radium Institute. Dokuchayev worked hard and in September 1947 he gained his diploma as a radioactivity specialist and within days he received his orders. He was to proceed to Base 10, a highly-secret industrial plant under construction to manufacture plutonium – the deadliest place on earth. Russia needed to produce at least 6 kg to build its bomb.

To find Base 10, Dokuchayev was told he had to take the train for Chelyabinsk, change for Sverdlovsk but alight at the stop for Kystym. When he finally arrived on October 19, after an exhausting trip, Kystym station was barely more than a wooden platform set in woodland, covered with the first snows of the winter, with no shelter, no seats and infrequent trains. Standing alone with his small suitcase Dokuchayev scanned the landscape, searching for 'a large house built in the Finnish style, which was impossible to miss' he had been told.

He spotted the villa and trudged through the heavy snow. Pushing open the large door he was confronted by two members of the MGB Border Regiment, clearly recognisable by their red and blue caps. The MGB had replaced the NKGB as Russia's state security police service. Dokuchayev was asked to show his credentials. He was informed that Base 10 was six miles away, near the Kyzyl-Tash Lake. However, he would have to wait to join more arrivals. By nightfall 10 others had walked from Kystym station, graduates from Moscow and Gorki. Conversation was forbidden. A truck struggled up the driveway to collect the new recruits for Base 10.

In the distance they saw the security lights piercing the dark. Soon the truck reached the first ring of high fencing topped with barbed wire. Beyond lay open ground with landmine signs, more barbed wire and lights. MGB guards ordered a roll call of the recruits. The site was vast, its perimeter extending for 36 miles. By 1970 this location would be a city with over one million inhabitants, while the near-by village of Ozersk, originally home to peasant farmers, would be changed into a huge chemical complex.

Accommodation in Base 10 was primitive, the hut barely habitable and a communal campfire providing the only warmth. Dokuchayev couldn't sleep, kept awake by the incessant noise of hammering and drilling from the construction work. Some nine miles away, under great secrecy, the construction of Russia's first industrial nuclear reactor – the Annuchka – was underway. Dokuchayev had been among the first batch of professional workers to arrive at Base 10. Within three months that number would grow to 30,000.

Breakfast on that first morning was a sorry affair, served in a large tent with snow blowing through the entrance whenever anyone entered. Dokuchayev strolled around the accommodation site, the eventual home for the engineers and technicians. Zeks – prisoners under the GULAG system – were everywhere, poorly clothed and always under guard. Curious to see the progress of the reactor Dokuchayev tried to bluff his way into the industrial area, but entry was vigorously denied.

Dokuchayev never did meet Yuri Bistrov, but one day Base 10's chief engineer failed to show up and his managers didn't dare question why. Construction was behind schedule and Bistrov was under pressure from his Moscow masters. An MGB squad had dragged him out of his office, pushed him into a car and drove him to a clearing in the woods. His crimes were read out aloud and Bistrov pleaded for mercy. After the execution his body was buried under stones. Efim Slavski, Bistrov's replacement, held the position for just two weeks. Equally inefficient at least his life was spared and he was allowed to remain on site as an engineer. By November the camp, now renamed Combine 817, was in the capable hands of Major General Boris Glebovich Muzrukov, a hard-liner and 'Hero of Socialist Labour'. He was the former head of Uralmash, the industrial combine that manufactured the T-34 tank.

In these early weeks Dokuchayev became increasingly frustrated. The reactor neared completion but the foundations for the radiochemistry facilities had yet to begin. He whiled away time reading, especially the book he had brought from Leningrad – *Nuclear Energy for Military Applications*, published by the Americans and written by the Princeton physicist Henry deWolf Smyth from Los Alamos. Published in January 1946 the Americans never realised, despite warnings from the British, that it was too early to go public with details of their nuclear research. The Russian Embassy in Washington purchased every copy it could lay its hands on and sent them to Leningrad and Moscow. That book was invaluable to Dokuchayev and he constantly re-read the chapter on the Hanford site, in Washington State, where three reactors produced plutonium and where there were two large radiochemical plants. The labour force at Hanford was 45,000, it was well fed and reasonably highly educated. At Combine 817, with one reactor and mainly unskilled workers operating in appalling conditions, Dokuchayev knew they needed a miracle.

General Victor Abakumov shared a similar view. During the liberation of Berlin and Vienna he had visited every nuclear facility and was impressed at the technology available to the German scientists. On the very day in December 1946 when the F-1 reactor in Moscow's Laboratory No. 2 had gone critical Beria had promoted Abakumov to MGB chief, tasking him specifically with the briefing of the Politburo on Soviet progress in the manufacture of its own atomic bomb. Articulate, but utterly ruthless, Abakumov took personal responsibility for the GULGMP system, part of the GULAG regime that governed the mineral and uranium mines. In addition to the Taboshar and Mailu-Su uranium mines Abakumov also ran Combine 817. Two of his senior officers, Colonels Egorov and Maltsev, reported daily on progress at the site and regular executions were ordered to show that any slacking would not be tolerated. It was vital that GKO 9887, the order that Stalin had signed to accelerate the bomb development, didn't fall behind schedule.

The work was backbreaking, especially for the former Russian PoWs who had been described as defeatists and criminals by Stalin for their surrender to German forces. Those who didn't perform were executed or returned to their previous prison camps. Some 5,000 such men toiled at Combine 817 in 1947, often starved and worked to death. Injuries festered as medical treatment was minimal. Dokuchayev, who had fought with such soldiers at Velikye Luki, was sickened at their treatment. Officers were allowed to keep their rank and uniforms, and for each year served at Combine 817 two years would be knocked off their sentence. Any association with the prisoners was banned but Dokuchayev did make friends with one Red Army captain and was able to smuggle extra food rations to him.

Given the slow pace of construction Kurchatov recalled Dokuchayev to Leningrad for a refresher course with Professor Petrzhak. The months sped by and after nearly a year Dokuchayev and 20 other scientists from the Radium Institute were ordered to Laboratory No. 2 and the NII-9 facility in Moscow. At Laboratory No. 2 Dokuchayev honed his skills on the F-1 reactor, monitoring levels of radioactivity in the uranium rods. Each week he also visited the 'hot lab' in NII-9 where plutonium recovery technology was under test, directed by Boris Nikitin, Andrei Bochvar and Zinaida Ershova. Kurchatov was also a regular visitor to view the apparatus under test that would eventually be copied on an industrial scale in Combine 817. Irradiated blocks transported from the F-1 reactor to NII-9 were dipped in solution, producing minute quantities of metallic plutonium.

This extraction process proved slow and tedious as the reactor had a capacity of 200 watts and only rarely was it boosted to 1,000 watts. Dokuchayev was enrolled into Nikitin's group and worked night and day measuring alpha, beta and gamma radioactivity. NII-9 produced a disappointing 10–15 grams of plutonium and morale fell as the scientists believed that the one reactor nearing completion at Combine 817, now renamed Chelyabinsk-40, would take many months to manufacture the 6 kg needed to build Russia's bomb. However, at least the technology was being perfected. Dokuchayev was promoted to head of radio metering, responsible for the monitoring of the complete process chain – from irradiated uranium blocks to the production of pure metallic plutonium.

The Radium Institute staff left NII-9 for Chelyabinsk-40 in May 1948, their technology now to be put to the real test. The site looked more welcoming to Dokuchayev this time – late spring had transformed the landscape and the prolific wild flowers were in bloom. The accommodation centre was complete and the prisoners had gone, transported elsewhere in the labour system. Dokuchayev enquired after his friend but no one knew if he had survived.

As soon as the group arrived they were taken to view the Annuchka reactor in Plant

A where the uranium blocks were to be irradiated. A radiochemical laboratory had been constructed in Plant B, where the blocks were to be dissolved to form a solution of plutonium nitrate. The deadliest part of the process, the manufacture of the metallic plutonium, was to be handled in Plant C.

There was great excitement on June 18 when Annuchka was finally switched on. Kurchatov, Beria and a number of Ministers had flown in from Moscow, expecting to witness a successful test. But the day ended in failure and embarrassment as Kurchatov ordered an immediate shutdown pending extensive modifications. Nikolay Antonovich Dolezhal, the reactor's head designer, was given just one week to rectify the problems.

Kurchatov's hopes of meeting his own deadline of August 1949 to manufacture the bomb, let alone Stalin's demand for August 1950, now looked doomed to failure. Their one industrial reactor, with its teething problems, could only run at 100 megawatts [100,000 watts]; but the three Hanford reactors each had a capacity of 250 megawatts with a combined capacity of 750 megawatts. To add to the growing dismay in Chelyabinsk-40, the scientists knew that the output from the sole radiochemical plant would, at best, operate at only half the output of one of the units in the US.

Stalin was furious at the delay and called Kurchatov, who could only reply that Dolezhal and his team were doing their best. Nikitin had also produced a disappointing estimate for Kurchatov, suggesting that Annuchka might only produce enough irradiated uranium to produce 100 grams of plutonium per day, and only if it was run at full capacity.

Dolezhal knew very well the price of failure and, with bated breath, on June 22 he restarted the reactor. Within hours it reached a capacity of 100 megawatts with 100 tons of uranium metal loaded into the pile. Kurchatov, back in Moscow, phoned Stalin with the good news. There ensued a debate in Chelyabinsk on whether the reactor should undergo rigorous testing to ensure that it was working correctly, but Kurchatov didn't have time on his side and would have none of it. The reactor was not switched off and Kurchatov ran the 100-ton load for three months.

The irradiated blocks were then stored for 45 days before they could be chemically treated. Production workers, wearing just leather gloves, gingerly carried some sample blocks to Plant B on December 22. Nikitin urged great care now and demanded that even the very smallest amounts of irradiated uranium were to be processed to test the radiochemical activity. In his laboratory in Plant B, Dokuchayev monitored alpha radiation after the blocks were dissolved. Negligible beta and gamma activity was detected. Dokuchayev presented his first findings to a delighted Nikitin who agreed that he should now start receiving the main output from the reactor.

From his calculations Dokuchayev estimated that the first 300 kg of irradiated uranium would yield 30 grams of plutonium. During the next three days he made more corrections to his machines and more irradiated blocks were brought from the reactor. If that level was maintained, Dokuchayev now estimated that 900 grams of plutonium would be ready within a month or so. Nikitin insisted that the rate was too slow, urging an immediate 10 per cent increase. He had received further instruction from Kurchatov in Moscow – 12 kg was now needed, enough for two bombs.

Radiation levels in all three plants were at incredible levels. No permissible levels had been set but the scientists believed that exposure of six roentgens, a measure of gamma radiation, was not too hazardous. Exposure zoomed to 48, eight times that level. It would later rise to 113.3 as safety measures were practically non-existent. At every stage of the process highly active and long-lived radionuclides were present. Despite the limited period that people were near the apparatus, it was inevitable that radiation sickness would occur.

Dissolving uranium in solution exacerbated the problem. In the radiochemical plant plutonium concentrate was delivered in containers of sheet steel, by hand, with no protection. Aleksandr Ratner, the deputy head of the Radium Institute, tried several measures for coping with the irradiated uranium but most ideas failed as technicians had to mix and wash the radioactive solution manually. The most dangerous processes involved uranium pulp filtration and packing of the extracted plutonium. No one at that time was fully aware of the dangers of inhaling radionuclides. In the storage facility in Plant C radioactive effluent was dumped within a large concreted area. Walls of reinforced concrete were clad with graphite blocks over two metres thick and the upper protective plate was strengthened with 40-millimetre steel rods to house the waste. Boys from the Kineshma Technical College, a school 200 miles north-east of Moscow, were responsible for the storage of this effluent. Their teachers had told them that Stalin, their great leader, needed workers on a secret project. The MGB had arrived with trucks and they, too, arrived at Kystym. Few of the boys survived. Other dirty and hazardous jobs in the three plants were left to women – graduates from the universities in Moscow, Voronezh and Gorki. Alpha particles permeated every building, with ventilation systems pumping radionuclides around each room. Outside, the birch trees withered and died.

Filiptsev, one of the senior managers, delivered the first batch of plutonium concentrate to Plant C for the production of metallic plutonium on February 26, 1949. Kurchatov was there to see it arrive. Dokuchayev came in for praise as Nikitin had reported to Kurchatov that the 10 per cent rise in the schedule level was being maintained thanks to tweaking of the process chain.

The senior scientists lived together in a house on the site that was nicknamed the 'Pickwick Club' due to the high number of academicians who resided there. Although not an academician, Dokuchayev enjoyed its facilities. Working in such dangerous conditions had created a strong camaraderie. Radiation sickness was rife but no one wanted to complain or let the side down.

Everyone toasted a major event in March when 8.5 kg of metallic plutonium was produced, more than enough for one bomb, despite it being full of cavities and slag inclusions that rendered it useless. Bochvar knew they could improve the process and one of his chemists, Reshetnikov, changed the lining in the crucible where the metal was melted, which did the trick. With that problem solved Nikitin estimated that 1 kg of pure metallic plutonium could be produced every two to three weeks, achieving the first target of 6 kg by the end of July. There must be no slippage, Kurchatov told Nikitin and Bochvar.

Kurchatov had now confirmed to Stalin that given the excellent progress at Chelyabinsk-40 the bomb could now be manufactured a year ahead of schedule. There were many visitors to the plants in July, and Dokuchayev was always pleased to see Kurchatov. Kurchatov had asked him for some plutonium samples to take back to Moscow to present to Stalin. He took Dokuchayev aside and asked the radiochemist if his apparatus could measure alpha activity with a high background level of beta and gamma. Only in a nuclear explosion, responded the chemist. That evening Dokuchayev played over in his mind that strange exchange. Kurchatov knew very well the capabilities of Dokuchayev's equipment.

As Russia's plutonium plant had buckled down to the rigid regime imposed by Kurchatov there had been frantic activity in KB-11, the codename for the facility in Sarov, on the River Techa. Established in April 1946, KB-11, or Arzamas-16 as it was later referred to, was the equivalent of Los Alamos. Under its first chief scientist, Vladimir Merkin, Arzamas became the design centre for the bomb. Yuli Khariton, Kurchatov's closest colleague, was relocated to Arzamas and soon took over.

For Arkadi Adamovich Brish his appointment in 1947 at Arzamas would lead to an involvement in the manufacture of Soviet atomic bombs that would last for more than half a century. An X-ray specialist in Moscow's Institute of Machinery, Brish gladly accepted the invitation in March that year to attend a presentation in the lecture theatre to listen to the highly-respected Lev Altschuller, a physicist who had already produced a number of sketches of a possible bomb design. Altschuller, one of the first employees at Arzamas, gave a speech that riveted the audience, including Brish and a journalist from *Pravda*. He addressed the young scientists and engineers about a top-secret project, which he couldn't name, stressing how vital it was to the security of the USSR that specialists came forward. That evening Altschuller's stirring speech filled the airwaves on Moscow Radio and the following morning *Pravda* printed it in full.

Originally from Minsk, the 30-year-old Brish immediately applied and was accepted. Even better, his salary of 1,000 roubles from the institute was doubled at Arzamas after he joined the team of 36 specialists. His first impression was one of bleakness. The nuclear centre was merely part of a rundown industrial plant in an area with hopeless communications and infrastructure. Builders had knocked 10 rooms together to form one large laboratory. Sand brought in on the soles of shoes covered the floors and the walls were grimy. As there was no accommodation the scientists had to cadge rooms in local houses. The conditions were depressing and General Pavel Zernov, in charge of administration, ignored the pleadings from the scientists to improve the facilities. Food was minimal and badly cooked. No visits or vacations were allowed and letters home were vetted. Well-armed guards patrolled the premises, keeping their charges under close surveillance.

Visits from Kurchatov were rare and Beria seldom bothered to view the progress of the design centre. Brish was responsible for the detonators that would be equally spaced around the spheres of plutonium in the bomb. In the first tests it was clear that the detonators were too sensitive, catastrophic if the problem wasn't resolved – the speed of detonation was also proving to be a problem. In January 1948, as Brish set up an X-ray experiment, a loud explosion was heard. Bloodied women scientists and technicians struggled out of a blazing hut, but there had been no fatalities.

Detonation was of key concern to the Russian scientists just as it had been in America. But here Kurchatov had the major advantage of being privy to stolen intelligence on two methods of firing device. The weapon, or gun method, where two equal plutonium spheres each of 3 kg collide at a speed of 2,500 metres a second, was one. A slower collision would not create the explosion, the plutonium would just melt. The Americans had perfected this method at Los Alamos, starting initially with firing uranium and plutonium 'bullets' into a uranium target. Because of the impurities of plutonium, these bullets had to be fired at a high velocity. After Kurchatov had sight of the American experience, the Russians had arranged their own trials on the waste ground in front of Laboratory No. 2. Physicists' Alexsandrovich, Merkin and Piatkin set up rifles loaded with uranium-tipped bullets, firing into targets to assess the explosive power and speed.

At Arzamas this method was abandoned as Khariton was uncertain that Chelyabinsk-40 would be able to produce the required 6 kg due to potential process losses. Instead, the scientists opted for implosion, successfully implemented by the Americans over Nagasaki.

Klaus Fuchs had given details of the implosion firing mechanism to Anatoli Yatskov, his NKGB controller, marking the pinnacle of his spying career. Within weeks these were in the hands of Kurchatov at Laboratory No. 2. In Los Alamos Richard Tolman, Professor at the California Institute of Technology, had suggested that fissionable material could be detonated by high explosive placed around a hollow sphere and crushing it into a critical mass. In effect, a core of fissionable material was suddenly compressed into a smaller size. The greater the density, the closer the nuclei are packed so increasing the chance of fission, or a chain reaction. Oppenheimer had agreed to a test on South Mesa, part of the Los Alamos complex. Experiments were also carried out at the Bruccton Explosives Research Laboratory in Pennsylvania with the support of George Kistiakowsky, who had helped in the manufacture of implosion charges.

America's early implosion experiments were encouraging, leading to the construction of a small site at Anchor Ranch, at Los Alamos, to take the tests further. Oppenheimer enlisted the help of John von Neumann, the Princeton mathematician working on ballistic trajectories in Maryland at the US Army's Aberdeen Proving

Ground, who modified the process. He said that shaped charges would produce a spherical detonation wave and that the method would be much faster than a gun. In addition, higher pressures would reduce the amount of active material required, increasing the efficiency of the atomic explosion. Fuchs had worked closely with von Neumann and they became joint owners of the patent.

Oppenheimer immediately adopted the implosion method and General Groves agreed to more funding to refine it further. First calculations suggested that an inward-moving spherical shock wave would be disrupted by the interference of detonation waves from the high-explosion segments and by instabilities arising as the tamper material was pushed into the heavier nuclear core by the explosion. An explosive lens to convert the detonation wave to a spherically convergent form was essential.

Kistiakowsky proved his worth in this department and on S-site; between December 1943 and May 1944, with the help of James Tuck, a member of the British team, he led the group developing the lens for the implosion gadget. Norris Bradbury, recruited to Los Alamos from the University of Stanford, helped in the casting. However, spirits fell in December 1944 when the implosion gadget failed on test. Within the next eight months problems with both the implosion and gun methods were solved and it was agreed that the uranium bomb, later employed over Hiroshima, would utilize the gun method. Implosion was reserved for the plutonium bomb to be used on Nagasaki.

Given Fuchs' drawings the scientists and engineers at Arzamas manufactured almost an exact copy of the American implosion device. Furthermore, Khariton now believed that it would work on just 4 kg of metal plutonium. This news had been conveyed to Chelyabinsk-40, but in the radiochemistry laboratory Dokuchayev and others remained hopeful of producing the required 6 kg.

There remained debate about the number of detonators necessary and their configuration. Brish was being worked off his feet. Finally, in the last week of August 1948 Khariton agreed with Major General Nikolay Dukhov, the bomb's key designer, and Altshuller that 32 detonators were to be used. In final tests the speed of detonation was 28 per cent better than originally achieved and Brish was congratulated.

The months now sped by in both Arzamas and Chelyabinsk-40 as work accelerated. Kurchatov and Khariton had the serious dilemma of what bomb to test. The team at Arzamas had built two – the first, a purely Russian design; the second, an almost perfect replica of the Nagasaki bomb. Kurchatov knew the first would take longer to perfect but as the Russians had been privy to the results of the Trinity Test the Nagasaki explosion and the US testing in Bikini in July 1946, testing the second was preferable. The explosion would still shock the world.

Beria paid a surprise visit to Chelyabinsk-40 in July 1949 much to Kurchatov's annoyance. There were doubts in Kurchatov's mind about whether Beria was more focused on his oil and gas responsibilities than on nuclear. Every time Kurchatov met with Beria in the Lubyanka, Beria had yet another model of an oil refinery in his office. This was the decade of the enormous post-war expansion of Russian oil-fields in the Volga-Urals. Dokuchayev was on the list of the people Beria wanted to meet and he was called to the telephone to take Kurchatov's call.

'Make Beria interested in what you are doing,' explained Kurchatov. 'Set up some instruments with plenty of flashing lights. Look very busy and try not to engage him in conversation.'

Beria flew in with his customary entourage and Kurchatov escorted him around all three plants. Dokuchayev remembered that Beria wore a blue sweater and slacks that day. Members of Dokuchayev's staff were at their desks, heads down. There was no shaking of hands.

'Hello,' said Beria. 'Comrade Stalin is expecting good work of you.' With that, he then walked out. As Dokuchayev started to dismantle the apparatus he had rigged up he noticed Kurchatov smiling back at him as he escorted Beria to his next appointment.

On August 5, 1949, Chelyabinsk-40 had done its work. Two hemispheres of metallic plutonium, each eight centimetres in diameter, had been manufactured in Plant C by the two engineers, Samoilov and Poido, and coated in nickel to prevent oxidation. Some 101 batches of plutonium in solution from the radiochemical laboratories had produced the required 6 kg.

There is a document authorizing the actual test of the bomb at Semipalatinsk in August 1949, but curiously Stalin never signed it, which puzzled the scientists. However, Stalin didn't want to be associated with the bomb's possible failure and had doubts whether the Soviet scientists were the measure of the Americans.

With the target met and the hemispheres delivered to Arzamas, the Chelyabinsk scientists had little time for a well-earned breather. The new laboratories in Plants B and C were nearing completion and Kurchatov demanded an even greater effort to increase the plutonium output. Some new safety measures had been installed. Fume cupboards had been constructed, made of polished stainless steel. At first the new facilities improved output but within days, alarmingly, the volume of finished plutonium fell by 40 per cent following uncontrolled precipitation and leakage in the new pure gold and platinum filters. Batches of plutonium had been processed for 14 days and left for 12 hours, after which the solution was poured through these filters before transfer by container to Plant C. The solution was poured into a vessel similar to a small coffeepot. More filtration led to deposits dripping onto the floor.

These improvements should have also limited the contamination, but in the rush to increase output the fume cupboards were left open and radionuclides freely circulated to further contaminate the laboratories.

On August 20 Dokuchayev was summoned to see Major General Muzrukov, the director of Chelyabinsk-40. Kurchatov had called from Moscow and his office had reserved a seat for Dokuchayev on the first available plane from Sverdlovsk. Dokuchayev felt apprehensive. A car collected him from Moscow's Vnukovo airport and the driver informed him that Kurchatov awaited him at Sredmash, the Ministry for Heavy Engineering that had day-to-day management of the bomb project. Dokuchayev offered his Chelyabinsk-40 pass at the security desk. A secretary showed him to the office of General Zadikyan, an Armenian. Kurchatov was gazing out of the window when Dokuchayev was called in.

'Hello Tankist!' boomed Kurchatov, as he turned with an outstretched hand. Kurchatov had always liked Dokuchayev and used the greeting on many occasions at Chelyabinsk-40, referring to the chemist's wartime career. Dokuchayev was introduced to Zadikyan, who Kurchatov had briefed on the exceptional work of the radiochemistry laboratories at the plutonium plant.

'We are going to test the piece,' whispered Kurchatov.

Dokuchayev feigned surprise – that news had been no secret at Chelyabinsk-40. He assumed that 'the piece' was the bomb. Kurchatov asked Dokuchayev if all his measurement and monitoring equipment was in working order. Now he understood the reason for Kurchatov's strange question in July.

'Of course,' replied Dokuchayev, feeling a little offended. 'We're all set.'

'Excellent,' said Kurchatov. Russia's premier nuclear scientist looked at Zadikyan and back to Dokuchayev. 'The test is going to be carried out within seven days. You must move your equipment to Semipalatinsk by train, as quickly as possible.'

The three men chattered for a time before Kurchatov told Dokuchayev to be at the Yakor Hotel at 7pm prompt, with a suitcase or travel bag. The Yakor no longer exists, but in 1949 it was a landmark hotel near to the Byelorussia railway station and regularly frequented by senior MGB officers.

Dokuchayev arrived early and as he mounted the stairs to the private room he heard voices, some recognisable. He entered and saw an anxious Kurchatov about to speak. In the room were 30 people, several in military uniform. The Radium Institute was well represented and Dokuchayev could see Vlasov, Gorshkov, Dzhelepov, Nikitin, Starik and Tolmachev – his colleagues from NII-9 and Chelyabinsk. Kurchatov spelled out very clearly what was to happen in the next few days and reiterated the need for complete secrecy. Downstairs, in the large lobby, guards kept prying eyes away from the meeting on the first floor.

The test date was August 29, at Semipalatinsk, a site chosen in 1946 in the near desert area of Kazakhstan. Kurchatov answered many questions before dinner was provided. Kurchatov's secretary had booked rooms and no one was allowed to leave the hotel that night. In the morning, after a restless night, Dokuchayev called his laboratory to instruct his assistants to begin packing the equipment. A train was due to leave from Chelyabinsk-40 for Semipalatinsk the next day.

At midday the group left the hotel for the drive to a military airport outside Moscow where two Soviet-built Dakotas waited for the flight to Sverdlovsk. Kurchatov and his close circle of colleagues departed first. Dokuchayev was in the second plane. Both aircraft landed on the recently constructed landing strip at Semipalatinsk, some 90 mile from the village. A number of two-story cottages had been reserved for Kurchatov, Beria and other Government officials, but for the scientists wooden shacks on the banks of Lake Irtysh provided only sparse accommodation.

A train had already left Arzamas en route to Semipalatinsk, travelling slowly and bristling with guards. On-board were Khariton, his deputy, Shchelkin, and 36 of the 75 members of staff. Much to his intense dismay, Brish missed out. Carefully stored on the train were the component elements of RDS-1, the first Soviet atomic bomb, ready for the critical final assembly at the test site.

CHAPTER 33

Van der Velde is given surprising news

Hans had prayed that Taboshar was behind him now as his plane landed at Vnukovo. Kurchatov had recalled him to Moscow, but not before he had been tasked with preparing a report for the head of the Russian atomic bomb project on the conditions in the uranium mining camps at Taboshar in Tajikistan and Mailu-Su in Kazakhstan. Pereverzev, Kurchatov's secretary, had met him at Vnukovo and escorted him to the waiting car. What a contrast, Hans mused, with his exit from the capital three years earlier when he had been pushed into a cattle-car by NKVD guards on a train bound for the deserted wasteland of Central Asia with hundreds of other unfortunates whose destiny was to dig uranium oxide.

Pereverzev was in good humour, pointing out to the German the beginnings of post-war reconstruction in the city. It was October 1945 and Moscow was slowly shedding its wartime austerity. Hans observed the many groups of German PoWs clearing rubble with their bare hands. Some were on scaffolding, laying bricks. During the early months of *Operation Barbarossa* these same men had believed they were invincible, trampling all over the Ukraine and Russia behind their panzer tanks. Now they were human fodder for Stalin, expendable labour. Hans shuddered when one large group brought the car to a halt. A PoW had attempted to see who was in the car and Hans had put a hand across his face.

The car slowed outside Laboratory No. 2, a large distinguished-looking building. The driver ignored the main entrance, stopping instead at the large gate to the side that guarded the entrance to the compound. Seeing Pereverzev, the guards waved the vehicle through. In the evening gloom Hans saw the outlines of rows of prefab huts under the trees. However, the driver had another destination – a lovely house out of character with the austere surroundings, constructed of wood and flooded with light. Pereverzev ushered the German into the foyer and left.

'Hello my SS friend,' called out Igor Kurchatov descending the grand staircase. 'You unexpectedly survived Taboshar, quite a remarkable feat. Come,' said the physicist, smoothing out his long beard. The house was lavishly furnished and smelt of polish. In the study Kurchatov sat behind his opulent desk and offered his guest a seat.

'How perverse,' Kurchatov said. 'In 1939 you start your scientific career at the Kaiser Wilhelm, the centre for nuclear physics in Germany, now six years later you are sitting in Russia's equivalent. What would your parents have made of it? Do you think they survived the war?'

Hans was still taken aback by such a welcoming reception. He smiled at Kurchatov. Thoughts of his parents had of course crossed his mind many times as he sat quietly in the church in Alma-Ata.

'You've been very resourceful,' continued Kurchatov, not waiting for a response. 'We sent you to Taboshar but to be honest we never believed you would survive. I was very surprised when I received a cable from Alma-Ata's NKVD office concerning your application to work in our laboratories. Of course I willingly gave my permission but Comrade Beria, in his usual way, vehemently opposed any move, even suggesting that you be sent to the Uigar-Sai uranium mine in Kazakhstan, where the conditions are even worse than Taboshar. Stalin finally authorized the request.'

'I can only thank you,' responded Hans quickly.

'Tell me about Taboshar and Mailu-Su, are they as bad as I hear?' enquired Kurchatov. 'I need an independent assessment, not the usual lies I'm used to receiving. You have a report for me?'

After an hour the housekeeper interrupted them. Comrade Flerov was waiting downstairs, just returned from another mission into Germany. 'Ask Georgii to join us,' said Kurchatov, 'and bring us some wine.'

Flerov was instantly recognisable. Hans had never forgotten his intense questioning in the Kremlin, especially over the activities of the isotope separation facility in Dresden. There was no surprise on Flerov's face as he saw the German. Hans could only guess that Kurchatov must have pre-warned Flerov about his expected guest. The housekeeper brought the wine and Hans nursed his glass before taking a sip, unsure of the situation in which he found himself. Kurchatov strode over to his gramophone, recently imported from New York with its stack of records.

With Bach wafting around the study Kurchatov returned to his desk and opened the bottom drawer.

Hans did a double-take when he saw the black notebook. Kurchatov tossed it to Flerov. 'The war is over, Hitler is defeated,' stated Kurchatov, raising his eyebrows at the German. 'Beria still dismisses your notebook as a clever forgery, contrived by either the Abwehr or British Intelligence, but he can't make up his mind which one. I and my colleagues, however, have made great use of it. Contrary to Comrade Beria's beliefs the formulae did work. You had written them down correctly, and they hadn't been doctored. But that doesn't clear you of being involved in a conspiracy.'

'I told you in 1942 that my notebook was genuine, you have my word. Why would I have risked my life if it wasn't?' retorted Hans indignantly, immediately regretting the annoyance in his voice.

'None of us can comprehend why Comrade Stalin has taken such a personal interest in you,' said Flerov, flicking casually through the notebook.

'I cannot help you. I have no idea why either,' replied Hans.

'Now that the war has ended, would you like to hear what happened to your colleagues at the Kaiser Wilhelm?' asked Kurchatov, helping himself to another glass of wine.

'Of course. Did the Red Army capture them when Berlin fell?'

'We found some, but Heisenberg, Wirtz and von Weizsäcker and others were taken by the British and Americans in the south of Germany. Our sources in London report that 10 are being interrogated at some country house near Cambridge. The Americans are insisting they be treated as war criminals and tried.

'It is on account of your former colleagues that I arranged your removal from Alma-Ata. Many of the scientists and engineers we did capture, who were involved in the German atomic bomb project, have agreed to work for us. They and their families are being transported to nuclear centres in the USSR as we speak. One group will come to the Elektrostal facility here in Moscow. This facility has only been in operation for a year. You will know of it only as Plant 12, where your uranium oxide from Taboshar is used to produce metallic uranium. Your presence may help in settling our German friends down in their new Russian environment. Comrade Savva Zolotukhin is the director and from tomorrow you will be working for him,' Kurchatov chuckled.

'You are to report to Dr Nicholas Riehl. That name will ring a bell, of course, it is one of the many names you included in your notebook. Riehl was the chief engineer of the Auer plant in Oranienburg, but unfortunately the facility was completely destroyed by an American bombing raid in the last month of the war and all uranium stocks destroyed.'

'I remember Riehl, I met him once at Gatow. Are you going to tell him about me?' asked Hans tentatively.

'Riehl will only be told that you were captured somewhere along the Taganrog to Mariupol road, researching into possible uranium sources,' said Kurchatov.

'But there were no uranium sources in that area,' Hans pointed out.

'That is no longer correct. Our geologists have identified one location to the north of Mariupol. It is too early to say, but radium has been found and, as you know very well, uranium oxide is often found nearby. You have nothing to fear. Few are aware of the real reason why you were in Krivaya Kosa, and Stalin has insisted that situation will remain. Incidentally, the mines in Lermontev in the northern Caucasus, your true destination, were reassessed by our mineralogists given the German interest in them and are now in production. They could be very productive over time.'

The wine flowed as Hans enjoyed the hospitality and he freely answered questions on some of the German scientists coming to Russia. It was late and Flerov offered to walk Hans to his quarters. They strolled through the compound, now in darkness. Only the glow of cigarettes smoked by patrolling guards was visible. In the guardroom the word was that Georgii Flerov was highly respected by Stalin. Kurchatov barely tolerated.

Both men halted in front of a tall building that Hans had seen earlier on the drive to Kurchatov's house. It was surrounded by barbed wire with two guards at its entrance, their rifles at the ready.

'Is this the reactor?' Hans enquired.

'Yes, but it's underground and far from complete. We won't be going critical for many months yet. The graphite is available but we are still very short of high quality metallic uranium. We are still combing Germany for supplies,' replied Flerov.

'Did the Nazis get this far? The only reactor I saw was the prototype in the underground laboratory in the Kaiser Wilhelm Institute for Physics,' asked Hans.

Flerov drew in his breath, pondering on how best to reply. He contemplated telling van der Velde how close the German scientists were in achieving their aim. At the Kaiser Wilhelm and later in Haigerloch and Hechingen, Heisenberg and von Weizsäcker had perfected the process, and the highly secret facility in Dresden had been a major worry for the Soviets since 1942. The RAF and US 8th Airforce had taken care of the problem with its massive aerial bombardment.

'No, the Nazis were years from building their bomb,' said Flerov flatly after a long pause. 'Let me show you to your room.'

Fuelled by the wine sleep came easily to Hans, but he was soon jolted awake as the door opened with a crash. Beria walked in, followed by a member of his bodyguard.

'We meet again. I hope you are well,' said Beria in his usual abrasive manner. 'Still peddling your stories, I hear, and I understand we are to send you to Plant 12, one of our most secret locations. We really are very careless.' Hans jumped out of bed and hastily dressed, panic-stricken at meeting Beria again.

'Now you are back in Moscow, I will be watching you. One false move...' grinned Beria, turning on his heel. His bodyguard lingered, pointing two fingers to the side of the German's temple and pulling an imaginary trigger before leaving to join his master.

* * *

Riehl was to prove an exceptional catch for the Soviets, but he was often rebellious. Kurchatov, Pervukhin and General Zavenyagin often wrote to Beria asking for better working conditions for the German scientists at Elektrostal. Beria turned them down. In his letter to Beria on October 2, 1946, Kurchatov warned of Riehl's worsening mental state and his constant yearning to return to Germany. This time better housing, accommodation and rations were provided. Riehl never stopped writing and complaining, but he was indispensable with his knowledge of metallic uranium manufacture. After the successful test in August 1949 he wrote to Stalin, demanding to know why he hadn't been invited to witness it. By 1953 Riehl was desperate for home, writing to Beria on May 6 and begging to leave. Zavenyagin responded to Beria's memo, insisting that the German would be a major loss and had to remain in the Soviet Union. Taking advantage of a trip to the uranium mines in Czechoslovakia in 1956 Riehl finally escaped to freedom.

In Elektrostal Hans had worked mainly in an administrative capacity, although from time to time had cause to visit other laboratories where German scientists were based. In Laboratory No. 5, located at Obninsk, 60 miles south of Moscow, many concentrated on uranium isotope separation and the building of a nuclear reactor. The facility was headed by Dr Heinz Pose, the former deputy director of the Kaiser Wilhelm Institute for Physics, who, with his family, had moved from Berlin in February 1946. Within three weeks Pose returned to Germany with General Victor Kravchenko and Major Kachkachian of the NKGB, on a recruiting mission to persuade more German specialists in the Soviet zone to work in Russia. Kravchenko returned to Moscow while Pose and Kachkachian visited Leipzig, and the Siemens and AEG plants in Mansfeld, located south of Magdeburg.

The Russians ploughed huge investment into Obninsk. As well as the reactor, 16 laboratories were constructed, almost all headed by Germans. Obninsk became a closed community, with entry and departure strictly controlled. The wives of the scientists taught the children. Pose, an influential and dedicated director, was best remembered as a regular entertainer on the piano. In 1952 the German group transferred to Sinop, near Sukhumi in Georgia, but Pose and his family remained in Obninsk at the request of Mikhailovich Mescheryakov, a senior director of the new Soviet nuclear research institute in Dubna, the closed scientific city. Sinop, divided into the secretive Laboratory H and the Agudzeri facilities, was the home for the group until 1955 when most of the Germans left for East Germany. Despite its secrecy the Russians allowed three British atomic physicists to visit in 1956 as part of a reciprocal arrangement to celebrate Khruschev's trip to Britain the same year.

Pose accepted an offer in 1957 from the University of Dresden to head the department of neutron physics, later becoming director of the Nuclear Physics Institute in the city and employing Klaus Fuchs, released early from jail in England.

In all, 200 Germans worked on the Russian nuclear programme, of which 53 were key scientists. Few, like Riehl, were treated well.

It was on a trip to Obninsk that Hans was urgently called to a telephone to take a call from Kurchatov. The date was August 21, 1949.

There had been no time for sleep as he arrived at Laboratory No. 2, passing lines of stationary trucks leading to the compound. For an hour he waited outside Kurchatov's office witnessing the same flurry of activity that he had seen at the Heereswaffenamt offices in Gatow one week before *Operation Barbarossa* Something was up and he could hazard a guess as to what it was.

The conversation was short. Hans could clearly see that Kurchatov had weighty matters on his mind.

'I've just returned from the Kremlin and a meeting with Comrade Stalin,' stated Kurchatov. 'Very shortly a tumultuous event will shock the world and I have been instructed that you should witness it. I'm in a hurry so please talk to Pereverzev who has the details.' That was the last conversation Hans ever had with Igor Kurchatov As Hans walked out the door he almost collided with Beria. He averted his eyes and hurried away, oblivious to the hate in Beria's eyes that bored into his back.

Pereverzev offered the German a chair and some coffee, which was most welcome, before reading out aloud the contents of a memo dictated some hours earlier.

'Reference: Hans van der Velde

'Given the exceptional service committed to the USSR by Hans van der Velde, Comrade Stalin in my meeting this morning has ordered he attend the testing of the 'piece' in Semipalatinsk. Van der Velde should attend the meeting of scientists and engineers at the Yakor Hotel at 7pm this evening for further instructions.

'On my advice to Comrade Stalin it was agreed that van der Velde should not attend as a civilian, as that may lead to questions from some quarters, especially from the scientists as to his exact role in the test. He must therefore wear a military uniform that would give the impression that he is a member of the heavy security that surrounds this operation.'

Kurchatov had signed the note and dated it August 21, 1949.

Hans could barely take in what Pereverzev had related to him as he ambled slowly to the visitors' accommodation hut where a bed had been reserved for him.

A final surprise awaited the former Wehrgeologen officer who used to wear the infamous black uniform of the SS. On the bed was the grey uniform of a major in the MGB, the successor organisation to the NKVD and the NKGB. That had been Kurchatov's idea – he was renowned for his wicked sense of humour.

CHAPTER 34

The day Russia entered the nuclear age

At the Semipalatinsk landing strip transport aircraft landed and took off every 10 minutes, such was the level of activity at the site of Russia's first ever nuclear test. The scientists had settled in and were equipping their laboratories. Dokuchayev, however, was near to panic. With just five days to go his apparatus had yet to arrive from Chelyabinsk-40. Together with a colleague he commandeered a lorry and drove over the rough terrain to the railway station where he was horrified, yet relieved, to locate two uncoupled goods wagons isolated on a branch line. He forced open a door and was astonished to be faced with a large Russian-style cooker. 'At least we will be able to eat,' he laughed to his associate. To their relief, the radio-chemistry instruments were found in the other wagon.

There were five laboratories on the testing ground, spread across three buildings and located about 30 miles away from the 180-feet high tower that held the 'piece' as Kurchatov called it – RDS-1, the plutonium bomb. Dokuchayev's team occupied a laboratory where material would be analysed as quickly as possible after the explosion. Next door were the biologists who had tethered a selection of animals in some ramshackle buildings a mile from the epicentre. If the animals weren't blown to pieces, they would be dissected. On the eve of the test, August 28, 1949, Dokuchayev and his team were ready, their equipment fully tested.

Kurchatov was angry at an unexpected snag. Low cloud and rain persisted as the pilots of two Petlyakov attack bombers, powered by two powerful Klimov engines and capable of 336 mph, had practised flying as steady as they could through the clouds. No Russian pilot had experience of flying through the turbulence that would be caused by a high-pressure explosion. Unfortunately, after one practice run a heavy landing damaged the undercarriage of one aircraft, rendering it unserviceable. If the inclement weather endured there was now doubt that the remaining Petlyakov could take off. The planes were to fly over the explosion epicentre to measure radiation levels as soon as the mushroom cloud had dispersed. Scientists from the Karpov Institute of Physical Chemistry in Moscow, pioneers of measuring radon in Taboshar, had manufactured radiation filter pods. Yak-9V aircraft had tested them first, but the Petlyakov planes were considered more suitable for the Semipalatinsk test site.

All was not lost, however. A year earlier the Radium Institute in Leningrad had built two secret monitoring stations, positioned 12 miles outside the city. Large dishes collected snow and rain in which strontium, antimony, silver and other materials could be isolated from the atmosphere. Measuring some six feet in diameter, these two dishes had proved incredibly accurate. From these samples the Russians could precisely monitor the composition of any American atomic test exploded anywhere in the world. The same dishes were now to monitor RDS-1.

By late afternoon engineers had checked one final time the positioning of RDS-1 at the top of the tower. There was an invitation to gather at Kurchatov's accommodation. 'Kurchatov was radiant, charming and polite to everyone,' remembered Dokuchayev, 'quite a contrast to an anxious Khariton, the science head from Arzamas-16.' At first Kurchatov seemed reticent in telling everyone the time of the test, but he then confided that it was to be 6am.

Kurchatov, his deputy Alexander Vinogradov and Boris Nikitin conducted one last tour of the laboratories. Beria arrived at the site and called an immediate meeting of the key scientists before putting in a call to Moscow. There had been surprise that Stalin wasn't to witness the explosion, the result of his untiring efforts to ensure that Russia became a nuclear power. Stalin had thought about going to Semipalatinsk but he continued to harbour doubts as to whether RDS-1 would work. In the event of failure at least he could blame Beria.

Dokuchayev retired to his makeshift bed in his laboratory, but he could only doze given his excitement. At around 8pm a Red Army colonel arrived and asked a surprised Dokuchayev to confirm his name with proof of identity. The colonel then broke the news that Dokuchayev had been selected by Kurchatov to be one of the eight observers in NP-2, the observation point six miles south of the epicentre. The radiochemist was ecstatic.

Before he left the colonel told Dokuchayev to assemble outside the laboratories at 2am, no later. 'He warned me not to oversleep,' recalled Dokuchayev, who actually didn't sleep a wink, constantly checking his watch. At 1.30am he walked outside to where a bus was waiting. A crowd had gathered as word had leaked out that the bus would be taking a chosen few for a grandstand view. There was a scramble to board but the colonel soon restored order. Only eight were to go he told the group of scientists. The colonel called out seven names: Vinogradov, Nikitin, Zeldovich, Mescheryakov – an observer of the American nuclear tests in Bikini Atoll in 1946, Major General Dukhov – the chief designer of RDS-1 and a great friend of Stalin, and Dukhov's adjutant, Ivan. Dokuchayev also claimed his seat, unable to believe he was in such exalted company.

Records confirm that eight observers did view the test from NP-2, one an MGB officer whose name has been omitted from official documents. With the lucky few chattering excitedly inside the bus at it waited to leave, the major had emerged from the shadows, his new credentials verified by the colonel. As the bus set off on its long and bumpy drive to NP-2, a distance of 40 miles, the former SS officer kept his own counsel.

Another bus had delivered nine further observers, this time at KP-1, the central control room located four miles north of the tower that held the bomb. Kurchatov alighted first, striding briskly into the underground bunker. Beria, General Osetrov, the head of security at the Semipalatinsk test site, Pereverzev, Flerov, Shchelkin, Pervukhin, General Zavenyagin and Khariton quickly followed. Inside was very basic. Next to the control room was an observation position with a wide slit in the concrete wall, and one periscope.

In NP-2 the bunker was merely a crudely dug hole with a periscope cemented into the sand. The bus driver had dropped off the eight observers and the colonel, then left. There was nothing for them to do but wait. The MGB officer kept his distance and walked out into the scrub in the dark. At 5.30am the sky lightened but the sun remained lost behind the rain clouds. It was pretty miserable and the observers questioned whether the test would be delayed. Rain looked imminent. The steel tower was clearly visible in the distance.

Connected to KP-1 by radio, the colonel alerted the observers to what was happening in the control centre. The command 'Ch', short for 'Chas', Russian for 'the hour', would blow the detonators that had been carefully positioned around the plutonium core by Brish in Arzamas, setting off the chain reaction. With minutes to go, the colonel reported that due to the inclement weather the test had moved back an hour to 7am. Some 10 minutes later the time was changed again, this time to 6.30am.

While they waited the group tried on their protective glasses that would shield their eyes from the glare of the explosion. The colonel repeated the instructions. They were to stand on the edge of the embankment and face the tower with their glasses on. After the command 'Ch', they should watch the explosion for no more than 20 seconds, as the first sonic wave would reach NP-2 some 10 seconds later. They must then jump into the dugout and remain facedown until it was safe to get up.

Zeldovich talked quietly with Mescheryakov, Vinogradov with Nikitin. Dokuchayev was introspective. At 6.29am the colonel called out at 10-second intervals. The eight observers stood on the embankment. Not all wore their glasses, some finding them too dark to see.

The sky lit up in a large ball of flame with vivid colours. 'It was like a giant welding torch,' Dokuchayev remembered. 'The flash terminated quickly, in a manner of seconds. The white semisphere was shortly followed by a rising column, white at the bottom and getting blacker as it rose to form a mushroom cloud.' Within seconds the mushroom hit cloud level, measuring a mile in height. Below, the air was sucked into its core. With hindsight Dokuchayev wished he hadn't worn the glasses so that he could have seen the real intensity of the light and colour.

The colonel had counted off the seconds before the sonic wave hit, a deafening roar of frightening intensity gathering speed and condensing into the hills of the Semipalatinsk desert. 'It was like the tank battle at Velikye Luki,' said Dokuchayev 'but one hundred times worse.' Once the wave passed, the group marvelled at the huge white and black cloud. Dukhov broke the silence. 'Long live Comrade Stalin,' he cried, 'I'll now become a Lieutenant General,' rocking with laughter.

Unexpectedly, the sun emerged from the clouds. The second shock wave passed not so intense as the first. Suddenly the wind increased in intensity, before dying away. The air was stuffy and hot to the skin.

There was only profound disappointment in KP-1. The slit in the concrete wall had been too narrow, limiting the view and observation of the full height of the mushroom. Beria was initially upset but he quickly regained his composure as the spectacle was overawing. He embraced Kurchatov, much to everyone's surprise. Never before had they witnessed the man express any elation or affection. Kurchatov, however, had other matters on his mind. He needed to urgently drive to NP-2 to talk to Mescheryakov in order to compare this test with the American Bikini Atoll explosions which Mescheryakov had witnessed at first hand.

Meanwhile, the observers at NP-2 were witnessing other events, and were horrified. The glint of the turrets of the two KV tanks carrying apparatus to measure radioactivity was clearly visible just yards from the epicentre. Aleksei Burzonian, the Russian Health Minister in charge of radiation safety, had considered his orders a great service to his country. To the observers in NP-2 his actions were suicidal. Both tanks stopped on the edge of the crater. Burzonian opened the hatch of one and looked into the morass of solidified and melted matter, breathing in the radioactivity. Minutes later a platoon of Red Army soldiers also arrived, they too without any breathing apparatus, but carrying radioactivity meters. Eventually they marched away, an officer striding out proudly at the front. Within moments of leaving the area some were terribly sick, already dying of radiation. Burzonian would be charmed. He would live for a further 20 years.

It took Kurchatov's driver two hours to reach NP-2 due to the detour he had to make. When he did arrive at 9am the scientists stood in line to greet him.

'Igor Vasilyevich,' Nikitin proudly declared, 'you have created something which is beyond this earth.' With tears in his eyes Kurchatov congratulated everyone, apart from the MGB major who stood away. Kurchatov, however, did acknowledge his presence and smiled. The major smiled back.

But it was Mescheryakov, the man who had done least on the project, who to everyone's surprise had the ear of his chief for a full 30 minutes. Away from the group the two whispered earnestly. Kurchatov had snubbed Zeldovich, the physicist who had established the very fundamentals of nuclear fission in Russia. Dokuchayev and the others had found it strange that Zeldovich wasn't at KP-1.

Not long after Kurchatov had left, another car was seen speeding towards NP-2. Its occupants were genuine MGB officers, Beria's bodyguards with an arrest order. The colonel argued with them but it was no use. Much to everyone's surprise the major who had not said a word all the time he was at NP-2 was bundled into the back of the car, which then sped off in the direction of the Semipalatinsk landing strip.

At 10am the bus arrived and Dokuchayev and his group returned to the laboratories. There was much work to do and no time for celebration. The KP-1 observers had also left, but not before Beria had called Stalin. The time difference was three hours between Semipalatinsk and Moscow but Stalin was already awake. Beria related the good news but was disappointed at Stalin's off-hand reaction. 'I know you had a good test,' was the jovial response. Stalin had already received calls from two of the many Army generals at the Semipalatinsk site. These men never returned to Moscow, nothing is known of their fate and Stalin never questioned their disappearance – Beria's bodyguards had rooted them out. Beria had personally wanted to break the news to the Soviet Premier.

In the radiochemical laboratory the first sample awaited Dokuchayev – a minute piece of the vaporized steel tower that had been sucked up into the atmosphere and deposited some distance away, now unrecognizable as metal and still warm to the touch. The biologists were already at work on a quivering dog, panting for breath, its eyes bulging and pouring fluid and blood from every orifice.

Early the next day three members of the radiochemistry team inspected the actual crater for samples. Dokuchayev, with two Radium Institute colleagues, Nikolay Vlasov and Nikolay Gorshkov had donned overalls, rubber gloves, Army boots, thick socks and underwear. The crater was now guarded by soldiers wearing just regular uniforms. Each scientist carried an Army kit bag and a dustpan and brush. They carefully picked their way around the crater's edge. The sintered sand was hot to the touch, even through their thick gloves. Vlasov's radioactivity measure showed a level of 50,000 microroentgens at the edge of the crater. When he clambered into the bottom of the crater, the needle went off the scale.

They spent 15 minutes at the epicentre, the maximum time limit they had set themselves. For as far as the eye could see the sparse vegetation had been destroyed. There was no noise, no birds. Dokuchayev observed that the shape of the crater was unusual. It was unlike that formed by a conventional explosive where the depression is usually relatively steep with ragged sides. Here, he stood in a crater resembling a symmetrical 'plate', five yards in diameter and just five feet in depth, full of rock, sand, parts of the bomb and general debris. The chemists had filled their kit bags and they returned to the car to remove the gas masks. The driver dropped them off at the nearest Army sanitation station, then carried on to the laboratories with the samples for analysis.

By late afternoon Dokuchayev experienced a sensation of intoxication, what he later described as 'false courage'. A radiological safety officer twice insisted he shower again in another attempt to rid himself of radiation. He felt dizzy and warm, too warm, and his eyes were sensitive to the daylight. A car took Dokuchayev back to his quarters on the banks of Lake Irtysh. He had a meal but felt nauseous. In a bid to beat off the sickness he dived into the water of the lake and swam around before drying off and sleeping for three hours.

The following day his eyesight was restored to normal but this time the sampling of the epicentre was conducted by Iosif Starik, the professor from the Radium Institute who had successfully led many of the search teams seeking out uranium oxide in the Kazakhstan and Uzbekistan deserts. Kurchatov visited the laboratories. Sampling continued on the first two days of September, but at the end of the second day an unexpected order from Moscow recalled the radiochemical team to

Leningrad and Chelyabinsk-40, to everyone's great dismay as much work was unfinished. Before they departed Semipalatinsk each scientist signed a secrecy agreement forbidding any disclosure, forever.

Stalin suppressed the news of the test. There were no parties and no champagne, unlike the American celebrations after the test in Alamogordo. Within weeks more nuclear facilities were commissioned. In Krasnoyarsk a new plutonium plant, Krasnoyarsk-16, was under construction, and in Tomsk and Verkh-Neivinsk, diffusion plants were put into operation to produce U-235. Kurchatov and Khariton studied designs from academician Keldysh on nuclear-tipped rockets, plans to power submarines and icebreakers with nuclear piles.

Pravda reported officially only on September 25, almost a month after the event. However, the Americans didn't need *Pravda* to confirm what they already knew. A fleet of B-29s patrolling Russian borders had picked up the explosion at Semipalatinsk with their sophisticated aerosol measurement devices attached to the nose and wings of the aircraft. Washington didn't share this confirmation at first with the British. Britain's Prime Minister, Clement Atlee, summoned his senior scientific advisor, Sir Henry Tizard, for an opinion. *'Have the Russians just produced an atomic bomb, or has a catastrophe just happened?'* he enquired. Tizard's written reply the following day was very short. *'I find it very difficult to believe that the Russians have produced a bomb in such a short time. An accident to an atomic pile could not be ruled out.'* Tizard also shared with Atlee an equally disturbing item from MI5. Klaus Fuchs was about to be unmasked as a Soviet agent of nine years standing.

Much of Russia's heavy bomber fleet was secretly already undergoing conversion to carry atomic bombs. General Zavenyagin wrote to Beria on November 1, to complain that the modification of the TU-4 bomb bays wasn't proceeding fast enough. The Tupolev aircraft, capable of flying non-stop for 3,600 miles, were almost exact copies of the Boeing B-29 Superfortresses, the same aircraft adapted to deliver the Hiroshima and Nagasaki bombs. In the latter months of the war against Japan a number of B-29s had made emergency landings on Soviet territory and the aircraft were confiscated and copied. Within ten years the USSR had a fleet of more than 420.

After the test Stalin began awarding medals and prizes. He had asked Beria to prepare a list of potential recipients. Alferov, Dukhov, Flerov, Khariton, Shchelkin and Zeldovich were the first to be awarded Stalin's Prize in the First Degree. Flerov also received 150,000 roubles and Dukhov was given the 'Hammer and Sickle' medal for his bomb design. All five men were provided with a dacha, a Pobeda car, education of their children at any Soviet educational establishment at the expense of the State and free travel for life. Kurchatov would receive every top award. In all there were 39 awards in the First Degree, 112 in the Second and 25 in the Third. Beria's initial list of possible recipients was returned with Stalin's handwriting scrawled across it: *'Why is Riehl missing?'* He didn't argue and added Riehl's name, but Stalin went further. As well as awarding the German scientist from Plant 12 Stalin's Prize in the First Degree, he gave him the title of 'Hero of Soviet Labour' and a payment of 350,000 roubles – a princely sum, equivalent to nearly $400,000 at that time.

One significant name was missing from the final list – a radiochemist who had survived the appalling early days of Chelyabinsk-40 and who was instrumental in developing the plutonium process that manufactured the material for the Semipalatinsk bomb. The former tank commander had no wish to be decorated. He still vividly remembered the harsh and unfair treatment meted out to the former Soviet PoWs in the construction of Chelyabinsk whose only wartime crime was to surrender to the Germans. To much amazement Yakov Dokuchayev had declined the Stalin Prize – he had no need of it.

The MGB had their own heroes, not just the four officers that were prominent in *Operation Enormoz*, the mission to steal the West's atomic secrets – Vladimir Barkovsky, Aleksandr Feklisov, Leonid Kvashnikov and Anatoli Yatskov. Other officers such as Anatoli Gorsky were also decorated. Not everyone benefited, however. Many Jewish members of the MGB were subsequently purged by Stalin, jailed and spent the rest of their lives without a pension, living in purgatory.

Kurchatov became increasingly dissatisfied with Stalin's plan to build a huge nuclear arsenal, but he was in a very small minority and he had to be mindful of his opinions. A year after Stalin's death the USSR, in a massive show of power, undertook its first military exercise using nuclear weapons. At Totsk, on September 14, 1954, Marshal Zhukov, the great wartime hero, commanded 45,000 servicemen as atomic bombs equivalent to 45,000 tons of TNT, or three times the power of the Nagasaki plutonium device, were exploded nearby. Not to be outdone the United States conducted eight similar exercises, but under better safety conditions.

During the period from 1945 to the end of all nuclear testing in 1996, some 2,050 bombs were exploded in total, of which the Americans tested 1,032 and the Russians 715. Of the remainder, France tested 210, Britain 45 and China 48. Only two bombs were ever used in anger.

* * *

For Hans, his witnessing of the bomb test at Semipalatinsk provided the stark realisation that he had merely been a conduit for transferring nuclear secrets from one dictator to another. Stalin, armed with his super weapon, would now be able to preserve a system that enslaved and murdered millions.

After his arrest at NP-2 Hans was taken to the landing strip for immediate transportation to Moscow. Kurchatov, who might have come to his aid, was of no help now. At the airfield Hans was ordered to change out of the MGB uniform. There were few other passengers on the flight, but Beria was among them. As he climbed aboard he glared triumphantly at the prisoner sitting between guards at the back of the plane. One of Beria's bodyguards, the same henchman that Hans had met in 1945 at Laboratory No. 2 after his summons from Alma Ata, pointed two fingers at his temple and laughed.

Constant refuelling stops had contributed to Hans' anguish as the aircraft flew inexorably closer to Moscow. When he tried to sleep he was prodded awake by the guards. Memories flashed in his mind – Maria, his girlfriend from Munich, his friendship with Franz and Helmut in Berlin, and above all the horrors of war he had witnessed in the Ukraine and Russia. He had never forgotten Lemberg and the wholesale slaughter of several hundred of the city's civilians in the jail, nor the death, for which he was responsible, of his Wehrgeologen colleague in Krivaya Kosa, mown down in a hail of bullets as he ran for his life. As a prisoner of the Russian sappers, Hans' nightmare journey in the sanya across the frozen Taganrog Bay to Yeysk was a recurrent nightmare. He feared now that his life had run its course, to end so soon after Russia had entered the nuclear era.

The aircraft banked sharply over Vnukovo before levelling out to land. Beria left first. His bodyguard grabbed Hans and half dragged him to the exit.

The final hand in the extraordinary story of Major Hans van der Velde, however, was yet to be played. Three other men appeared, also in MGB uniform, the senior officer flashing an order bearing Stalin's signature. A scuffle ensued, but the diminutive yet forceful officer stood his ground. Beria's bodyguard rushed away to make a desperate phone call. Stalin had played his joker and within the day he would spirit Hans out of the Soviet Union forever, repaying the debt he owed to the SS officer.

CHAPTER 35

Meeting Malone

The cryptanalysts were puzzled by the regular use of the term *Material G* in the wartime radio traffic from the Russian Consulate in New York. But by early 1948 American code breakers, assisted by experts in Britain, were coming tantalisingly close to identifying the expression. *Venona* was soon to uncover its first great secret. The breakthrough came in February 1949 and the results were unambiguous. British Foreign Office telegrams sent from London to the Embassy in Washington during 1944–1945 had been passed to Soviet agents. There had been a traitor in the British Embassy with access to the most confidential of documents, including letters to the Ambassador from Winston Churchill, the Prime Minister, and Anthony Eden, the Foreign Secretary.

Elizabeth recalled the buzz around the Embassy in March 1948 as rumours first circulated from the Ambassador's floor. She had spent her war years in the War Office, in a top-secret department dealing with the funding of nationalist groups in the Balkans. The news of her posting and subsequent promotion to Washington was exciting after a trying period in post-war Berlin working with a group of three Army officers, among them Goronwy Rees, who was a great friend of the diplomat Guy Burgess. She had grown tired of Rees, brilliant though he was. He could never be relied upon and was never around when needed, always with the excuse that some other department needed to utilise his language skills. His whereabouts were often shrouded in the general chaos that was Berlin in the weeks and months after Germany's surrender. No one at that time was aware that Rees, recruited by Burgess and codenamed *Gross* by the Soviets, had provided the NKVD and NKGB with wartime secrets.

The most senior female employee in the Embassy, Elizabeth spent much of her time at the Pentagon. There had been heated argument in Berlin between the British and Americans over expenditure in their respective occupied zones. The British, with the bigger zone and the greatest number of PoWs, refugees and displaced persons, felt strongly that the Americans should at least pay an equal share of the monthly expenditure. An impasse ensued, leading to the creation of a joint administrative operation codenamed *Bizonia*, with Washington the obvious base location.

Each week Elizabeth had met a representative in the Pentagon and for days they would pore through the stack of bills from Berlin, apportioning payment on a strict 50:50 basis and striking a balance. If the Americans had underpaid, a cheque made out in dollars was handed over and she would immediately deposit it with a US grain agency to pay for another vital consignment to bankrupt Britain.

Working in America's capital was an exhilarating experience for Elizabeth. The Embassy staff worked hard, but played hard as well, frequenting the bars in

Georgetown, especially the Nat King Cole and the Mayflower restaurant. It was around November when the rumour that a wartime employee had spied for Russia became more than just a topic of conversation. Everyone received notification that someone would shortly be arriving from London to interview all staff, at all levels.

Christmas came and went, and only in January 1949 did Major Sampson finally appear. He was friendly and good-looking, as more than one female employee quickly observed. The reputation of the MI5 officer had gone before him – Sampson was the 'spycatcher', in charge of internal security and by all accounts tough and gritty. After an exhausting session at the Pentagon it was Elizabeth's turn to be interviewed. She was asked to expound on her daily routine, who she met and what she did for social activities. After a week Sampson flew back to London and business at the Embassy returned to normal.

Sampson's report completely exonerated present staff. However, he had been disturbed by the accounts of the apparent lifestyle of Donald Maclean, who had returned to London in October 1948 to prepare himself for a posting to Cairo. Elizabeth and other members of staff were disgusted that the Ambassador had never disciplined the diplomat. If the same boorish behaviour were exhibited by anyone else there would be an immediate return ticket to London and an unpleasant appointment with the head of personnel followed by dismissal. Sampson was thanked for his report but his remarks on Maclean remained in the file, his warnings unheeded.

Maclean had been posted to the Embassy in 1944 as First Secretary. Most mornings he had appeared the worse for wear, his clothes dishevelled, reeking of stale cigarettes and yesterday's booze. He and his American wife, Melinda, enjoyed the privilege and trappings of diplomatic status. Their nightlife was the talk of the Embassy, and the gossip had intensified – Donald and Melinda were 'swingers', not choosy about dallying with either sex. The bingeing grew out of control, but still the reprimand never came. They had a close circle of friends, people who would protect Maclean if events spiralled out of control – as they invariably did.

One such friend was Sir Ronald Campbell, the Foreign Office representative in Washington who was closely concerned with *Tube Alloys*. Atlee, Britain's Prime Minister, had sought Campbell's opinion on the reorganization of *Tube Alloys* after the war had ended – the very report that Atlee, Bevin, Cripps and Anderson had discussed in Downing Street on August 10, 1945, the day after *Fat Man* had been dropped on Nagasaki.

If Philby was the agent held in the highest regard by the Soviets, Maclean was considered the most intelligent, the brilliant mind who many contemporaries in their misguided opinions expected to reach the upper pinnacles of the Foreign Office. The son of Sir Donald Maclean, a Cabinet Member in Ramsay Macdonald's National Government, Maclean had begun to pass intelligence in 1938 when he worked in the Paris Embassy. His controller was Katie Harris, who photographed the stolen documents from her apartment nearby before returning them to her charge. Donald was soon infatuated with her and they started to sleep together. Of British origin, Harris, codenamed *Gypsy* and *Adder*, had been recruited into the Comintern in the 1920s and had worked for the NKVD since 1931. Moscow had deliberately arranged a female controller for Maclean as it was worried about his homosexuality. In Paris bars a drunken Maclean would anonymously move around picking up soldiers and anyone else who caught his fancy. With Paris hastily evacuated after the German invasion of the city, Maclean and his wife-to-be, Melinda, fled to Bordeaux. A British warship later conveyed them and other British citizens to Britain.

From London, Maclean, using the codenames of *Homer* and *Leaf*, fulfilled his potential at the Foreign Office. On September 15, 1941, he handed a package to the NKVD *resident* Colonel Anatoli Gorsky that concerned British and American foreign policy on Iran, the Baltic States and Byelorussia. Also included was a report on the Foreign Office's dealings with the exiled Polish Government in London, confirmed from another impeccable source; one of the exiles was a fellow NKVD agent. Of particular interest to Moscow was correspondence between Churchill and Roosevelt on possible ideas to convince Russia that an Allied invasion of Japan might be feasible sometime in the future if launched from Soviet soil. Stalin held Maclean in great store.

In the course of the next three years before his posting to Washington Maclean had passed over to his controllers numerous Foreign Office secrets, including reports on Churchill's plans to strike a separate peace deal with Hitler in order to thwart Stalin's plans to expand USSR influence into Central and Eastern Europe. Anthony Blunt, working in MI5 and codenamed *Tony*, had provided documents on the same subject.

The behaviour of Maclean in London, however, was as bad if not sometimes worse than in Paris. He had become an inveterate bisexual, a situation that angered his wife. Konstantin Kukin, the NKVD *resident* who had taken over from Gorsky, was so concerned about the situation that he cabled Moscow many times, suggesting that Maclean's antics could compromise other sources. Such misdemeanours were quickly forgotten though when Maclean passed over to Kukin one last package before his passage to Washington. The contents were of particular interest to Stalin. They were copies of the actual transcripts of Churchill's conversations with Tito and Shubanich, the head of the Croatian Peasant Party, over the limitation of influence of the Yugoslav Communist Party in a post-war environment. Kukin was able to obtain confirmation for Stalin through another of his usual channels, James Klugman, who was responsible for MI6 contact with partisans in Yugoslavia and SOE agents in the Balkans.

Settled into the Washington Embassy Maclean soon established contact with his new controller. Among the documents the First Secretary gave to the Russians was British and American strategy for a world at peace after the defeat of Germany and

Japan. Privy to most of the correspondence of Winston Churchill to both Roosevelt and then Truman, Maclean was perfectly positioned for the NKGB.

Once the war with Germany was over Maclean still didn't disappoint his Russian masters, providing Stalin with Allied intentions for the restructuring of Europe. On three separate occasions, July 5, 6 and 10, 1945, the British diplomat compromised the most sensitive of secrets by handing over countless copies of documents. Because of Maclean's undoubted value Moscow remained sympathetic to his drinking – but his controller cabled to say it had become almost out of control, just as Kukin had written some years earlier in London. By this time Maclean had been in the employ of Soviet Intelligence for 15 years, far longer than the usual period. NKGB chiefs now speculated that Maclean might, afterall, be a double agent. Moscow decided to let Maclean run his natural course as a spy.

Drink or sexual misdemeanours certainly didn't affect promotion and Maclean relished his new role as the Embassy's Head of Chancery. This new administrative position now gave him daily and unfettered access to the diplomatic bag from London and all of its contents. He also became the British representative on the Combined Policy Committee, which made him privy to the written exchanges between Atlee and Truman on questions of nuclear policy in what was a very sensitive period for the Atlantic alliance. The revelations of GRU officer Igor Gouzenko, the defector from the Ottawa Embassy, that British and Canadian scientists had betrayed atomic secrets had substantially soured relations.

General Groves, not surprisingly, had very much welcomed Truman's decision to limit the spread of nuclear technology by banning international co-operation, including the British and certainly the French who he disliked most of all. As a result, the Combined Policy Committee was given only a very limited mandate – essentially to source and allocate supplies of uranium oxide. America had infuriated Britain by purchasing almost the entire stock and future production in Canada. Britain was left with access only to the Belgian Congo and South African ores.

Maclean had been allocated an advisor, an expert on atomic matters – Dr Wilfred Mann, the British physicist and MI6 scientific representative in Washington. Both men attended the Combined Policy Committee meetings in the Atomic Energy Commission building. Maclean was never aware that Mann, too, was in the employ of Russian Intelligence.

On Mann's trips back to London to brief Perrin and his colleagues, he always found time to meet his case officer. At the end of 1947 Mann passed to the *rezidentura* in the Soviet Embassy the fine detail of the deal that Britain had been forced to sign with the Americans. Britain had agreed to waive the right of veto on the dropping of an atomic bomb. Furthermore, the US had insisted that two-thirds of all uranium oxide mined in the Belgian Congo and South Africa be shipped to American ports. With American money propping up an ailing post-war economy Britain had no choice but to agree. On another trip, in February 1948, Mann gave the London *rezidentura* the technical details of a fleet of adapted long-range US bombers that were on constant alert in the north Pacific to monitor the fallout from any Russian nuclear explosion.

Sir William Stephenson, head of Britain's intelligence liaison group in New York, unwittingly had provided intelligence at the very highest level to Maclean and Mann. One such report concerned British monitoring of the Soviet nuclear programme. The Moscow archives do not make it clear if it was Maclean or Mann who on August 15, 1948, passed to the Russians the news that Stephenson had been informed that the Soviet bomb would be exploded sometime in 1949. That leak terrified Moscow and an immediate investigation was launched to uncover the Russian source.

By the time Kim Philby arrived in Washington on October 20, 1949, as MI6's liaison with the CIA and the FBI, Maclean had been gone a year. Moscow had made the decision that its contact with Philby would be kept to a minimum, certainly in the beginning as the FBI would be monitoring the movements of Britain's senior intelligence officer in the US. Distrust of Britain had deepened with the news that *Venona* had already decoded the cover name of *Rest* as Klaus Fuchs. Philby's FBI contact had also informed him that the cryptanalysts were uncomfortably close to discovering the identity of *Homer*. There were nine candidates but five, of which Maclean was one, were high on the suspect list. The arrival of Burgess, the notorious hard-drinking homosexual, in Washington as Second Secretary had worsened the situation.

Meredith Gardner, *Venona*'s expert decoder, whittled down the nine names to one and by April 1951 *Homer* was confirmed as Maclean. Events moved quickly. On April 25 Mann was relieved of his duties on nuclear matters and replaced by the much-respected Dr Robert Press, an attaché in the Embassy. Burgess left the Embassy for London on May 1, while in London John Cairncross was transferred from the Treasury to the Ministry of Supply that same day. Three days later an astonished Washington Ambassador received a secret cable from London saying that Burgess, too, was a traitor. Many people were now under suspicion, none more so than university contemporaries of Burgess and Maclean. An anxious Philby, sitting in Washington, had further urgent meetings with his controller from the Russian Embassy. He now feared he was under surveillance – not just from the FBI, but now from his own side, MI6. On May 16 Philby received a phone call from London with the news from a colleague that the interrogation of both Maclean and Burgess was now imminent. Risking his own discovery Philby took a cab into Georgetown, walking around several blocks before diving into a seedy bar. He hadn't been followed. That night a cypher was transmitted to Moscow with Philby's information.

Maclean and Burgess defected to Russia on May 25.

* * *

Highway 695 encircles Baltimore, a city with some of the worst slums in America but also host to internationally renowned institutions such as the John Hopkins Hospital. To the west of the city the Park Heights Avenue turnoff leads to the suburb of Owings Mills. Park Heights continues for miles and set back in gentle hills covered with heavy snow is Rainbow Hall, a Baptist retirement home. It was Sunday, February 13, the day before Valentine's Day – the time 11am. Sunday was no different than any other day, according to the first resident I met while attempting to locate a nurse. Visitors were rare, I was told. The sitting room was unbearably warm as residents read their newspapers or stared vacantly around them. One woman in her armchair pointed at a white speck on the carpet, telling everyone in earshot that it was her newspaper and she wanted to read it. A kindly old man walked over, picked up the imaginary newspaper and returned it to the grateful owner.

I had come to Owings Mills to meet Wilfred Mann, now aged 92. In coded transmissions to Moscow his controllers had given him the codename *Malone*, because of his Irish ancestry.

Given the lack of a receptionist all I had to go on was a photograph taken 20 years ago, which he had sent to a friend in Oxford. No one in the sitting room fitted his description. In a wheelchair sat a Navy veteran proudly wearing his ship's cap. A woman resident chattered away to him, saying nothing in particular.

I heard voices from another room and here a helpful nurse, a large and jolly woman, gave me Mann's room number and pointed down a corridor to a lift. On the first floor I walked past another sitting area, then a tiny kitchen until I reached the last but one door on the left, his name clearly visible.

I had telephoned several times in the past fortnight. Mann had been talkative, coherent and very receptive to the suggestion that I might visit him. He offered to prepare a light lunch for the occasion but I told him that he shouldn't go to any trouble. The day before I was due to fly I called again to check that everything was fine for my visit, and it was.

On my plane to Dulles airport in Washington I re-read the transcripts of my taped interviews I had conducted with a number of KGB veterans. Four interviews had been with Colonel Vladimir Barkovsky who had an in-depth personal knowledge of Russian penetration in Britain and America.

One KGB officer had provided greater detail on Maclean's activities in Washington and his defection with Burgess from a KGB officer who had served in London at a high level and had at one time access to all 78 volumes of files relating to Maclean. Several years ago these were held in a secret Moscow archive. Permission to view them was only rarely granted from their keeper Colonel Georgi Goncharov. The NKVD had never really trusted Mann and the files suggest that he might have been a double agent. I had been keen to ascertain the relationship between Mann, Maclean and Philby, and the extraordinary friendship Mann had enjoyed with James Jesus Angleton, the late head of the Counter-Intelligence Department of the CIA.

For decades Moscow had perpetuated the story that it was Maclean who stole the *Maud Report*, the document describing in detail how Britain on its own had intended to build 36 atomic bombs between 1941 and 1943. The veteran KGB officer Colonel Anatoli Yatskov, a key member of *Operation Enormoz*, the group who specialised in stealing atomic secrets, had used 'doctored' documents for his memoirs, persevering with the deception. Barkovsky, too, tried to feed the convincing lie to the West in the early 1990s. However, it was Cairncross who stole the *Maud Report*, not Maclean. Even high-flyers in the Foreign Office, such as Maclean, never had access to atomic secrets in 1940 and 1941. Mann, Eric Rideal and Patrick Blackett, all advisers to the Maud Committee, had fleshed out the detail of the *Maud Report* for Gorsky and Barkovsky.

During Maclean's spell in Washington he relied heavily on Mann. Philby, however, was wary of the physicist, reflecting later in a debriefing session in Moscow that he disliked his MI6 colleague and suggesting that all KGB contact with him cease. He described Mann as 'flaky'. Their coldness towards each other had not passed unnoticed by colleagues.

The defection of Burgess and Maclean had been carefully arranged, according to another veteran KGB officer who knew both Philby and Maclean well in London and who participated in their debriefings in Moscow. There have been so many theories, many false and put out by Major Yuri Modin, Maclean's last Soviet case officer in London. One report suggested that Burgess and Maclean had caught a train to Paris, after arriving by boat in France from Southampton. In Paris they had met old friends and got drunk before being spirited away. The real account was very different and certainly one which the two British diplomats had never envisaged.

Philby had warned Moscow on May 16 that the two were to be interrogated by MI5 as soon as permission was granted by a reluctant and embarrassed Foreign Office. Another source, this time from within MI5, had already conveyed that same message to Colonel Nicholas Rodin, the MGB *rezident* in the London Embassy. An anxious Rodin sent an alarm signal to Moscow – a signal only used as a last resort when an agent is in dire risk of exposure.

For Yuri Modin, a defection operation was long overdue. He had learned from other contacts that Maclean in his drunken moods had begun to brag to all and sundry that he was a Russian agent of many years standing. Burgess, too, was both unreliable and unpredictable. The Ambassador in the Washington Embassy had sent him home over his behaviour. Rodin hoped that Moscow would soon act.

In Moscow, Rodin's cable *'Homer is in danger, authorise Plan No. 1 or Plan No. 2. Propose No. 2'* had been expected given Philby's warning from Washington. Maclean's file was sent to Lt General Victor Abakumov, the head of the MGB for a decision. Stalin and Beria were kept informed of developments. Over the years there had been many reports on Maclean's behaviour, two of which were from two former Washington case officers, Major Boris Kreshin and Major Nikolay

Vladakin. At that time Moscow had even considered using an officer from the New York Consulate, Colonel Pavel Lukianov, to try and improve the relationship. The news that Burgess had now also been uncovered had grave implications. It was abundantly clear that both diplomats would quickly crack under British or American interrogation and implicate others.

Within two days General Sergei Savchenko, the deputy chief of the Foreign Intelligence Directorate, replied to Rodin. He agreed to Plan No. 2, which entailed the use of the Russian merchant fleet. Alongside each ship's captain there were always two intelligence officers, one GRU the other MGB. The defection procedure had been rigorously followed, with final sanction approved by Abakumov. The use of the two standard code words 'Krilov' and 'Vladimerov' in the cable provided authorisation.

The same cable was transmitted to the *rezident* in Paris, Colonel Aleksei Krochin, who would provide a 'battle cover' group for the operation. The next day another cable, this time naming Burgess and Maclean, was sent to Paris in the midst of countless others to disguise it in case transmissions were being monitored by British Intelligence. A third and more detailed cable followed. An MGB officer from London flew to Paris to provide photographs of the intended defectors.

Escape to Finland had been Plan No. 1. Russia literally ran its northern neighbour, paying huge annual bribes to senior police officers and Government Ministers. They were given cash, valuable hunting rifles, furs and jewelry. Such bribery included payments to Urho Kekkonen, the Finnish Prime Minister, who later became President upon the death of Kusti Paasikivi. Post-war Finland pursued a friendly foreign policy towards Russia and Kekkonen helped Russian Intelligence in any way he could. From Helsinki a special 'sealed' train ran uninterrupted to Moscow. In this instance, however, Finland was considered too risky given the large MI6 presence in Scandinavia.

On Friday May 25, the day set for the defection, Burgess and Maclean behaved normally but didn't use the telephone as they knew it would be bugged. That evening they set out to Southampton to catch the ferry to St Malo, the beginning of a new life behind the Iron Curtain. Modin cabled Moscow to confirm that the operation had begun. In his Washington office an angry Philby was on tenterhooks. For years he had dreaded that the antics of his Cambridge friends could lead to the compromising of his own position.

Colonel Sergei Volokitin, the deputy *rezident* from the Paris Embassy was in charge of the 'battle cover'. He hovered outside the Post Office, the agreed meeting place at St Malo, with a newspaper under his arm. He recognised the two men walking towards him from the photographs he had been given. They shook hands, exchanged pleasantries, and immediately set off in the two waiting cars. Volokitin and his team had anticipated a possible shoot-out with either British or French Intelligence officers that might be tailing the Foreign Office men. Apart from carrying the usual automatic pistols, they carried the standard armoury for liquidation officers – glass phials with toxic substances and delicately manufactured cigarettes that included a single bullet and a firing mechanism. Pointed close towards the mouth such miniature guns were deadly.

They drove to Brest to meet the Russian ship, constantly checking for a tail, but no one followed. In the car Volokitin gave instructions to his two charges, omitting to say that in the event of any trouble the diplomats would be immediately executed and their bodies dumped by the side of the road. Volokitin had been an excellent choice – murder was in his blood. He had honed his skills in 1941 when operating in the Caucasus, followed by operations in Poland and Byelorussia. Prague was Volokitin's killing ground post-war, quietly executing politicians who dared speak out against Soviet rule and influence.

To Volokitin's horror the quayside at Brest was empty. Sensing a trap he remained in the car with Burgess and Maclean whilst his men took up defensive positions. It was quiet, too quiet. Finally Volokitin ran to a telephone to call Paris. There had been a slip-up and the ship had unexpectedly docked at Bordeaux, not Brest, the anxious Embassy official told him.

On the long drive south Burgess demanded that Volokitin purchase whisky. As the alcohol did its work Burgess leered and waved at young men as they drove through the villages. He became abusive when Volokitin told him to calm down. Maclean said little, lost in his own thoughts.

At Bordeaux Volokitin quickly located the grain carrier, but Burgess now presented a serious problem. He was roaring drunk and incapable of walking properly. Volokitin pushed Burgess hard into the car seat and forced sleeping pills deep down his throat. Maclean was horrified and cried out. With his men surrounding the car Volokitin went aboard to speak to the ship's captain and the leader of the new 'battle cover'. Minutes later Burgess was dragged up the gangway, Maclean following meekly behind. Volokitin handed over a case of whisky before he and his group began their return to Paris. Deep in the bowels of the ship Burgess was dumped on a bunk bed in the tiny cabin and passed out. Maclean sat on the other bunk, nursing a bottle of whisky he had been given. Two armed guards were positioned outside. In the radio room a coded message was transmitted to Moscow.

Under orders to avoid British waters the captain headed west into the Atlantic. The ship skirted Ireland before heading north, aiming for the Skagerrak and Copenhagen. Inside their cabin Burgess and Maclean continued their drinking, left alone by the 'battle cover' and crew. Provisions were taken aboard in Copenhagen, but the Englishmen remained locked in their cabin despite their protestations.

By the time the ship sailed from Copenhagen and into the Baltic Sea recriminations had been raging for days in London and Washington. Philby and Mann had been interviewed several times, as were several members of MI5, including Lord Victor Rothschild. Churchill, who had been voted back as Prime Minister in

February 1950, launched a full investigation but it was soon hampered – especially as a number of the runaways' friends were senior officers in Britain's highly secret Counter-Intelligence groups, the 'K' and 'D' Divisions. Questions were raised about the nefarious activities that had taken place in Rothschild's apartment in Bentinck Street, not far from Harley Street in London's fashionable West End.

Rothschild, in late 1940, had headed F-3, the intelligence unit combating German saboteurs in Britain. With Tessa Mayer, his second wife and F-3 colleague, now pregnant, they vacated the apartment to settle in the country. Burgess and Blunt had moved in and it became a standing joke amongst the intelligence community who attended the often-riotous parties that secret files were to be seen scattered around the rooms. In the bedrooms, boyfriends and 'rent boys' offered their favours. At Bentinck St the champagne and wine flowed copiously. Guy Liddell, director of 'D' Division, was a frequent visitor. A few years earlier, in the very same apartment, Rothschild had introduced Liddell to Blunt.

From the outset Bentinck St had been a problem for Moscow. Gorsky had been summoned to Moscow to explain how he had allowed this situation to develop. It was strictly against procedure to allow association between agents. On his return to London Gorsky spoke to Blunt, now in a senior role in MI5, and ordered him to move out. With his usual flamboyant style Blunt refused, and the parties continued. Moscow reluctantly agreed to accept the *status quo*.

The ship sailed through the Gulf of Finland, Leningrad its final destination. Burgess was almost uncontrollable, moaning at the hardness of his bunk and the lack of facilities. The case of whisky purchased by Volokitin had already been consumed. Moscow had radioed that it wanted the two men sober and forbade any further alcohol.

Colonel Kulikov and his 'battle cover' met the ship in Leningrad and a convoy of cars sped to the railway station where a three-carriage train awaited, each one wired to record every sound, whisper and conversation. As the train slowly pulled away the debriefing process began. Burgess asked for a drink but Kulikov brushed aside the plea – sobriety was now the order of the day. Isolated from one another, Burgess and Maclean were asked by English-speaking interrogators to recall every movement during their last days in England. Moscow was keen to quickly ascertain whether MI5 had connived in the defection, despite what appeared to the contrary in the headlines of Western newspapers.

The train never reached Moscow and the two British diplomats didn't receive the official welcome they had expected. It stopped on the tracks in the middle of the night 10 miles out of the capital in Serevrjannombor, the 'Silver Forest'. Both men were unceremoniously bundled off the train and into a waiting car to be driven to a 'safe house' a short distance away, well hidden by trees.

There had been internal squabbling over which MGB department would be responsible for the intensive debriefing that was expected to take more than a year. Usually this was tasked to the Committee for Information, a completely independent intelligence agency that remained very much apart from Counter-Intelligence. However, given the unique status of Burgess and Maclean it was agreed that interrogation would be a joint effort under the direction of Lt General Michael Belkin, the officer who had arrested the Swedish diplomat Raoul Wallenberg in Budapest in July 1944.

In the 'Silver Forest' the house was well away from investigative Western journalists scouring Moscow, eager to report any sighting of the defectors. One of the first visitors was General Leonid Raikhman, who led a unit so secret that only Stalin and Beria knew its task. There was a mole in the Politburo, a source who reported to MI6. Philby and Maclean had often alerted Moscow to the agent but they never found out his name. This file was closely guarded and despite Philby's seniority in the organisation his attempted access was always denied. Raikhman spoke to Maclean for some time, discussing possible suspects. One name was high on Raikhman's list – Yakov Kapustin, a key figure in the Leningrad Communist Party. Kapustin had lived in London with an English girl for a number of years and Raikhman was convinced that the girl was an MI5 plant. Maclean could offer no help.

The interrogators prioritised their questioning, outwardly always courteous and friendly. First they needed to assess whether Burgess and Maclean were double agents by determining why they had been able to obtain so much classified material. Second, they had to prove they hadn't been used as 'disinformation' channels. During breaks in the questioning the diplomats wrote down the names and responsibilities of every colleague they had worked with over their long careers as Russian agents. Burgess grew exhausted, became flippant and suggested he be returned to London.

After two weeks Stalin's intelligence chiefs were no nearer in clearing the two of playing a double game but much useful material had been gained. Of particular interest to the Russians were the activities of the British Embassy in a neutral Stockholm during wartime and the role of Wallenberg and his family as the mediators of separate peace discussions between Britain and Germany. A special team met with Maclean for long discussions on British and American nuclear development.

It was decided to move Burgess and Maclean to Kuibyshev, where they remained for three months before transfer to Moscow. Burgess, given the name Andrevich Eliott and the codename *Twin*, hit the bottle and refused to participate in any further questioning. Maclean, named Modzoevsky and *Hicks*, continued to be co-operative. Now under the umbrella of the 2nd Directorate of Counter-Intelligence both were still suspected of being double agents, but that didn't stop officers from various departments wanting to work with them. Debriefing only ceased in 1953.

In all his time in Moscow Burgess felt homesick and yearned for London, but he had his uses for the KGB and other government agencies. In July 1956 a British Government delegation visited Moscow to brief the Russians on the unfolding Suez crisis. The delegation was taken aback as Burgess arrived at a reception in the Sovietska Hotel where he performed wonderfully in analysing British policy on

Israel. As the British politicians were wined and dined by their hosts, Burgess circulated shaking everyone's hands and discussing old friends. Although Burgess's appearance had been officially sanctioned, his visible friendliness towards the British worried the KGB who sent a report on him to Khrushchev, the Soviet Premier. Previous fears of being a double agent were rekindled and Burgess was kept away from foreigners thereafter. Following his death the rumour persisted that the troublesome Burgess had been poisoned by the KGB's renowned toxic laboratory.

* * *

The door to Mann's room in the retirement home in Owings Mills was slightly ajar, but from within there was no sound. I knocked gently several times before I slowly pushed the door open. The room was small, a bookcase covering almost one wall, to the right a bed. Mann, his back towards me, sat motionless and hunched forward in the wheelchair that was facing the winter landscape.

Outside in the corridor other residents shuffled by and I was uncertain what to do. I thought I should find the nurse, thinking I had arrived too late to listen to what Mann had invited me from England to hear. Still Mann hadn't moved. Then I remembered what he had told me on the telephone. Each night a nurse gave him his pills, the effects lasting well into the morning. With hindsight I wished I had arranged the appointment for the afternoon or the early evening, but he had been insistent about lunch.

Born August 4, 1908, Mann had been educated at St Paul's School, London, one of the best schools in the country, and Imperial College where he studied physics. After Imperial he spent time with Niels Bohr in Copenhagen and visited California to work on cyclotrons with the pioneering Ernest Lawrence in the Radiation Laboratory at Berkeley. With the Second World War looming, Imperial wanted their bright former student back to work with Professor George Thomson, newly co-opted into the Ministry of Aircraft Production, to conduct experiments on U-235 separation. In the summer of 1941 Mann had constructed his 'Jitterbug', a small-scale model of a uranium-separating device, encouraged in his pioneering work by Professor Simon at the Clarendon. This unique machine had resembled an ice-cream maker with membranes made from 'Dutch Cloth', a chemically-manufactured substance full of minuscule perforations. The Ministry of Supply had frantically scoured the country for supplies that were known to exist pre-war.

Mann was one of the brightest talents in *Tube Alloys*.

It is unclear now why Lt Commander Eric Welsh and Michael Perrin decided to use Mann in nuclear intelligence. After Thomson had agreed to the proposal Mann was moved into Shell-Mex House, the home of Britain's wartime scientific intelligence, where the wider secrets of *Tube Alloys* were shared with him. Vladimir Barkovsky was one of his Embassy case officers and together they shared meals in out-of-town restaurants. But their favourite meeting place was in London's Kew Gardens where both men enjoyed discussing the splendid flora.

Mann was sent to Washington in 1942 as part of the scientific exchange programme. He was attached to the National Bureau of Standards and the US Navy in the physics laboratory of John Hopkins, but still reported to Welsh. Together with the US scientist Merle Tuve, Mann designed close proximity fuses for shells, an invention used to great effect to bring down German V-1 rockets over England.

As Chadwick began to discuss British participation in the *Manhattan Project* much of this documentation was kept in his safe in Washington, to which Mann also had access. On trips home Mann saw Barkovsky, sometimes his Embassy colleagues, Boris Kreshin or Konstantin Kukin. On one visit Barkovsky had made a duplicate key for Mann from an impression that the physicist had made. At the end of the war Welsh had moved Mann to Canada as an advisor on the British nuclear project at Chalk River, only to return to Washington as the MI6 advisor to Maclean on the Combined Policy Committee. Mann also now became close to Angleton at the CIA.

When it was confirmed that Maclean and Burgess were traitors Mann was immediately tainted by association. Never again would he work for the British Government in any capacity. Interrogation in London proved inconclusive and Mann was allowed to go to America, where he took up the position as head of the National Bureau of Standards' radioactivity section, a role he held until 1980. From time to time he and his wife Miriam visited Oxford, staying in a cottage at Boars Hill. In the sensational events in 1979 when Sir Anthony Blunt, the keeper of the Queen's paintings, was publicly named as a spy, a physicist from Imperial was also implicated, but not named. In an attempt to clear the slur on his reputation Mann wrote a short autobiography, published by Robert Maxwell's Pergammon Press, using diary entries to refute that he was the so-called 'Fifth Man'; John Cairncross had yet to be publicly identified as a Russian agent and given that infamous 'title'.

On my first telephone conversation with Mann we had casually chatted about the party scene in Washington, when both Burgess and Philby worked in the Embassy. In Philby's house on Nebraska Avenue parties often degenerated into a binge, with Burgess at his most mischievous and egged on by a drunken Philby. Miriam would go home early, leaving her husband to enjoy himself.

We had spoken about his relationship with Maclean and Angleton. Mann had confided in me that Eric Welsh never trusted Angleton and he told me the reason why. One of Welsh's agents, Mann wouldn't say who, had uncovered information so sensitive that he declined to share it with his superiors at MI6. Yet Welsh had taken Mann into his confidence. In a whisper Mann related to me the startling event that had taken place in London in 1944.

Angleton had worked for the legendary General 'Wild' Bill Donovan, the head of the OSS, and in London during the war he had established very close ties with members of MI6 and MI5. Welsh and Angleton were like 'peas in a pod', said Mann, mavericks that could never be team players. With the demise of the OSS and the introduction of the CIA in 1947 Angleton's reputation had grown, forever preaching that he would weed out any KGB agents in the organisation. Despite his claims he never found any.

There was no movement in the wheelchair, but I observed Mann's shoulders gently rising and falling.

I walked into the neat and orderly room. Beautifully bound leather copies of Browning adorned the bookshelf and framed photographs of his late wife and other members of his family were on his desk. For a minute I stood there, until his eyes opened from his deep sleep and he offered a frail hand in welcome.

The conversation was slow, painfully so. We spoke first about Imperial, but those years were too far in the past and he had little interest. Since 1980 he had opted for a quiet retirement, out of sight of prying journalists still searching for his untold story.

I gently probed for more detail on his long friendship with Angleton. But he quickly tired. I had brought with me from London a copy of his autobiography *'Was there a Fifth Man? – Quintessential recollections'*, written under Angleton's instigation.

'There are five people on the cover, Burgess, Maclean, Philby and Blunt,' I enquired. 'When you wrote the book John Cairncross hadn't been publicly exposed. The fifth, in the middle, is a blank outline. Were you that man?'

He glared at me, temporarily in full control of his faculties.

'Yes,' he replied.

I wanted him to repeat what he had just admitted.

'Are you saying you spied for the Soviet Union?'

Mann didn't respond this time.

'So you were the *Fifth Man*?' I tried again.

'I could be.'

Suddenly the tiny room felt claustrophobic. I couldn't hold his gaze any longer and I struggled for something to say. At that moment a nurse entered to check on her patient.

'Could you take a photograph of Dr Mann and me?' I asked.

As the camera flashed Mann said, quite loudly, 'This is a very bad idea.'

I thanked the nurse, who then left.

'Why did you really come here?' Mann asked coldly. I had overstayed my welcome, it was time to leave Owings Mills.

On the way out of the retirement home I noticed the Navy veteran was soundly asleep, oblivious now to the woman still talking to him. In the car park I sat in my rented car, replaying my tape. I thought I detected Mann at his window staring down at me.

Back in England I made a phone call to an apartment in Moscow, the home of one of Russia's greatest ever spymasters.

'I have seen Mann. He's terminally ill.'

There was silence on the line.

'Tell me more about your meeting,' replied Barkovsky finally, in that quiet and unassuming tone of his. 'Did he confess to you?'

Mann, the scientist who had shared with Russia the early secrets of the nuclear age, is dead now. There were no obituaries in the British newspapers, despite his wartime scientific contribution on both sides of the Atlantic and his winning the US Navy Ordnance Development Award and the US Army Medal of Freedom, with Bronze Palm.

Only the very few in Moscow were ever privy to the files that described the extraordinary bond Mann shared with Angleton. Welsh, that gnarled hard-drinking controller of a network of MI6 undercover agents known only to him, came so close to solving the puzzle. He had discovered the truth about Angleton but never realised that Mann fitted into his jigsaw of suspicion.

Surprisingly, Welsh had shared those innermost misgivings with Mann, his MI6 prodigy – but why had Mann now shared those private conversations with me? Perhaps he knew he had only a short time left to live; no one could hurt him now.

Mann had been privy as to why Philby hadn't defected at the same time as Burgess and Maclean. Philby had wanted to and urged his Washington controller to arrange it. Burgess and Maclean had carried too much baggage and Philby knew he would be a prime target for the MI5 interrogators. Furthermore, an episode in 1944 had been observed that with skilful investigation would prove his treachery. Moscow, however, ordered him to remain and bluff it out, but the MGB knew that whatever the outcome Philby was now dispensable, his career in British Intelligence effectively over. If Philby, too, had disappeared there would have been a witchhunt of unparalleled proportions and the MGB might easily have lost their most prized asset – James Jesus Angleton.

CHAPTER 36

Ultimate Deception

Dateline: December, 2000
Location: Exmoor, Somerset, England

Completely and utterly enthralled by the journalist's story, I hadn't moved from my chair for hours. He had done almost all the talking, as he promised he would. I had added personal detail only where it was necessary. The Russian Intelligence officer escorting me on the train from Moscow to Helsinki in August 1949 had assured me that all traces of my existence in Russia had been expunged on Stalin's orders. It was very clear that hadn't been the case. The journalist had been given access, at the highest level, to whatever now existed in Moscow on my capture, interrogation in the Kremlin and my life in Russia.

According to the journalist a wall of silence had been enforced on the inhabitants of Krivaya Kosa for several decades. KGB officers acting on the direct order of Stalin had swarmed over the village just days after my departure to England in 1949, threatening banishment if anyone ever related the events of February 23, 1942.

The journalist had ventured to the southern Ukraine to visit the village, now renamed Sedovo after a famous Ukrainian writer who was born there, to find people who might remember the raid of the Soviet sappers who had ventured over the ice of Taganrog Bay in their sanyas. In the summer months the kosa, the largest in Taganrog Bay, is apparently now a huge holiday camp, a mass of humanity with young Ukrainians sleeping rough on the sand or in makeshift tents, their cars flattening the sunflowers. From the British Museum he had acquired a copy of a 1938 map of the Taganrog area to identify the key points of the village as it was during the war.

I was astonished to learn that at the end of the kosa, which stretches for several miles, the beacon used by the sappers as a marker in 1942 still remained. Unfortunately the khattas, the tiny dwellings that once stood on the edge of the bay, had collapsed into the sea as the coastline crumbled. Gone, too, was the German watchtower that I had seen in flames as the huge Russian had dragged me aboard the sanya. Residents had informed the journalist that in November 1943, as the Russians advanced on German positions around the Sea of Azov, Yak-9 fighters and T-34 tanks had shelled the garrison. The Germans, outnumbered and on near-starvation rations, fought a ferocious rearguard action and used the remnants of the watchtower for firewood. The Red Army liberated Krivaya Kosa after two years of occupation.

The journalist had prepared for me a sketch of the village centre, but I couldn't recall any detail for him. He had failed to locate the Cossack house I had stayed in

for those few hours with Conrad, my unfortunate Wehrgeologen colleague. M
only recollection, apart from the bloodstains on the floor caused by the deaths c
the previous incumbents, was that the roof had been tiled with green slates, a trad
tion in the area.

One resident he had met was Simonova Prokopenko, aged eight in 1942, who ha
lived just 100 yards from the spot where my Opel car came to a halt in the snov
drift. I studied the photograph of the old schoolhouse, now boarded up after the roc
had collapsed. The journalist said the schoolhouse was next door to the buildin
where Conrad and I had eaten and drunk strong Ukrainian beer just hours befor
the raid. Other photographs of Krivaya Kosa showed how little this Cossack settle
ment had changed since wartime. Simonova fondly recalled the kindness of th
German sergeant billeted with the family, who had given her sweets on her birtl
day. Her cousin, Maria Danilova, still lived next to her, the large house barel
changed from the time of its occupation by German and Rumanian officers. Unlik
Simonova, Maria had declined to talk. She had sat in the garden pondering th
request for some time but then walked inside and waved the journalist and Nikola:
his Russian translator, away. Even after all these years the experience of the wa
was too painful to relate, despite a generous offer of money. She was not about t
share her wartime experiences with an inquisitive foreigner.

Near the schoolhouse they had encountered a drunk, a young man who was keen t
accept any incentive. He spluttered out the name of one of the village elders and ha
pointed vaguely in the direction of where Zoya Samsonovich's home could be foun

Nikolay soon found it and knocked on the door. Zoya subsequently proved quit
a find for the journalist. Aged 20 in 1942, Zoya and her partisan husband, Gavril
Ivanovich, had risked their lives to provide intelligence for Colonel Ilya Starino
and his men based in Yeysk, the fishing village on the southern shore of Taganro
Bay. For more than an hour and for the very first time, she had told her story. The
had sat in her garden, surrounded by angry flies attracted by overripe tomatoe
accompanied by several intrigued grandchildren. She explained that as soon as th
bullets began to fly around her khatta during the raid she had hidden under the be
and prayed. When the conversation turned to the captured SS officer she becam
reticent, but she offered the name of the chief partisan, Nikandr Sklerov, who migl
help. He still lived in the village but Zoya hadn't seen him for 20 years and onl
vaguely knew his address. It was getting late and she was tiring but Zoya agreed t
take the journalist to Sklerov's home the following day.

The journalist and Nikolay had returned to Donetsk and discussed this excitin
development. Sklerov had been a major participant in the extraordinary story of th
raid on Krivaya Kosa. Early the next morning with the summer temperature soarin
to over 35 degrees Centigrade they again were driven south to the village, taking
break occasionally to view the wartime Soviet tanks mounted high on pedestals a
memorials to the ferocious tank battles that had taken place where now there wer

sunflower fields. The Ukrainians revered their dead. In Krivaya Kosa Zoya had climbed into the car and gave instructions to the driver. In a street on the north side of the village she bellowed at the driver to stop and off she strode with her walking stick. She had been right about the street but not the house number. One by one she banged her heavy stick on the front doors. It must have looked very amusing to the road hawkers who sold warm Ukrainian beer from their tents on the pavements.

The red star, denoting a hero of the 'Great Patriotic War', the Russian name for the war with Germany, hammered high into the sidewall provided the clue. Holidaymakers, short-term tenants of a converted out-house in the garden, had stared as an animated Zoya had gesticulated to someone peering through a window that was partly covered up with old newspapers. Sklerov had been asleep. Her job done Zoya insisted the taxi driver take her home. Blearily wandering out into the sunshine Sklerov, wearing a cap, sat under a tree. At first he ignored Nikolay and the journalist, only relenting when a wad of money was placed into the pocket of his shirt. It transpired that Sklerov's wife was seriously ill in Mariupol. She desperately needed life-saving drugs but the hospital administrator had denied treatment unless funds were made available.

The former partisan had miraculously survived the war, but in January 1943 after he escaped from Krivaya Kosa to enlist in the Red Army he found there was no record of his key intelligence work for Starinov and he was given the very lowest rank. Apparently that was a sore that had festered to this day. Only some years later did Sklerov receive the official recognition he deserved. Given the heat the journalist had purchased some beer and Sklerov had demanded several refills. Only then was he prepared to talk at length about the episode that had been kept secret for so long.

The journalist later visited Novoazovsk, formerly Budenovsk. This important garrison village for the Germans in 1942 had now grown into a dormitory town for the more affluent workers of Mariupol, home of the world's largest steel works. Starinov in Moscow had provided the journalist with the address for Vladimir Venediktov, a retired history lecturer and local historian. For years they had corresponded. In the 1950s Venediktov had been jailed for 10 years for distributing anti-Stalinist literature. In his voluminous files Venediktov had the details of every one of the 110 raids in Taganrog Bay that had been mounted by Starinov and his men. Venediktov had maintained a military museum in Budenovsk but it had closed due to lack of funding. The journalist showed me Venediktov's photograph – he looked resplendent with his long silver beard and curling moustache.

In recent years Venediktov had acquired the diaries of Colonel Frederick Schmidt, the senior German officer in charge of the garrisons in Budenovsk and Krivaya Kosa in 1942. Schmidt had been part of the push into the Caucasus in spring 1943 but the Ukrainian partisans would never forgive him for his brutality in the villages. An executioner had tracked him down and butchered him in a savage revenge. The diaries had remained in Kiev until the 1990s when the widow of the executioner posted them to Venediktov. The news of Schmidt's execution had been loudly cheered in Krivaya Kosa. The senseless slaughter of Anna Borisovna Podolskaya is still solemnly commemorated. Abused by Rumanian soldiers Anna had struck out for Taganrog, carrying her much-loved guitar. Soldiers in a passing truck had coldly shot her down on the road.

I was, of course, very curious to hear what this historian had recorded about my capture. The journalist replied that Venediktov had grinned at the mention of the name Major Hans van der Velde. He passed a letter to Nikolay, written by Starinov, who translated the relevant paragraph out aloud.

'Major Hans van der Velde, with a colleague, had been driving from Taganrog to Mariupol. About 2 km outside Krivaya Kosa, near Obruivski, his car, an Opel Kapitan, broke down in the snow and ice. They walked into the village. Later, the car was towed to the house in the village not far from the schoolhouse. In the early hours of February 23, 1942, gunfire was heard and van der Velde was seen to rush outside. Not participating in the gunfight, he hauled the tarpaulin off the Opel and started the engine in a bid to escape. Sergeant Major Maxim Alekseyevich Repin killed him and his colleague. A briefcase was found.'

Only in 1995 did Venediktov hear the real version from Starinov – the German had not been killed, but captured and taken to Moscow. Venediktov had further elucidated that after the raid the bodies of the German and Rumanian soldiers had remained in the snow for more than a day as the garrison in Budenovsk was slow in responding to the attack, believing that the road into the village would be extensively mined. That would explain, said the journalist, why Starinov didn't encounter any opposition when the sappers were unexpectedly ordered by Major General Tsyganov, the commander of the 56th Army in Rostov, to return to Krivaya Kosa in daylight to search for any intelligence that may have been missed. On the main raid the Russians had suffered only one casualty – the result of a faulty hand grenade that quickly put paid to the young sapper who had attempted to throw it. A large monument was built in Krivaya Kosa to his memory. It stands very close to the schoolhouse.

In 1967, the 25th anniversary of the raids across Taganrog Bay, veterans met for the first time since the war. Their extraordinary actions were reported in Rostov's newspaper under the headline 'The icemen of Taganrog Bay'. Starinov had given the journalist the cuttings. Parties were held in the villages of Margaritovka, Semibalki, Port-Katon, Yeysk and Shabelsk, the stanitsas on the southern shoreline where they had been billeted. In Semibalki there was a special salute to the Spanish members who had bunked on the Primorskii farm. Rafael Kano, Antonio Esmeralda, Jesus Rodrigues and Jose Vieska, four who learned their trade under Starinov in the Spanish Civil War, toasted lost companions such as Manuel Belda, the first casualty. Tsyganov had died but his deputy Colonel Zhurin, nicknamed the 'king of sabotage', spoke movingly about the bravery of the 125 sappers that had comprised this elite group of saboteurs. There was no mer tion in these celebrations of the capture of an SS officer at Krivaya Kosa during the raid of February 23, 1942, nor of the finding of the 'atomic' notebook.

A regular visitor from Rostov to the control centre at Yeysk during the raids, Zhurin had recalled the bitter winter of 1941–1942 and the gales that blew over the frozen Taganrog Bay, which literally knocked the sappers off their feet. The laden sanyas had rotated like ferris wheels when the gusts were exceptionally strong. In the early raids the Cossack horses couldn't move because their legs splayed, their horseshoes ineffective in the icy conditions. In Shabelsk the blacksmiths had solved the problem by forging horseshoes with long spiked crampons. For the sappers, who experienced the same problem, the blacksmiths manufactured similar soles for their felt 'valenki', their boots.

The newspaper had described the individual heroism of several of the sappers, including the elusive Maria Belova, the agent who operated behind enemy lines in constant danger of discovery. Maria had run many of the partisan groups that supplied vital intelligence as to the strength of the enemy garrisons.

During my long day with the journalist I had grown increasingly grateful for what he had discovered. It seemed that Barkovsky and Starinov never doubted the part I had played in the building of the Soviet atomic bomb. I had recalled to the journalist how appalled I had been at the test site in Semipalatinsk at the realization that I had handed over the nuclear secrets of one dictator to another. However, during my many years in England I had increasingly come to the view that Russia would have built it anyway – perhaps I had merely shortened the timeframe. Hearing for the first time how Balezin and others had evaluated my notebook was fascinating. Of course I would never forget Flerov, Kurchatov and Khlopin. Nor could I ever forget Stalin and Beria.

With enormous effort and research the journalist had compiled the biographies of the numerous scientists, intelligence agents and military men that had contributed in whatever way to the construction of the bomb. The eye-witness account of Yakov Dokuchayev from the NP-2 observation post where I, too, had been a member of the privileged few that day, left me spellbound. The journalist left me a photocopy so I could read it again at my leisure. Dokuchayev would have seen my arrest by the two members of Beria's bodyguard, but that wasn't in the account.

I had smiled as I read my own biography. That, too, the journalist had thoughtfully photocopied. Stalin had personally presented awards some months after the test. I surprised the journalist when I told him that Stalin had decorated me with his highest award in his Moscow dacha just before my sudden departure from the Soviet Union in 1949 just days after the Semipalatinsk test.

* * *

The journalist's story had been exhausting for both of us, but his tale wasn't finished, he explained. He suggested moving on to a quiet pub on Exmoor. I recommended the Tarr Steps Hotel, which enjoys a magnificent view of one of the prettiest valleys.

My wife remained at home as we set off in his car, slipping quietly through the village, over the old narrow bridge spanning the River Barle and up to the moor. I directed him to Hawkridge and the very steep road that took us down into the heavily wooded valley, leading up to the hotel, next to the Bronze Age Clapper Bridge.

As the day was unseasonably mild we sat in the garden and waited for our drinks to arrive, enjoying the views and the rays of the winter sun. The birds sang and the blue sky was a patchwork of vapour trials of high-flying aircraft making for European destinations.

'I envy you,' said the journalist, breaking the silence. 'I'd love to live here.' The drinks arrived.

Given that the Russians had provided me with a complete new identity in 1949, his search to find me had been difficult but a source in Moscow had helped. German archives had proved to be an avenue of dead ends when he attempted to investigate my background. The Bundesarchiv in Aachen and the Militararchiv in Freiburg, organisations with records of military personnel from 1920 to 1945, surprisingly had no file on me. Berlin was the only hope but the Deutsche Dienstelle, with the most complete archive of the Second World War, drew another blank.

He had contacted an American working in Government telecommunications in the US whose father, as a sergeant in post-war Berlin, had purloined Waffen-SS and SS personnel files from the Berlin Document Centre. My name wasn't amongst them. The journalist then wrote to an adjutant of Wiking, who searched his own meticulous records of the SS division that saw so much action during the invasion of Russia. The adjutant could only confirm the existence of a special detachment, a Wehrgeologen group that took orders only from Berlin.

What had remained of the personnel records of the Kaiser Wilhelm Institute for Physics, now the Max Planck Institute, offered nothing. Only few personnel records had survived the NKGB ransacking in the immediate days after the end of the war. Intriguingly, one related to Professor von Weizsäcker. A letter written by D Bewilogua confirmed von Weizsäcker's starting day at the Kaiser Wilhelm as October 15, 1936, with a salary of 300 Reichsmarks per month.

It seemed I was a man without a past, but then this journalist had been extraordinarily resourceful. He had found the files of my interrogation in the Kremlin and my subsequent stay in the Soviet Union and had established key KGB contacts.

Darkness had now descended over Exmoor, only the lights from the bar and the dining room illuminating the garden. Despite my warm coat I now felt cold and suggested he took me home. On the journey we crossed a cattle-grid and the journalist stopped the car, waiting for some Exmoor ponies to cross the road.

He turned his head towards me.

'Would you like to know what became of Maria, your girlfriend in Munich?' he said softly.

That was like a hammer blow.

'Of course,' I stammered.

'You probably remember the day; spring, April 1936, Walchensee, in the German Alps,' he stated flatly.

'How could I forget it? During lunch with my parents and Maria Hitler arrived, with Himmler and Baldur von Schirach,' I replied.

'Hitler always loved a pretty face and apparently he was quite taken with Maria. From his veranda in the coffee-house he heard her talking about her Russian travels with her father. Initially he was just curious but Himmler the following day established that Maria's father was an industrialist in the chemical sector.

'Maria was flattered when the letter arrived and she sounded out her father. At first she decided against accepting the invitation to travel to Berlin for an interview in a Government department that sounded suspiciously like the Abwehr. However, the letter alluded to Maria being able to use her fluency of Russian, so within the month she found herself in the office of Lt General Franz Bentivegni, head of Abwehr-3, the highly secretive department that dealt with Counter-Intelligence and subterfuge in Russia. After an intensive selection process Maria underwent training to become an Abwehr agent.

'When you saw her for the last time at the Rheinischer Hof in Munich she was awaiting her first assignment. Maria never told her father about her role in German military intelligence, but he suspected as much after an old friend confided that the Abwehr had been checking into the family background. He would never put his daughter's life in peril by informing you of her new career. More times than not, he wanted to. When you gave Maria the names of your father's print workers in Dachau, you assumed her father was instrumental in their release. Actually, Maria never told him, she used her own contacts. The SS had little time for the Abwehr but even the Dachau commandant must take the call when a department head of the Abwehr comes on the phone.

'Maria never forgot you and in May 1941, just weeks before the start of *Operation Barbarossa*, she wrote you a letter, handing it to her father with the understanding that if anything happened to her he would hand it over to you. I have no idea what happened to that letter.

'Prior to the invasion, Abwehr activity increased in the Soviet Union. Despite the alliance between both countries the respective security services distrusted each other. The NKVD and GRU had built up cells in Berlin and in other German cities. In Russia the Abwehr encountered little difficulty in finding and recruiting disaffected Communists, especially Ukrainians who hated the Stalin regime. With the invasion imminent, Soviet sympathizers in Germany knew they were at serious risk and fled. The Gestapo and the SD ruthlessly weeded out many.

'The Abwehr, never trusted by Hitler, incurred heavy casualties in the invasion. For the duration of the war the Abwehr put 150 spying groups into Soviet territory, but only two groups ever made it back to Germany – a terrible result. In May 1945 the NKGB captured Bentivegni and he was interrogated for weeks, finally breaking down to reveal the full extent of Abwehr operations within the USSR and German occupied territories.

'There were two Abwehr attempts on Stalin's life, the most audacious in 1944 codenamed *Zeppelin*. A light aircraft landed behind the Soviet lines in a field near the city of Smolensk on September 6 and two Abwehr operatives ran for cover from the plane. Both were dressed in Soviet uniforms. The man was a seasoned 33-year-old saboteur, a Russian who had worked for German Intelligence since the outbreak of war. His name was Peter Ivanovich Shilo and he was dressed as a major in SMERSH – the Soviet Counter-Intelligence Service. After some cosmetic work Shilo had taken on the identity of Major Tavrin, a 'Hero of the Soviet Union', who had a permit to enter the Kremlin.

'Shilo's accomplice was a German woman, fluent in Russian, who wore the uniform of a sub-lieutenant of the Red Army. Using their rank they commandeered an Army motorcycle and sidecar. Driving through the night, staying off the main roads to avoid roadblocks, they reached the outskirts of the Russian capital. In the pannier of the motorcycle was an incredible device – a panzerknakke. Abwehr engineers had designed a strong protective metal sleeve into which either operative would slide a forearm. Attached to the sleeve was a sliding mechanism upon which a tiny rocket containing a high explosive could be fitted.

'Stalin would often address an audience of troops at the Kremlin in the Hall of Columns. The Abwehr's plan was to infiltrate and fire the rocket. Even if *Zeppelin* succeeded, the chance of escape for the Abwehr agents was negligible. A military policeman manning a roadblock ringing Moscow saw the motorcycle approaching and flagged it down. Suspicious, he called over his colleagues. The agents were quickly rumbled.

'Interrogation took place at the Lubyanka. As well as the miniature rocket launcher, the Russians found a radio-controlled mine in the sidecar, to be placed at the Bolshoi Theatre on the eve of a forthcoming state holiday. The Bolshoi had been the alternative plan, to wipe out the entire Politburo.

'Under torture both admitted their roles in the Abwehr, but they weren't executed immediately. They were moved to a 'safe house' in Moscow where the NKGB forced them to transmit false intelligence to Berlin in the hope that continued traffic might identify other groups operating in Russia. Berlin wasn't fooled. For a while the Abwehr went along with the ruse, knowing full well that the operation had been compromised, but then stopped answering. The last communication signalled the death sentence for the two agents and execution took place in the underground killing chamber of the Lubyanka.

'I'm sorry to tell you, but the female agent was your Maria. By all accounts she was a very brave woman. It is sad to think that both of you landed up inside the Lubyanka, but at different times. There is some evidence that she may have been poisoned with experimental drugs from that dreadful toxic laboratory before her execution. Captured Germans, especially Abwehr agents, were guinea pigs for much of the testing. You were lucky and avoided that painful fate.'

I shuddered, suddenly reliving my own moments with the odious Dr Mayranovsky.

My wife had been concerned at the time I had been away. I invited the journalist into our tiny kitchen as I went upstairs to find a box, the one given to me in 1949 by Stalin. I took the lid off and gently lifted out the medal, giving it a rub with my sleeve.

'So this is Stalin's Prize for your assistance in building his atomic bomb, can I touch it?' asked the journalist, smiling.

'Go ahead. Stalin considered his award to be higher than Lenin's, but most historians would probably disagree.'

'You must be very proud,' he said, returning the medal to me.

'Perhaps.'

'I need to leave, it is a long drive back to London. Before I go you should know something about that MGB officer who rescued you from Beria's thugs at Vnukovo airport in Moscow after your arrest in Semipalatinsk. He's still alive, but poorly. Each year he visits a KGB hospital for a full screening – Russia takes good care of its intelligence veterans. After escorting you to Helsinki, on Stalin's instruction, he enjoyed a brilliant post-war career as an intelligence officer. Do you have any idea who he was? I leave it to you to guess.

'For your safety it was essential that the aircraft from Semipalatinsk be met by someone Stalin could trust. He called this intelligence officer, untainted by Beria or his hoodlums, who was in Moscow awaiting his next international assignment having already proved his worth in one foreign capital. Within the hour he had been briefed and he drove to the airport with a signed order from Stalin.

'Stalin had guessed correctly that Beria would try some stunt in Semipalatinsk but he believed you would be safe in NP-2; how wrong he was.

'On the surface Beria displayed loyalty to Stalin, but he detested him and the feeling was mutual. Both were born in the same mould I suspect. Stalin usually stood aside, allowing Beria freedom in liquidating troublesome colleagues or enemies. Beria had a favourite execution site, a secluded wood outside Moscow where the bodies rotted quickly in the rich soil. However, he never personally pulled the trigger; he had his own executioners only too pleased to carry out such a service. It was customary for Stalin and Beria to utilize the intelligence services to spy on each other. Stalin knew the names of every woman from the intelligence services who had slept with Beria. Zardo was a special favourite. Before the war she was a NKVD operative in Paris.'

We stood there, in an English kitchen, somehow divorced from events of sixty years ago. It seemed like an eternity before the journalist spoke again. It was as if he was mentally prompting me to say something, anything. My wife had nervously busied herself in the room next door, deeply regretting her suggestion to me that the journalist should visit after his phone call.

Finally, the journalist stretched out his arm to shake my hand. He walked out to his car. He opened the driver's door but didn't get in. Instead he lit a cigarette and stared at the blackness of the Exmoor sky.

'Time to make dinner,' said my wife quickly.

I went back upstairs, to return the medal to its place of safe keeping, but something troubled me. My hand moved to other items in the box, things of greater sentimental value to me. One was Stalin's second present on my departure. Despite the years its content hadn't faded. On a number of pages there were pencil marks in Russian, probably made by Igor Kurchatov who in my incarceration in the Lubyanka had felt like a friend.

The journalist had told me earlier that day that in 1946 Vladimir Barkovsky, who had returned to Moscow from his London posting, had tried unsuccessfully to locate the notebook with its secrets of the German atomic bomb. Kurchatov had denied any knowledge of its very existence. In later years Barkovsky had tried on several occasions but the trail always went cold. There was a rumour that it lay in the sealed security box of Georgii Flerov, Stalin's favourite scientist.

I can still clearly remember that train journey through the Finnish countryside, en route to Helsinki in 1949, aboard a strange train with its tiny circular windows. All I had was a small bag of possessions that someone had collected for me from Plant 12, the isotope plant near Moscow where I worked, and the box which Stalin had given me in his study at his dacha on August 31. The MGB officer had brought for the journey a flask of coffee and he shared it with me. He had looked disinterested as the tall pines flashed by. I had opened the box and almost jumped for joy. There was the notebook with Stalin's medal. Kurchatov must have returned it to Stalin. The two sheets of folded paper, with the drawings that so intrigued Flerov during my interrogation in the Kremlin, were missing; perhaps Stalin had kept them as his own memento. Finland and freedom drew inexorably nearer. I had closed the box and drank the warming coffee. My mind had been whirling with questions, none of which I could formulate an answer to. I had only half listened when my escort spoke about his new posting to the United States, in Washington. Finland was close. Russia was behind me now.

The smell of dinner brought me back to the present. I shook the dust from the notebook before replacing it in the box; my box of secrets. I glanced at another memento – the small phial of uranium oxide I had taken from Alma-Ata as reminder of Taboshar.

Only then did I realise why the journalist hadn't left. He was sitting in his car, the engine idle.

I cursed.

My wife was upset. She, too, had seen the red glow of the cigarette. Something was wrong, he had said he was going, she cried.

Turning on the outside light I walked over to the car.

'Yes?' he said, expressing no surprise.

'There are some loose ends,' I said rather feebly.

'All good stories have a beginning, middle and an end. Do you smoke? I didn't light up during the day.'

'Go ahead, don't mind me.'

'Please could you sit in the car, and would you turn that light off?'

From the kitchen window my wife looked anxiously out through the curtains into the blackness. Dinner would have to wait.

I composed myself.

'Who was Franz?' I enquired. 'I felt I knew him, but I didn't know him at all, did I?'

'That is probably true. Before I can provide you with an answer though, I need to describe what had happened in the Cabinet Room in No. 10 Downing Street on August 10, 1945. Clement Atlee, the Prime Minister, had hosted the meeting and Sir Stafford Cripps, Ernest Bevin and Sir John Anderson were present. The previous day the second atomic bomb, *Fat Man*, had exploded over Nagasaki.

'On the invitation of Anderson, Lt Commander Eric Welsh and Lt Colonel Michael Perrin had been invited into the Cabinet Room – both were unknown to Atlee.

'Churchill's Chancellor of the Exchequer, a close friend and confidant and keeper of so many wartime secrets, began his briefing to the newly elected Prime Minister and the two Ministers. There were to be no interruptions as Anderson explained in great detail an extraordinary operation, sanctioned by Churchill. Welsh appeared disinterested. Perrin, a small and wiry man, with little humour, was more circumspect. He sat stiffly, one leg over the other, hands in lap.

'Anderson had solicited the help of Welsh, he explained, and between them they had conceived the idea – the ultimate deception. British Intelligence would provide Stalin with the schematic drawings of the German nuclear reactor and the atomic bomb – the very drawings that Rudolf Hess had brought with him on his solo flight to Britain on March 10, 1941, so carefully drawn and annotated by Professor von Weizsäcker. Once Stalin saw them, believed Anderson, he would need no more convincing that Hitler, his supposed ally, harboured military ambitions further east than Czechoslovakia and Poland. Hitler in the possession of an atomic bomb could see his Third Reich stretch all the way to the Pacific coastline of the USSR.

'For the operation to succeed the diagrams needed to fall into Russian hands using a channel trusted by Stalin and Beria, as they had a healthy mistrust of easily gained intelligence. The mechanics were hatched in Welsh's cage, the metal monstrosity that the Lt Commander used as his office on the fourth floor of Shell-Mex House, the centre of Britain's wartime scientific intelligence.

'One of Welsh's most valuable MI6 agents in Germany, the scientific publisher Dr Paul Rosbaud, continued Anderson, was too valuable to be risked. Instead, Welsh decided to utilise *John*, the contact for Professor Karl Friedrich Bonhoëffer, the Kaiser Wilhelm physicist, and Bonhoëffer's brother-in-law, Dohnanyi, the deputy head of the Abwehr. *John* was a middle-ranking German civil servant working in one of the Berlin Ministries who was a proven double agent with a courier chain that had already passed much material to London via Switzerland. He had been recruited into British Intelligence before the war to serve both Welsh, his master, and the beautiful Colonel Zoya Ribkina, his NKVD mistress in Moscow who ran the *Rote Kapelle*, the *Red Orchestra*. Ribkina knew that *John* enjoyed contacts at the very highest level in Berlin and she would have believed the integrity of the diagrams if they had been stolen from Bonhoëffer's safe or the Abwehr. Bonhoëffer didn't work closely with von Weizsäcker and his group in the underground laboratory but, given his long-standing relationship with Heisenberg, he had been aware of the uranium project.

'The operation was quickly dropped after reports from Berlin confirmed that the Germany-Russia pact was near to breaking point. Aerial reconnaissance had observed large German troop movements, including the elite Waffen-SS, moving to holding points in the east. The invasion was months, possibly weeks away.

'If you haven't guessed, *John* was your friend, Franz.

'What quickly resurrected the ultimate deception was the name of Hans van der Velde, said Anderson. Franz had cabled Welsh some months earlier saying that he had met you and that you worked for the Kaiser Wilhelm Institute of Physics and the Heereswaffenamt. Over time Franz had hoped that your talents could be exercised in an intelligence capacity, but he wasn't going to push the matter. It was only after you had told him that you kept a comprehensive notebook that Franz quickly got a message through to Welsh. Anderson and Welsh agreed with Franz that the acquisition of your notebook and the Hess diagrams by the Russians would greatly enhance the operation's value. Bonhoëffer or Dohnanyi wouldn't be needed. Through Franz you were to be recruited into the *Red Orchestra* and he didn't think you would decline. Given your position in the German nuclear programme you would have been in a position to acquire the diagrams. Franz would have passed both documents to his NKVD controller.

'Anderson persuaded Churchill to agree with the plan. As an imminent ally Anderson argued, Russia would need every assistance Britain could provide. Even the greatest secret of all – the development of an atomic bomb – needed sharing. Welsh arranged that the diagrams be smuggled into Berlin. Anderson now insisted on the greatest secrecy – there were to be no minutes of meetings, nothing.

'Your unexpected conscription into the Wehrgeologen a week before the invasion again led to cancellation of the operation. But your sudden reappearance in Berlin

November 1941, on leave after the capture of Kharkov, led to urgent meetings in London. At this stage Welsh brought Michael Perrin into his confidence as the deputy director of *Tube Alloys* now had an intelligence role. It was outlined to Churchill by Anderson what Franz had in mind. Churchill gave his permission. Your chances, however, were regarded as very slim given that you had to engineer your capture.'

The journalist lit another cigarette, the moon casting an eerie glow on the River Barle gently meandering downstream to Dulverton.

'Only by sheer luck did Franz remain undetected throughout the war. Despite his efforts he was never given any reward for his loyalty, which is so typical of the British, unlike the French who rewarded foreigners for bravery and heroism. I can confirm that the Gestapo arrested Helmut, your other drinking chum from Meinekestrasse. Even under extreme torture Helmut gave nothing away, suffering a lingering death in the Gestapo headquarters in Prinz Albert Strasse, strung up over a beam, his neck slowly tightened on to a meat hook. That was the usual method for traitors.

'One flaw in the van der Velde operation was confirmation. Franz, using his con-tacts, at best might hear that you were missing in action, an indication that you had been taken, and that possibly you had succeeded. But, by the same token, you could also be dead. Captured SS officers didn't live long.

'After the war the record of German dead in *Operation Barbarossa* was incom-plete. Hundreds of thousands of German prisoners languished in Russia in prison camps, or worked in Moscow rebuilding the city. In June 1945, Franz, now a mem-ber of the Allied administration of Berlin, had access to Wehrmacht and SS opera-tional files. A Major van der Velde had been reported missing, no body recovered, in Krivaya Kosa in February 1942, according to a report from headquarters in Taganrog. The details of the action were vague.

'Concerned, Welsh flew to Berlin for consultations with Franz. Europe was now engaged in post-war reconstruction, funded by American money. London had a new priority, the Cold War, and the enemy was the USSR. It would be unhelpful, deeply embarrassing in fact, if our American friends heard of this British-inspired wartime mission. Systematically Hans van der Velde was purged from every record. An English officer, Major Blunt – not to be confused with Blunt the traitor – tem-porarily managing the closed Kaiser Wilhelm institutes, scoured what the Russians hadn't taken and destroyed all evidence of your employment. German military records, mainly under British control, were also cleansed. Officially, you no longer existed. Your parents in Munich were informed in 1942 that you were missing in action, presumed dead.

'For Welsh, the operation never happened. Perrin, too, kept his silence.

'When America joined the war in December 1941 Britain's Prime Minister had hoped you were dead, your mission unfulfilled. Welsh did ask Franz to discretely make inquiries, but given that the Wehrgeologen was attached to the SS he didn't try too hard. Churchill often enquired of Anderson if there was any news from Franz about you, but there wasn't.

'With the world about to witness the beginning of the nuclear age following the bombing of Japan, Churchill, voted out of office by a war-fatigued electorate, decided that Atlee should be informed of the operation for which he had given his sanction. Churchill was also fearful of the repercussions if news ever leaked out that the British had deliberately provided the Russians with German nuclear secrets.

'In the weeks after the Japanese surrender the new Cabinet debated long and hard on whether Britain should develop its own nuclear capability, as the Americans had banned any further collaboration. The nation needed rebuilding and money was scarce. Sir Stafford Cripps strongly opposed a British deterrent as did another powerful voice, Hugh Dalton, the wartime head of the Special Operations Executive. Ernest Bevin, an unlikely proponent, persuaded Atlee that Britain should carry on and perhaps even share our technology with the Russians.

'In the first major post-war debate in a packed House of Commons on August 16, 1945, Atlee had addressed its members, many still in military uniform. *'I think it is fitting that today I should pay a tribute to one of the main architects of our victory,'* said Atlee. *'In the darkest and most dangerous hour in our history this nation found in my Right Honorary Friend the man who expressed supremely the courage and determination never to yield which animated all the men and women in this country.'* The speech was short; Atlee aware of the attention focused on the former Prime Minister.

'Churchill, as usual, was in fine oratorical form. *'Six years of total war have convinced most people that had the Germans or Japanese discovered this new weapon, they would have used it upon us to our complete destruction with the utmost alacrity,'* he proclaimed, reporting that Britain's financial contribution to the development of the bomb was £500 million, a huge amount given other war priorities.

'It was a fine speech, ended by the following: *'I must say that I am in entire agreement with the US President that the secrets of the atomic bomb shall so far as possible not be imparted at the present time to any other country of the world.'*

'Hardly the truth, of course, but wouldn't any great patriotic leader have sanctioned your mission in a bid to defend the freedom of his country? Every member of the House stood and applauded.

'So, now you know. The mission of Major Hans van der Velde was dreamt up by British Intelligence, not the *Red Orchestra* as Franz led you to believe.

'You have another question, don't you?' asked the journalist in the darkness, 'one that has bothered you ever since your capture in Krivaya Kosa.'

'Yes,' I replied.

'Have you no idea, not at all?'

'None. Why did Stalin let me live and why did he protect me from Beria?'

'You have Ivan Maisky, the Russian Ambassador to London, to really thank. On evening in January 1942 he returned to the Embassy. In his pocket he had a memo addressed to Churchill, despite Anderson's insistence to the contrary that there were to be no records of the van der Velde operation.

'A few hours earlier Anderson had dictated the note to his secretary and demanded the only carbon copy be handed over to him. By the time the courier delivered the original to Churchill, Anderson had flopped into his usual armchair at the Athenaeum, one of his favourite clubs. He ordered a whisky before opening his briefcase to peruse the daily clutch of War Cabinet papers. Out of the corner of his eye, Anderson observed Maisky slide into a chair beside him. Both men talked of the war and news from the Eastern Front.

'The well-practiced sleight of hand was barely detectable. Maisky downed his drink and left, leaving Anderson to his reading. In his Embassy car the Ambassador could barely believe what he was reading. Rather than summarise, Maisky instantly decided that Stalin should see the original. Maisky knew he could count on the discretion of the Embassy's political attaché with his indispensable photographic skills. An hour later Maisky returned to the Athenaeum, slipping the carbon copy back to Anderson.

'Stalin, therefore, had full warning of the ultimate deception. He had the written evidence you were genuine, but a dupe of MI6. Anderson's note had been very explicit, with detail about yourself, your notebook and the Hess diagrams. Why had he written the note? There's only one obvious answer, which I'm sure you can work out for yourself.

'Beria, of course, was correct in his intuition that the 'atomic' notebook might have been a British or German ploy, but he would never know why. According to the files in Moscow Stalin never told him. Your day-long interrogation in the Kremlin wasn't intended as a mere charade. Stalin felt he could make use of you, as his pawn. He was angry at the constant reticence of his top scientists in forming a decision on whether Russia should restart its nuclear programme. It was clear from NKVD and GRU intelligence that the USSR was well behind in the race to build a bomb. By inviting Georgii Flerov, the physicist who felt it had been a terrible mistake to stop the project in the first place, to the interrogation Stalin had hoped that Abram Ioffe might be jolted into action. The 'discovery' of the notebook and the Hess diagrams had given Stalin the ammunition he wanted. Perhaps now you can begin to understand why Stalin spared your life?

'The photographs of Anderson's memo to Churchill had been sent in the diplomatic bag to Moscow and placed in the *Athenaeum* file, opened by Stalin's secretary, Poskrebyshev, as Maisky had begun his profitable liaison with this key member of the War Cabinet. When Stalin asked Poskrebyshev for the file during your interrogation in the Kremlin he needed to re-read the note from Maisky to determine whether you had lied. I guess you hadn't.

'On receiving Maisky's sensational material from London in January Stalin had personally contacted Major General Tsyganov in Rostov and instructed him to call if there was any unusual event in his sector of the Southern Front regarding a member of the Wehrgeologen. Stalin was curious as to how an SS officer would try to effect his own capture. A baffled Tsyganov duly complied. When Tsyganov cabled Stalin on February 23, 1942, about the raid on Krivaya Kosa and what had been found Stalin demanded a second raid on the village in case something had been missed. Stalin was just being thorough.

'He could have left you to the mercy of the local NKVD in Rostov, but he now realised you would have a value in Moscow.

'After your interrogation your usefulness was at an end, but Stalin admired your courage. Sending you to Taboshar may have led to death from the mines but it kept you out of Beria's grasp. After your abduction in Semipalatinsk Stalin accepted the inevitable. Spiriting you out of the country was the only option. All traces of your existence in the Soviet Union, as in Germany, were expunged, but not the *Athenaeum* file.

'As Welsh had direct intelligence responsibility for *Tube Alloys* he had been a regular visitor to Churchill's bunker, often remaining late in the evening. Both men hit it off, especially over a bottle of malt whisky and cigars. Just weeks before the ending of the European war Churchill had confided in the MI6 officer about a matter troubling him ever since the 'Big Three' meetings had begun. Often Churchill shared the most sensitive of information with Stalin but he had the disturbing impression that the Soviet dictator was always aware of what he had just been told.

'There was no real evidence against Sir John Anderson, only an intriguing report received by MI6 before the war that the NKVD had recruited a senior British civil servant with a scientific background. He had been an exchange student for a year in Germany. With resources that person could have been tracked down but war had intervened and there were other more important matters for MI5. However, with its Registry now back in London from Blenheim Palace, Welsh suggested to Churchill that he would do some digging. Welsh began by studying the backgrounds of any one who had access to War Cabinet secrets, starting with its Ministers. The discovery that Sir John Anderson had studied in Leipzig in 1904 after graduating from Edinburgh was an unexpected development. Coincidentally, Anderson's research had been into the properties of uranium.

'Flimsy stuff, but Welsh had Anderson tailed. He decided against making request for MI5 watchers in case word leaked out that a Cabinet Minister was under surveillance, preferring instead to use two retired detectives he knew from Special Branch. Every movement was monitored. Just days before the General Election of July 26 Welsh met the detectives to study the log. His heart skipped a beat when one detective produced a list of some visitors to the Athenaeum over a period of weeks, at the times when Anderson was in the club. A regular was Fedor Gusev, Maisky's replacement as Russian Ambassador in 1944.

'Welsh checked the frequency of the War Cabinet meetings, cross-referencing them with his log. The MI6 officer was convinced he had his man.

'Proving it was another matter. If Anderson had spied for Russia during his days as Governor of Bengal and during spells at the Home Office and other Government departments he was a highly experienced agent who had covered his tracks well. Churchill could hardly believe what Welsh relayed to him. He ordered the Lt Commander not to repeat his suspicions to anyone – that suited Welsh, notorious for his single-mindedness and for operating alone.

'Welsh carefully thought through the trap that would ensnare Anderson, but he needed assistance. He turned to Perrin, one man he felt he could trust.

'Thanks to regular information from a senior scientist in the American team in Los Alamos, Welsh was always up to speed on the developments in the US. General Groves, parsimonious in divulging *Manhattan Project* detail to his British allies, would have been outraged to discover that many documents, supposedly for the eyes of only US scientists and military, found their way to Welsh and Perrin in London.

'One report definitely not shared by Groves was the announcement that enough plutonium had been produced at the Hanford facility for a third bomb, far more powerful than those to be dropped on Hiroshima and Nagasaki. This nuclear bomb was to be a deterrent against any further Soviet threat during Stalin's annexation of Eastern Europe. Just days after the German surrender Groves had let it be known that *'the real enemy was Stalin'*. Berlin was a hotbed of speculation. One urgent NKGB cable to Moscow even suggested that the Allies would attack Russia through northern India. These were anxious days and world leaders held their breath.

'Welsh had decided that he would set the trap on the very day that Anderson was to explain the van der Velde mission to Atlee, Cripps and Bevin at No. 10 Downing Street – August 10, 1945.

'That day as Welsh listened with disinterest to Anderson in the Cabinet Room he reflected that within hours the fly, hopefully, would be caught in the web.

'Anderson was good, very good, thought Welsh as Churchill's closest wartime colleague spoke of the details of the numerous interrogations of Hess and the disclosure that Hitler's deputy had brought with him a diagram of a prototype German nuclear reactor and the first design for a bomb. Atlee and his two Ministers were stunned at the audacity of the van der Velde operation in which success or failure remained unconfirmed.

'The meeting at an end, Atlee had profusely thanked Anderson, expressing the hope that the former Chancellor of the Exchequer's skills could be utilised for the country again, perhaps as head of the new atomic authority that Atlee wanted to establish. Atlee, Churchill's deputy for most of the war, had no questions about van der Velde and the ultimate deception. It was a wartime secret he had never been privy too. Now as leader of Britain's new administration he was desperately keen to forget the past and rebuild the nation.

'Welsh had typed the note himself in the early hours of that morning in his flat in

Vanden Court, Petty France, close to St James's Park. Headed *Top Secret – Read and Destroy*, the highest classification for any Government document, Welsh read it through a final time and signed it. He then organized its delivery to Anderson's rooms to coincide with the timing of the meeting in the Cabinet Room.

'Hurrying back to his metal cage from Downing Street, Welsh's hand was never far from the phone. It rang. Anderson was on the move from his office, said the caller, and in a hurry. Out in the Strand Welsh hailed a cab. Time was of the essence. As Welsh paid off his fare outside the Athenaeum his other detective, waiting outside, confirmed that Gusev had arrived just moments earlier.

'Gusev was a Molotov appointment, a 'second generation' careerist in the Soviet Foreign Ministry, a bureaucrat. He had dreaded each session with Anderson. Where Maisky was deft of hand, Gusev was awkward and Anderson kept their meetings in the Athenaeum to a minimum. Dutifully Gusev filed his weekly report to the colonel in charge of the Kremlin intelligence service.

'Welsh bounded up the stairs of the gentlemens' club and walked quickly into the bar to observe Anderson speaking softly but forcefully to the Ambassador who appeared to be paling by the second. Welsh strode towards them, startling them.

"Ambassador,' said Welsh, 'I think you should leave immediately. You may have urgent business to attend to.' Gusev looked stunned. Something was wrong, very wrong. He was like a scared rabbit caught in car headlights. He muttered something inaudible and fled.

'Forever the politician, Anderson smiled thinly, offering Welsh a drink. Welsh shook his head.

"Earlier this afternoon,' began Welsh, 'you received a note from me with the highest security regarding information I had received from the United States. The source I will not disclose, suffice it to say the contents were important enough for you to call the Russian Embassy. I observed you informing the Ambassador that America, unbeknown to ourselves, had built a third atomic bomb as a deterrent against the Soviets.'

"Try and prove it,' sneered Anderson.

"I can't, as you know very well. I can hardly invite the Russian Ambassador to be a witness for the prosecution at the Old Bailey,' replied Welsh.

"What happens now?' asked Anderson, his voice calm.

"First I need to call Winston Churchill,' Welsh responded. 'I promised him that I would do so, once it was over. Understandably he feels badly betrayed, as do I. Never once did I doubt your integrity during the years we worked together. Churchill felt your treachery should be reported to Atlee and let him decide your fate. I advised caution – many events in the war are best left outside the public domain. He agreed. My superiors will not be informed, nor will Atlee. Instead you will withdraw from public life.

"There must be no autobiography, memoir, nothing, you understand. I will ensure that on your death, whenever that may come, your files will be closed for such a long period that no one will care by such time they are released. Atlee will invite you to chair the new advisory committee on atomic matters, as you are the obvious candidate. He may be persistent and you will reluctantly accept but step down after a decent interval. Don't attempt to contact your Soviet friends. From now on your life will be under continual scrutiny. If you go outside this boundary I will personally guarantee a swift end to your miserable life.'

'Anderson looked shocked as the implications of his discovery sank in.

"Are you going to tell me when you were recruited?', asked Welsh.

"I take it from what you have said that I am free to walk away?', responded Anderson.

"Shamefully that is the case. You can go home and reappraise the rest of your life.'

"In which case I don't have to answer your question,' snapped Anderson, picking up his briefcase and storming away. 'You can discover that for yourself.'

'What happened next?' I asked the journalist, totally fascinated.

'As Welsh watched Anderson go, he called out. Anderson turned, glowering at Welsh, who held out an outstretched hand. Anderson dug deep into a pocket of his crumpled suit and handed over the incriminating memo. "There is no third bomb, is there?', said Anderson wryly. "I'm not at liberty to confirm or deny,' replied Welsh.

'The MI6 officer walked slowly back to Shell-Mex House, deep in thought. He had called Churchill from a private room in the club. Welsh felt uncomfortable that he had acted alone, even under Churchill's direct order. Some secrets were best hidden, the great man had said softly on the telephone, even from the heads of MI5 and MI6.

'In Trafalgar Square Welsh watched as voracious pigeons were fed seed by Londoners, ebullient that the six-year nightmare of war was at an end. Britain had come though it, as the victor. Courting couples held hands as the famous fountains sprayed a hazy mist over the square. Welsh gently cursed himself for never finding the time to enjoy a lunchtime recital in the National Gallery as many of his staff had done.

'He took out the note handed back by Anderson. The third bomb was true, of course, and the Americans were never going to tell the British. In American eyes Britain and its far-flung empire had been consigned to the historical past. Only America now had the power to combat Stalin's new brand of hard-line Communism, the scourge that threatened the free world. President Truman had already ordered that the bomb be made ready to be delivered to a US airforce base in Germany, only two hours flying time from Moscow.

'A week earlier Welsh had received interesting news from Berlin. There had been countless Russian defections. Moscow was powerless, despite issuing general threats of reprisals on families left behind. A friendly officer in the X-2 Counter-Intelligence branch of America's OSS, the predecessor to the CIA, had cabled Welsh that an NKGB operative, fearful of another Jewish purge within the organisation, had defected with his family. Mindful of the Soviet penetration in Britain's intelligence services the officer had established contact with the OSS, now extensively active in former German-occupied Europe. To show his value the Russian had provided the OSS with many documents from Moscow, including several cables from the Russian Embassy in London. Welsh had flown to Berlin to collect them. Clearly there had been leaks at the highest level of the British Government. Andersen could not have been the only culprit, believed Welsh. He had already informed Churchill about his suspicions concerning Sir Stafford Cripps.

'Slowly Welsh tore up his typed note and strolled through Trafalgar Square, throwing the tiny pieces into the sky. With the warm sun on his back he turned into the Strand and stopped at his favourite pub near Shell-Mex House. Perrin was already at the table with two pints of beer, there was much to discuss, even to celebrate.

'Fedor Gusev needed more than a stiff drink. He was near to panic after the confrontation in the Athenaeum. Espionage he believed should be left to the NKGB and GRU who skulked in the shadows of London parks or waited for contacts at subway stations. Back in the Embassy he composed himself, but he was very concerned that Anderson had been compromised. Stalin would not be pleased. Gusev needed advice and fast. Sending a cable to Moscow would have to wait.

'The phone rang for an interminable time before it was finally answered by the cultured English voice. Gusev related the events of the late afternoon, admitting the covert relationship that Maisky and now he had enjoyed with Sir John Anderson. Within the hour there was the promised return call. On the description that Gusev had provided, the man at the Athenaeum who had accosted Anderson and the Ambassador sounded like Welsh, he was told, an officer from the sister intelligence organisation who he had little time for and, by all accounts, was one of Churchill's midnight drinking friends.

'What had happened was worrying, said the caller, and couldn't easily be checked out without arousing suspicion. If Gusev's suspicions that Anderson had been set up were correct, the operation would have needed the highest authorisation.

'Gusev listened, nodding his head in agreement, the caller guarded in his choice of words. That evening Gusev sent Stalin a coded cable. As expected the news of the third bomb prompted an immediate reply demanding further clarification. The Ambassador made no mention of the events at the Athenaeum.

'Gusev returned several times to the club, never for one moment expecting Anderson to show; each time the absence of Anderson was reported back to Moscow. After two weeks Gusev called the house in Central London again and was informed that Atlee had appointed a reluctant Anderson to be the director of the nuclear programme. In MI5 there had been no mention of any treachery, which was deeply puzzling. He advised Gusev to alert Stalin that Anderson had been discovered.

'Relieved that his espionage duties were at an end, Gusev uneventfully served out the remainder of his term in London and returned to Moscow in 1949 just months before the breaking storm over Fuchs's treachery. His predecessor, Maisky, who had been so effective in establishing London as the main source for intelligence, was already out of favour. After London Maisky became the Deputy Minister of Foreign Affairs, attending the 'Big Three' conference in Tehran in November 1943. In 1947, after the purging of Molotov, Maisky was dismissed but in 1952, the year before Stalin's death, he was imprisoned for his 'Jewish connections', reportedly 'confessing' to all charges. The Russian Supreme Court tried him for 'Misconduct on diplomatic duties to the detriment of the State'. Gorsky, the NKVD *rezident* who had worked under him in London, testified for the prosecution. Beria allowed Maisky to be transferred from jail to the Komnata Otdykha, the special 'rest rooms' in the Lubyanka, where prisoners received better treatment.'

* * *

The moon had long since disappeared behind the clouds and the rain had fallen steadily. It was past midnight. My wife had long given up peering out through the curtains. My old bones ached.

'Is it your intention ever to publish in a national newspaper? Every paper would want this story,' I asked.

'Have no fear on that score,' responded the journalist. 'I have merely been a part in the process of discovery – make what you will of that statement. With the century drawing to its close British Intelligence wanted to finally close its files relating to the early atomic years and there is only one man alive who could provide some answers – Vladimir Barkovsky, the veteran Russian spymaster and keeper of all the Soviet atomic secrets of his day. Somehow he had to be tempted to talk.

'Apart from the known traitors such as Fuchs and Nunn-May there was no real information as to the depth of Soviet penetration in the British nuclear efforts. The more I dug into the secret Russian files the more I unearthed. I found details of scientists and intelligence officers who worked on *Tube Alloys* and the *Manhattan Project* who were never discovered, nor the politicians who were responsible for policy. In addition, only now have we realised the full significance of your 'atomic' notebook in the manufacture of Stalin's bomb.

'Fuchs was lucky to avoid the death sentence, but in the United States the Rosenbergs were put to death. After his early release from jail in 1959 Fuchs moved to East Germany, working in the nuclear research facility at Rossendorf, near Dresden, and lecturing in the city's university. Students remember him as a 'loner'. Curiously, the Stasi always ensured that textbooks used by the students had pages removed where there were mentions of Fuchs. He married Greta Keilson, a long-time friend, and died in Dresden on January 28, 1988.

'There remained the mystery of what happened to many of Fuchs' papers, written in Birmingham, New York, Los Alamos and Harwell. After Fuchs' arrest in 1950, John Corner, the head of theoretical physics at Aldermaston, formerly requested that Harwell send him all the German physicist's papers. Harwell prevaricated for months but finally released them. Despite the pressures of managing up to 80 physicists Corner found time to archive the papers into 100 topic folders which he maintained in his office. Eventually the files were transferred into the large walk-in safe in Aldermaston's administrative block and only one person, apart from Corner, given access.

'Some years later Corner requested one of the files and sent a written request to the records officer in charge of Aldermaston's new archival system. To Corner's utter astonishment the request was returned with a note stating that none of Fuchs' documents could be traced, in all likelihood they had been sent to the head office of the UKAEA, Britain's atomic energy authority, in Charles II street in London, to be destroyed. The officer had added the words, 'What a terrible loss', to the note. Despite his position in Aldermaston, an angry Corner never discovered why the papers had been removed without his permission.

'The Ministry of Defence still pushes the line that some of the papers were kept, but most were destroyed. Of course they exist, they are buried in the sub-basement of the MI5 building in Thames House. Given their content it was paramount they were removed from Aldermaston to a location where no one could ever read them again. An agreement had been signed in 1958, whereby Britain and America agreed to officially share past and present nuclear secrets. This had created concern, even fear, in certain Government departments. The British had no intention of ever releasing to the Americans the full extent of Fuchs' wartime development work on the atomic bomb in Britain or, indeed, his papers involving his work in America.

'Robert Lees, the powerful and somewhat frightening director of security of the UKAEA, issued an edict around 1958 that papers not necessary to current work were to be immediately destroyed. A frightening atmosphere pervaded the offices of the UKAEA, Aldermaston and Harwell as vast numbers of documents were burnt in incinerators. Squads of security officers descended onto offices in secret locations throughout the country and encouraged staff throughout to sift their filing cabinets, especially those records that dealt with *Tube Alloys*. To this day no one can elucidate on the almost wanton destruction of Britain's early atomic records.

'I have been offered a highly plausible explanation why Lees and his staff went about their task with the degree of enthusiasm they did. By the end of the war the British had woken up to the probability that *Tube Alloys* had been extensively compromised to the Soviets. At all costs this revelation needed to be kept from the Americans, who remained intensely anti-British thanks to the treachery of Fuchs.

'Thankfully, some wartime records did survive the great purge and in 1963 many dusty files were found in a Government basement by Margaret Gowing, the official historian appointed by the Ministry of Defence to write a sanitized history of *Tube Alloys* for public consumption. The basement yielded an incredible discovery. Stuffed behind the box files was a box of Kellogg's corn flakes. Curious, she picked up the rather squashed packet and she found a document inside. Gowing had located part of the original Frisch-Peierls Memorandum, the sensational feasibility study written by the two physicists that carefully explained for the very first time that only a small amount of U-235 was necessary to manufacture an atomic bomb, the very essence behind *Tube Alloys* and the *Manhattan Project*. Although she tried Gowing never found out why such an important and historic document had been neglected in the way it was. Incidentally, the other half of the Memorandum was later found, also by accident, in letters belonging to Sir Henry Tizard, Churchill's wartime nuclear advisor. It is a terrible indictment that the public files in the Public Record Office in Kew Gardens have little relevance to what really transpired during the war years on the atomic bomb.

'Who gave Lees the order to burn the records? In his security position, the instruction would have come from the Ministry of Defence in turn advised by MI5.

'Nunn-May's papers also remain out of the public domain. After his release from jail he accepted an offer to teach in Ghana, as no university in this country would touch him. From time to time he visited England and on one occasion called Margaret Gowing to tell his side of the story. Sadly, she declined to meet him.

'When Cairncross was first interrogated in 1951 it became clear that every major scientific secret during the war might have been compromised, not just *Tube Alloys*, but Bletchley Park and Porton Down. Britain had developed the jet engine, but that, too, had been leaked to the Russians. Cairncross never went to jail, instead he enjoyed the clear air and delights of Switzerland, released through lack of any real evidence.

'After the arrest of Fuchs suspicion fell on many scientists on both sides of the Atlantic. Bruno Pontecorvo, the Italian physicist at Harwell, escaped before the net closed on him and suspicion fell on his friend Enrico Fermi, one of the leading scientists in the *Manhattan Project*. KGB files on Fermi exist in the Department S archive with reports filed by Maria Masia, one of its officers. Peter, her husband and chief of section in the 4th Directorate of the NKVD, had run the desperate operation to liquidate Igor Gouzenko, whose defection compromised the North American networks. There is a possibility that Fermi, one of the greatest physicists of the century, passed on nuclear secrets to the Russians.

'It is funny, isn't it?' said the journalist, 'we fought with the Russians, died for the same cause, yet only covertly were secrets shared that might help shorten the war. With the passing of time do we forgive the traitors that were in our midst? I never fully discovered the extent that Robert Oppenheimer compromised the *Manhattan Project*, or how Wilfred Mann, Eric Rideal and Patrick Blackett had undermined *Tube Alloys*. But Blackett was useful even in the 1960s. At one select KGB briefing in a venue east of Moscow, attended by Barkovsky and other officers who specialised in scientific intelligence, Blackett was mentioned as an exceptional contact. Elevated to the House of Lords, he died in 1974, his name revered with an annual

Blackett Lecture that continues to this day.

'I know the identity of *Moor,* the physicist strongly suspected by Perrin and controlled by Barkovsky from 1941 to 1946. As he is still alive I cannot reveal his identity but I have met him twice. I also had the greatest luck in finding a woman who often came into contact with Ruth Kuczynski, Russia's spy queen who operated in Oxford as *Sony*a. The woman's husband had worked as a scientist and up to 1972 a file existed on him in the Russian Embassy in London.

'Other *Tube Alloys* names liberally litter the Russian archives – Dr Nicholas Kemmer, who worked in the Cavendish and in Montreal, is one. After the war Kemmer was employed at the University of Edinburgh. A former KGB officer confirmed that in the 1960s contact might have been re-established. Each trip to Moscow yielded more names and raised more questions. Eventually I devised a system whereby I emailed in advance of my visit a series of questions to one of my KGB contacts.

'Lord Victor Rothschild's role in Britain's atomic bomb efforts is not very clear, suffice it only to say that he seemed to have influence in several MI5 departments during the war. He was clever, but there is a paper trail in Moscow beginning with a letter written in 1934 from an intelligence officer in the London Embassy about his recruitment. Given his close friendship with the Cambridge group of spies it was inevitable that Rothschild was interviewed by MI5, but his influential friends ensured it was never a serious interrogation. I have on tape considerable detail of the 35-year period he spied for Russia, including his time as advisor to Edward Heath when he was Prime Minister. Rothschild was a mastermind behind one of the KGB's most auspicious post-war operations. The idea was hatched in the Lubyanka and, enlisting Rothschild's help, the KGB tied up MI5 and MI6 for a generation. Rothschild, for a time a candidate to head MI5, had quietly fuelled the speculation in British Intelligence that Roger Hollis, the director of MI5, had been a Soviet agent recruited in China.

'You may remember the furore in the national newspapers over the allegation that Hollis may have been a spy. Only a public statement by Margaret Thatcher supposedly cleared Hollis, but his reputation was forever tainted. It had been a stunning KGB operation. Hollis never was a spy.

'There are thousands of reports and notes relating to early British and American atomic efforts held in the KGB's archives in the Lubyanka and in Yaseneva, the huge intelligence complex some 20 miles south of the city. The archive in Yaseneva is housed on the first floor below ground level and is held on microfiche. All the film used for photographic work during the war had perished. It didn't last once developed.

'Perrin had suspicions about a number of scientists but these were only hunches. From time to time he shared those names with an American physicist from Los Alamos who had CIA clearance. After the war Perrin continued in Government office as the deputy controller of the Directorate of Energy until 1951 before accepting a knighthood and joining the Wellcome drug company. Following his retirement and to his death in 1990 he remained forever silent about his wartime responsibilities.

'Welsh, his lungs decayed through heavy smoking and his liver rotted by whisky, passed away in 1954. Completely against standing security service regulations he destroyed all of his papers. Over one weekend he burnt everything on a bonfire in his garden, destroying records of both *Tube Alloys* and other projects he had been involved with. Some fellow MI6 officers, however, heaved a sigh of relief when Welsh was placed in his grave.

'Anderson became Lord Waverley in 1952, history kindly recording his long-standing Government record. He died in 1958, his papers closed to the British public for 75 years after his death. It will be 2033 before historians can review his heavily filleted file.

'In Moscow, despite his great age, Barkovsky still travels to Yaseneva, researching the KGB's operational history. He works four days a week but has Wednesday off. Barkovsky is tired now and his health is failing.

'I interviewed Barkovsky on four occasions and the tapes of these extensive private conversations are fascinating. At our final session he listened intently to what I had unearthed over my two years of research. He had guided me, of course, prodding me in different directions and providing contact names, never wanting anything in return. I remain mystified why Barkovsky had been willing to devote so many hours with me, given his reputation for absolute secrecy. Occasionally he gave me copies of intelligence articles published in Moscow, carefully pointing out the inaccuracies.

'On the last time I met him we drove him home. I asked him to name the agents of his generation who had impressed him the most. 'Philby,' he replied with no hesitation. 'He was very dedicated.' Donald Maclean came a close second, 'he had a brilliant mind,' said Barkovsky.

'As we reached his home Barkovsky gently shook my hand and in his quiet voice told me I had done better that he expected me too. Intriguingly, he said that there was one big secret he would take to his grave that had involved one of his agents. I think I know what he was referring to, but that will take time to uncover. He denied knowing anything about the existence of *Agent D*. This uniquely placed agent had obtained a document that had reported a meeting between Churchill and Hitler. I have no further information. But I know the meeting happened somewhere in Switzerland.

'I never saw Vladimir Barkovsky again. We had fixed up a further appointment. However, on the day I called to confirm that I would see him at the Gypsy restaurant, the rendezvous used by spy chiefs of past times, another voice answered the phone, gruffly stating that Barkovsky had left Moscow on urgent business. That was a lie, but not unexpected. He had had to report to the FSB every appointment we had made.

'No spymasters can ever claim to have 'clean' hands and Barkovsky is no exception. He made enemies, including Lt General Pavel Sudoplatov, the head of Department S. These old adversaries met for the last time in December 1993, when Barkovsky made a surprise visit to Sudoplatov's Moscow apartment. The conversation was superficially friendly but the tone was icy. For his research Barkovsky needed more background on Katie Harris, the remarkable agent recruited into the NKVD in 1931 and assigned in 1936 to Maclean in Paris. After a stint in Mexico City she had returned to Moscow in 1946, and up to 1951 penetrated the MI6 network in Riga, Latvia. Jewish, Harris was purged and jailed, released in 1954 but prohibited from living in Moscow. She had lived out her remaining years in Gorky. Her files in the KGB archives are incomplete and Barkovsky had hoped that Sudoplatov could fill in some gaps.

'I did make one mistake in my dealings with Barkovsky. In one of our conversations I mentioned the name of a physicist, a junior member of *Tube Alloys*. He had agreed to meet me at his home on the River Thames after one Moscow trip. Barely an hour after my return to England, the phone rang. The scientist, who had enjoyed an outstanding post-war career in Harwell was frantic, almost frightened. He screamed at me saying that he could never meet me now or at any time in the future. I could only assume that he had received a disturbing phone call from someone he hadn't seen or heard from since 1946.

'We've reached the end,' the journalist said stifling a yawn. 'Time for both of us to get on with the rest of our lives.'

I nodded my head in the darkness. This day had been a voyage of discovery for me. At the same time it was clear that I had shared an inextricable link with Vladimir Barkovsky. In our own respective ways we had given Stalin his bomb.

The journalist switched on the car headlights, lighting up Withypool Common in the distance. I got out. He wound down the window and extended his hand.

'Major Hans van der Velde, I can see why Stalin was fond of you,' he smiled. The car pulled out of our driveway. Suddenly it stopped and he shouted back.

'How remiss of me. I forgot to ask – do you know the whereabouts of your 'atomic' notebook?'

'No idea, none whatsoever,' I lied. For a moment his foot remained on the brake. Even in the darkness I detected the shake of his head – he knew.

I watched as the rear lights went past the village shop and the Royal Oak pub before heading up the hill to Dulverton.

The moon had come out again to bathe Exmoor with a silvery luminescence. I suddenly remembered I hadn't asked the journalist his name… and he hadn't offered it.

EPILOGUE

Dateline: December 10, 2000

'There are some loose ends,' said the publisher on the telephone. 'I hope you don't object to me calling you at home?'

'No. It's good to hear from you, my people tell me the operation worked like a dream.'

'The book idea was brilliant, but I was really surprised that Vladimir Barkovsky fell for it, granting me all those interviews. He was taken aback, however, the last time I met him when I said that the book had been written under the name of 'Jerry Dan', his operational codenames in Britain and America. He thought about it for a while and then laughed.'

'Did you find the 'atomic' notebook?'

'Forget it, it is a long lost relic of the Second World War. But yes, I do know where it is. It is of no consequence now.'

'Barkovsky really helped you then?'

'He did. Without him I wouldn't have been able to unravel the story. Thanks to Barkovsky I was able to see Colonel Starinov, and despite his great age his memory was perfect. Through Starinov I met others who had a connection including the widow and son of Stepan Balezin. About 10 years ago Alexander Balezin wrote a short book about his father and included detail of van der Velde's notebook, but it was heavily vetted by the KGB before publication. Much was omitted.'

'Your journalistic and publishing cover has served us well over the years. Iran was the first time you worked for us, wasn't it?'

'Yes, in 1978 I travelled to Tehran to talk to the Central Bank and the Ministry of Finance, ostensibly to discuss country risk and Iran's attractiveness to the international banking community. What was a real worry, however, were those Iranian government loans personally guaranteed by the Shah through his Pahlavi Foundation, funded secretly offshore from siphoned-off oil revenues. For years bank lending to Iran had been highly profitable as bankers were assured that support from the Foundation was as good as a state guarantee.'

'And your involvement?'

'Your agency and others were very worried at the financial exposure to the banking system if the Shah was thrown out. I provided financial details of the Foundation and its worldwide assets. When Ayatollah Khomeini created an Islamic republic the Central Banks in Europe and North America collectively agreed not to disclose the full extent of their exposure after Khomeini's refusal to honour past debt. You will remember that one medium-sized British bank was quietly bailed out without any leak to the newspapers.'

'You helped out in the BCCI problem, I believe, shortly afterwards?'

'Correct. Several trips to Abu Dhabi were necessary to uncover the secret list of BCCI's shareholders and the details of the bank's trust fund in the Caribbean, used to finance bribes to politicians in several countries, including Britain. I inveigled myself into the confidence of Sheik Abedi, BCCI's Pakistani-born chief executive, a shadowy figure who tucked many Middle East governments away in his back pocket.'

'Were the murder allegations regarding BCCI true?'

'Probably. I sometimes visited Abedi in his suite at the Grosvenor House. He had a sinister presence about him and he always surrounded himself with bodyguards. Abedi himself provided me with a diagram of the bank's complicated ownership structure. In another envelope he handed to me was a wad of one-hundred dollar bills and a written offer to join the bank in a publicity role. I handed this back. Over lunch one day at BCCI's City office an executive whispered to me nervously about an internal 'hit-squad' that had murdered two members of staff in Abu Dhabi, the centre of the bank's operations. Their bodies were fed to the sharks in the Persian Gulf. It was surprising the authorities didn't close down BCCI sooner; the Bank of England had monitored its activities for years.'

'What was your next operation?'

'Probably South Africa, I can't remember the year now. Arguably this was my most dangerous assignment. An assistant governor of the Reserve Bank and his family had been brutally murdered in their home in Pretoria.'

'Why did we become involved?'

'Washington and London suspected foul play. The assistant governor was the IMF representative in the Reserve Bank. Every central bank has a director with responsibility for IMF liaison. The IMF had been forewarned by him that a huge scam operated in the Reserve Bank, allowing South African politicians and companies to spirit their wealth out of the country without incurring stringent financial penalties. A year after the murders one of my contacts, a press officer in Volkskas, a Pretoria-based bank, and a former employee for BOSS, was prepared to talk.'

'I suppose BOSS carried out the killings. At whose behest?'

'An aide to John Vorster, the Prime Minister.'

'I've only been aware of you since I became director. During the 1990s we were impressed by the intelligence you provided to us on the growing Mafia influence in the Russian petroleum industry. We shared some of that with our American cousins.'

'Good.'

'You mentioned loose ends.'

'I visited Major Hans van der Velde. He's well for his age. Each year he still receives money from one of the KGB accounts in London; an extraordinary Stalin legacy. Can we leave him alone, even though he arrived somewhat illegally in Britain in 1949?'

'Not a problem. I must say, what he did was incredibly brave, although probably very stupid.'

'You know I have a manuscript. I want to publish, with the necessary changes of course.'

The journalist heard the deep intake of breath at the other end of the telephone.

'MI5 will try to stop you, with good reason. You've accused Churchill of passing German nuclear secrets to Stalin, with the connivance of Sir John Anderson, his Chancellor of the Exchequer, who turned out to be a Russian agent of long-standing.'

'You could use your influence. Readers of the book will find the accounts of van der Velde and Barkovsky hugely interesting. I promised van der Velde I wouldn't publish, but he'll be dead soon. With regard to Churchill, he only sanctioned the van der Velde operation. It was Anderson, for obvious reasons, who argued for the mission to go ahead.'

'It's impossible.'

'I repeat, why? The book is written as historical fiction.'

'Look, let me make myself very clear. This operation caused huge ructions within MI5 after it found the tapes and documents in the raid on your house. Even the Prime Minister was informed. It would be political suicide if I now had to admit to MI5 that the operation had all been my idea.'

'Will you ever tell MI5?'

'Not on my watch. The sole intention was to ascertain, once and for all, the full extent of Soviet scientific espionage in wartime and post-war Britain. For decades vested interests within MI5 ensured that there were few real investigations. Our concerns were pushed aside, barely considered. It was clear that not just the atomic bomb project had been compromised. We were angry that every scientific secret this country possessed had been passed to Russian Intelligence and MI5 seemed unconcerned in finding the perpetrators. It was the Americans who discovered Fuchs through *Venona*, not the British. Nunn-May only came to light by a Russian defection in Canada. MI5 interviewed Cairncross, but it was hardly an interrogation. And what happened? We let him go to enjoy the delights of Switzerland. Pathetic. What you have done, using the cover of writing a book, is to confirm many of our past suspicions. We knew that Barkovsky was keen to talk, but never in our wildest dreams did we believe he would open up as much as he did. Nor did we know that you would find a contact that had access to the First Chief Directorate archives in the Lubyanka – that was a real bonus.'

'Yes it was. I started off researching nuclear secrets and within months other more interesting names began turning up in the documents – Robert Maxwell, Harold Wilson, Victor Rothschild and others. What did MI5 think of me?'

'At the moment their Counter-Intelligence people can't fathom you out. We were asked to check our files if we had any record of you but, of course, we denied any knowledge.'

'Do I take it as read that MI5 intercepted my phone, fax and email?'

'You can. You were also tailed when you met Barkovsky at the National Hotel.'

'I thought as much. Everything about that visit to Moscow was odd; I sensed it.'

'I will consider your publishing request but I may have to disappoint you. In the meantime push your intentions with your MI5 channel. I'll soon get to hear about it. What other loose ends are there?'

'There's the matter of Oxford.'

'Ah yes, Oxford – an embarrassment MI5 thought it had solved many years ago. Your two new names suggest that we hadn't been as thorough as we should have been. However, it is an MI5 matter, and they wouldn't like us to interfere.'

'Both the man and the woman are very old, they wouldn't stand up to even gentle questioning, especially him. Please tell MI5 not to go in too hard.'

'Agreed. The scientist I understand was NKVD reporting to Barkovsky, and the woman was GRU handled by *Sonya*. Is that right?'

'Yes. That scientist from the Clarendon was agent *Moor,* one of the top suspects on Michael Perrin's list of probable Soviet agents. MI5 had interrogated him in the 1960s as part of the Peter Wright investigation regarding Roger Hollis and his MI5 deputy, Mitchell. There were suspicions but no proof. The KGB has confirmed that *Moor* had been very useful to the Soviet atomic programme.'

'And the woman, she was just a courier?'

'That's right, and a very good one. Her husband had been recruited into the GRU before the war, courtesy of Professor Patrick Blackett who recommended the physicist to a GRU talent-spotter. Before he emigrated to Britain he had conducted nuclear research in the top German university for physics. It was standard GRU and NKVD practice to order the Russian Academy of Sciences to invite foreign scientists to visit important research facilities in Moscow and Leningrad. These invitations were usually accepted. The scientists would be lavishly wined and dined by their Soviet hosts and to those inclined to be 'helpful', generous financial inducements were offered. One such incentive was made to this physicist but there were several times in Oxford when he had second thoughts on handing over Britain's atomic bomb secrets. The GRU threatened him, however, if he stopped. His wife later became the courier – the conduit for contact with Ruth Kuczynski and Len Beurton.'

'I understand you received a letter from this woman describing her relationship with Ruth and Len?'

'Yes, your people have seen it.'

'I have to admit that neither MI5 nor ourselves ever sufficiently unravelled the extent of the Kuczynski network in Britain. The father – the economist – we were never able to get a handle on. He had access to much of our pre-war and wartime economic policy. With regard to Ruth and her brother Jürgen, God only knows how good those two really were.'

'They were both exceptional agents according to Barkovsky. Jürgen was instrumental in finding Fuchs and he enrolled many others in Britain into the Soviet cause. The GRU couldn't have been happier when Jürgen joined the US Army in October 1944 with the rank of colonel. Initially he worked as a military statistician on a base in East Anglia before his posting to Allied Headquarters in Germany to sit on the British-American committee tasked with the economic rejuvenation of the country. Another of the projects Jürgen assisted in was the US Strategic Bombing Survey – the results of this analysis on wartime bombing strategy were passed to Moscow. As a hugely experienced GRU talent spotter he established new contacts in post-war Germany ensuring that Cold War military secrets were never safe from Russian hands. In late 1949 after being warned that Fuchs was soon to be unmasked Jürgen fled to East Berlin. He often met Barkovsky over the next 20 years or so. Even though Jürgen had 'retired' Barkovsky was only too pleased to use his experience. Jürgen died on August 6, 1997, after publishing more than 200 books. He had become an accomplished East German Marxist historian. Much of his extensive library went to the Humboldt University on the Unter den Linden in Berlin. Ruth, too, was in a league of her own. It is now very clear that the GRU cell she ran in Oxford was more extensive than we previously believed. There remains the unsolved puzzle of her penetration into MI5 when the organisation was based at Blenheim Palace during the first years of the war. She had one major source. As we know, this source was a woman.'

'That's true. Can we talk about *Scott*. Are you certain *Scott* was an Oxford-based agent for the NKVD?'

'That was what I was told. He was a radar scientist, I have given your people his name. According to the NKVD archives *Scott* even had helpers. I think you must assume that the Clarendon had been badly compromised.'

'You never gave us a name for *Pirate,* one of the agents mentioned in that 1943 document you obtained on Russian activities in Britain during 1942?'

'People in Moscow clammed up as soon as I mentioned the codename, but I haven't given up. I believe he may have been a colleague of Welsh. What did you make of the Victor Rothschild tapes, I hope you found them as fascinating as I did?'

'These new disclosures could create difficulties. There are still people around who maintain he was clean. Rothschild's involvement in the KGB plot to smear Hollis and Mitchell is just extraordinary. I have listened to your tape several times, trying hard to understand how Rothschild might have been able to set it up.'

'I hope you were impressed at the level of intelligence I managed to purloin on Mann, Blackett, Bernal, Rideal and, of course, *Moor*?'

'Our files were sketchy by comparison, apart from Bernal who never shied away from telling anyone that he was a Communist. Learning about Professor Rideal, a key advisor to *Tube Alloys* and a specialist on centrifuges, was a blow. Even now the CIA might get very worked up to hear that Rideal reported private conversations he had had with General Groves to Moscow.'

'Rideal's controller was Barkovsky.'

'Yes, you said. What was his codename?'

'It was an odd one, but very simple. Barkovsky called him *Alkit*, the name of the men's military and civilian outfitters that had branches in London, Oxford and Cambridge. Apparently Barkovsky would meet Rideal either in the store, or sometimes outside. Barkovsky ran him until 1946.'

'How did you find out about Walter Layton, the pre-war editor of *The Economist*? That little gem really threw MI5. He had been highly valued during wartime and helped out on the secret government propaganda programme. We honoured Layton with a Peerage.'

'I asked *Bluebird* to help with Layton. Have you informed the Americans about the members of Oppenheimer's secret cell and the identity of *Perseus*?'

'I'm mulling over that one. I need a favour on another matter, and those revelations might be useful. I guess you haven't mentioned the identity of *Perseus* in your book because he is still alive. Do you think that Barkovsky ever sussed you out?'

'Hard to tell. It is unlikely that I'll ever see him again but he doesn't mind me calling him at his apartment.'

'How is your relationship with *Bluebird*?'

'It's fine. Did MI5 record my telephone calls with him?'

'Yes, I've been given the transcripts.'

'Actually *Bluebird* was a nickname the MI5 'watchers' had given him when he was a senior KGB officer in London in the early 1970s. He often had a hectic daily routine. If *Bluebird* wasn't on a tennis court, he would be in a pub, chatting up another blonde, or in Soho visiting film distributors to peddle his Soviet-produced 'merchandise'. I assume that MI5 still owns the property almost opposite the Embassy, which it uses for electronic surveillance?'

'Probably.'

'At that time the Russians, too, had sophisticated listening equipment. Whilst the 'watchers' were radioing in the movements of Embassy members, the Russians were able to unscramble the MI5 transmissions immediately. It became a standard joke within the Embassy – as the 'listeners' monitored the MI5 transmission '*Bluebird* leaving Kensington Palace Gardens by either the north or south gate', in his car *Bluebird* would be informed and he became adept at dodging the 'tails'. The KGB loved playing games at MI5's expense, given its ability to intercept the radio traffic from across the road. As Embassy staff deliberately queued for buses in Bayswater the KGB, at a distance, observed 'watchers' joining the queue. They knew that MI5 had planted 'bugs' in the Ambassador's suite of offices and in the general reception areas of the Embassy. The MI5 'bug' in the lift not only transmitted conversation but could also identify the very floor the lift was on. *Bluebird* and his fellow officers used the lift to the wrong floor, alighted and then used the stairs.'

'I'm sure that MI5 would be very amused to hear more but watch yourself *Bluebird* has a nasty streak. When he ran the UK desk in the Lubyanka in the late

1970s he authorised the liquidation of a British journalist in Moscow. Has *Bluebird* located the document on the Soviet penetration of the Conservative Party?'

'I'm using my other source as *Bluebird* doesn't have the clearance to the archive.'

'Will *Bluebird* name the Westminster cell of MPs he personally controlled?'

'*Bluebird* was very helpful in the operation we've just closed but he's quite concerned about any disclosure as all these agents are alive. Occasionally he's worried about being found out. His pension, meagre as it is, would be immediately terminated and then there's the threat of a possible jail sentence in Vladimir prison. As you know, Mr Putin takes a dim view of retired KGB officers spilling secrets of the past. However, *Bluebird* has been paid well for his services in the past 12 months.'

'Your other source – has he seen the document?'

'He has.'

'Do you know yet how many names are mentioned in it?'

'In the limited time he had in the archive, he says there are five Members of Parliament, all men. The names meant nothing to him, apart from one, who I've already discussed with you.'

'Don't send any documents over the Internet when you are in Moscow. The FSB is now intercepting all Internet traffic from the Moscow area. You could be found in a very short time. I suggest you use your normal channel, the risk is far less.'

'OK. Did MI5 establish the identity of *Agent D*?'

'That's a puzzle it has yet to solve.'

'So you haven't told them?'

'No, let them work it out for themselves. According to the files we first reported our suspicions more than 40 years ago. I understand he sat on several intelligence committees during the war, eventually becoming very friendly with Churchill.'

'*Agent D* was held in high regard in the NKVD according to my source.'

'I daresay, given he gave to the Russians the details of Churchill's trip to the Vatican in 1944 to negotiate with German generals a separate peace arrangement that would have isolated Stalin. Your two documents on the Vatican negotiations should give MI5 a steer in the right direction.'

'There is more on *Agent D*. He regularly met another Soviet agent, not a controller or someone from the Embassy. Curiously it seems they were aware of each other's nefarious activities.'

'What are you saying?'

'This person worked for the FBI, whose Soviet codename was *Lemon*. She was a woman.'

'And *Lemon*'s identity?'

'That I don't know. You would need to check which FBI agents were stationed in London during the war.'

'Interesting. Thank you.'

'*Elsa*. I haven't mentioned this codename either.'

365

'Who is *Elsa*, wasn't that a wartime name unearthed by *Venona* in the States? She worked in government?'

'No, we had our own *Elsa*. This one worked for MI5.'

'A name please, there weren't many female officers in those days.'

'No. For the moment I'm not prepared to identify *Elsa*.'

'You have shared the other names with us, why not her? I thought you worked for us.'

'There is more to uncover. For years you chased your tails uncovering male spies and yet, right under your noses sat *Elsa*, very pretty by all accounts but downright dangerous and horribly effective.'

'What did *Elsa* steal?'

'She handed over to her Russian controller in London the Allied plans for the D-Day landings in 1944.'

'My friend, you know too much. Tell me more about Maxwell, you seem convinced we had something to do with his untimely death.'

'I am.'

'You would be foolish to believe everything you hear in Moscow. We never liked him but that doesn't imply we killed him.'

'Let me give you some perspective on Maxwell's spying career. I won't start with Berlin, you know how he was recruited. The Soviet relationship with Maxwell had proved fruitful but in 1951 contact was severed with the arrest and purging of Major General Dmitry Utekhin for supposed contact with underground Jewish organisations. Thereafter Fedotov, head of the KGB's Counter-Intelligence department, banned any further involvement. After Stalin's death Khrushchev purged the Soviet intelligence services and within two years Maxwell returned to the fold.

'Maxwell travelled to Moscow in 1954. To the new regime at the KGB he appeared as a fledgling international publisher of some influence. At his hotel he was introduced to Colonel Bogdan Dubenski, an officer who would be at Maxwell's side for a number of years as the Russian publishing ventures grew. Dubenski changed Maxwell's codename from *Tolmatch* to *Fedorov*, the name of a famous 16th century Russian printer. During the visit in 1954 Maxwell met Academician Topcheyev, the chief scientific secretary of the Russian Academy of Sciences, who granted Maxwell the exclusive rights to publish Soviet scientific papers and journals abroad. Funding arrangements were put into place by the Ministry of Finance, with the KGB channelling money into Maxwell's offshore accounts.

'Full responsibility for Maxwell resided with Department No. 7, the KGB section that dealt with the recruitment of foreign journalists as Soviet agents. With Dubenski's departure to head the Norwegian KGB station, Colonel Norman Borodin, aka Gruzenberg, became the active case officer. Gruzenberg later became deputy chief of Counter-Intelligence.

'On March 22, 1956, Major General Ivan Serov, accompanied by Lt General Ale

Gribanov, arrived at Heathrow on board the inaugural flight of the Tupulov 104. No one at MI5 expected the head of the KGB and one of his deputies to suddenly turn up in London. Actually it was a handy blind for more serious discussion at the Embassy concerning the impending Khrushchev and Bulganin visit to Britain in April. A source within MI5 had disclosed to the Russians some weeks earlier the details of MI5's operation to eavesdrop on the Russian Premier and his 16-strong entourage, including the infamous Commander Buster Crabb scheme to attach a magnetic listening device on the hull of Khruschev's moored cruiser, the *Ordzhonikdze*.'

'Are you saying that the KGB had prior warning of Crabb's operation?'

'At least a month, apparently, and I don't know the name of the MI5 source. Crabb was well known to the KGB, as it had tracked his MI6 activities in Latvia establishing the nationalist underground groups. An experienced frogman, Crabb was captured in the water and tortured by a KGB interrogation team on board the ship.'

'What has the Serov trip to do with Maxwell?'

'Serov and Gribanov returned to Moscow on March 28 but before they left they had two secret meetings in the Embassy. The first was with Maxwell, the other with Victor Rothschild.

'The following year, in February, Serov received a one-page memo, marked '*Top Secret*', from the KGB's First Deputy Chairman, Major General Lunyov and Gribanov. Borodin had prepared the document. The Soviets wanted to celebrate the 40th anniversary of the Revolution and Maxwell had agreed to produce documentary films of the Bolshoi Ballet and a production of 'Swan Lake' for distribution in London and New York, but he needed funding for the projects. Your people have the document but let me read it to you.

'*TOP SECRET*

'*To the chairman of KGB, State Security Committee of the Council of Ministers of the USSR*'

'*To Army General Comrade Serov, I A*'

'*Date 25 February 1957*'

'*Following the request of the Organisation concerning attracting prominent representatives from the West for positive propaganda of Soviet science and achievements in connection with the future celebration of the 40th anniversary of the Great October Socialist Revolution, the following is for your consideration:*

'*We have undertaken measures assuring the involvement of an influential business representative from England, R Maxwell, who is connected with one of the Labour Party leaders, Harold Wilson.*

'*Aiming to maintain business and conspiratorial contacts with Maxwell we have identified his broad commercial possibilities. In connection with this we feel it feasible to meet Maxwell's request to become a foreign producer of documentary films 'The Bolshoi Ballet' and 'Swan Lake', which are planned to be shown between*

1957 and 1958 in the United States, Europe and in other countries.

'*Given the importance of further work with Maxwell and the feasibility of significant economic benefits of his publishing activity, we feel it necessary that the Ministry of Foreign Trade Bank and Ministry of Culture of the USSR receive guidelines of the Organisation regarding co-operation with him, in addition to more funding.*

'*Signed: First Deputy Chairman of the KGB*
'*Major General K Lunyov*
'*And the Head of the 2nd Chief Department*
'*Lt General O Gribanov*'

'Serov duly signed, granting Maxwell his money. For a long time there has been suspicion that the KGB funded some of the Maxwell ventures. Now we have the proof.

'Serov came to London again in 1957 for more meetings with Maxwell and Rothschild.

'As Maxwell's legitimate relations with the Russians expanded he dealt with Mezhdunarodnaya Kniga, the Moscow publishing house of the Ministry of Foreign Trade of the USSR. In 1965 Maxwell published one of his biggest Russian works – *Economics of Nuclear Energy*. Payments were conducted through the All-Union Agency for Copyright – a KGB front created for Russian authors. All authors and publishers were required to use this organisation.

'Given Maxwell's strong personality Moscow decided against using a controller from the Embassy in London and contact often proved sporadic. That situation changed partly when Vitali Lui, better known to us as Victor Louis, the Moscow representative of the newspaper mogul Lord Rothermere, introduced himself to Maxwell. Recruited in a Soviet labour camp in the early 1950s, Louis had risen through the KGB ranks to become a colonel some 10 years later. He married a British woman and expanded his horizons. Entertaining was important for Louis and he held lavish tennis parties for the foreign community in his dacha near Moscow where the heads of MI6 and the CIA stations freely networked with KGB officers. So much for the Cold War.

'Using his cover as a journalist Louis maintained contact with many British politicians and businessmen. Major General Vecheslav Kevorkov, director of Counter-Intelligence, handed Louis the important task of maintaining the Soviet intelligence relationship with Taiwan at a time when official contact was difficult due to the relationship with China. Louis was often asked to check out the accuracy of Maxwell's information. On one visit to Moscow in 1968 Maxwell passed to the KGB the details of his secret discussions with the Israeli Government on proposals to restore diplomatic relations between both countries. The KGB sent Louis to Tel Aviv to verify the proposal.

'As well as Louis, another key KGB contact for Maxwell was Colonel Igor Prelin, head of the so-called public relations department in the KGB, who reported to General Oleg Kalugin. With each passing Soviet premier Maxwell was a highly valued contact through his access to politicians and Governments throughout the West

368

An MP from 1964 until 1970 he was especially useful in conducting KGB probes.

'Maxwell had now turned into an intelligence maverick. He revelled in the company of Brezhnev, whose memoirs he published, organized by the premier's interpreter Suchodrcv, a KGB officer. Maxwell later established strong contacts with Yuri Andropov, head of the KGB from 1967 to 1982 and briefly general secretary of the Communist Party before his death in 1984.

'Maxwell's international reputation grew. He purchased the *Daily Mirror* and in America he bought publishing houses, newspapers and airline databases.'

'Did the KGB fund any acquisition in Britain?'

'Probably, but not the *Daily Mirror*. The KGB did help with some of the start-up funding for *The European*, his short-lived pan-European publication. But publishing soon became a sideline for Maxwell in his relationship with the KGB.'

'Explain.'

'Senior Russian Government officials were laundering Communist Party funds into hard currency accounts, using the KGB as a conduit. Maxwell helped, given his wide knowledge of the offshore banking system. Furthermore, he became party to appropriations from bogus joint ventures, some in the notoriously corrupt Russian petroleum industry. Grateful politicians ensured that Maxwell benefited. Sofia and Prague were his favourite locations for clandestine liaisons regarding these transactions.

'In London Maxwell only felt comfortable dealing at Ambassadorial level. Leonid Zamyatin, the Soviet Ambassador, however, never warmed to the publisher but did take his calls. Meetings would be arranged at the Embassy, but after the cursory greetings Zamyatin would duck out and leave Maxwell to discuss matters with his intelligence officers.

'On becoming the head of the KGB in 1988 Vladimir Kryuchkov personally took over the supervision of Maxwell, but two officers maintained their liaison. Yuri Kolesnikov, a veteran officer who had worked in Rumania and Israel and who had been deputy chairman of the anti-Zionist committee was one. The other, Colonel Igor Constantinov, had been expelled from London station in 1971. Gorbachev and his wife, Raisa, often entertained Maxwell.

'Kryuchkov facilitated Maxwell in purchasing rights for scientific publishing in the GDR, Poland and Bulgaria and was in negotiation at the time of Maxwell's death over a license for all scientific publishing in the USSR. Maxwell's most audacious joint venture was the film production company, to be funded by the KGB yet headed by the publisher. The idea was not new. In the 1970s the KGB had used the guise of Sovexport, a marketing company, to sell Russian-made movies and documentaries in the West. London became its centre and KGB officers had actively cultivated major and minor film stars, including a very sexy young lady who starred in several productions from the Hammer Film Studios who frequently attended parties at the Embassy. Maxwell and Kryuchkov were well into discussions on this new venture, but with his death it was dropped. The newspapers would have a field day if they got the story that his company pension funds were to be further raided to set up a KGB film studio. However, by this time Maxwell was effectively broke, openly lying to his bankers.

'Maxwell had agreed to another commitment – publishing the KGB publication *Intelligence and Counter Intelligence*, a journal for serving and retired KGB veterans. The Central Statistical Section of the KGB had drawn up a contract but it remained unsigned.

'The KGB told me that MI6 was now monitoring Maxwell's phone calls and faxes from your listening facility in Scotland. It was aware that Maxwell was discussed by the Joint Intelligence Committee, on which you sit with your colleagues from MI5, GCHQ and Ministry of Defence Intelligence. The Russians knew that the CIA head-of-station in London often voiced his concerns about Maxwell when he attended JIC meetings.

'Events moved quickly now. Maxwell had two visits in June 1991 from KGB officers. Shebarshin was the first, followed by Yakushkin, the US *resident*, who travelled through London en route to Moscow. Maxwell was trying desperately to roll over debt and hide the massive holes in the pension funds. On October 31 he flew to Gibraltar to join his yacht, the *Lady Ghislaine*.

'Using the listening station in Gibraltar every movement of the yacht in the Canary Islands was closely monitored by your people. After the crew retired for the night on November 5, leaving Maxwell to continue his heavy drinking, the Special Boat Squadron, selected members of your secret military wing, the Increment, were close by. As Maxwell urinated over the side an arm silently closed around his mouth and he was dragged into the water. Maxwell struggled violently but he was no match for the two wet-suited divers. The SBS men stripped the dead Maxwell of his clothes so, to the world's press, the event had all the signs of an unfortunate accident. Days later, when Maxwell's bloated body was found, the Spanish autopsy certified death by heart attack and drowning. On November 9, after his body had been flown to Israel for burial, at the Institute of Forensic Medicine Israeli doctors confirmed quite different results, clearly observing lesions on the back, shoulders and hands. Furthermore, severe bruising was visible under Maxwell's right ear and the muscles on his left shoulder were torn, the result of being pulled into the water and the unequal struggle for life. There were no traces of a heart attack or coronary thrombosis.

'In Moscow there was relief over his death. Not only had Maxwell been in the employ of the KGB, for decades he had flirted with the intelligence services of Israel, Iran, Iraq and Libya. Maxwell had offended the Ayatollah and for years had been a target for the Iranian secret services. Gaddafy, too, had fallen out with Maxwell and the Libyan dictator had hired a former CIA 'freelance' to hunt down the publisher.

'The tidying up of loose ends in Moscow had begun the day after Maxwell's death. Vadim Biryukov, one of Maxwell's past KGB controllers and an agent with strong links with foreign journalists was murdered in his garage after first enduring unspeakable torture. It was widely believed that Biryukov, a key figure in the laundered funds operation, had in his possession the secret account numbers in the offshore banking centres. In the days that followed other acquaintances of Biryukov mysteriously disappeared.

'Yes, the British liquidated Maxwell, but with the knowledge and connivance of the KGB, which had agreed to MI6's request to cover up Maxwell's spying career that had spanned more than 45 years. In the interest of both countries it was important that Maxwell's past be concealed, especially now that Russia was in the grip of fundamental change. Does this account of his death square with the facts, as you know them?'

'That's unfair. You know I can't answer even if I wanted to. But have you discounted a totally 'freelance' operation, he had numerous business enemies?'

'The KGB insisted the Increment took him out. The killing enabled the organisation to unwind the Maxwell scams – they had become an embarrassment.'

'Your Increment notion isn't plausible and why should the Russians tell you that we connived together in a cover up?'

'I wondered about that at first but then it became clear that so many officers in the KGB, past and present, had had some level of communication with Maxwell. In a way the Russians rather wanted to boast about their long relationship with him. No one ever trusted him and there were always doubts as to which intelligence service he felt most committed to, but he had been very useful. He never disappointed – there was always a new deal, something new for the Russians to consider. You would be interested to hear that on occasions he often alluded to the KGB that he worked for you.'

'He did, but a long time ago and nothing current at the time of his death. Did any of your sources come across any document that detailed the politicians in this country that Maxwell had bribed with KGB money for favours? There were a number.'

'I never asked.'

'Pity. I understand you have obtained another document on Maxwell?'

'Yes, it is dated June 23, 1980. The KGB note relates to a 'soft' credit of $8 million due to Maxwell which had been stopped by the Russian Ministry of Finance. The payment was to be made through several Soviet banks in Switzerland and channelled to a number of Maxwell's businesses. These credits were usually repaid through the National Westminster Bank. There is no suggestion that NatWest was aware of Maxwell's dealings with the KGB. There can be no doubt, now, that Maxwell was on the KGB's payroll. I managed to obtain one of the four copies made of the document – the copy that went to the KGB Secretariat.'

'Do you expect to receive more material on Harold Wilson?'

'Probably. How far advanced are your people in confirming what I've given you to date?'

'A small team has been put together to sift through all the K Branch material, the MI5 department set up in the 1970s to investigate Soviet penetration of the Labour Party.'

'You are including those meetings that Wilson held with the Soviets over the question of the Ukrainian gold lying in the vaults of London's banks, that were concluded in December 1947?'

'We shall. Remind me about those meetings and Wilson's involvement.'

'In the war he was director of economics and statistics at the Ministry of Fuel and Power and a key member of the British delegation that visited Moscow. A Ukrainian family had deposited the gold in question back in the 19th century with the East India Company at an interest rate of five per cent per year. In 1858 when the company was disbanded it was transferred to the Bank of England. Only after a relative took up the case did the Russians and a representative from the Bank of England, a Colonel Robert Mitchell, begin negotiations in 1922. The British, in their normal style, acknowledged the gold's existence but no more than that. The NKVD joined the new negotiations in June 1937, but only in 1947 did both countries conclude an outcome. Now President of the Board of Trade, and at 31 the youngest Cabinet Minister since William Pitt the Younger in 1792, Wilson signed the agreement. The Russians were given a harsh deal. Essentially the British kept the gold as reparations for wartime military aid. Furthermore, the British received 750,000 tons of Soviet wheat at an abysmally low price; grain it could ill afford. Quite rightly the Russians raised the issue again in the 1950s and in 1967 when Wilson was Prime Minister. Kosygin, in London to discuss a Russian proposal that Wilson should intermediate to bring peace in Vietnam, agreed to settle mutual claims over the gold.'

'Was that the end of it?'

'No. In July 1986 Shevardnadze on a trip to London brought up the question with the Thatcher Government, but was rebuffed.'

'So what happened to the gold?'

'The Bank of England still has it, and the value has grown to quite a huge sum. It belongs quite legitimately to the Ukrainians.'

'So Wilson was recruited during the early negotiations?'

'During his trip to Moscow Wilson met several Soviet diplomats, all employees in the intelligence services, but he was already an agent. James Klugman, the SOE officer, had talent spotted Wilson in 1943 after being tasked to identify possible recruits, especially those with links to the Labour Party. Konstantin Kukin, the NKVD *rezident* in London, ran Klugman who reported that Wilson might be eminently suitable. The civil servant was a socialist but could be independent of the pro-Labour line. Wilson met Kukin and by all accounts they struck up a strong friendship. However, Wilson steadfastly declined to enter into an agent's relationship – an 'agentura' – with the NKVD, remaining an 'agent of influence'. The KGB officer who ran Wilson for several years was Nikolay Hlyistov, the same officer incidentally who had some dealings with Maxwell. Hlyistov had been in London as a postgraduate at the LSE, and he is a name your organisation is very familiar with. You later banned Hlyistov from entering Britain, and the US followed suit. Today, I understand, that ban remains in place and the very mention of his name touches a raw nerve. He's now chairman of a Moscow insurance company.'

'According to your material Wilson was very active for the KGB during his first period as Prime Minister. What level of intelligence was being provided?'

'In 1964 Wilson provided a great deal on British foreign policy. For example, Russia was keen to hear Britain's assessment of Lyndon Johnson's new administration, the reaction in London to China testing its atomic bomb and new British policy to broaden relations with Eastern Europe and the USSR. On other matters Wilson gave the Soviets an inside track on the British plans to exchange the Russian spy Gordon Lonsdale for Greville Wynne and the establishment of Quadragon, a secret department in the Ministry of Defence. The following year, the coup in Indonesia, the German Bundestag programme to revise state borders in Europe and Britain's view over the power struggle in Russia between Brezhnev and Podgorny for the position of party first secretary were just some of the issues discussed at Cabinet and later shared by Wilson with the KGB. Britain's policy towards the conflict between India and Pakistan in 1966, the death of Shastri, West Germany's nuclear potential and relations towards China with the advent of the Cultural Revolution were also of major interest. Should I carry on?'

'Enough. The real difficulty MI5 had with Wilson was discovering the identity of the go-between between himself and Hlyistov.'

'So I understand but now you know his name. Given the go-between achieved high public office I guess that will be another secret that will never make the public domain.'

'On your forthcoming trip to Moscow will you try to locate the Gaitskell file?'

'I already have; it's not at the Lubyanka or in Yaseneva.'

'Where is it?'

'Omsk.'

'Why Omsk?'

'All the KGB personnel records from 1940 to 1965 have been moved to the FSB office in the city. A special permit is required to view the files.'

'Does *Bluebird* still stick to his version of Gaitskell's sudden death in January 1963?'

'He's never waivered. The poison came from the KGB's toxic laboratory and was never detected in the post-mortem. Moscow had taken the decision that it wanted to elevate Wilson to lead the Labour Party. Gaitskell needed to be eliminated.'

'Has *Bluebird* conveyed to you yet how the poison was administered?'

'No.'

'Tread with great caution my friend, sometimes I worry about you.'

The line went dead.

Ultimate Deception

The Black Sea Area

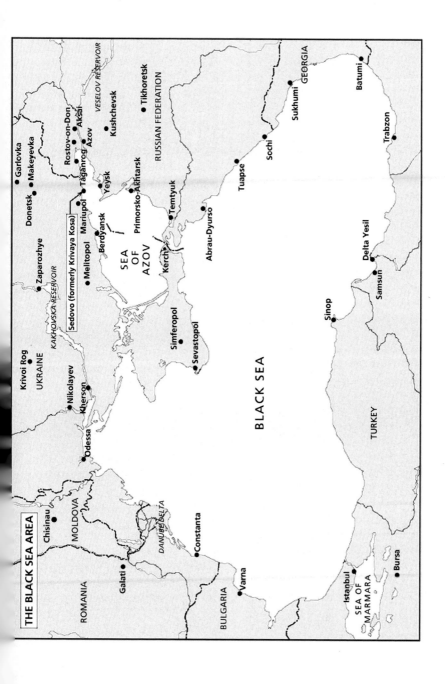

The centre of Krivaya Kosa

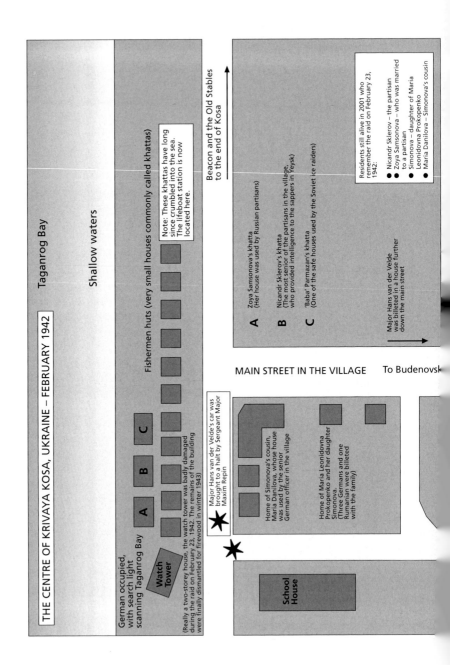

THE CENTRE OF KRIVAYA KOSA, UKRAINE – FEBRUARY 1942

Taganrog Bay

Shallow waters

Fishermen huts (very small houses commonly called khattas)

Note: These khattas have long since crumbled into the sea. The lifeboat station is now located here.

German occupied, with search light scanning Taganrog Bay

Watch Tower

(Really a two-storey house, the watch tower was badly damaged during the raid on February 23, 1942. The remains of the building were finally dismantled for firewood in winter 1943)

Major Hans van der Velde's car was brought to a halt by Sergeant Major Maxim Repin

Home of Simonova's cousin, Maria Danilova, whose house was used by the senior German officer in the village

Home of Maria Leonidovna Prokopenko and her daughter Simonova. (Three Germans and one Rumanian were billeted with the family)

School House

MAIN STREET IN THE VILLAGE   To Budenovsk

Beacon and the Old Stables to the end of Kosa

A   Zoya Samsonova's khatta
(Her house was used by Russian partisans)

B   Nicandr Sklerov's khatta
(The most senior of the partisans in the village, who provided intelligence to the sappers in Yeysk)

C   'Baba' Parmazan's khatta
(One of the safe houses used by the Soviet ice raiders)

Major Hans van der Velde was billeted in a house further down the main street

Residents still alive in 2001 who remember the raid on February 23, 1942:

● Nicandr Sklerov – the partisan
● Zoya Samsonova – who was married to a partisan
● Simonova – daughter of Maria Leonidovna Prokopenko
● Maria Danilova – Simonova's cousin

The Sea of Azov and Taganrog Bay

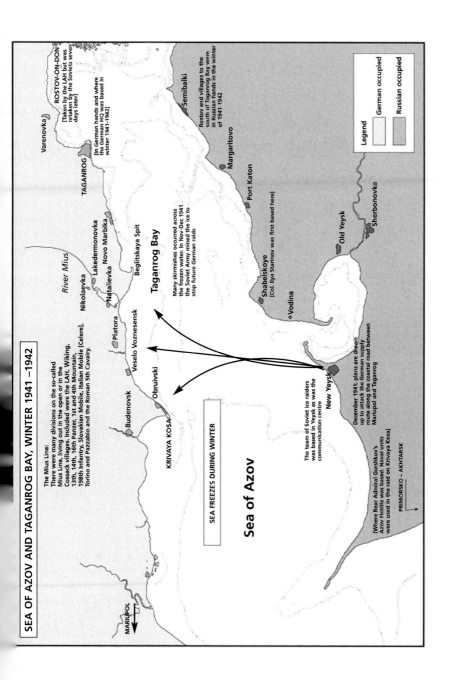

SEA OF AZOV AND TAGANROG BAY, WINTER 1941–1942

The Mius Line:
There were many divisions on the so-called Mius Line, living out in the open or in the Cossack villages. Included were the LAH, Wiking, 13th, 14th, 16th Panzer, 1st and 4th Mountain, 198th Infantry, Slovakian Mobile, Italian Mobile [Celere], Torino and Pazzabio and the Roman 5th Cavalry.

ROSTOV-ON-DON
[Taken by the LAH but was retaken by the Soviets seven days later]

Varenovka

TAGANROG
[In German hands and where the German HQ was based in winter 1941–1942]

Semibalki

Rostov and villages to the south of Taganrog Bay were in Russian hands in the winter of 1941–1942

Margaritovo

River Mius

Nikolaevka

Lakedermonovka

Natalievka Novo Marbika

Beglitskaya Spit

Platora

Taganrog Bay

Many skirmishes occurred across the frozen water. In Nov–Dec 1941 the Soviet Army mined the ice to stop future German raids

Port Katon

Veselo Voznesensk

Shabelskoye
[Col. Ilya Starinov was first based here]

Obrulvski

Vodina

Old Yeysk

Budenovsk

Sherbonovka

KRIVAYA KOSA

New Yeysk

December 1941: plans are drawn up to attack the German supply route along the coastal road between Mariupol and Taganrog

SEA FREEZES DURING WINTER

The team of Soviet ice raiders was based in Yeysk as was the communication centre

Sea of Azov

[Where Rear Admiral Gorshkov's Azov Flotilla was based. Naval units were used in the raid on Krivaya Kosa]

PRIMORSKO – AKHTARSK

MARIUPOL

Legend

☐ German occupied

▨ Russian occupied

iii

The raid on Krivaya Kosa

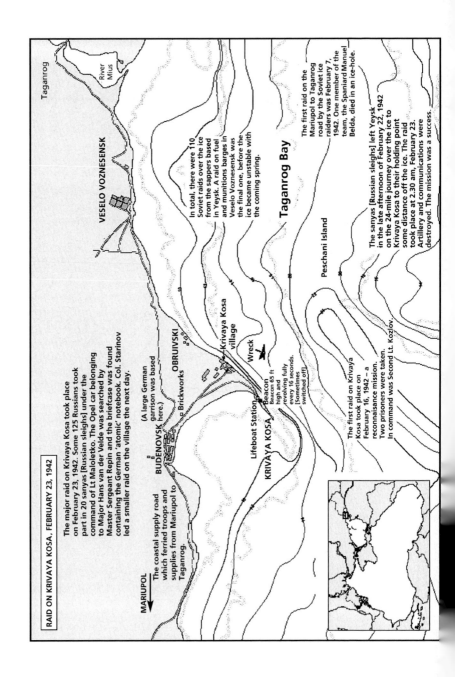

RAID ON KRIVAYA KOSA, FEBRUARY 23, 1942

The major raid on Krivaya Kosa took place on February 23, 1942. Some 125 Russians took part in 20 sanyas [Russian sleighs] under the command of Lt Maloletko. The Opel car belonging to Major Hans van der Velde was searched by Master Sergeant Repin and the briefcase was found containing the German 'atomic' notebook. Col. Starinov led a smaller raid on the village the next day.

MARIUPOL

The coastal supply road which ferried troops and supplies from Mariupol to Taganrog.

BUDENOVSK
(A large German garrison was based here.)

OBRUIVSKI
Brickworks

KRIVAYA KOSA
Lifeboat Station
Beacon
Beacon 65 ft high and revolving fully every 16 seconds. [Sometimes switched off]

Krivaya Kosa village
Wreck

The first raid on Krivaya Kosa took place on February 16, 1942 – a reconnaisance mission. Two prisoners were taken. In command was Second Lt. Kozlov.

VESELO VOZNESENSK

In total, there were 110 Soviet raids over the ice from the sappers based in Yeysk. A raid on fuel and munitions barges in Veselo Voznesensk was the final one, before the ice became unstable with the coming spring.

Taganrog Bay

Peschani Island

The first raid on the Mariupol to Taganrog road by the Soviet ice raiders was February 7, 1942. One member of the team, the Spaniard Manuel Belda, died in an ice-hole.

The sanyas [Russian sleighs] left Yeysk in the late afternoon of February 22, 1942 on the 24-mile journey over the ice to Krivaya Kosa to their holding point some distance off the ice. The raid took place at 2.30 am, February 23. Artillery and communications were destroyed. The mission was a success.

Taganrog

River Mius

Characters

Colonel Vladimir Borisovich Barkovsky, KGB
Barkovsky arrived in Liverpool, England, in February 1941. He worked as political attaché at the London Embassy, first with Anatoli Gorsky, then Konstantin Kukin, the respective heads of the London NKVD station. His ultimate superior in Moscow was Lt General Pavel Fitin, the head of the th Directorate. Using his camera skills, learned at the Malakhovka NKVD training school, Barkovsky photographed hundreds of documents provided to the NKVD from Philby, Maclean, Burgess, Cairncross, Blunt and Mann. In 1945 Barkovsky was appointed Major. During his time in London from 1941–1946 Barkovsky ran his own ring of 20 contacts, of which six were primary sources. In 1949, as a Lt Colonel, Barkovsky was commissioned to work in the Washington Embassy out after only one month he was posted to the New York Consulate. He, with three other officers, was recalled to Moscow in 1950 after the arrests of Fuchs and Julius and Ethel Rosenberg. During 1950–1956, Barkovsky remained in Moscow but he travelled to the US twice a year on his diplomatic passport. In 1956 Barkovsky was appointed KGB *resident* in New York, his main task to replenish the networks after the defection of Elizabeth Bentley to the FBI in 1948. He remained in New York until 1963. From 1963–1969 Barkovsky was deputy head of the Science and Technology Intelligence [STI] department in Moscow, responsible for the overall control of scientific agents in the Western hemisphere. Between 1970–1984, Barkovsky was a professor lecturing in one of the KGB's institutes and during this period he began to write the official history of the organisation. Barkovsky is regarded as one of the most able Russian spymasters of his generation. The events in Krivaya Kosa in February 1942, and the finding of Hans van der Velde's 'atomic' notebook, continued to intrigue the spymaster to his death in 2003.

Characters

Vladimir Barkovsky
He always preferred wearing a suit when he met his agents in London in 1941–1946. Shortly after his arrival, he purchased a suit from the tailor, Austin Reed, in Regent Street. One of his favourite meeting places was Kew Gardens.

Vladimir Barkovsky
Dressed in the uniform of political attaché in the London Embassy.

Operation Enormoz
The four key members of the special NKVD group of officers set up in wartime to steal atomic intelligence from Britain, the United States and Canada. They met only infrequently in later years to celebrate their achievements. *From left to right:* Colonel Anatoli Antonovich Yatskov [New York 1941–1946], Colonel Leonid Romanovich Kvashnikov [New York 1943–1945; became head of S&T in 1952], Colonel Vladimir Borisovich Barkovsky and Colonel Aleksandr Semyonovich Feklisov [New York 1941–1946 and London 1947–1950; the last case officer for Klaus Fuchs].

Characters

Colonel Vladimir Barkovsky, outside the Kurchatov
Institute, Moscow.

The special conference held in Laxenburg, outside Vienna, in 1999 would have been the last for many
of the Russian atomic specialists who were present. The event was mainly sponsored by the US
Government and there were 100 delegates from the US, Britain and Russia. Under discussion was the
development of Russian nuclear weapons during the Cold War. Vladimir Barkovsky is at the centre
of this grouping of Russian nuclear scientists. To the right is Arkadi Brish, the scientist who worked
at Arzamas, the Russian nuclear design centre, who was responsible for the detonators for RDS-1, the
bomb exploded at Semipalatinsk in August 1949.

Characters

Vladimir Barkovsky, outside his apartment block in Moscow.

The apartment block in winter.

Characters

Colonel Ilya Starinov
Codenamed *Rudolf Wolf* when he led the Russian and Spanish subversive brigades in the Spanish Civil War, his exploits became legendary. Starinov returned to Moscow in 1939, after three years in Spain with 300 Spaniards who later fought for the Soviet partisan army. Already a holder of Lenin's highest award for valour, Starinov acquired a formidable reputation as a saboteur during the war with Germany. He and his teams of sappers systematically mined Kharkov before the Germans entered the city in 1941, with the help of Nikita Khrushchev, the head of the city's Military Council. When Khrushchev became Soviet Premier, the two often met to toast the murderous devastation exacted on the Germans during the Soviet retreat. During the winter of 1941–1942, Starinov headed the special group of 125 Russian and Spanish sappers, based in Yeysk, south of Rostov-on-Don, that travelled across the ice of Taganrog Bay in sanyas [sleighs] to disrupt German military supplies from Mariupol to Taganrog. It was during the raid on February 23, 1942, at Krivaya Kosa, that Sergeant Major Maxim Repin found the 'atomic' notebook in Major Hans van der Velde's briefcase after a firefight near the schoolhouse in the village. Starinov was not on the raid himself, but visited the site some hours later after an order from his commanding officer, Major General Tsyganov, commander of the 56th Army. Within days of the raid Starinov flew to Moscow with the 'atomic' notebook, where he met Stepan Balezin, the deputy to Sergei Kaftanov, Stalin's scientific advisor. Starinov didn't return to the Taganrog area after his meeting with Balezin. During the German retreat from the Soviet Union and Eastern Europe in the latter stages of the war, Starinov commanded a number of sabotage groups. With the advance on Berlin, Starinov, on the staff of General Konev, ran a partisan squad that dismantled German mines. After the war Starinov became an explosives advisor to the KGB, with many of his students becoming veterans of the war in Afghanistan. In 1970 Starinov met with Kaftanov, their first meeting since the war, to discuss the contribution which van der Velde and the 'atomic' notebook had made to the Soviet atomic bomb programme. After celebrating his 101st birthday on August 2, 2000, in Moscow, Starinov died the following November. His funeral was covered on national television.

Characters

Colonel Ilya Starinov
Photograph taken in Spain during the Spanish Civil War. His sabotage team was responsible for the wrecking of more than 80 trains. On one occasion Ernest Hemingway visited the group, on assignment for a US newspaper, but Starinov declined to meet him. There was a one million-peseta reward for the capture of Starinov. Included in his team were Manuel Belda and Domingo Ungrier, two Spaniards who would be involved in the Red Army ice raids across Taganrog Bay in 1941–1942. Belda lost his life on the ice during one of the first practice raids.

Colonel Ilya Starinov
Pictured with his wife in 1940.

Characters

Dr Yakov Dokuchayev
During the war Dokuchayev served as a tank commander in the Battle of Velikye Luki in the Ukraine. After the war he volunteered for 'dirty work', training as a radioactivity measurement specialist in Leningrad. Dokuchayev was one of the first scientists at Combine 817, Russia's first plutonium producing facility. He was surprised when Igor Kurchatov asked him to attend the testing of the Soviet atomic bomb at Semipalatinsk in August 1949, where he was one of eight observers at the NP-2 observation point. Shortly after the explosion, Dokuchayev was a member of a group that entered the bomb crater to obtain samples for analysis. He later wrote an account of the bomb test that was never published, mainly because he had had the temerity to refuse an award for his work on the bomb.

Characters

Master Sergeant Hans Demleitner

A veteran of the German 1st Mountain Division Demleitner maintained a unique collection of photographs taken throughout the war. His camera recorded the horrific massacre of civilians in the Ukrainian city of Lemberg in July 1941 by the retreating NKVD. Soon after Lemberg was taken Demleitner had been ordered to locate the jail and take photographs of the massacre. He spent the winter of 1941–1942 with his division living under canvas on the River Mius. After the war he returned to his home in Kochel in Bavaria and became an historian. Not far from his home was the wartime experimental rocket site. Demleitner was proud of the huge number of Red Army troops he had personally killed in battle or executed. He ended his life in March 2001, shooting himself in the head with a military revolver in the same room in which this photograph was taken.

Professor Carl Friedrich von Weizsäcker

One of the key physicists in Hitler's atomic bomb project based at the Kaiser Wilhelm in Berlin. He joined the Kaiser Wilhelm in 1936 and attended the meeting in Berlin on September 26, 1939, called by the Heereswaffenamt, the Army Weapons Office, to discuss the possibility of building an atomic bomb. In the early days of the war von Weizsäcker was conscripted, but served only 14 days in the Wehrmacht after Peter Debye, the Kaiser Wilhelm's director, successfully pleaded for his release. On July 17, 1940, von Weizsäcker submitted a report to the Heereswaffenamt that a nuclear reactor would be able to produce the element 93, or neptunium, which would decay into element 94, highly fissionable plutonium, and confirmed that this material could be used for the construction of an atomic bomb. Von Weizsäcker received a telephone call from Rudolf Hess, Hitler's deputy, requesting a meeting just two weeks before Hess flew to Scotland. The meeting lasted for some time and nuclear issues were discussed. With other Kaiser Wilhelm colleagues, von Weizsäcker moved to a converted laboratory in Hechingen. The German reactor was constructed in nearby Haigerloch. Hechingen was overrun by Moroccan troops and von Weizsäcker was worried for his safety, but within hours the French arrived followed by members of the Alsos Mission. Interrogated at Farm Hall, England, he formed a strong relationship with Major Rittner, the MI6 intelligence officer who ran the day-to-day interrogation team. His father, Ernst, worked for Joachim von Ribbentrop at the German Foreign Office before becoming Hitler's diplomat in the Vatican. Von Weizsäcker's brother became President of Germany.

Characters

Dr Wilfred 'Basil' Mann
Inventor of the 'Jitterbug', the prototype uranium separation machine, at Imperial College in 1941. A physicist, Mann was involved in the original discussion on the British atomic project for the *Maud Report,* whereby the British would construct 36 bombs. Mann moved from Imperial and worked in intelligence for Michael Perrin and Lt Commander Eric Welsh at *Tube Alloys* in Shell-Mex House, in the Strand. From 1942 Mann worked for the British Commonwealth Scientific Office in Washington as supervisor in British and Russian scientific co-operation. In addition, with the US National Bureau of Standards, Mann helped develop proximity fuses, which were used on shells in England to shoot down German V-1 rockets. The US Navy awarded Mann the Naval Ordnance Development Award in May 1946 for this work. The US army also honoured Mann the Medal of Freedom, with Bronze Palm. After a short period with the British nuclear programme in Canada Mann returned to Washington as a member of MI6, advising Donald Maclean on atomic matters, reporting to Welsh, and liaising with James Angleton of the CIA. Under suspicion after Maclean's defection, Mann was replaced by Dr Robert Press, an attaché at the Embassy. From 1951–1980 Mann worked at the US National Bureau of Standards, and headed the radioactivity department. He later became a naturalised American citizen but was accused in 1979 of being a Soviet agent, the same year Anthony Blunt was publicly named as a wartime spy. Mann was a double agent, working for both British Intelligence and the NKVD, the Russians believing he was part of the British wartime *Double X* operation. During the war and in the post-war period Mann had been in regular contact with Gorsky, Kukin, Kreshin and Barkovsky. The author visited Mann in Rainbow Hall, a retirement home in Owings Mills, near Baltimore, just months before he died in March 2001. KGB veterans confirm that Mann was a Soviet agent of considerable influence. His codename in NKVD transmissions from London was *Malone*. In his debriefing sessions in Moscow Philby argued that Mann was unstable and his information should not be relied upon.

Characters

Igor Kurchatov

A photograph of the early members of the Soviet atomic bomb programme. Kurchatov, known affectionately as 'The Beard' is standing in the second row, sixth from the left. A former student of Abram Ioffe, the leading physicist in the Soviet Union, Kurchatov was tasked by Stalin to build an atomic bomb by August 1950. Kurchatov achieved Stalin's demand one year ahead of schedule. Kurchatov met Stalin regularly to discuss developments and maintained two offices where he could view all stolen Western nuclear intelligence – one room in the Kremlin, the other near Beria's office in the Lubyanka. Relations with Beria, who took over the project from Molotov, were bad and the dislike was mutual. Typically Beria despised anyone who enjoyed the personal trust of Stalin, especially a scientist. With a number of Jewish scientists working for him, Kurchatov always had to be on his guard against Beria who was renowned for his Jew-baiting. Kurchatov won four major awards from Stalin but, remembering his own early hardship and humble upbringing, he gave away all the monies that came with such honours to local orphanages. He also had a strong sense of humour. As a member of Nikita Khrushchev's party on the state visit to England in 1956, Kurchatov presented a paper at Harwell. For the first time British scientists could openly question the head of the Soviet atomic bomb programme. Protocol dictated that the paper be given in Russian, despite Kurchatov's excellent English. There was much good humour in the conference hall at the top secret establishment, especially when Kurchatov explained the workings of an apparatus built by the Soviets that was capable of measuring up to one million degrees centigrade. He grabbed some chalk and drew a bizarre drawing on the blackboard to much laughter from the audience. The whole event was taped by MI5, edited and sent to the Prime Minister.

Igor Kurchatov

He died in February 1960, aged 58, in his dacha having been nursed by his wife. Her photograph is on the left of the mantelpiece.

Characters

The Kurchatov Institute
The former Laboratory No. 2 is steeped in Russia's nuclear history. This huge bust of Kurchatov celebrates its founder. On the grass, three physicists carried out wartime experiments using rifles, firing uranium bullets, to replicate similar US detonation tests in Los Alamos.

Igor Kurchatov
Hidden behind trees on the Kurchatov compound is Kurchatov's house, beautifully timbered and built in 1945 by Academician Shchusev, the famous Russian architect. On Stalin's instruction Kurchatov was to enjoy every luxury. Kurchatov hosted dinner parties for his scientists, whom he would encourage to sing after overindulging on Georgian wine and vodka. A heavy smoker, he tried desperately to break the habit, failing each time. Adjoining the dining room is a small balcony where, towards the end of his life, Kurchatov had whispered conversations with Andrei Sakharov, the Soviet scientist who was key in the development of Russia's hydrogen bomb, successfully tested in 1953. Kurchatov and Sakharov became vocal in warning the world about the dangers of nuclear power for military use.

Characters

Stepan Balezin

Scientific deputy to Sergei Kaftanov, Stalin's scientific advisor. Before the war Balezin worked with Kaftanov, who was in charge of Russia's higher educational system. Balezin was responsible for the universities. He volunteered to fight but was immediately returned to Moscow on the orders of Kaftanov who now held a senior position on Stalin's Defence Committee, the GKO. Colonel Starinov passed the 'atomic' notebook, found on Major Hans van der Velde, to Balezin for evaluation. Balezin asked Aleksandr Leipunsky, the Kharkov physicist who had been jailed in a pre-war purge on scientists, for his opinion. General Pokrovsky, the NKVD's explosives expert, also provided a report. Both opinions were negative but Balezin believed that the contents of the notebook were genuine. Stalin was in regular contact with Balezin, especially for advice on Kurchatov's appointment as head of the bomb project. Balezin was instrumental in the setting up of Laboratory No. 2. Flerov became a great friend.

Stalin's scientific advisors

Kaftanov relied on four deputies. Balezin is on the left.

The GKO

Stalin's Defence Committee, the GKO, sometimes worked out of 11, Rozhdestvenka – a grand old building five minutes walk from the Kremlin. Balezin had an office here and this is where he met Starinov, who brought the 'atomic' notebook to Moscow.

Characters

Lt General Pavel Anatoli Sudoplatov, NKVD
Stalin entrusted Sudoplatov with the running of a number of top-secret NKVD departments. One was Department S, formed in 1944 to assess stolen atomic intelligence. It was disbanded in 1947. Sudoplatov's office was in the Lubyanka but the department was based in Ostozhenka St. He was arrested after Stalin died in 1953.

Colonel Zoya Ribkina, NKVD
She was the controlling officer for the *Red Orchestra* as head of the German desk at the Lubyanka. Very pretty, her conquests included Count von der Schulenburg, Germany's wartime ambassador to Moscow, whose office she bugged. She knew the Wallenberg family, assisting in supplying Swedish steel supplies for the USSR in exchange for platinum. Ribkina alone knew all the names of the *Red Orchestra* operatives keeping a diary of their activities. After the war she was purged by Stalin and sent to Vorkuta as chief of operations, running informants within this dreadful camp where thousands died. Allowed to return to Moscow she became a writer. She wrote the biography of Lenin's mother and another book about Lenin's stay in Finland. Kim Philby befriended Ribkina after his defection.

Professor Arkadi Adamovich Brish
One of the original members of Arzamas-16, the design centre for Russia's atomic bomb. He was responsible for the detonator configuration for RDS-1, the bomb exploded at Semipalatinsk in August 1949, but was disappointed not to witness the test.

Characters

Nicandr Sklerov
The senior of the three wartime Ukrainian partisans in Krivaya Kosa who, at great risk, provided intelligence to Colonel Starinov in the winter of 1941–1942. His intelligence led to the capture of the two prisoners, just days before the main attack on the garrison on February 23, 1942. Sklerov witnessed the firefight near the schoolhouse on that date. He had also agreed with the other partisans that he would execute the traitorous schoolmaster in the nearby village of Budenovsk. The schoolmaster, wounded by Sklerov, managed to escape to Mariupol. The red star on the fence and the wall of his house denotes a veteran of the Great Patriotic War, the war against Germany. He still lives in the village.

Characters

Yuri Kolesnikov – Robert Maxwell's last KGB controller
During the Second World War Kolesnikov was a Second Lieutenant who fought in the Ukraine, winning the Order of the Red Banner. At the end of the war he worked in Rumania as an NKGB *illegal*, followed by a spell in Palestine and the new Jewish state of Israel. Jewish, Kolesnikov was one of hundreds of members of the NKGB/MGB who were purged from the service on the orders of Stalin and Beria. However, he was regularly used by the KGB during the 1970s and 1980s. In the early 1980s Kolesnikov became deputy chairman of the highly-secret Anti-Zionist Committee, based in Moscow, which was set up by the KGB and the Central Committee. In this capacity he met Robert Maxwell on a number of occasions. Maxwell was still keen to find out what had happened to his parents and family during the German invasion of Eastern Europe and Kolesnikov offered his assistance. The Anti-Zionist Committee, managed by Colonel Mark Krukpin of the KGB's Counter-Intelligence Department in the Lubyanka, monitored the contacts of Jewish organisations in the USSR with Jewish entities abroad and neutralised Soviet dissidents. In overall charge was General Philip Bobkov, the First Deputy Chairman of the KGB and head of the Fifth Ideological Department. The Committee was disbanded in 1990. Bobkov's deputy, General Gennady Titov, met Maxwell from time to time.

Characters

Zoya Samsonova
Her husband, Gavrila Ivanovich, was one of the three partisans in Krivaya Kosa. She vividly remembers the two raids in February 1942.

Simonova Prokopenko
Aged eight in 1942 she still lives in the same house which housed German and Rumanian soldiers. She was terrified when Starinov's saboteurs raided the village.

Vladimir Vasileyvich Venediktov
Historian and long-time friend of Ilya Starinov outside his house in Novoazovsk, formerly Budenovsk. He has records of all 110 raids made by Starinov's saboteurs on the northern shoreline of Taganrog Bay in the winter of 1941/1942.

Krivaya Kosa

The road from Taganrog to Mariupol
The surrounding area remains as bleak as it was
in 1942. Vegetation is scarce. Major Hans van
der Velde travelled this road from his base on the
River Mius to Krivaya Kosa.

The main street of Krivaya Kosa, now Sedovo

The end of the kosa
Krivaya Kosa is the longest of the sandbars that are a feature of Taganrog Bay and the Sea of Azov.

Krivaya Kosa

Village life
Much of the village is unchanged since the war. It remains mainly a rural and fishing community, but some villagers commute to the huge steel works in Mariupol.

The road to the watchtower
Up this dusty road was the German watchtower, a large two-story building that fronted onto Taganrog Bay. It was badly damaged during the raid of February 23, 1942, and was finally demolished by the Germans for firewood a year later.

Krivaya Kosa

The schoolhouse
It is now derelict and in a dangerous condition. The khattas, or small huts, in front of the building have long since fallen into Taganrog Bay as the shoreline has eroded. Just yards away, in the early hours of February 23, 1942, a firefight took place here. Major Hans van der Velde crashed his Opel car into a snowdrift and the 'atomic' notebook was discovered in his briefcase.

Colonel Friedrich Schmidt
He was the senior German officer based in Budenovsk, close to Krivaya Kosa. On his right is Nikolay Duschenko, the Russian starosta, or administrator, appointed by the occupation forces. Duschenko, despite his position, was well liked by the villagers and helped out as best he could. Schmidt, a hardened Nazi, left the area after the 1941–1942 winter, joining the Spring offensive on Rostov and the Caucasus. The partisans hunted him down in the Caucasus and executed him.

The beacon
Situated on the kosa, the original was rarely switched off in the winter of 1941/1942.

Berlin

The Kaiser Wilhelm Institute for Physics, Dahlem, Berlin
The main centre for Germany's wartime atomic bomb project. It is now part of a university complex. To the right is the Van der Graaf generator.

Harnack House
Part of the Kaiser Wilhelm compound. Lectures on the atomic bomb took place here. It was also a leisure centre for the scientists and technicians. At the end of the war the building was used by the American military as an officers club.

Berlin

The Kaiser Wilhelm Institute for Physics, Dahlem, Berlin
The entrance to the underground nuclear laboratory. The Americans sealed this in 1945 because of radioactivity fears.

Berlin

The former Kaiser Wilhelm Institute for Chemistry, in Dahlem, Berlin, where Otto Hahn and his colleague, Fritz Strassman, conducted the first nuclear fission experiments in December 1938. The experiments stunned the scientific world and were an alarming warning that an atomic bomb was possible. After the war the institute was closed. However, it was re-established in Mainz in 1949 by Strassman and Josef Mattauch as the Max Planck Institute for Chemistry.

The front entrance of the Kaiser Wilhelm Institute for Physics, now the Max Planck Institute and used by students in the university campus that occupies much of the former Kaiser Wilhelm site.

Haigerloch

The entrance to the underground facility in Haigerloch, southern Germany, which housed the German nuclear reactor. The Reichsforschungsrat, the National Research Council, took over the running of the nuclear project from the Heereswaffenamt, the Army Weapons Office, in February 1942 and decided to convert this wine and beer cellar under the town's historic church into a nuclear facility as Berlin was under threat from Allied bombers. In the nearby town of Hechingen, 12 scientists from the Kaiser Wilhelm Institute for Physics, including Heisenberg and von Weizsäcker, set up a laboratory in a former textile factory.

The B8 experimental reactor in Haigerloch was built as a concrete cylinder deep in the cellar. Once in operation normal water occupied the space between the reactor's outer concrete shell and the inner shell made of aluminium that contained a vessel made of magnesium. The space between the two vessels was filled with graphite weighing 10 tons and 664 small rectangular blocks of uranium attached to the circular graphite lid that was bolted onto the reactor. Heavy water was gradually pumped into the inner vessel, triggering a chain reaction. The photograph is of a replica of the original reactor that was dismantled by the Alsos Mission, the small group of British and American officers tasked with finding German nuclear scientists and materials. All the reactor components went to America. No part was allowed to come to Britain.

Walchensee and Kochel

The Café Bucherer on the banks of Lake Walchensee, southern Germany. On April 16, 1936, Hitler, his adjutant Hoffman, Baldur von Schirach, the head of the Hitler Youth, and Heinrich Himmler arrived for lunch to the complete surprise of the staff and other guests. Hitler and his group sat on the verandah to the right of the photograph, overlooking the other guests who sat at tables on the lawn. Hitler enjoyed his vegetarian lunch and drank only water. He signed a photograph of himself and dated it. That photograph hung on a wall in the restaurant until the end of the war, thereafter it was hidden away in an attic for the next 50 years.

The experimental rocket site in Kochel, southern Germany. The two wind tunnels still exist under this building and are used as storage space by the German ceramics company that presently occupies the site. In Kochel the German rocket specialists had completed the design for a two-stage rocket that had the capacity to reach the east coast of the United States. Werner Heisenberg, Hitler's top atomic scientist, whose wooden lake-side chalet was only a short distance away in the village of Urfeld, was well aware that an atomic warhead on a German rocket was feasible.

Moscow

Lubyanka-3 is one of a group of buildings off Dzerzhinsky Square in central Moscow which houses the Russian Intelligence services. A number of FSB departments are located in this building, including the History Room, which the author visited. The History Room occupies one floor and displays photographs and details of many covert KGB operations and those of its predecessors, the Cheka, OGPU, NKVD, NKGB, and MGB. The FSB social club is also in Lubyanka-3 where in a modern Russia rock bands play to the employees most Friday nights. From Lubyanka-3, under this busy road, is a passageway that leads to the killing chamber where countless numbers of Lubyanka prisoners were shot in the traditional method – a bullet in the back of the head.

Moscow

Laboratory No 2 – Moscow
The entrance to the underground F-1 nuclear reactor, hidden away in the woods of the Kurchatov Institute. At one time this was one of the most closely guarded facilities in the USSR.

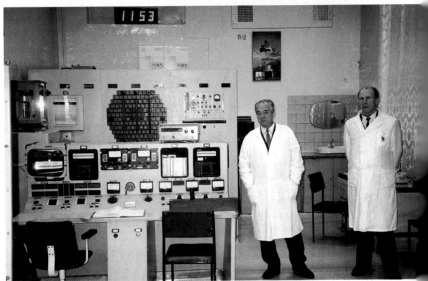

The control room
The F-1 reactor went critical at 11.53pm on December 25, 1946. Beria, who was in the room, hugged Igor Kurchatov before calling Stalin with the news.

XXX

Moscow

Left: The reactor
Comprised of graphite and uranium, it was constructed to the plans stolen in Chicago where Enrico Fermi, the Italian scientist, had built the world's first reactor on the squash courts of the university in 1943.

Below: The head of the reactor
Spent fuel is piled alongside. It is held together with lead, hammered together with nails. On the top are layers of cadmium. The European Union has been asked to provide funds to make the reactor safe.

Moscow

A naval periscope
Kurchatov had it rigged up outside the reactor so he could view the reaction. It still functions today.

Reactor materials
The reactor is made up of layers of graphite and uranium, seen here in the control room.

Wartime and early post-war nuclear research and development

Russia

[After Stalin had been informed by Truman at Potsdam that on July 16, 1945, the US had successfully tested a nuclear device in New Mexico, he initiated the term *Problem No. 1* for the Russian atomic bomb project on returning to Moscow]

Krivaya Kosa

The village was renamed Sedovo after the war. It is located on the northern shoreline of Taganrog Bay in the Sea of Azov. The 'atomic' notebook was found in the briefcase of Major Hans van der Velde, an SS officer and physicist attached to the Wehrgeologen. The raid on Krivaya Kosa by Red Army and naval saboteurs, was led by Lt Maloletko, under the command of Colonel Ilya Starinov in Yeysk, acting on intelligence provided by Nicandr Sklerov, a Ukrainian partisan. The raid began at 2am on February 23, 1942. The content of the 'atomic' notebook, describing in detail the German nuclear bomb project, was one of the key factors in Stalin's decision to restart Russia's atomic efforts that had been abandoned after the German invasion in June 1941.

Institutes

All-Russia Institute of Aviation Materials [VIAM] – Moscow: Given responsibility for much of the work on the F-1 nuclear reactor in Laboratory No. 2. By 1945 it was a major source for materials and equipment on the atomic project.

Institute of Chemical Physics [IKHF] – Moscow: Began work on the bomb in 1943. By 1945 it had responsibility for plutonium chemistry and reactor corrosion protection.

Institute of Organic and non-Organic Chemistry [IONKh]: Began work on the bomb in 1943, researching into industrial heavy water production, plutonium chemistry, industrial recovery methods and materials for diffusion isotope separation under the supervision of the Radium Institute.

Institute of Physical Chemistry – Dnepropetrovsk: Established in the 1930s for isotope separation and heavy water research. Allocated 78,500 roubles by the Uranium Commission in 1940 to assess feasibility of an atomic bomb. Overrun by German forces in 1941. Many of the staff were executed by the SS.

Institute of Physical Chemistry – Odessa: Limited nuclear research. German forces overran it in 1941.

Institute for Physical Problems – Moscow: Peter Kapitsa was director until his acrimonious resignation from Stalin's committee looking into uranium issues.

Geochemical Institute [GEOKHI] – Moscow: Worked on the nuclear reactor in Laboratory No. 2.

Kharkov Physical Technical Institute [KhFTI] – Kharkov: Set up by the Leningrad Physical Technical Institute in 1930, it became a key pre-war nuclear centre with a Van der Graaf generator. Deputy Prime Minister Mikhail Pervukhin proposed in 1937 that a cyclotron should be built but construction fell behind schedule and it was not complete before the German invasion. The institute suffered Stalin's purge in 1938 and one of Russia's most renowned scientists, Lev Landau, was imprisoned; many other scientists were arrested. Allocated 223,000 roubles by the Uranium Commission in 1940. A special German unit captured the institute before the retreating NKVD could destroy it in November 1941 and the SS executed unco-operative scientists. Much of the apparatus was dismantled and re-erected in Munich. By the end of 1945, the institute developed uranium isotope separation methods.

Karpov Institute of Physical Chemistry – Moscow: Studied the effects of uranium oxide on workers in the uranium exploration sites. An aerosols laboratory pioneered radiation filter pods first tested on Yak-9V aircraft and later on PE-2 aircraft. Poor visibility prevented the PE-2 from flying over the Semipalatinsk test site in August 1949. In 1950 the institute established a laboratory in Taboshar to study the effects of radon.

Lebedev Physical Institute of Academy of Science [FIAN] – Moscow: Located at the Russian Academy of Sciences [Department of Physics and Mathematics], it was a major uranium research centre in the late 1930s. By the end of 1945 FIAN had responsibility for nuclear reactor calculations and neutron physics, assisting in the construction of the F-1 reactor in Laboratory No. 2. A cosmic ray research department opened. In 1950 all work on particle accelerators was stopped in Laboratory No. 5 and transferred, with the staff, to FIAN.

Leningrad Physical Technical Institute [LFTI] – Leningrad/Kazan: The focal point of nuclear research in Russia in the 1930s, founded by Abram Ioffe in 1918. The first Soviet conference on atomic physics was held in the institute in September 1933. The fifth, and last such event, was held in Moscow in November 1940. With the threat of the German and Finnish encirclement of Leningrad, apparatus and staff were moved east to Kazan. By the end of the war LFTI was again operational with responsibility for isotope separation methods and cyclotron studies.

Leningrad State Optical Institute: Involved in the Russian defence industry and carried out nuclear research in the 1930s. Its director was Sergei Vavilov.

Mining Museum – Leningrad: Evacuated during the war to Kazan. One of the very few institutions funded by the Uranium Commission in 1940.

Nitrogen Industry Institute: By 1945, a producer of heavy water.

Orgstoiproyekt Design Institute [GSPI]– Angarsk and Sverdlovsk: In 194 Vitali Khlopin, Boris Nikitin and Aleksandr Ratner from the Radium Institut managed research into obtaining plutonium from irradiated uranium on an industrial scale.

Physics Institute – Kiev: Directed by Aleksandr Leipunsky from 1944.

Radium Institute for Academy of Sciences [RIAN] – Leningrad: Established in 1922 and run by Academician Vladimir Vernadsky. RIAN conducted much of the early work on radium and uranium extraction. Allocated 330,000 roubles by the Uranium Commission in 1940. The institute was evacuated during the war. By 1945 RIAN had responsibility for plutonium and uranium chemistry, and cyclotron studies.

Rare Metals Institute [GIREDMET] Moscow: Began work on the bomb in 1943. Uranium ores were delivered from Taboshar, Tajikistan, in 1944.

Rontgenology and Radiology Institute: In 1945 it had responsibility for emergency response training in the uranium institutes and laboratories.

Semyonov Physical Chemical Institute – Leningrad/Moscow: One of the four main nuclear research centres at the end of the 1930s. Allocated 35,000 roubles by the Uranium Commission in 1940.

Urals Industrial Institute: By 1945 it manufactured fine gauze for diffusion separation installations.

Laboratories

Laboratory No. 1 – Kazan: Academician Ioffe was made head of this nuclear laboratory in September 1942.

Laboratory No. 2 – Moscow: The building was initially to be used for the Institute of Experimental Medicine but instead it was taken over for the nuclear project, headed by Igor Kurchatov. The start-up of its cyclotron was September 8, 1944. By the end of 1945 the laboratory employed 180 scientists and engineers. Russia's first physical reactor, the F-1, went critical at 11.53pm on December 25, 1946. Isaak Kikoin ran the diffusion separation department; Georgii Flerov, the heavy-water reactor; Lev Artsymovich, electromagnetic isotope separation; Mikhail Kornfeld, new heavy water production methods; and Yuli Khariton, theoretical and experimental study of the nuclear explosion process and the bomb design specifications. It is now the Kurchatov Institute, but not directly involved in atomic weapons.

Laboratory No. 3 – Moscow: This was the Centre for Theoretical and Experimental Physics, under the scientific management of Academician Abram Alikhanov and V. Vladimirsky. Work started at the end of 1945 to develop heavy water reactors, a thorium/plutonium reactor and a cyclotron. A cosmic ray study department was also added. Much of the heavy water work, conducted under Kornfeld in Laboratory No. 2 was transferred here.

Laboratory No. 4 – Moscow: Work started in 1945 on centrifugal isotope separation.

Laboratory No. 5 – Obninsk: Set up on May 13, 1946, on the former premises of a school for Spanish children near Obninsk, 60 miles south west of Moscow. It was run by Dr Heinz Pose, with 33 other German nuclear scientists who were invited, or coerced, to work in the USSR at the end of the war. The Germans developed uranium isotope separation methods. A reactor was built and by 1952 a total of 16 laboratories were in operation. The German group was transferred to Sukhumi in Georgia that year. Pose, with his family, remained in Obninsk.

Laboratory No. 9 [also referred to as *NII-9*] – Moscow: Situated near Laboratory No. 2, with a 'Hot Lab'. The eminent radiochemist, Zinaida Ershova [Russia's 'Madame Curie'] worked here, obtaining pure plutonium from irradiated uranium. The process was perfected and installed in the plutonium plant in Chelyabinsk. Several German scientists worked at this highly-secret facility.

Alexandrov Laboratory – Kazan: Igor Kurchatov worked in Department 10 on a magnetizing project with a group of other scientists in 1941, before joining Ioffe at Laboratory No. 1 in Kazan.

Arzamas-16 [codenamed *KB-11* during the early years] – Sarov: Home of the Russian Experimental Physics Research Institute, in the Nizhegorod oblast on the River Techa, a tributary of the Oka. This was the design centre for the Russian bomb, established in April 1946, headed first by Vladimir Merkin and then Yuli Khariton, Kurchatov's most trusted colleague.

Dubna – the secret scientific city located near the village of Novo Ivankovo: Building began in 1946. By December 1949 the Dubna Synchotron Laboratory was operating with the commissioning of Russia's first synchotron, which used magnets of 5–6 metres in diameter. In 1951 more laboratories were constructed.

Electrovacuum Laboratory of NKEP [the Electricity Industry Narkomat] – Moscow: By 1945 this laboratory had responsibility for vacuum technology for electromagnetic isotope separation.

Russian Academy of Sciences laboratories – Kazan: Several of its facilities moved to Kazan from Moscow at the beginning of the war. Many Russian Government departments moved to the city during the German invasion.

Russian Academy of Sciences – Kazahk branch, Alma-Ata: Its uranium analysis laboratory was set up in 1944 by the Radium Institute in Leningrad, handling ores from Taboshar, Mailu-Su and other mines.

Sukhumi and Agudzeri nuclear laboratories – Sinop, Georgia: The majority of the 150-plus invited or coerced German scientists worked in the two facilities.

TSAGI [former Aero/Hydrodynamics Laboratory]: Began work on the bomb in 1943.

Plants and production sites [*most of these plants managed by the NKVD/NKGB*]
AO Bismuth – Ukraine: Location for manufacturing metallic uranium after the war.

Base 5 – Verkh-Neivinskii: Established in 1947 to produce highly enriched U-235, using methods developed by Kikoin. It became fully operational in 1949, directed by Zinaida Ershova and V. Shevchenko.

Base 9 [Plant 814] – Verkhniaia Tura, North Urals: Electromagnetic separation plant using methods developed by Artsymovich, constructed in 1949.

Base 10 [later Combine 817 and Chelyabinsk-40] – Kystym/Chelyabinsk: Russia's first industrial-scale plutonium, hexafluoride and graphite plant on the Kyzyl-Tash Lake, commissioned in mid-1947. The plutonium process for RDS-1, the first Soviet bomb, began on June 19, 1948.

Chirchiksky Enterprise – Uzbekistan: By 1946, this plant produced heavy water, but supplies proved inadequate.

Combine 6, Central Asia: Uranium facility.

Dorogolmilov Plant: Metal production plant, supplying copper to Laboratory No 2.

Glavpromstroy – Moscow: Uranium facility.

Krasnoyarsk – 16: Plutonium plant commissioned in 1949 to complement Combine 817 after the successful test of RDS-1.

Moscow electrode plant: By August 1945 workers at this plant, working closely with Goncharov and Pravdiuk at Laboratory No. 2, had established a process to produce high-grade graphite.

NII-42: Established in 1943 to produce hexafluoride and heavy water.

Nizhniaia Tura: Plant for electromagnetic division of uranium isotopes.

NKHP [Chemical Industry Narkomat]: Established in 1943.

Plant 12 [Elektrostal] – Moscow: Several German scientists worked here producing pure metallic uranium for use in the F-1 reactor in Laboratory No. 2.

Plant 26 – Sverdlovsk: Kikoin and Lange built and successfully tested a centrifuge for U-235 separation with good results.

Plants 28, 544 – Udmurtia Glazov, 815: Production centres.

Plant 906 – Dneprodzerzhinsk, Ukraine: Uranium facility.

Tomsk-7: Thermal diffusion plant for the division of uranium isotopes.

VEI: Established in 1943.

Uranium mining sites [*all controlled by the NKVD/NKGB*]
Bukhovo – Rodopi Mountains, Bulgaria: Production began in March 1945 with 300 mining engineers flown in from Russia. Within a year the mine, managed by Colonel Schors, a hard-line officer, produced 1.5 tons of uranium oxide per week.

Joachimsthal – Erzebirge Mountains [Ore Mountains], Czechoslovakia/ German border: Long-established uranium mine and key in the wartime

German nuclear project. Radium had been extracted in the late 19th century and used by Madame Curie in Paris. The facility was taken over by an NKGB team in 1945, run by General Michajlov. The Czech premier, Klement Gottwald, personally handled the administration transporting all production to Russia. In 1946 uranium oxide output totalled 100 tonnes, rising to 800 tonnes by 1950. In the months after the end of the war the Soviets estimated that 60,000 forced labourers were needed. German PoWs were a major source of labour. These PoWs were released in 1952 and replaced by labour from 16 camps in Czechoslovakia, mainly Camp X11 and Camp Rovnost. From 1950–1960 casualties at Joachimsthal totalled 29,880 due to the high levels of radiation and poor protection procedures.

Leninabad and Khodzhet – Respublika Karakalpakistan, west Uzbekistan: Two uranium mining areas near the town of Nukus.

Maili-Su - Kazakhstan: Major uranium mine – from where few returned.

Piatigorsk [Lermontev] – north Caucasus: Location for post-war uranium extraction. Exploration had taken place in the 1930s but ceased. This site was of particular interest to the Germans during the invasion. Details of the site were found in Hans van der Velde's briefcase.

Plant 18 – Taboshar, north Tajikistan: Major uranium mine and one of 70 sites in Central Asia. Tens of thousands died here from radiation, the exact death toll is unknown. A number of British and French officers who had been PoWs in German-held camps in Central Europe, but not released after the Soviet occupation, worked here until they died. Uranium from Taboshar was used in RDS-1, the first bomb. A biophysics institute was eventually established.

Uigar-Sai – Kazakhstan: Uranium mine.

Zheltye Vody – Ukraine: Uranium mine.

Organisations
Department S: Formed in 1944 as Group S, reformed on October 20, 1945, headed by Lt General Pavel Anatoli Sudoplatov. It was tasked to re-evaluate stolen atomic intelligence amongst other duties. Sudoplatov's office was in the Lubyanka but the department was based in Ostozhenka St. Department S had 12 sections: [1] American intelligence; [2] British scientific intelligence; [3] European expertise on nuclear issues; [4] Translation of stolen nuclear and scientific documents; [5] Interrogation of foreigners, mainly British and French officers; [6] Recruitment of Soviet physicists and chemists; [7] Analysis and preparation of surveys and monitoring; [8] Legal and media matters, such as TASS and other Soviet press agencies; [9] Co-operation with Soviet Counter Intelligence agencies; [10] NKVD branch supervision and other domestic agencies [11] Supervision of uranium extraction in Eastern Europe; [12] Secretariat including reports to Stalin and Beria. Department S was disbanded in May 1947

Department K – affiliated to the NKVD: November 1945–December 1946, run by Sudoplatov. This was a combined intelligence unit specifically tasked to obtain atomic secrets from the West.

GRU [Soviet military intelligence]: Managed by Lt General I Ilyichev. The GRU initially ran Klaus Fuchs until atomic intelligence was passed over to the NKVD on Stalin's instruction.

NKVD – 4th Directorate: Based in the Lubyanka, it was headed by General Victor Kravchenko who was responsible for development of new weapons. Some 400 scientists were based at highly-secret facilities and strict conditions were imposed. Kravchenko had a number of scientific intelligence agents operating outside the USSR.

NKVD – 5th Directorate: The main department for atomic intelligence, based in the Lubyanka and controlled by Lt General Pavel Fitin.

State Defence Committee [GKO] – one of the locations was Rozhdestvenka, 11, Moscow [a short walk from Red Square]: Stepan Balezin, the senior of four deputies to Sergei Kaftanov, the scientific advisor to Stalin, met Colonel Starinov here to discuss the contents of the 'atomic' notebook found at Krivaya Kosa.

SMERSH: Originally established by Stalin in February 1941 as a military intelligence department, but it was merged into the NKVD. Emerged again in April 1943, under State Security Commissar CP. Yukhimovich. A Counter-Intelligence section was added, GUKR SMERSH, headed by General Abakumov, to counteract the activities in Russia of the Abwehr. SMERSH established a large operation in Karlhorst, Berlin, on the fall of the capital, headed by General Ivan Serov. His main responsibility was to locate German rocket and nuclear scientists. SMERSH always operated independently from the other Soviet Intelligence services, which was a constant cause of friction. It was disbanded in June 1946.

TSKTI NKTM [Heavy Machinery Narkomat]: By 1945 it had some responsibility for the F-1 reactor.

SREDMASH – Moscow: The department in charge of the development of the bomb – headed by Zadikyan who worked closely with Kurchatov.

Russian Embassies and Consulates: NKVD/NKGB and GRU officers in New York, Washington, San Francisco, Mexico City, Stockholm, London and Ottawa, and after the war in Paris and Canberra.

USSR NKHP [Chemical Industry Commissariat]: This location has in its possession an inventory of materials and documents received by GRU from its agents prior to September 1945. There are 142 documents [4,853 pages in total], and 14 stolen samples of uranium and uranium compounds, high-purity heavy water, graphite and beryllium.

Universities

Kiev: Carried out some pre-war nuclear research, but never became a major centre.

Moscow [MGU]: Some pre-war research, but purged heavily by Stalin. A training facility was established in October 1945 for technicians and engineers on plutonium manufacture.

Gorki: Active departments in nuclear research.

Kharkov: Active departments in nuclear research.

Moscow Institute of Engineering and Physics [MIFI] Moscow Institute of Physics and Technology [MFTI]: Specialised universities established in November 1945 to train nuclear physicists.

Test site

Semipalatinsk Kazahkstan: Work started in 1946 to prepare the site. Russia's first atomic bomb, RDS-1, was exploded here on August 29, 1949. The first H-bomb, RDS-6, was tested here on August 12, 1953.

Britain

[Britain used the codename *Tube Alloys* or *TA* for its project in the early years of the war when it was developing its own bomb, as outlined in the *Maud Report*. During the later co-operation with the Americans from 1942–1945, the codename continued in use]

Universities and laboratories

Armament Research Establishment, Fort Halstead – Sevenoaks, Kent: In 1947, as Britain decided to manufacture its own nuclear deterrent, the task fell to William Penney to create a special group at Fort Halstead. Penney selected 35 of his top staff to begin work on the bomb. Space finally ran out so Aldermaston was created.

Aldermaston: A dedicated weapons group was set up in 1950, with Penney given the title of Chief Superintendent of High Explosives.

Atomic Energy Research Establishment (AERE) – Harwell, Berkshire [former RAF station]: Established in the last months of the war. First Harwell pile (codenamed *GLEEP*) became operational on Friday, August 15, 1947. Harwell's cyclotron operated its first full trial on December 2, 1949. Hanger 8 used by the Nuclear Physics Department.

Atomic Energy Research Establishment (AERE), T.R.E – Great Malvern, Worcestershire: Its synchrotron became operational October 10, 1947.

British Thompson Houston Co, Research Laboratories – Rugby: At one time most of its research team were involved with *Tube Alloys*.

Cavendish Laboratory – Cambridge: Many of its nuclear scientists went to the Montreal Laboratory and Chalk River, Canada, in the last years of the war.

Chemical Research Laboratory – Teddington, Middlesex: Established in 1935.

Clarendon Laboratory – Oxford: The Clarendon's wartime nuclear work, mainly on isotope separation, was managed by Professor Franz Simon.

Department of Colloid Science – University of Cambridge: Headed by Professor Eric Rideal, an advisor to Professor George Thomson on the *Maud Report.*

Department of Mathematics – University of Manchester: Its mathematicians, mainly Tolansky, were involved in some of the early uranium calculations.

Imperial College – University of London: Thomson headed the Maud Committee. Imperial conducted early uranium experimentation on separation with the 'Jitterbug', a prototype uranium separation machine. Imperial's report on the use of uranium for the Ministry of Aircraft Production on May 5, 1940, was quoted in the *Maud Report* in June 1941.

Jesus College – University of Oxford: Staffed mainly by personnel from the Clarendon. Researched into metal corrosion.

Kings College – University of London: Several scientists working on the project were evacuated to the University of Bristol because of the German blitz.

George Holt Physics Laboratory – University of Liverpool: Professor James Chadwick moved to Liverpool in 1932 where he embarked on building a cyclotron.

Medical Research Council [MRC]: Limited early post-war work.

National Physical Laboratory – Teddington, Middlesex: Established in 1918, in the late 1930s it began research into the manufacture of uranium metal. Managed by the Royal Society.

P6 Experimental Station – Rhydymwyn, Mold, north Wales: Disused government building, taken over by ICI and the Clarendon for research and development of industrial-scale separation machines. In 1944 a team from P6 visited Oak Ridge to see the faster electromagnetic process. No Americans were ever entertained at P6 but all research from this facility was shared with Britain's partner. As the electromagnetic process moved to the fore in America testing at P6 slowed down and it closed finally in March 1945 with its machines transported elsewhere.

Porton Experimental Station – Porton Down, Wiltshire: Undertook radioactivity experiments. There was also collaboration between the Clarendon regarding the use of Porton's electron microscope in 1944.

Radiochemical Centre – Amersham: Involved in early post-war research.

University College – University of London: Undertook only limited research into nuclear work.

University of Birmingham: Three groups located here were run by Professor Rudolf Peierls, Mark Oliphant and Professor William Haworth. Later in the war a group from the Clarendon, led by Henry Shull Arms, took over Oliphant's premises as that team had departed for America.

University of Bristol: Headed by Neville Mott, and joined by Allan Nunn-May and Powell from Kings College, London.

University of Jerusalem: The Jerusalem Potash Company experimented in the Dead Sea on heavy water in October 1945, financed by *Tube Alloys*.

Y.P Laboratory [in the grounds of ICI Metals] – Witton, Birmingham Staffed by the Clarendon and handled research into membranes.

Universities that assisted AERE as at December 1, 1950: Liverpool, Birmingham, Cambridge, Edinburgh, Glasgow, Oxford, Imperial College, Reading, S Bartholomews's Hospital. By 1953: St Andrews, Birkbeck College, Birmingham, Bristol, Cambridge, Durham, Exeter, Imperial College, Leeds, Lerdon (in the Netherlands), Liverpool, London, Nottingham, Oxford and Sheffield.

Plants and production sites

British Oxygen Company: Planning began in 1946 on a liquid nitrogen plant.

Capenhurst – Cheshire: Gaseous diffusion plant for U-235, compromised to the Soviets by Klaus Fuchs.

Metropolitan-Vickers Electrical Group (Metro-Vick) – Trafford Park Manchester: Designed and built early model diffusion units.

Imperial Chemical Industries: From 1934 ICI had experimented with heavy water. The wartime plants involved with *Tube Alloys* were: Billingham, Co Durham [heavy water and the development of a diffusion plant]; Widnes [manufacture o uranium metal]; Winnington [general research into uranium]; and ICI Metals in Birmingham. ICI Kings Norton started up in October 1945.

Mond Nickel Company [subsidiary of International Nickel] – Birmingham Investigated a number of metallurgical problems related to the manufacturing of uranium

Morgan Crucible Company: Involved with the work at P6 and at various IC locations.

Percy Lund Humphries and Co Ltd: Subcontracted by ICI Metals to handle work on the manufacturing of uranium in 1941.

Sharples Centrifuge Company – London: Subcontracted by ICI Metals to manufacture uranium metal.

Springfields – Lancashire: Centre for uranium production, compromised to the Soviets by Klaus Fuchs.

Sun Engraving Company Ltd: Manufacturers of nickel and copper membrane used by the *Tube Alloys* teams at the University of Birmingham.

Woolwich Research Department – Woolwich Arsenal, London: A key wartime nuclear experimental centre.

Windscale – Cumberland: Post-war facility for plutonium production, compromised to the Soviets by Klaus Fuchs.

Organisations

Atomic Energy Production Division – Risley, Warrington: One of the key centres early post-war.

British Atomic Energy Diffusion Mission – New York: Group of British scientists who worked with the Kellex Corporation on diffusion after it was decided that Britain and America would co-operate on nuclear research.

Department of Scientific and Industrial Research [DSIR] – London: Established on December 1, 1941, at 16 Old Queen Street under W. Akers, the head of *Tube Alloys*.

Directorate of Tube Alloys – London: Based in the Ministry of Supply, fourth floor, Shell-Mex House, Strand. Michael Perrin, Deputy Controller of *Tube Alloys* based here.

Ministry of Aircraft Production – Millbank, London: Responsible for initial work on the atomic bomb project in 1940–1941.

United Kingdom Scientific Mission – 1800 K Street, Washington DC: Handled British wartime scientific co-ordination with the US and Russia. No foreign scientists were given access to Hanford, the plutonium plant.

Non-Ferrous Metals Research Association – London: Undertook research into the properties and manufacture of uranium metal.

MI5/MI6/RAF Intelligence – London: Based mainly on the fourth floor of Shell-Mex House. Lt Commander Eric Welsh, head of nuclear intelligence, had his metal 'cage' on this floor. After the war the intelligence services involved with Britain's atomic bomb programme remained in Shell-Mex House before relocating to St Giles Court, Holborn, Charles II Street and Ormond Yard, near St James Square.

Royal Aircraft Establishment [RAE] – Farnborough, Hampshire: Responsible for the initial work done on the atomic bomb project in 1940–1941.

The Treasury – Whitehall, London: Office of the Chancellor of the Exchequer, Sir John Anderson, who had personal charge of *Tube Alloys* from September 1941 until the end of the war.

The Extra-Mural Research Group – London: Based in Shell-Mex House. It was the temporary name of the bomb project in the first few months after the war.

Canada

Chalk River – north west of Pembroke, 130 miles west of Ottawa: Several hundred Canadian, British and French personnel were involved in the nuclear project, managed by the British. Defence Industries of Canada built a nuclear pile at Chalk River, codenamed *NRX*. The zero reactor, codenamed *ZEEP*, was operational in September 1945. *NRX* went critical on July 22, 1947.

Montreal Laboratory [McGill University– Montreal]: Many of the staff from the Cavendish Laboratory, University of Cambridge, were based here, including Nunn-May.

Nuclear Research Centre – Ottawa: Extensively compromised by the GRU, through the Russian Embassy in Ottawa. A number of Canadian scientists were identified following the defection of Igor Gouzenko.

Germany

[In 1939, a committee agreed in the Kaiser Wilhelm to proceed with a nuclear weapon and thereafter the term 'Uranverein' was used to refer to further discussion of the project]

Institutes and laboratories

Celle laboratories: Research into isotope separation.

Dresden: Highly secret laboratory for isotope separation, bombed by the RAF and the Americans in 1945. A number of scientists and technicians were captured by the NKGB and taken to work in the Soviet Union at Laboratory No. 5.

Freiburg: Research into isotope separation.

Institute for Physical Chemistry – Hamburg: Research into production of heavy water, and isotope separation, directed by Paul Harteck.

Kaiser Wilhelm Institute of Chemistry – Dahlem, Berlin: In December 1938 Otto Hahn and Fritz Strassman successfully concluded that uranium was fissionable. In 1949 the institute was re-established in Mainz by Strassmann and Josef Mattauch as the Max Plank Institute for Chemistry.

Kaiser Wilhelm Institute of Physics – Dahlem, Berlin: Peter Debye was the director, succeeded by Kurt Diebner and under the military control of the Heereswaffenamt. It was the main centre for the nuclear programme. Later the institute and 12 scientists, including von Weizsäcker and Heisenberg, moved south to a former textile factory in Hechingen. In April 21, 1945, the Hechingen facility was overrun by Moroccan troops.

Kaiser Wilhelm Institute of Physical Chemistry – Dahlem, Berlin: Directed by Peter Adolf Thiessen, an ardent Nazi. The institute was partially evacuated in September 1943 to other areas of Berlin, mainly Falhenhagen, Arensdorf and Petershagen.

Kaiser Wilhelm Institute for Medical Research – Heidelberg: Directed by Walter Bothe. *The Alsos Mission* [the group of American and British Intelligence officers and scientists tasked to locate Germany's nuclear weapons programme] took away documentation in March 1945.

Manfred von Ardenne Laboratory – Lichterfelde, Berlin: Run by Baron von Ardenne, specialising in the building of accelerators and electromagnetic isotope separators. It was plundered by an NKGB group, headed by General Zavenyagin, on May 19, 1945. Von Ardenne and his wife, Bettina, were transported to Moscow on May 21, 1945.

Neutron Institute – Vienna: Established by the University of Vienna in 1940 as a nuclear research centre, financed directly from Berlin and managed by Georg Stetter. From the summer of 1944 some work was dispersed to nearby villages. In Mautern, 50 miles from Vienna, work began on a 900kV installation to obtain powerful neutron beams but materials from Hamburg never arrived because of bombing. With the Red Army advancing, equipment from the three Vienna institutes was moved to Tumersbach, close to Salzburg, and the library and research documents to Schwallenbach, in Wachau. The scientists and technicians fled to Salzburg. The Russian 337th Border Regiment captured the Vienna institutes and its deputy commander, Major Barannikov, sent a report to Beria on what had been found between April 25–May 10, 1945.

Physics Institute – University of Vienna: Headed by Stetter before he moved to the Neutron Institute.

Radium Institute – Vienna Academy of Science: Headed by Gustav Ortner.

Stadtilm – Thuringia, south of Erfurt: Walter Gerlach, Kurt Diebner and Karl Wirtz fled Berlin accompanied by a number of trucks with what was left of the Berlin stock of uranium and heavy water. The facilities at Stadtilm were poor so the stocks were eventually taken to Hechingen and Haigerloch.

Technische Hochschule – Breslau: Group of chemists based here.

Tailfingen – near Balingen, southern Württemberg: Hahn and his team moved out of Berlin to carry on research in March 1944.

University of Bonn: A cyclotron was constructed here.

University of Kiel: Research on mass spectroscopic studies and isotope separation.

University of Göttingen: Research into isotope separation.

University of Leipzig: Key centre run by Werner Heisenberg. Prototype L IV reactor built using 140kg of heavy water and 750kg of uranium metal powder. It was destroyed by fire in June 1942 and all work ceased in Leipzig. Heisenberg moved full-time to the Kaiser Wilhelm in Berlin.

University of Munich: Research into isotope separation and heavy water production, headed by the chemist Claus Clusius. In 1943 the British were very concerned about the development of two new volatile gases. Walter Gerlach was based in Munich before he took over the atomic bomb project in 1942 in Berlin.

University of Strasburg: At the end of November 1944 the *Alsos Mission* discovered papers relating to the German uranium project, left by von Weizsäcker who was Professor of Physics, but who spent little time in the university.

Organisations

Des Amtes fur Physikalische Sonderfragen der Forschungsanstalt der Deutschen Reichspost [Department for Specialized Physics] – Berlin: Closely involved with the activities of the Kaiser Wilhelm.

Heereswaffenamt [Army Weapons Office] – Gatow, Berlin: Orders were given on September 8, 1939, to a number of scientists to report to the Army Weapons Bureau to work on atomic fission. Head of the science division was Professor Erich Schumann. The Heereswaffenamt called a meeting of selected scientists on September 26, 1939, to discuss the possibility of Germany developing and building an atomic bomb. The Heereswaffenamt had its own radiation laboratory where, right up to the end of the war, Kurt Diebner tried to develop a nuclear reactor.

Reichsforschungsrat [National Research Council] – Berlin: Took over the running of the nuclear project from the Army Weapons Office in February 1942, then run by Walter Gerlach. On February 26, 1942, Bernhard Rust, German Minister for Research and Education, had a meeting with the top atomic scientists to review progress on the bomb in Grunewaldstrasse 35, Steglitz, Berlin.

Plants and production sites

Auer Company – Oranienburg, suburb of Berlin: Chemical company that manufactured purified uranium for the nuclear project, under Dr Wirth, the company's senior scientist. Forced labour came from local concentration camps.

Haigerloch – near Stuttgart: The site of the experimental B8 reactor, chosen in 1943 as Berlin came under incessant Allied air attack. The rental agreement was signed on September 1, 1944, to use this former wine and beer cellar under the castle for a monthly rental of RM100. Heisenberg, Wirtz, Hahn and von Weizsäcker closely monitored the building of the reactor. The last experiment on B8, in April 1945, showed a seven times increase in neutrons. Wirtz then hid the uranium blocks and heavy water. The facility was taken by French troops and the *Alsos Mission* arrived on April 23. The material was found three days later, hidden in the basement of a nearby mill.

IG Farbenindustrie – Munich and Frankfurt-am-Main: Chemical manufacturer producing metallic uranium.

Siemens: A number of the company's laboratories worked on purification of graphite as a possible moderator in a reactor, as an alternative to heavy water.

Uranium producers and mines
Aue – Erzebirge Mountains (Ore Mountains), Czechoslovakia/German border: Uranium oxide mine near Joachimsthal.

Gastein [upper reaches of the Danube] and Oberschleima [lower Silesia]: Small uranium mines.

Joachimsthal – Erzebirge Mountains (Ore Mountains), Czechoslovakia/ German border: Main source for uranium oxide.

Mauer AG – Scheningen: Uranium producer.

Rohestoffgeselschaft – Berlin: Involved in the transportation of uranium oxide to laboratories in Berlin and elsewhere.

Trebacher Chemische Werke – Klagenfurt, Austria: Austrian uranium producer with mines in the villages of Treibach and Foorlach.

Heavy water plants
Norsk Hydro – Vermork, Ryukan, central Norway: Ill-fated attempt to destroy this plant in November 1942 by British Commandos. An Allied bombing raid in 1943 only temporarily put the plant out of action. The Germans on February 9, 1944, attempted to transport the remaining stock of 150 gallons to Germany, but the *Hydro* ferry was blown up by Norwegian partisans.

Leuna – 10 miles west of Leipzig: By 1942 the plant was operational, but only small supplies of heavy water were produced.

Japan
[There were two separate atomic bomb projects during the war, codenamed *Ni Project* and *F Project*]

Army Aviation Technology Research Institute – Tokyo: Instigator of Japan's work on producing an atomic bomb.

Dai-Ni High School – Sendai: Professor Tadayoshi Hikosaka, one of Japan's foremost nuclear experts, worked here. By November 1944 he and other Japanese scientists were aware of the properties of plutonium.

Fukushima Prefecture: The only known location in Japan where uranium oxide was found in any sizeable quantities. Other uranium supplies came from Korea and Malaysia.

Imperial University – Kyoto: Towards the end of the war the Japanese Navy sponsored its own research into producing an atomic bomb, under Professor Bunsaku Arakatsu. The codename was *F Project* – the *F* referring to fission, but the staff was small in number. Uranium was separated in Kyoto using the centrifugal process. The Kyoto group of physicists made their last report to the Imperial Navy in July 1945.

Imperial University – Tokyo: The most prestigious university in Japan. The head of the physics faculty was Professor Ryokichi Sagane, who in October 1940 assisted Lt Colonel Suzuki of the Imperial Army with the preparation of a 20-page report on the feasibility of a bomb.

Institute of Physical and Chemical Research [RIKEN] – Tokyo: Founded in 1917. It was the largest private scientific research establishment in Japan. Lt General Yasuda asked RIKEN in April 1941 to proceed at speed on building the atomic bomb. Yoshio Nishina, the head of the project, reported to the military in May 1943 that U-235 could be produced using the thermal diffusion method. Separation devices were complete by March 1944. The codename was *Ni Project*, using the first two letters of Nishina's name. Some of the staff were dispersed to radar research leaving only 15 scientists and engineers allocated to the programme. The funding of the *Ni Project* had been limited to just Yen 2 million. The US airforce on April 13, 1945, destroyed RIKEN's facilities, so ending Japan's desire for atomic weapons.

Navy Technology Research Institute: A committee of the best physicists in the country was assembled to discuss the problems of building a bomb. There were 10 meetings in all between July 1942 and March 1943, concluding that conventional weapons would win the war in the Pacific.

United States
[selected sites only]

[The codename *Manhattan Engineering District* was used in the early months of the atomic bomb programme, but the name *Manhattan Project* became the general term]

By December 1941 the US government had awarded 16 research and development contracts on the then fledgling nuclear project, totalling $300,000, to the following:

Columbia University, Princeton, Standard Oil Development Co, Cornell University, Carnegie Institute, Iowa State College, John Hopkins University, University of California, University of Chicago, University of Minnesota, National Bureau of Standards, University of Virginia.

Fast neutron studies commissioned at: Carnegie Institute, National Bureau of Standards, Cornell University, Rice Institute, Stamford University, University of California, University of Chicago, University of Indiana.

Aberdeen Proving Ground in Maryland: Run by the US Army.

Alamogordo air base – New Mexico: On the Trinity site, 210 miles south of Los Alamos, on July 16, 1945 at 5.29am, the world's first atomic device was tested.

Argonne National Laboratory – Chicago: Became a key centre post-war.

Bruceton Explosives Research Laboratory – Pennsylvania: Run by US Bureau of Mines.

Columbia Nuclear Laboratory – New York: In June 1940 nearly all the work on the chain reaction was concentrated at Columbia under Pegram, Fermi and Szilard.

Clinton Engineering Works – Tennessee: Plant run by the University of Chicago.

Dahlgren Proving Ground: Run by the US Navy – first drop tests done here.

Hanford Engineering Works – Washington State: Plutonium plant built by the US Army and Du Pont. Produced the plutonium for the Nagasaki bomb.

Kellex Corporation – New York: Subsidiary of Kellogg. Worked on diffusion process with British scientists.

Livermore Laboratory – California: Home of the large cyclotrons.

Los Alamos National Laboratory – New Mexico: The main centre for the *Manhattan Project*.

Metallurgical Laboratory – University of Chicago: Established in early 1942.

National Bureau of Standards: Top physics institute in the US.

National Research Defence Committee [NRDC] – Washington: Dr Vannevar Bush, chairman.

Oak Ridge – Tennessee: Housed the electromagnetic and diffusion plants. The U-235 for the Hiroshima bomb manufactured here.

Office of Scientific Development [OSRD] – Washington: Dr Vannevar Bush the director, Dr James Conant of Harvard, his deputy.

Radiation Laboratory and other facilities – Berkeley, University of California: Linked to Los Alamos.

Westinghouse: Prepared designs for isotope centrifuge in 1941.

A SELECTION OF DOCUMENTS
FROM THE KGB ARCHIVES

Included are many relating to the atomic bomb and the wartime Soviet penetration in Britain and America.

Some key translations of documents:

➤ Churchill's trip to the Vatican to attempt peace negotiations with the Germans – dated August 27, 1944. page lxiii

➤ The NKGB agent, codenamed _Malone_, who worked in the special scientific unit of MI5 and MI6 which managed the British atomic bomb project – dated August 23, 1945. page lxxvii

➤ The confirmation that _Agent D_ was a senior member of SIS who worked closely with Guy Liddell, head of Section B of Counter-Intelligence – dated April 8, 1945. page lxxx

➤ The listing of the key NKVD agents involved in scientific espionage in Britain, _List, Ellie, Scott, Alkit, Pirate_ and _Valet_ – dated January 26, 1943. page lxxxiii

➤ Professor Robert Oppenheimer, chief scientist in the Manhattan Project, and his role in aiding Russian Intelligence – dated October 2, 1944. page lxxxvi

➤ Professor Robert Oppenheimer, the second document, again confirming that he was a secret member of the US Communist Party – dated January 7, 1946. page lxxxix

➤ Robert Maxwell, and the request to the head of the KGB to formalise his payments – dated February 25, 1957. page xci

➤ Robert Maxwell, the second document, showing how payments were made to his companies by the KGB – June 24, 1980. page xciii

Notes:
Many documents describe the 'English' and not 'British'.
The question of Uranium-235 is generally referred to as a 'problem'.
The footnotes to the documents have been added by KGB archivists.
Occasionally the KGB archivists use the word 'original' on documents.

Document 1

[Помета Е.М.Потаповой] Справка: экземпляр выдержки из перевода этого доклада на русский язык и отзыв академика Курчатова о его ценности находятся во 2-м томе аг[ентурного] дела «Энормоз[8])», стр. 20—38[9]).

Оперативный архив СВР России. Д.82 072, т.4, л.17. Подлинник. Опубликовано: *А.А.Яцков, В.П.Визгин.* У истоков советского атомного проекта: роль разведки. 1941—1946 гг. что материалам архива внешней разведки России //ВИЕТ. 1992. № 3. С. 108.

1) Собственный заголовок документа: «Справка на № 7073, 7081/1096 от 3.X.41 г. из Лондона».

2) Датируется по дат., указанной в заголовке этого документа, и дате документа № 108.

3) См. примечания 3 к документу № 106.

4) См. примечание 4 к документу № 106.

5) Возможно, имеется в виду отчет Комитета M.A.U.D., руководившего до середины 1941 г. исследованиями возможности цепной ядерной реакции. Комитет возглавлял Дж.П.Томсон. Р.Пайерлс пишет об этом периоде: «Летом 1941 г. Комитет M.A.U.D. выпустил свой последний отчет. К этому времени американские физики на небольших образцах измерили сечение деления урана-235 и обнаружили, что оно того же порядка, что и значение, принятое нами с Фришем, хотя все же немного меньше его. Доклад M.A.U.D. содержал вывод, что атомная бомба осуществима, и описывал работу, которую необходимо было выполнить для ее создания» (*Р.Пайерлс.* Перелетная птица. Воспоминания физика //Природа. 1993. №12. С. 90).

6) Сечение деления (англ.).

7) См. примечание 6 к документу № 106.

8) «Энормоз» (от англ. enormous — огромный) — кодовое название проблемы атомного оружия, установленное 1-м Управлением НКВД СССР.

9) Суда по содержанию, помета не могла быть сделана ранее 29 сентября 1943 г. (Дата избрания И.В.Курчатова академиком).

№ 108

**Записка начальника 4-го спецотдела НКВД СССР
наркому Л.П.Берии[1]) о работах по использованию
атомной энергии в военных целях за рубежом
и необходимости организации этой работы в СССР**

10 октября 1941 г.

Присланные из Англии сов[ершенно] секретные материалы Британского правительства, касающиеся работ английских ученых в области использования атомной энергии урана для военных целей, содержат два доклада Научно-совещательного комитета при Английском комитете обороны по вопросу атомной энергии урана и переписку по этому же вопросу между руководящими работниками комитета.

Судя по этим материалам, в Англии уделяется большое внимание проблеме использования атомной энергии урана для военных целей. Необходимо отметить, что обсуждение всех вопросов, связанных с решением этой проблемы (вопросов на то, что проводимое в этом направлении, по-

242

видимому, находятся еще в стадии теоретических и лабораторных исследований, имеют часто практический характер. В частности, из материалов видно, что английские ученые на основе расчетов выбрали оптимальный вес урановой бомбы, равный 10 кг, прорабатываются вопросы, связанные с выбором типа аппаратуры, пригодной для изготовления взрывчатого вещества, и произведены примерные расчеты стоимости постройки завода урановых бомб. Все это свидетельствует о том, что предварительные результаты теоретических и экспериментальных работ, проведенных в Англии, дают основания для подобного обсуждения.

Однако в материалах нет точных данных о том, что на основании всех обсуждений Комитетом обороны принято решение о постройке опытного завода. Между тем, именно этот вопрос представляет наибольший интерес, так как только в случае положительного решения можно сделать безусловный вывод о том, насколько реальны факты, изложенные в материалах. Сообщения агента «Вадима[5])» от 20.9.41 г. и 4.10.41 г. имеют несколько несистематический характер и в более ранних сообщениях говорится о том, что на заседании Комитета начальников штабов принято решение о срочной постройке в Англии заводов урановых бомб. В сообщении же от 4.10.41 г. приводятся данные, ранее изложенные в докладах Научно-совещательного комитета. Выдержками из этих докладов и заполнено все сообщение.

На основе изучения присланных материалов можно сделать следующие выводы:

1. Материалы представляют безусловный интерес как свидетельство большой работы, проводимой в Англии в области использования атомной энергии урана для военных целей.

2. Наличие только имеющихся материалов не позволяет сделать заключения о том, насколько практически реальны и осуществимы различные способы использования атомной энергии, о которых сообщается в материалах.

Имея в виду исключительное значение успешного решения проблемы практического использования атомной энергии (проблема, над которой работают в течение десятков лет крупнейшие ученые мира), считал бы необходимым:

1) поручить заграничной агентуре 1-го Управления НКВД СССР собрать конкретные проверенные материалы относительно постройки аппаратуры и опытного завода по производству урановых бомб;

2) создать при ГКО СССР специальную комиссию из числа крупных ученых СССР, работающих в области расщепления атомного ядра, которой поручить представить соображения о возможности проведения в СССР работ по использованию атомной энергии для военных целей.

Вопросами расщепления атомного ядра в СССР занимались: академик Капица — Академия наук СССР, академик Скобельцын — Ленинградский физический институт и профессор Слуцкий[3]) — Харьковский физический институт[4]).

В.Кравченко
10.10.41 г.

Оперативный архив СВР России. Д.82 072, т.3, л.12—13. Автограф.

1) Далее в заголовках документов: Л.П.Берия.
2) См. примечание 3 к документу № 106.

243

lii

This is a note from General Victor Kravchenko to Lavrcnty Beria, dated October 10, 1941, regarding the Soviet acquisition of the *Maud Report* from Britain that detailed Britain's plans to build 36 atomic bombs.

The document in full:

No. 108

Top secret materials of the British government sent from England concerning the studies of English scientists on the use of uranium atomic energy for military purposes contained two reports of the scientific advisory committee [the committee chaired by Lord Hankey] *to the English Defence Committee* [the War Cabinet] *on the question of uranium atomic energy and correspondence relating to this matter among the leading employees of the committee.*

Judging by this material the English are paying great attention to the question of using uranium atomic energy for military purposes. It is necessary to mention that the discussion of all arising issues [despite the fact that work carried out in this direction probably is still at the stage of theoretical and laboratory research] is of a purely practical nature. In particular, it is clear from these materials that English scientists on the basis on their calculations, have selected the optimal weight of a uranium bomb equal to 10 kg. The scientists are working on issues connected with the choice of the type of apparatus suitable for the manufacture of the explosive and they have carried out approximate calculations relating to the cost of building a plant to produce uranium bombs. All these testify to the fact that preliminary results of theoretical and experimental studies carried out in England provide a basis for such discussion.

However this intelligence does not contain precise data on whether the Defence Committee has taken a decision to build an experimental plant. In the meantime it is precisely this question which is of the greatest interest to us because only in the event of a positive decision one can draw an unconditional conclusion concerning how real are the facts set out in the materials we have received. Information of the agent 'Vadim' [Anatoli Gorsky, the NKVD *rezident* in the Russian Embassy in London] *of September 20, 1941 and October 10, 1941 is misleading. In the September message he says that at the meeting of the scientific advisory committee a decision has been taken urgently to build in England a plant to manufacture uranium bombs. Yet in a message of October 4, 1941 unclear information is cited which was earlier presented in the reports of the scientific advisory committee. The whole of this transmission is filled with extracts from these reports.* [There were several cyphers from London with details of the *Maud Report*, and Kravchenko's note to Beria is unclear as he mentions October 10, yet cites the one of October 4].

On the basis of the study of these materials one can draw the following conclusions:

1. *The intelligence is of undoubted interest as it confirms the work being carried out in England in the use of uranium atomic energy for military purposes.*

2. *This limited availability of intelligence precludes a conclusion on how in practical terms the various ways of using atomic energy mentioned are real and physical.*

Bearing in mind the exceptional significance of a successful solution to the problem of practical use of atomic energy [a problem that for decades the greatest scientists of the world have been working on] I suggest immediate action:

1. *To task the foreign agents network of the NKVD USSR to collect specific authentic materials relating to the building of apparatus and experimental plant to manufacture uranium bombs.*

2. *To set up a special commission made up of major Soviet scientists working on nuclear fission to be attached to the Defence Committee of the USSR. It would be tasked to advise on the development of atomic energy for military purposes in the USSR.*

Academician Kapitsa from the Academy of Sciences of the USSR, Academician Skobeltsyn from the Leningrad Physics Institute and Professor Slutskii from the Kharkov Institute have all been extensively involved with the problems of fission.

V Kravchenko

Oct 10, 1941

№ 117

Из оперативного письма № 4 1-го Управления НКВД СССР резиденту лондонской резидентуры А.В.Горскому о задачах в области научно-технической разведки

15 марта 1942 г.

Линия работы — техника

По линии техники перед нами сейчас стоит большая необходимость в получении как информации, так и конкретных материалов по проводимым в В[ашей] стране работам в области: 1) военной химии — отравляющим веществам и защите от них; 2) бактериологии — изысканиям новых бактериологических средств нападения и защиты; 3) проблемам урана-235 и 4) новым взрывчатым веществам.

Всем этим вопросам сейчас уделяется исключительное внимание и в Вашей стране необходимо максимальное усилие для освещения этих вопросов.

По вопросам бактериологии, урану-235 и ВВ нами уже давались указания как письмом, так и телеграфом [1]. [...]

В вопросах технической разведки проявляйте максимум осторожности [2].

«Виктор» [3]

Оперативный архив СВР России. Д.77666, т.2, л.6. Подлинник.

---

[1] См. примечание 3 к документу № 91.
[2] Фраза вписана П.М.Фитиным от руки.
[3] См. примечание 5 к документу № 91.

Translation of Document 2

A directive from Lt General Pavel Fitin to Anatoli Gorsky, the NKVD London *rezident*, dated March 15, 1942. *Victor* was Fitin's codename in the NKVD.

The translation of text and archivist's footnotes:

No. 117

Direction of work- technical

In the technical area we are facing a great need to obtain information and specific materials on work carried out in your country in the field of:

1.   *Military chemistry – poisonous substances and protection from poisonous substances*
2.   *Bacteriology – studies of new bacteriological means of attack and defence*
3.   *Problem of Uranium-235*
4.   *New explosives*

These questions are attracting considerable attention at present in your country and it is necessary to make maximum efforts on them.

On questions of bacteriology, Uranium 235 and explosives we have already given you guidelines both by letter and by telegraph. [1]

In questions of technical intelligence please be very careful [2]

Victor [3]

[1] See note No. 3 to document no 91
[2] This phrase was handwritten by P. M. Fitin.
[3] See note No. 5 to document no 91

Operative archive SVR Russia. D.77666, Vol. 2, Sheet 6. Original

№ 118

Из оперативного письма № 2 1-го Управления НКВД
СССР резиденту нью-йоркской резидентуры В.М.Зарубину
о задачах в области научно-технической разведки —
о проблеме урана-235

27 марта 1942 г.

«Максиму»

П. № 7 (ХУ¹))

Обстановка настоящего времени настоятельно требует мобилизации всех
имеющихся у нас возможностей для развертывания разведывательной работы
в разрезе заданий, данных в п. № 4 (1941 г.), и др. указаний и, особенно,
по химии ОВ, защите от ОВ, вопросам бактериологии и проблеме урана-235.

Для этого считаем необходимым сообщить Вам о ряде лиц, которых нужно
немедленно же привлечь к нашей работе. Среди них будут и те, задания на
связь с которыми уже давались в наших письмах за 1941 г. [...] ²).

9*   259

Translation of Document 3

A directive from Moscow sent to the New York NKVD *rezident*, Vasily Zarubin,
on the acquisition of scientific intelligence, including U-235. It is dated March
27, 1942. In it was a list of scientists in the US who were already providing intelligence to their Soviet controllers. Zarubin was codenamed *Maksim*. The (XY)
was the codename for scientific intelligence used in cyphers.

No. 118

To Maksim

*The situation at present firmly demands the mobilisation of all possibilities we
have within the scope of tasks given in letter No. 4 [1941] and other guidelines:
in particular on chemistry of toxic substances, protection from toxic substances,
issues in bacteriology and the problem of Uranium-235.*

*We believe it necessary to inform you about a number of people who must be
immediately involved in our work. Among them will be those people already mentioned in our letters in 1941 for you to contact. [...].*

базы проверить полученную развединформацию и ее недостаточностью. 11 февраля 1943 г. ГКО повторяет поручение о подготовке доклада уже в другой формулировке, но с тем же требованием дать заключение и ответ на вопрос — возможно ли создание атомного оружия (см. документ № 141).

4) Последний абзац документа — уклончивая приписка В.М.Молотова, в ней речь идет о проекте Постановления ГКО № 2542сс от 27 ноября 1942 г. — см. документ № 132.

№ 128

Распоряжение ГКО № 2352сс
«Об организации работ по урану»[1]

28 сентября 1942 г.
Сов. секретно

Москва, Кремль

Распоряжение Государственного комитета обороны
№ 2352сс

28 сентября 1942 г.   *Об организации работ по урану*[2]

Обязать Академию наук СССР (акад[емик] Иоффе) возобновить работы по исследованию осуществимости использования атомной энергии путем расщепления ядра урана и представить Государственному комитету обороны к 1 апреля 1943 года доклад о возможности создания урановой бомбы или уранового топлива[2].

Для этой цели:

1. Президиуму Академии наук СССР:

а) организовать при Академии наук специальную лабораторию атомного ядра[3];

б) к 1 января 1943 года в Институте радиологии[4] разработать и изготовить установку для термодиффузионного выделения урана-235;

в) к 1 марта 1943 года в Институте радиологии и Физико-техническом институте[5] изготовить методами центрифугирования и термодиффузии уран-235 в количестве, необходимом для физических исследований, и к 1 апреля 1943 года произвести в лаборатории атомного ядра исследования осуществимости расщепления ядер урана-235.

2. Академии наук УССР (акад[емик] Богомолец) организовать под руководством проф[ессора] Ланге разработку проекта лабораторной установки для выделения урана-235 методом центрифугирования[6] и к 20 октября 1942 года сдать технический проект казанскому заводу «Серп и молот» Наркомата тяжелого машиностроения.

3. Народному комиссариату тяжелого машиностроения (т. Казаков) изготовить на казанском заводе подъемно-транспортного машиностроения «Серп и молот» для Академии наук СССР к 1 января 1943 года лабораторную установку центрифуги по проекту проф[ессора] Ланге, разрабатываемую Академией наук УССР.

4. Народному комиссариату финансов СССР (т. Зверев) передать к 1 нояб-

---

ких обоснований проводимых работ. О значении этой проблемы[2] нами неоднократно Вам подчеркивалось. [...]

«Виктор»[3]

Оперативный архив СВР России. Д.77666, т. 2, л. 14. Подлинник.

1) См. примечание 3 к документу № 91.
2) Далее так в документе.
3) См. примечание 5 к документу № 91.

№ 127

Записка заместителя председателя ГКО В.М.Молотова[1] И.В.Сталину о проектах распоряжений по возобновлению работ в области использования атомной энергии

27 сентября 1942 г.

Вношу на Ваше утверждение проект распоряжения Государственного комитета обороны «Об организации работ по урану», внесенный Академией наук СССР (т. Иоффе) и Комитетом по делам высшей школы при Совнаркоме СССР (т. Кафтановым)[2].

В проекте распоряжения предусматривается возобновление работ по исследованию использования атомной энергии путем расщепления ядра урана.

Академия наук, которой эта работа поручается, обязана к 1 апреля 1943 г. представить в Государственный комитет обороны доклад о возможности создания урановой бомбы или уранового топлива[3].

Второй проект тт. Иоффе и Кафтанова (о добыче урана) требует дальнейшей проверки и будет внесен на утверждение ГОКО особо[4].

В.Молотов
27/IX

АП РФ. Ф.22, оп.1, д.95, л.103. Подлинник.

1) Далее в заголовках документов: В.М.Молотов.
2) К записке приложен проект распоряжения, завизированный В.М.Молотовым (АП РФ. Ф.22, оп.1, д.25, л.104—106). Распоряжение — см. документ № 128.
3) ГКО поручило подготовку доклада А.Ф.Иоффе от 25 апреля 1943 г. Возможно, что имеющее отношение к этому документу (см. в книге: И.В.Курчатов. Избранные труды (в трех томах). — М.: Наука, 1984. Т. 3. С. 22—57). В докладе изложены вопросы, начиная с открытия явления радиоактивности, а также дан обзор данных по цепной ядерной реакции. И хотя И.В.Курчатов пишет, что при определенных условиях бесспланный процесс будет бурно развиваться и может закончиться взрывом исключительной силы (там же, с. 52), в докладе присутствует некоторая неопределенность, вероятно,

This is Stalin's order to restart work on the atomic bomb, dated September 28, 1942.

Translation of text and the archivist's footnotes in full:

No. 128

Instruction of GKO No. 2352 ss

On the organisation of work on uranium [1]

September 28, 1942   *Moscow, the Kremlin*

Top secret

On the organisation of work on uranium

To order the Academy of Science of the USSR [Academician Ioffe] to resume work on the feasibility of using atomic energy through the splitting of the uranium nucleus and to submit a report by April 1, 1943 on the possibility of producing a uranium bomb or uranium fuel. [2]

For that purpose:

1.   *To the Presidium of the Academy of Science of the USSR.*
a.   *Organise a special laboratory on the atomic nucleus attached to the academy. [3]*
b.   *By January 1, 1943 in the Institute of Radiology [4] and the Physics Technical Institute [5] to produce Uranium-235, using centrifugal and thermal diffusion methods, in an amount necessary for physical investigation, and by April 1, 1943 to carry out research in the atomic nucleus laboratory on the feasibility of splitting the Uranium-235 nucleus.*
2.   *The Academy of Science of the Ukrainian Republican [Academician Bogomolets] – to develop under the supervision of Professor Lange a project of a laboratory installation for Uranium-235 production using a centrifuge [6] and by October 20, 1942 to submit the technical project to the Kazan plant 'Serp i molot' of the People's Commissariat of Heavy Machine Building.*
3.   *People's Commissariat of Heavy Machine Building [Commissar Kazakov] to produce at the Kazan plant for the Academy of Science by January 1, 1943 a laboratory for centrifugal installation based on Professor Lange's project.*

4. The People's Commissariat for Finance [Commissar Zverev]....[some of the copy of this document is illegible]

5. To order the People's Commissariat for Ferrous Metals [Commissar Tevosian], the People's Commissariat of Heavy Machine Building [Commissar Lomako] to allocate and ship by November 1, 1942 to the Academy of Science the following materials subject to technical specifications of the Academy.

a. People's Commissariat for Ferrous Metals – various types of steel – 6 tonnes.

b. People's Commissariat for Non-Ferrous Metals – 0.5 tonnes, and also to order People's Commissariat of Heavy Machine Building to allocate two lathes for production.

6. People's Commissariat for Foreign Trade [Commissar Mikoyan] is to buy abroad, based on applications of the Academy of Science, apparatus and chemicals for 300,000 roubles for the atomic nucleus laboratory.

7. Chief Directorate of Civil Aviation [Commissar Astakhov] by 5.11.1942 to ensure supply to by air to Kazan' from Leningrad of 20 kg of uranium and 200 kg of apparatus which belong to the Physics-technical Institute for Physics Research. The Sovnarkom of the Tatar ASSR [Commissar Gafatullin] is to present by 15.10.1942 to the Academy of Science premises in Kazan' with an area of 500 sq. m for their atomic nucleus laboratory and housing for 10 scientists.

Chairman of GKO I. Stalin [7].
[Note:] Signature on the list – see GOKO-2354 [8]

AP.RF F.22 1.95 d.99-101, original
Footnotes

1. In the right-hand top corner of the first page of the document the word 'project' has been crossed out; the month and the date and instruction number are hand written. In the title of the instruction the word 'uranium' was crossed by hand and then written in again by hand above the line. On examination of the documents two copies of this instruction were found, typed separately but identical in content. The document is accompanied by a distribution list, the final text of the instruction was sent to: V. M. Molotov, S. V. Kaftanov, A. F. Ioffe, V.L. Komarov, Ya. E. Chadaev, excerpts mentioned in the text to those responsible for implementing specific instructions (AP RF F.22 ts.1 1.95 1.102)

2. See note 3 to document 127.

3. Here the reference is to Laboratory No. 2 (this name was given to it in

1943). This laboratory was created on the basis of LFTI in Kazan, subject to the decision of GKO no. 2872ss of 11 February 1943. The laboratory was transferred to Moscow, see document no. 144, on the first composition of the laboratory see document no.177a, 180.

4.   *Thus in the document – information on an Institute with such a name was not found. There was an Institute of X-ray and radiology of NKZ USSR but there is no information on its participation in this work until 1946 in documents known to us. Perhaps there is a typo in the text and it's the Radium Institute that is meant. In the distribution list there is no mention of the head of either Radiological or Radium Institute.*

5.   *Probably LFTI is meant here.*

6.   *In 1942 Lange worked in Ufa in the Physics and Mathematics Institute of the Academy of Science of the Ukrainian SSR. On the essence of Lange's project and its implementation – see docs. no. 147, 162, 164. Several telegrams sent to the Academy of Science of the Ukraine in Kazan, addressed to A. F. Ioffe for 1942 dealing with the progress of centrifuge design have been preserved.*

27.10 –'... The technical project is finished. Sent today urgently to Kazan' to the plant 'Komsomolets'.

5.11 'So far could not leave, I will go in the next few days, will bring working technical drawings.' Lange.

6.11. 'On the 10th the working drawing will be finished. Lange leaves at first opportunity'. Palladin (Archive of RAN F.2 op. 1a(4))d.236 l.48-51).

7.   *No signature.*

8.   *The reference is to the 'List of questions to be approved in the Central Committee of the party' as of 28.09.1942 (AP RF f.22 op 1 d.95 l.116).*

№ 1694

СООБЩЕНИЕ
РЕЗИДЕНТУРЫ НКГБ СССР В РИМЕ
О ПЕРЕГОВОРАХ НЕМЕЦКИХ ПРЕДСТАВИТЕЛЕЙ
С ЧЕРЧИЛЛЕМ В ВАТИКАНЕ
ОБ УСЛОВИЯХ СЕПАРАТНОГО МИРА[1]

27 августа 1944 г.

Черчилль был принят папой не в пятницу, как сообщают газеты, а в среду. Черчилль был без свиты, лишь с одним личным секретарем. После беседы с папой он посетил государственный секретариат Ватикана, где его ожидал Вейцзекер, который, как упорно утверждают в Ватикане, возглавляет немецкую делегацию, прибывшую для переговоров с англичанами. Беседа Черчилля с Вейцзекером была непродолжительной.

Англичане выдвинули условия:

1. Полная капитуляция немцев и быстрая оккупация Германии.

2. Детальные переговоры о территории будут вестись после оккупации, против чего возражают немцы.

3. Воскресить партию христианских демократов и земледельцев, которые должны составить большинство в правительстве.

4. Временная администрация должна находиться в англо-американских руках.

5. Немедленное возвращение аннексированных Германией территорий.

6. Немцы должны сотрудничать в устранении опасности коммунизма.

Что касается Ватикана, то он настаивает на скорейшем формировании немецкого правительства, с тем чтобы избежать при оккупации Германии какого бы то ни было просоветского правительства.

Архив ПГУ КГБ, арх. № 235, л. 15.
Подлинник

---

[1] См. том 3 настоящего сборника, документы № 757, 780, 805, 837, 919, 970; том 4, документы № 1137, 1302, 1354, 1448, а также документы № 1601, 1634, 1635, 1654.

The NKVD had an almost direct line of communication to the discussion taking place in the summer of 1944 in the Vatican between Allied representatives, Pope Pius XII, Ernst von Weizsäcker – Hitler's Vatican Ambassador – and a number of German generals. On July 24, Cardinal Francis Spellman, the head of the American Episcopacy, and Myron Taylor – an American catholic multi-millionaire, president of United Steel and personal envoy of President Roosevelt, met with the Pope and von Weizsäcker. Hitler's Ambassador was covertly working for a group of German military officers headed by General Walter von Brauchitsch and Field Marshal Wilhelm Keitel, to try to conclude a peace agreement with the Allies just two months after the Allied D-Day landings. At the meeting von Weizsäcker put the following peace conditions to the two Americans: the Rhine reverts to French and British control as it was under the Weimar regime; Austria was to become an independent state; Poland receives its old borders with Germany but without the corridor in Danzig, in exchange for the Memel district; and a new military government in Germany was to be formed from generals who were not compromised by Nazism. Lastly, the Allies were to preserve the integrity of Germany. Keitel was executed in October 1946 after standing trial at Nuremberg.

In August it was Churchill's turn to visit the Pope, to present his own proposals. This meeting that took place on August 27, 1944, is recorded in the following NKVD document.

Translation of text and the archivist's footnotes:

No. 1694

Message of the rezidency of the Soviet NKGB in Rome on the talks of German representative with Churchill in the Vatican concerning the conditions of a separate peace [1]

Churchill was received by the Pope, not on Friday as the newspapers have reported, but on Wednesday. Churchill came without his entourage, only with one personal secretary. After his talk with the Pope he visited the state secretariat of the Vatican where von Weizsäcker was expecting him, who as they continued to insist in the Vatican, heads the German delegation, which has arrived for talks with the English. Churchill's talk with von Weizsäcker was not long.

The English put forward the following conditions:

1.   *Complete German capitulation and speedy occupation of Germany.*
2.   *Detailed negotiations concerning territory will be conducted after the occupation – the Germans have objections.*
3.   *To revive the Christian Democrat Party and farmers who have to make up the majority in the government.*
4.   *Provisional administration has to be in Anglo-American hands.*
5.   *Immediate return of territories annexed by Germany.*
6.   *The Germans have to co-operate in eliminating the danger of Communism.*

As far as the Vatican is concerned it insists on a speedy formation of the German government in order to avoid any pro-Soviet government during the occupation of Germany.

Archive of the First Chief Directorate of KGB. Archive number 235. Sheet 15. Original.

[1] See volume 3 of this collection, documents numbers 757, 780, 805, 837, 919, 970: volume 4, document numbers 1137, 1302, 1354, 1448 and also document numbers 1603, 1634, 1635, 1654.

питания, деньгами в сумме 400—450 руб. совзнаками, пропусками для возвращения через линию фронта и взрыв-веществами, как указано выше.

В инструктаже о поведении в советском тылу им рекомендовалось выдавать себя за детей, родители которых погибли или находятся в Красной Армии, а о взрыв-веществах говорить, что это украденный уголь, предназначенный для обмена на хлеб.

В ночь с 27 на 28 августа вся эта группа была попарно сброшена с двух транспортных самолетов в районах крупных железнодорожных узлов.

Розыск выброшенных на территории Белоруссии парашютистов продолжаем.

Народный комиссар государственной безопасности БССР

Архив КГБ БССР, ф. 3, оп. 3, д. 2, лл. 437—442.
Копия

№ 1702

ДИРЕКТИВНОЕ УКАЗАНИЕ ИНТЕЛЛИДЖЕНС СЕРВИС РЕЗИДЕНТАМ СИС ЗА КОРДОНОМ ПО ВОПРОСУ РАЗВЕДЫВАТЕЛЬНОЙ ДЕЯТЕЛЬНОСТИ В ОТНОШЕНИИ СОВЕТСКОГО СОЮЗА И НАЦИОНАЛЬНЫХ КОМПАРТИЙ[1]

[Август 1944 г.]

Наблюдались случаи, когда наши резиденты при соответствующих обстоятельствах затруднялись принимать решение в вопросах, связанных с коммунизмом и советскими агентами.

Надо иметь в виду следующее. СССР является союзником, с которым мы сотрудничаем в получении разведывательных данных о противнике и его разведке[2]. Вместе с тем советская разведка вербует агентов с целью получения секретной информации

---

[1] Добыто закордонной агентурой НКГБ СССР.

[2] По предложению Англии и США внешняя разведка органов госбезопасности СССР заключила с английской разведкой в 1941 г. и с американской разведкой в 1943 г. соглашения, в соответствии с которыми стороны должны были передавать друг другу разведывательную информацию по Германии, оказывать помощь в проведении диверсий, заброске на территорию врага агентуры, в организации с ней связи и т. д. Однако на практике контакты с разведками наших союзников по их вине носили эпизодический характер и результаты оказывались малоэффективными. Более того, англичане, например, разрабатывали наших агентов, которые должны были забрасываться в Германию с территории Англии, всячески провоцировали их на отказ от работы в тылу немцев, склоняли их к невозвращению в Советский Союз. Подобное сотрудничество не удовлетворяло внешнюю разведку СССР, и вскоре после открытия второго фронта оно полностью прекратилось.

48*

у нас. Кроме того, коммунистические партии других стран представляют собой движение с революционными и разрушительными целями. Сила, влияние и престиж этих партий начиная с 1941 г. во многих случаях значительно возросли, и имеется тенденция к их дальнейшему росту. Конечной целью указанных партий является захват власти в своих странах, хотя, по крайней мере в настоящее время, их деятельность направлена на поддержку усилий в войне против нацистской Германии.

Таким образом, наша разведывательная деятельность в этих условиях должна тщательно планироваться, с тем чтобы не создавать правительству Его Величества затруднений дипломатического порядка в его отношениях с советским правительством и другими союзниками. Сотрудники в деле получения военных развединформацией других стран в деле получения военных развединформацией данных, резиденты должны соблюдать строжайшую осторожность, с тем чтобы обеспечить безопасность нашей собственной организации и ее отношении с чиновниками или агентами. Все, что касается нашей организации, ее личного состава или методов работы, следует скрывать от них, за исключением тех случаев, когда разглашение некоторых сведений абсолютно необходимо для проведения каких-либо мероприятий.

В то же время необходимо добывать и сообщать всю доступную информацию о составе и методах работы секретной разведывательной службы Советского Союза или различных компартий.

При этом следует помнить, что коммунисты, особенно наиболее опытные из них, имеют, как правило, длительный опыт и практику обращения к конспиративным методам, а возможно, и к разведывательной работе[1]. При настоящих обстоятельствах им следует пытаться проникнуть в СССР или в его официальные миссии. Попытки проникновения в организацию компартий других стран могут предприниматься сотрудниками, имеющими специальную подготовку или задания центра. Под понятием «проникновение» имеется в виду просачивание или вербовка агентов на советской территории, в советских миссиях или среди членов компартий с целью собирания разведывательной информации об СССР или компартиях.

Далее. Необходимо соблюдать величайшую осторожность в установлении связи с другими союзниками, особенно с поляками, информация о которых со СССР и коммунистической деятельности является в некоторой мере тенденциозной, и они к тому же склонны создавать трения между правительством Его Величества и советским правительством. В подобных случаях надо придерживаться следующей позиции. Соглашаясь получать любую информацию, которая нам может быть передана о коммунистическом движении, мы не склонны, однако, сотрудничать в работе против любого другого союзника (включая Россию) там,

где существует контакт по этому вопросу между резидентами СИС и союзными разведчиками или органами безопасности. Такое сотрудничество следует продолжать только после консультации с центром, если его продолжение не вызовет риска дипломатических осложнений. Устанавливать новые связи для обмена информацией по данному вопросу с союзными разведчиками без одобрения центра не следует. Короче говоря, резиденты должны собирать всякую информацию о коммунистических организациях и отдельных членах без риска осложнений, тогда как вопросы связи с союзными разведками и внедрения агентов должны решать только после консультации с центром.

В отношении выполнении заданий центра по этому вопросу необходимо в дальнейшем руководствоваться изложенными выше указаниями.

Подлинник

[1] Так в тексте документа.

Архив ПГУ КГБ, арх. № 235, лл. 112–113.

№ 1703

МЕМОРАНДУМ ПО ОТЧЕТУ АГЕНТА ЧЕТВЕРТОГО УПРАВЛЕНИЯ НКГБ СССР «ИЧИАНА»[1] О ВЫПОЛНЕНИИ ЗАДАНИЯ В ТЫЛУ ПРОТИВНИКА

[Август 1944 г.]

2 июня 1943 г. в тыл противника под видом перебежчика из Действующей Красной Армии был переброшен агент «Ичиан» с заданием вступить в «Туркестанский легион», установить связь с туркестанской эмиграцией и внедриться в ее руководящие круги, а также заинтересовать разведывательные органы противника и эмигрантские круги якобы действующей в г. Ашхабаде «шпионско-националистической группой» с целью перехвата каналов связи противника с действующими в Туркменской ССР антисоветским подпольем.

После перехода агента поступили документальные данные, что он принят противником, который заинтересовался его легендой.

23 марта 1944 г. на базу оперативной группы Четвертого управления НКГБ СССР к переходу на ее сторону было подготовлено около 200 человек, однако план был раскрыт и немцами. В результате боевых действий опергруппой было уничтожено свыше 100 солдат полка,

[1] См. том 4 настоящего сборника, документы № 1166, 1207, 1234, 1235, 1240, 1271, 1273, 1276, 1282, 1299.
[2] После установления «Ичианом» контакта с оперативной группой Четвертого управления НКГБ СССР в районе г. Баранович перешло 49 солдат и офицеров «Ост-мусульманского полка СС» во главе с «Ичианом»[2].

757

This document was a directive by the head of Britain's SIS, MI6, to the heads of department regarding the operational difficulties of spying on a wartime ally. A copy was quickly passed by an NKGB agent within SIS to his Russian controller from the Embassy in London. It is translated in the Russian style leaving in terms such as 'rezident.' The archivist's footnotes are revealing, especially the second. The document is dated August 1944.

No. 1702

Directive instruction of the intelligence service to SIS rezidents abroad concerning intelligence activities in relation to the Soviet Union and national Communist parties [1]

There have been incidences when our rezidents in certain circumstances have had difficulties in taking decisions in matters concerned with the USSR and its agents.

One has to keep in mind the following.

The USSR is an ally with whom we co-operate in obtaining intelligence on Germany and German intelligence [2]. However we realise that Soviet Intelligence is recruiting agents to spy on us. The Communist parties in other countries are movements with revolutionary and destructive aims. The power, influence and prestige of these parties starting from 1941 have grown significantly and it will grow further. Ultimately the aim of these parties is to seize political power although at present their activities are directed towards supporting the war effort against Nazi Germany.

This means that our intelligence activity in these conditions must be thoroughly planned so as not to cause diplomatic difficulties between His Majesty's government and the Soviet Union. With regard to obtaining military intelligence from Russian civil servants or from Communists from other countries, rezidents must maintain the strictest secrecy so as not to compromise our own organisation. Anything that pertains to our organisation, its personnel or methods of work, has to be hidden from these agents except in those operational cases when disclosure of certain information is absolutely necessary.

It is necessary to obtain and transmit any accessible information on the composition and methods of work of the secret intelligence services of the Soviet Union and from Communist parties throughout Europe. We must remember that Communists, in particular the most experienced of them, are very experienced in using clandestine methods and intelligence. [3]

Due to present circumstances we should not attempt to penetrate into the USSR or its official missions. Attempts to penetrate the Communist parties may only be undertaken by specially trained employees who have been tasked by the Centre.

Furthermore, we must take the greatest care in establishing contacts with other allies, especially the Poles, whose information about the USSR and Communist activity is tendentious. Poles tend to create friction between His Majesty's government and the Russian leaders. In such cases one should adhere to the following position. While agreeing that we must obtain intelligence we should not co-operate with them in working against our ally. Intelligence gathering on the Soviet Union must be left to SIS rezidents and Allied intelligence officers. Any other co-operation can only now be sanctioned by the Centre so to lessen the risk of diplomatic complications. No new contacts can be established without prior approval from the Centre.

Archive of the First Chief Directorate of the KGB, archive no. 235, pages 112–113.

[1] Obtained by the foreign agents network of the NKGB USSR.
[2] Based on proposals made by the intelligence services in England and America in 1941, and later American suggestions in 1943, we agreed to share information with each other on Germany. In addition we rendered assistance in conducting sabotage which included parachuting our people into enemy territory to set up communications with agents. However, in practice, this co-operation was poorly co-ordinated. Our Allies were to blame and the results were ineffective. Moreover the English tried to turn our agents who were to be parachuted into Germany from the territory of England. In every possible way the English provoked them to refuse to work behind the German lines and they attempted to persuade them to defect. After the Second Front was opened our intelligence services terminated any further co-operation.
[3] This is what is in the text.

United archive of SVR Russia. D.82072, Vol. 3, Sheets 12–13. In his own handwriting.

№ 2120

СООБЩЕНИЕ РЕЗИДЕНТА НКГБ СССР В БЕРЛИНЕ О ВЕРБОВКЕ НЕМЦЕВ В АНГЛИЙСКИЕ И АМЕРИКАНСКИЕ ВОЙСКА

3 августа 1945 г.

Из ряда новых источников подтверждается, что англичане и американцы вербуют в свою армию немцев из лагерей военнопленных. В первую очередь, это летчики, танкисты и артиллеристы. Вербуемым объясняют, что они нужны для войны с Японией, для работы в полиции, для службы в оккупированных районах взамен союзных военнослужащих, посылаемых теперь на родину. Вербуемым обещают обеспечить через несколько лет приём и американское гражданство или английское подданство и возможность выезда в Америку или Англию. Такая пропаганда имеет большой успех ввиду крайне неблагоприятной перспективы жизни в Германии в ближайшем будущем. В районе Фленсбурга англичане предлагают вступить в их армию всем ученикам старших классов немецких гимназий, а также молодёжи последнего года призыва в гитлеровскую армию, выпускаемой из лагерей военнопленных. За это обещают хорошее материальное обеспечение.

Вербовка немцев в союзные армии порождает среди немецкого населения всевозможные кривотолки о якобы предстоящей вскоре между СССР и союзниками, когда новая германская армия будет ими обучена. Высказывают предположения, что война начнётся или на немецкой территории, или путём вторжения в Советский Союз через Иудино.

Архив ПГУ КГБ, арх. № 241, л. 378.
Подлинник

№ 2121

ИЗ ПРОТОКОЛА ДОПРОСА БЫВШЕГО НАЧАЛЬНИКА ОТДЕЛА «АБВЕР-3» ГЕНЕРАЛ-ЛЕЙТЕНАНТА ГЕРМАНСКОЙ АРМИИ БЕНТИВЕНЬИ ФРАНЦА

6 августа 1945 г.

Вопрос: Какие задачи поставил перед Вами Канарис и систему подготовки войны против Советского Союза?

Ответ: Канарис поставил передо мной общую задачу: подготовить контрразведывательные органы абвера к войне против СССР. Разработка и проведение конкретных действий в области контрразведки лежала на мне как на начальнике отдела «Абвер-3». Канарис лишь предупредил меня, что всю подготовку к войне нужно вести в строжайшей тайне, не называя каких-либо приказаний, приказов или распоряжений.

Вопрос: Что Вы конкретно сделали для подготовки войны против СССР?

Ответ: По контрразведывательной линии мною были предприняты следующие меры:

подготовка низовых органов абвера к ведению активной контрразведывательной работы против СССР в условиях военных действий;

дезинформирование иностранных разведывательных органов, в частности советской разведки, в том смысле, что германское правительство придерживается якобы мирных тенденций, улучшения отношений с Советским Союзом;

мероприятия в области почтовой, телеграфной и телефонной связи для обеспечения тайны в вопросе переброски войск на восток.

Вопрос: Что было Вами предпринято в области подготовки низовых органов абвера к контрразведывательной работе против СССР в условиях военных действий?

Ответ: Во все абвергруппы, которые до этого времени действовали с войсками против Франции, Бельгии и Голландии, были введены лица, владеющие русским языком, были заполнены все вакантные места в абвергруппах. В начале июня 1941 г., связавшись с верховным командованием германской армии, я узнал, какое количество абвергрупп потребуется для Восточного фронта, и расписал эти абвергруппы по армиям.

В абвернтеллах, которые работали на Восток (абверштелле «Кенигсберг», абверштелле «Штеттин», абверштелле «Бреслау»

¹ См. том 5 настоящего сборника, документы № 1510, 1607, а также документ № 2028

In the first months after the war with Germany had ended, Berlin was alive with rumour of the immediate onset of the Third World War. This NKGB note confirms the high state of alert in Moscow.

Information of the rezident of NKGB USSR in Berlin on recruitment of Germans to English and American armies

No. 2120

August 3, 1945

A series of new sources confirm that English and Americans are recruiting Germans from POW camps into their armies, such as pilots, tank crew and artillery men. Those recruited are being told that they are needed for the war with Japan, or in the police, to serve in territories occupied by the Allies in lieu of Allied military personnel who are returning home. They are being promised that after several years they will be awarded American or British citizenship. Such propaganda is very successful given the poor prospects that will exist in Germany for some time to come. In the region of Flensburg, the English are offering high-school students the opportunity to join the British army. The youngest and most recent conscripts into Hitler's army are being released from POW camps. The English are offering them material security if they enlist.

Recruitment of Germans into the Allied armies generates among the German population all sorts of false rumours concerning an allegedly forthcoming war between the USSR and the Allies, especially as the new German army will have been trained by the Allies. Assumptions are being made that the war will start either on German territory or by way of invasion of the Soviet Union through India.

Archive of the First Chief Directorate of the KGB, archive no. 250, page 378

Original
[The Document, No. 2121, which is also shown on page lxix refers to the NKGF interrogation of Lt General Franz Bentivegni, the head of Abwehr-3 – the section in German Intelligence which carried out Counter-Intelligence work against the USSR during wartime.]

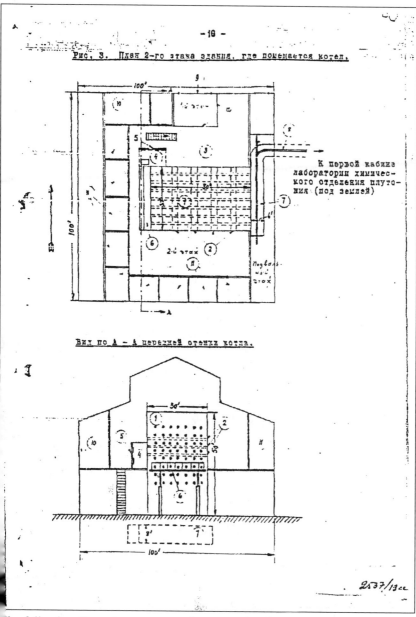

Рис. 3. План 2-го этажа здания, где помещается котел.

К первой кабине лаборатории химического отделения плутония (под землей)

2-й этаж

Подвальный этаж

Вид по А – А передней стенки котла.

2537/13сс

The following diagrams were part of an extensive document that was delivered to the NKGB in March 1949 by a scientist in Oak Ridge, Tennessee. They were redrawn and translated into Russian. Uranium for the Hiroshima bomb came from Oak Ridge.

Document 9

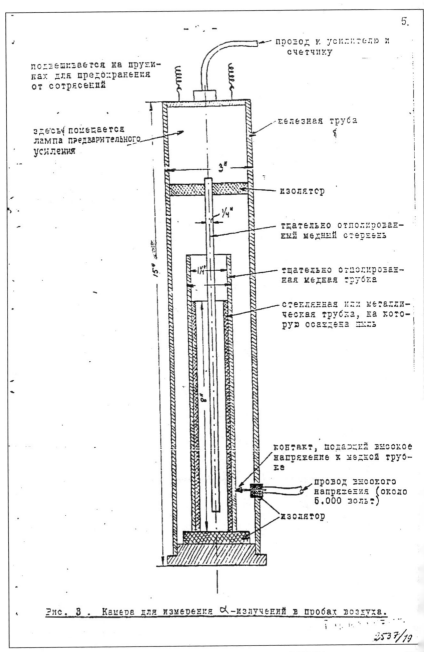

Рис. 3 . Камера для измерения α-излучений в пробах воздуха.

Oak Ridge: Many of the drawings stolen by the NKVD/NKGB were very specifi[c]
This is a diagram of an apparatus to measure alpha radiation in air samples.

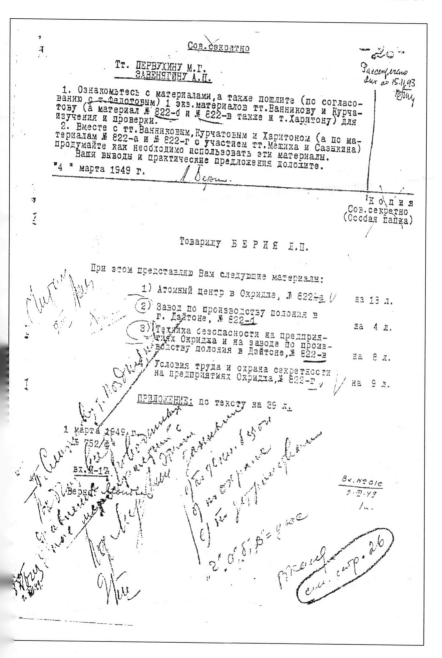

Сов.секретно

Тт. ПЕРВУХИНУ М.Г.
ЗАВЕНЯГИНУ А.П.

1. Ознакомьтесь с материалами, а также пошлите (по согласованию с т.Федотовым) 1 экз. материалов тт.Ванникову и Курчатову (а материал № 822-б и № 822-в также и т.Харитону) для изучения и проверки.
2. Вместе с тт. Ванниковым, Курчатовым и Харитоном (а по материалам № 822-а и № 822-г с участием тт.Мешика и Сазыкина) продумайте как необходимо использовать эти материалы.
Ваши выводы и практические предложения доложите.

"4" марта 1949 г.   Л.Берия.

К о п и я
Сов. секретно
(Особая папка)

Товарищу Б Е Р И Я Л.П.

При этом представляю Вам следующие материалы:

1) Атомный центр в Окридже, № 822-а   на 13 л.

2) Завод по производству полония в
   г. Дэйтоне, № 822-б   на 4 л.

3) Техника безопасности на предприятиях Окриджа и на заводе по производству полония в Дэйтоне, № 822-в   на 8 л.

4) Условия труда и охрана секретности
   на предприятиях Окриджа, № 822-г   на 9 л.

ПРИЛОЖЕНИЕ: по тексту на 29 л.

1 марта 1949 г.
№ 752/ф

Вх.М-17.

Верно:

These are two documents relating to atomic intelligence given to the Soviets and top-level Russian discussion about the contents. The people referred to in the first document: Kurchatov [scientist], Fedotov [NKGB General who was chief of Intelligence Directorate], Khariton [scientist], Mezhik [NKGB Lt General who was deputy chief of Soviet atomic administration from 1945–1953, reporting directly to Beria] and Sazykin [NKGB Lt General and one of the four deputies to Lt General Pavel Sudoplatov in Department S]. The second document, dated March 1, 1949, provides an indicator of how much material was being stolen in the United States by Russian Intelligence.

TOP SECRET

To Comrades Pervukhin, MG, and Zavenyagin, AP

1: *Familiarise yourselves with the materials and also send [after agreeing with Comrade Fedotov] one copy of materials to Comrades Vannikov and Kurchatov [and material no. 822-B and 822-V, also to Comrade Khariton] to study and check.*

2: *Together with Comrades Vannikov, Kurchatov and Khariton [and as far as materials no. 822-A and 822-G with Mezhik and Sazykin] think how it is necessary to use these materials.*

Report on your conclusions and practical proposals.

March 4, 1949

Signed: *L. Beria*

Copy
Top secret [special folder]

To Comrade Beria, LP
Enclosed for you the following materials

1. *Atomic centre in Oak Ridge, no. 822-A – 18 pages*
2. *Polonium manufacturing plant in Dayton, no. 822-B – 4 pages*
3. *Health and safety at Oak Ridge and polonium manufacturing plant a Dayton, no. 822-B – 8 pages*
4. *Work conditions and protection of secrecy in Oak Ridge plants, 822-G - 9 pages*

Enclosure text 39 pages

March 1, 1949

№ 2142

СООБЩЕНИЕ РЕЗИДЕНТА НКГБ СССР В ЛОНДОНЕ ОБ АКТИВИЗАЦИИ ДЕЯТЕЛЬНОСТИ АНГЛИЙСКОЙ РАЗВЕДКИ ПРОТИВ СССР[1]

23 августа 1945 г.

Информация «Малона»[2].

1. 17 августа сего года глава английского департамента индустриальных и научных исследований Айплтон[3], беседуя в присутствии «Малона» с начальником его конторы, сообщил, что первая атомная бомба была сделана из элемента-49, а вторая — из урана-235. В свое время резидентура сообщала, что американцы кодируют названия химических элементов путем написания последних цифр атомного номера и атомного веса. Поэтому указанная выше цифровая величина 49 обозначает элемент с атомным номером 94 и атомным весом 239, то есть плутоний-239.

2. В конце прошлой недели в контору «Малона» поступила расшифрованная телеграмма турецкого посла в Москве от 10 августа. Этой телеграммой турецкий посол информировал свой МИД о том, что:

а) на советское правительство произвело сильное впечатление военное применение атомной энергии, но оно намеренно скрывает это впечатление;

б) в Советском Союзе также ведутся работы в направлении использования атомной энергии, и в них принимают участие академики Капица и Иоффе;

в) английское посольство в Москве проявляет интерес к состоянию советских работ в области использования атомной энергии.

3. В апреле сего года контору «Малона» посетил сотрудник 2-го Управления СИС капитан военно-воздушных сил Барроу, который сообщил, что во изменение прежних распоряжений было разрешено начать работу против СССР, но не непосредственно, а с территории пограничных стран и использовать для этого всевозможные каналы. В июле сего года «Малон» лично ознакомился с меморандумом директора СИС генерала Мензиса[4], в котором говорилось, что в соответствии с требованиями

---

[1] См. документы № 2078, 2110, 2111, 2120.

[2] Агент НКГБ СССР, сотрудник специального технического бюро 2-го отдела Интеллидженс сервис.

[3] Айплтон Эдуард Виктор — профессор, член британского национального комитета радиотелеграфа, президент Международного научного радиосоюза, с 1939 г. — секретарь департамента научных и индустриальных исследований Великобритании.

[4] См. том 6 настоящего сборника, документ № 1859.

военного министерства на ближайший период должна быть развернута работа против СССР, и была проведена следующая классификация стран, могущих быть использованными как база для ведения разведработы против СССР: пограничные страны и другие страны, имеющие связь с СССР.

4. В учреждении «Малона» известно, что налаживается сотрудничество английских и французских разведок для работы против всех стран, включая СССР. В Париже создана объединенная организация под названием «Англо-французское бюро связи». Начальник французского отделения СИС находится в настоящее время в Париже, где принимает участие в организационном оформлении указанного бюро.

5. Техническая разведка против СССР также будет усилена в недалеком будущем. В настоящее время контора «Малона» приступила к составлению картотеки на советских ученых и научно-исследовательские организации по материалам официальных советских технических, научных и других публикаций. Одним из источников разведывательной информации о научных достижениях Советского Союза станет «Англо-французское бюро связи», в котором постоянно будет работать представитель конторы «Малона». С французской стороны технической разведкой будет руководить профессор Рока, занимающий в настоящее время пост редактора научно-исследовательского отдела французского адмиралтейства и являющийся английским агентом с 1942—1943 гг.

«Игорь»

Архив ПГУ КГБ, арх. № 251, лл. 386—387.
Подлинник

С конца 30-х годов в ряде промышленно развитых стран мира начались исследования проблемы практического использования атомной энергии. Во Франции, Англии, США и Германии эти исследования были направлены на изыскание способов создания атомного оружия. С мая 1941 г. аналогичными изысканиями занялись и в Японии. В силу разных причин к середине второй мировой войны в числе активных разработчиков проблемы остались только США и Германия.

В США эта работа с августа 1942 г. получила кодовое название «Манхэттенский проект». «Манхэттенский проект» осуществлялся в строжайшей тайне. (Даже Трумэн, занимая пост вице-президента США, ничего о нем не знал.) Руководитель проекта генерал Л. Гровс признался впоследствии, что такая секретность была направлена прежде всего на то, чтобы о работах не узнал Советский Союз.

В СССР теоретическая сторона проблемы практического использования атомной энергии была решена к лету 1941 г. Великая Отечественная война и достигнутые результаты в разрешении указанной проблемы на Западе заставили СССР с октября 1942 г. также заняться военным аспектом проблемы. К этому времени в вопросах создания атомного оружия мы отставали от США и Германии на два-два с половиной года. «Наши знания, из чего и как делать атомную бомбу, — вспоминал один из участников ее создания академик Г. Н. Флеров, — были получены из довоенных работ известных советских физиков, и наши достижения стали результатом

This NKVD transmission from Konstantin Kukin, the London *rezident* who took over from Anatoli Gorsky alerted Moscow to the news that the British and French were about to establish a secret MI6 bureau in Paris to monitor Soviet atomic developments. Kukin's informant is Wilfred Mann. Kukin also reports other key developments. The second footnote confirms that *Malone* is a Soviet agent working in British Intelligence.

The translation of text and the archivist's footnotes:

No. 2142

Report of NKGB rezident in London on the intensification of activities of British Intelligence against the USSR [1]

August 23, 1945

Information from Malone [2]

1. *On August 17 this year, the head of the English Department of Industrial and Scientific Research, Appleton [3], during a conversation in the presence of Malone with the head of his section, said that the first atomic bomb was made from element-49, the second from Uranium-235. Earlier the rezidentura reported that the Americans are coding the names of chemical elements by writing the last digits on the atomic number and the atomic weight. Therefore the value 49 mentioned above signifies an element with an atomic number of 94 and atomic weight of 239, namely plutonium-239.*
2. *At the end of last week Malone's office received a deciphered telegram of the Turkish ambassador in Moscow dated August 10. In this telegram the Turkish ambassador informed his Ministry of Foreign Affairs that:*
a. *The Soviet government was very impressed by the military use of atomic energy, but it is concealing this impression intentionally;*
b. *In the Soviet Union they are also working on using atomic energy, and the academicians Kapitsa and Ioffe are taking part in this work;*
c. *The British Embassy in Moscow has demonstrated an interest in the state of Soviet research in the use of atomic energy.*
3. *In April this year Malone's office was visited by an employee of the second directorate of SIS, an airforce captain, Barrows,* [Barrows was a Flight Lt. in RAF Intelligence] *who reported that former instructions were changed, and it has been permitted to start work against the USSR, not on its territory, but from the territories from neighbouring countries and to*

> *use various channels for that purpose. In July of this year Malone had per-*
> *sonally read a memorandum of General Menzies [4], director of the SIS,*
> *which said that in accordance with the demands of the War Ministry, in the*
> *near future, activities against the USSR should be launched and the fol-*
> *lowing classification of countries which could be used as a base to con-*
> *duct intelligence work against the USSR: neighbouring countries and*
> *other countries which have links with the USSR.*

4. *In Malone's establishment it is known that co-operation between British*
   and French intelligence services is being set up to work against all the
   countries including the USSR. In Paris a joint organisation under the
   name 'Anglo-French Liaison Bureau' has been created. The head of the
   French section of the SIS is presently in Paris where he is involved in
   organisational issues of the above mentioned bureau.

5. *Technical intelligence against the USSR will also be strengthened in the*
   near future. At present Malone's office started to put together a file index
   on Soviet scientists and scientific research organisations based on materi-
   als from official Soviet technical, scientific and other publications. The
   Anglo-French Liaison Bureau will become one of the sources for intelli-
   gence information on Soviet scientific achievements, in which a represen-
   tative from Malone's department will be working permanently. On the
   French side Professor Rocard will be heading technical intelligence; at
   present he holds the post of the director of the scientific research section
   of the French Admiralty and has been an English agent from 1942-1943.

Signed: *Igor*

Archive of the First Chief Directorate of the KGB archive file number 251, pages
386–387

Original

1. *See documents No. 2078, 2110, 2111, 2120.*
2. *Agent of the NKGB, employee of the special technical bureau of the second*
department of the intelligence service [SIS].
3. *Appleton, Edward Victor – professor, member of the British national commit-*
tee of radiotelegraphy, president of the international scientific radio union from
1939 and secretary of the Department of Scientific and Industrial Research of
Great Britain [DSIR].
4. *See volume 6 of this collection, document number 1859.*

№ 1940

СООБЩЕНИЕ РЕЗИДЕНТУРЫ НКГБ СССР В ЛОНДОНЕ ОТНОСИТЕЛЬНО ПЕРЕГОВОРОВ А. КЕССЕЛЬРИНГА[1] С АНГЛИЧАНАМИ И АМЕРИКАНЦАМИ ПО ВОПРОСУ О КАПИТУЛЯЦИИ НЕМЕЦКИХ ВОЙСК В ИТАЛИИ[2]

8 апреля 1945 г.

Агент ФБР «Лемон» рассказала нашему агенту «Д»[3], что от работника УСС (организация Донована)[4], который на днях прибыл из Италии в Англию, ей стало известно, что до перевода Кессельринга с итальянского на западный фронт сам Кессельринг или 2 высших немецких офицера от его имени вели с союзническим командованием в Италии переговоры о капитуляции немецких войск, находящихся на итальянском фронте.

«Д» сообщил об этом Лидделу[5], который неохотно подтвердил правдоподобность данной информации, но продолжать разговаривать на эту тему не пожелал.

Архив ПГУ КГБ, арх. № 244, л. 257.
Подлинник

---

[1] См. том 5 настоящего сборника, документ № 1750.

[2] См. том 3 настоящего сборника, документы № 757, 780, 805, 837, 919, 970; том 4, документы № 1137, 1302, 1354, 1448; том 5, документы № 1603, 1634, 1635, 1648, 1654, 1694, 1718, а также документы № от 16.02., 07.04.

[3] «Д» занимал видное положение в английских спецслужбах.

[4] См. том 5, документ № 1650.
Донован Уильям Джозеф — один из организаторов стратегической разведки США, генерал-майор. В годы гражданской войны в СССР был представителем американского правительства при штабе Колчака. Разведывательной работой начал заниматься в период первой мировой войны. По его проекту в июле 1941 г. был создан Комитет по координации информации, на базе которого в 1942 г. образованы Управление стратегических служб (УСС) и Объединенный разведывательный комитет, подчиненные Объединенному комитету начальников штабов. Возглавлял УСС до 1946 г. (см. том 3 настоящего сборника, документы № 829, 844).

[5] Лиддел Гай — начальник отдела «В» английской контрразведки. Отдел получал, оценивал разведывательные материалы и намечал их использование. «Д» имел служебный контакт с Лидделом.

Translation of Document 12

The third archivist footnote of this document describes the seniority in the British Secret Service of *Agent D* and in the fifth footnote *Agent D* is described as being a colleague of Guy Liddell, head of Section B of Counter-Intelligence. The document also confirms that the NKGB had an agent in the FBI, who operated under the codename of *Lemon* – a woman and probably London-based. The second footnote further confirms that the Kremlin knew about every British and American meeting that had taken place in the Vatican regarding peace talks with German politicians and senior officers and the exclusion of any Russian influence in a post-war Germany.

The translation of text and the archivist's footnotes:

No. 1940

A message from the NKGB rezident's network of the USSR in London regarding the talks between A. Kesselring [1] and the English and the Americans in the matter of German army capitulation in Italy [2]

April 8, 1945

The FBI agent, 'LEMON', told our 'Agent D' [3] that she learned from an OSS employee [Donovan's organisation] [4], recently arrived from Italy to England, that until Kesselring was transferred from Italy to the Western Front, he and two other senior German officers had conducted talks with the Allied Command in Italy, regarding the capitulation of German armies based on the Italian Front.

'D' told this to Liddell [5], who unwillingly confirmed the likelihood of this information but did not wish to elaborate further on this subject.

Archive PGU [First Chief Directorate] KGB
Archive Number 244 sheet 257

Original

[1] See volume 5 of this collection, document no. 1750.
[2] See volume 3 of this collection, documents no. 757, 780, 805, 837, 919, 970; volume 4 document no. 1137, 1302, 1354 and 1448; volume 5 documents no. 1603, 1634, 1635, 1648, 1654, 1694 and 1718.
[3] Agent D held an important position in the British Secret Service.
[4] See volume 5, document 1650. Donovan, William Joseph – one of the organisers

lxxx

of US strategic intelligence, Major General. During the civil war in the USSR, he was the representative of the American government attached to Kolchak's head-quarters (Admiral Kolchak). Donovan began his involvement in intelligence during the First World War. In July 1941, on the basis of Donovan's project, the Committee for Information Co-ordination had been set up. As a result, in 1942, the Directorate of Strategic Services [OSS] and the United Intelligence Committee were established subordinate to the United Committee of Chiefs of Staffs. He headed the OSS until 1946. [see volume 3 of this collection, documents no. 829 and 844].

[5] Guy Liddell – head of Section B of British Counter-Intelligence. This section received and assessed intelligence materials and planned their use. D had contact with Liddell, because of his work.

...ственные группы, возглавив их опытными работниками и снабдив имеющимися в НКВД—УНКВД материалами и списками лиц, подлежащих немедленному аресту.

Немедленно по прибытии в освобождаемые города и районы организовать изъятие руководящих лиц немецкого административного и хозяйственного аппарата: бургомистров, членов, полицейских, старост и других.

Одновременно с этим выявлять и арестовывать всех активных немецких пособников из населения, оставшегося на оккупированной немцами территории.

Налаживая агентурно-оперативную работу, восстанавливать связь с проверенной агентурой и осведомления, организовывать выявление и последующий арест оставленных немецко-фашистскими оккупантами нелегальных шпионско-диверсионных групп и одиночек, радистов, предателей и изменников Родины, а также ликвидацию бандитских групп.

В практической работе городским и районным органам и командированным оперативно-следственным группам и командированным оперативным работникам центрального аппарата НКВД.

О результатах проведенной работы каждые 5 дней доносить СССР телеграфно.

Народный комиссар внутренних дел СССР
Подлинник

ЦОА КГБ, ф. 12ос, оп. 5, д. 23, лл. 44—45.

№ 1089

**СПРАВКИ ПЕРВОГО УПРАВЛЕНИЯ НКВД СССР
О РАБОТЕ АГЕНТУРЫ
НКОЙ РЕЗИДЕНТУРЫ НКВД СССР ПО ЛИНИИ
АУЧНО-ТЕХНИЧЕСКОЙ РАЗВЕДКИ В 1942 г.**

26 января 1943 г.

...го за 1942 г. от агентуры было получено около 3000 листов по различным техническим вопросам. В основном материалы оказались ценными и были использованы ...сностью и научно-исследовательскими организациями.

...тем 3 настоящего сборника, документ № 619.

---

1) материалы «Листа» по бактериологии. Они содержат ценные сведения об организации и направлении работы в Англии по подготовке к бактериологической войне, содержат данные по экспериментальным исследованиям и пр.;

2) отчеты «Эллис» по цветным металлам и сплавам. Наибольший интерес представляли отчеты в части исследования алюминиевых и магниевых сплавов;

3) материалы «Скотта» и «Помощника» по радиолокационной аппаратуре.

Как положительную сторону в работе следует также отметить вербовку таких ценных агентов, как «Аккит», «Пират», «Валет»...

Начальник Первого управления НКВД СССР
Подлинник

Архив ПГУ КГБ, арх. № 77666, т. 2, л. 31.

№ 1090

**ИЗ ДОКЛАДНОЙ ЗАПИСКИ
УНКВД ПО КАЛИНИНСКОЙ ОБЛАСТИ № 1/399
В НКВД СССР
О КОНТРРАЗВЕДЫВАТЕЛЬНЫХ, КАРАТЕЛЬНЫХ
И ВОЕННЫХ ОРГАНАХ ПРОТИВНИКА,
ДЕЙСТВОВАВШИХ В г. ВЕЛИКИЕ ЛУКИ
В ПЕРИОД ЕГО ОККУПАЦИИ**

26 января 1943 г.

Материалами следствия по делам арестованных предателей и изменников Родины установлено, что в г. Великие Луки во время его оккупации действовали следующие контрразведывательные, карательные и военные органы противника: тайная полевая полиция (ГФП); полевая жандармерия; городская полиция; районная полиция; полевая комендатура; местная комендатура.

I. Тайная полевая полиция

Аппарат тайной полевой полиции прибыл в г. Великие Луки вслед за передовыми частями немецкой армии и разместился в здании бывшего горотдела НКВД (Краснофлотская ул.). Арестованные содержались в городской тюрьме и бывшем КПЗ горотдела НКВД.

Основными задачами ГФП в первые 3—4 недели являлись:

1) выявление оставшихся в городе и в районе коммунистов и партийно-советских работников;

The NKVD document which reports on the activities of the top scientific agents in Britain in 1942, namely *List, Ellie, Scott, Alkit, Pirate* and *Valet*.

Translation in full:

No. 1089

Information of the First Directorate of NKVD USSR on the work of the agents network of the British rezidence of the NKVD USSR on scientific, technical intelligence in 1942

26th January 1943

Altogether in the course of 1942 we have received about 3,000 sheets of material from the agents dealing with various technical questions. In the main the materials stand out to be valuable and were used by [British] *industrial and scientific research organisations.*

Among the most valuable materials one should mention:

1. Materials on bacteriology obtained by 'List'. They contain valuable information on the organisation and direction of work in England relating to preparation for bacteriological warfare, site data on experimental research etc.
2. Reports from 'Ellie' on non-ferrous metals and alloys. There are interesting reports relating to the study of aluminium and magnesium alloys.
3. Materials on radar devices obtained by 'Scott' and his assistants.

As a positive aspect in our work, one should also mention the valuable work of agents 'Alkit', 'Pirate' and 'Valet'.

Signed: *Head of the First Directorate NKVD USSR*

First Chief Directorate of the KGB archive, archive No. 77666, volume 2, sheet 31

Original

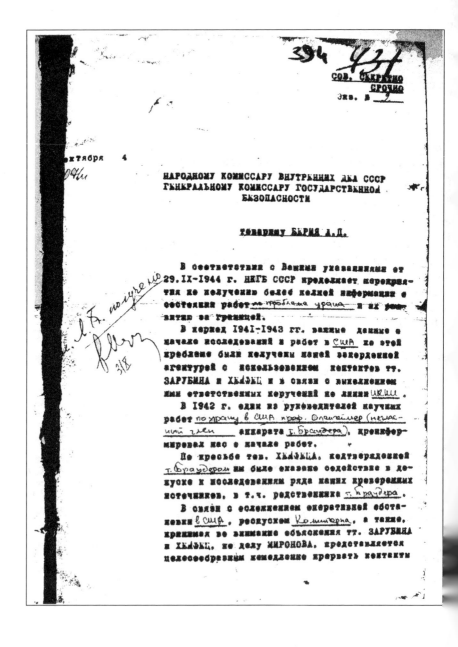

394

СОВ. СЕКРЕТНО
СРОЧНО

Экз. №

октября 4

НАРОДНОМУ КОМИССАРУ ВНУТРЕННИХ ДЕЛ СССР
ГЕНЕРАЛЬНОМУ КОМИССАРУ ГОСУДАРСТВЕННОЙ
БЕЗОПАСНОСТИ

товарищу БЕРИЯ Л. П.

В соответствии с Вашими указаниями от 29.IX-1944 г. НКГБ СССР продолжает мероприятия по получению более полной информации о состоянии работ по проблеме урана и их ведении за границей.

В период 1941-1943 гг. важные данные о начале исследований и работ в США по этой проблеме были получены нашей закордонной агентурой с использованием контактов тт. ЗАРУБИНА и ХЕЙФЕЦ и в связи с выполнением ими ответственных поручений по линии ИККИ.

В 1942 г. один из руководителей научных работ по урану в США проф. Оппенгеймер (негласный член аппарата т. Браудера), проинформировал нас о начале работ.

По просьбе тов. ХЕЙФЕЦА, подтвержденной т. Браудером им было оказано содействие в допуске к исследованиям ряда наших проверенных источников, в т.ч. родственника т. Браудера.

В связи с осложнением оперативной обстановки в США, роспуском Коминтерна, а также, принимая во внимание объяснения тт. ЗАРУБИНА и ХЕЙФЕЦ, по делу МИРОНОВА, представляется целесообразным немедленно прервать контакты

- 2 -

руководства и активистов КП США с учеными и
специалистами, участвующими в работах по
Урану.

НКГБ просит получить согласие Инстанции.

НАРОДНЫЙ КОМИССАР ГОС. БЕЗОПАСНОСТИ СССР
Комиссар Государственной безопасности I ранга

/МЕРКУЛОВ/

Верно

отпечат. 3 экз.
№1-т.Берия
№2-Секр. НКГБ
№3-I Упр.НКГБ

т.КОССОД
...р. НКГБ СССР

PROFESSOR ROBERT OPPENHEIMER

First document

There is a document procedure that has been utilised in Russian Intelligence for decades. In the case of highly sensitive information a document is typed up but gaps are left for a senior officer to complete. He will by hand fill in these gaps and underline. In the case of this document, the NKGB officer, Colonel Kossov, completed what was necessary.

The translation in full:

394 [431 is crossed out]
Top Secret
Urgent
Copies – 9

To the People's Commissar of Internal Affairs of the USSR and General Commissar of State Security

<u>*Comrade Beria LP.*</u>

In accordance with your instructions of September 29, 1944 the NKGB continues its work to obtain fuller information on the state of progress on the <u>uranium problem</u> and its development abroad.

In the period 1941–1943, important data on the beginnings of research and work in the <u>USA</u>, concerning this problem was received by our overseas agents network using contacts of Comrades Zarubin and Kheifets, and in connection with their implementation of important tasks to do with uranium.

In 1942 one of the leaders of scientific work on <u>uranium in the USA, Professor Oppenheimer [secret member of Comrade Browder's network]</u> informed us about the beginning of the work.

At the request of Comrade Kheifets, confirmed by Comrade Browder, he provided assistance in gaining access to research of several reliable sources we have, including a relative of Comrade Browder.

Due to complications in the operational situation in the USA, the dissolution of the Comintern, and taking into account the clarifications of Comrades Zarubin and Kheifets in the case of Mironov, it seems expedient to break immediately the contacts of the leadership and the activists of the Communist Party of the US with scientists and specialists participating in the work on uranium.

NKGB asks to obtain the consent of the top leadership.

Signed: *Merkulov, Commissar of State Security of the USSR First Rank*

October 2, 1944

Typed in 3 copies
1. Comrade Beria
2. Secretariat of the NKGB
3. First NKGB Directorate

Prepared by: *Comrade Kossov, NKGB USSR*

[Приложение]

***Справка на ученых и административных лиц, упоминаемых в разделе
«Состояние разработки проблемы использования атомной энергии
в капиталистических странах»***

Сов. секретно

США

1. Комптон Карл Тейлор, профессор физики. Американец. Родился 14 сентября 1887 года в городе Вустер, штат Огайо. В 1939–1940 гг. член Управления военных ресурсов, с 1940 г. — член Исследовательского комитета национальной обороны. Является братом профессора физики Комптона Артура Холли.

2. Комптон Артур Холли, 1892 г. рождения. Американец. Известный физик. С 1923 г. — профессор физики в Чикагском университете. В 1927 г. получил Нобелевскую премию по физике. Написал ряд работ по Х-лучам и электронам. Член Национальной академии наук США. Председатель Американского физического общества. Начальник отдела Управления научно-исследовательских работ в США.

Комптон Артур Холли состоит членом совещательной группы, вместе с другими видными физиками, при комиссии по контролю над новым видом оружия.

Является братом профессора физики Комптона Карла Тейлора.

3. Юри Гарольд, 1893 г. рождения, американец, известный физик. Профессор Колумбийского университета. За работы по открытию тяжелой воды был награжден Нобелевской премией.

4. Оппенгеймер Роберт, 1906 г. рождения, профессор Калифорнийского университета. Американский еврей. Негласный член компартии Америки.

Руководитель лаборатории технических проблем, связанных со сборкой составных частей атомной бомбы.

Является членом совещательной группы, вместе с другими видными физиками (Лоуренсом, Комптоном и Ферми), при комиссии по контролю над новым видом оружия.

5. Ферми Энрико, 1901 г. рождения. Итальянец. Крупный ученый в области теоретической физики. Бывший профессор Римского университета. В 1939 г. эмигрировал из Италии в США, где занял должность профессора физики Колумбийского университета. Принимал участие в создании атомной бомбы и присутствовал на полигоне во время испытания.

Член совещательной группы при комиссии по контролю над новым видом оружия.

6. Лоуренс Эрнест Орландо, 1901 г. рождения, американец, физик, профессор Калифорнийского университета. Занимался изысканиями в области структуры атома, атомного ядра, влияния радиоактивности в применении физики, биологии и медицины.

Основатель новой системы устройства по разрушению атомных ядер.

Почетный член Академии наук СССР.

Был председателем научного конгресса, состоявшегося в связи с общим конгрессом советско-американской дружбы.

7. Тейлор Хью Стотт, 1890 г. рождения, американец. Окончил Ливерпульский университет, Нобелевский институт в Стокгольме, Высшую техническую школу в Ганновере. Профессор физической химии в Принстонском университете. Автор многих работ по физической химии. Награжден несколькими медалями научных учреждений Англии, США и Бельгии. Состоит членом многих научных обществ США и Европы.

С 1 июля 1945 г. — директор Принстонского университета.

PROFESSOR ROBERT OPPENHEIMER

Second document

In the KGB archives is a 20-page document entitled *'The status of development of the problem of using atomic energy in capitalist countries'*. This extensive and highly-detailed document is dated January 7, 1946, and was prepared by Lt General Pavel Sudoplatov, who ran a number of KGB departments, including Department S which was charged by Stalin with re-evaluating all atomic intelligence obtained in Britain and the United States during wartime. This document details all the nuclear centres in Canada, the US, Britain and France. It also includes the names of every key nuclear scientist with a short biography on many of them.

Opposite is a copy of the relevant page of this document that lists the scientists in the US.

As in other KGB documents highly confidential information is underlined. Robert Oppenheimer is listed at No. 4. It reads *'Robert Oppenheimer, born 1906, Professor at the University of California, American Jew'*. The words *'secret member of the US Communist Party'* are underlined. There is also an underline for the second scientist on the list: Arthur Compton of which the author has no further information.

Сов. секретно

ПРЕДСЕДАТЕЛЮ КОМИТЕТА ГОСБЕЗОПАСНОСТИ
ПРИ СОВЕТЕ МИНИСТРОВ СССР
Генералу армии тов. СЕРОВУ И.А.

5 февраля 1957 г.

Во исполнение поручения Инстанции о привлечении видных представителей деловых кругов Запада к пропаганде достижений советской науки и культуры в связи с предстоящим празднованием 40-годовщины Великой Октябрьской Социалистической Революции, докладываем на ваше рассмотрение:

В проводимых нами мероприятиях принимает участие влиятельный предприниматель из *Англии Р. Максвел*, связанный с одним из руководителей *Лейбористской партии Г. Вильсоном.*

В ходе поддержания делового конспиративного контакта с *Максвелом* нами установлены его широкие коммерческие возможности. В связи с этим считаем целесообразным удовлетворить просьбу *Максвела* выступить в качестве зарубежного продюссера документальных фильмов "Большой Балет" и "Лебединое озеро", намеченных к прокату в 1957-58 гг. в США, Англии и других странах.

Принимая во внимание важность дальнейшей работы с *Максвелом*, учитывая возможность значительного экономического эффекта от его издательской деятельности, представляется необходимым, чтобы Минвнешторг и Минкультуры СССР получили по вопросу сотрудничества с ним соответствующие указания Инстанции, дополнительные средства и квоты.

ПЕРВЫЙ ЗАМЕСТИТЕЛЬ ПРЕДСЕДАТЕЛЯ КОМИТЕТА
ГОСБЕЗОПАСНОСТИ ПРИ СОВЕТЕ МИНИСТРОВ СССР
- Генерал-майор /К.ЛУНЕВ/

НАЧАЛЬНИК 2 ГЛАВНОГО УПРАВЛЕНИЯ
- Генерал-лейтенант /О.ГРИБАНОВ/

Исполнитель: Н.Бородин

ROBERT MAXWELL

First document

In this document the highly-sensitive underlined material has been completed by Colonel Borodin, who was one of the contacts for Maxwell. The word 'Organisation' in the text refers to the KGB.

Translation in full:

TOP SECRET

To Chairman of KGB, State Security Committee of the Council of Ministers of the USSR

Army General Comrade Serov, I.A

Date 25 February 1957

Following the request of the Organisation relating to attracting prominent representatives from the West for the positive propaganda of Soviet science and achievements in connection with the future celebration of the 40th anniversary of the Great October Socialist Revolution, the following is for your consideration:

We have undertaken measures assuring the involvement of influential business representatives from England including <u>R. Maxwell</u>, who is connected with one of the Labour Party leaders, <u>Harold Wilson</u>.

Aiming to maintain business and conspiratorial contacts with Maxwell we have identified his broad commercial possibilities. In connection with this we feel it feasible to meet Maxwell's request to become a foreign producer of documentary films 'The Bolshoi Ballet' and 'Swan Lake' which are planned to be shown between 1957 and 1958 in the United States, Europe and in other countries.

Given the importance of further work with Maxwell and considering the feasibility of significant economic benefits of his publishing activity, we feel it necessary that the Ministry of Foreign Trade Bank and Ministry of Culture of the USSR receive respected guidelines of the Organisation regarding the opportunities for cooperation with him, in addition to extra funding and quotas.

Signed: *First Deputy Chairman of the KGB*
Major General K. Lunyov

And the *Head of the 2nd Chief Department*
Lt. General O. Gribanov

Prepared *by N. Borodin*

Agreed [with Serov's signature]

285

Министру финансов СССР
тов. ГАРБУЗОВУ В. Ф.

24.06.80   1071-ц

Уважаемый Василий Федорович!

В соответствии с Вашим указанием совзагранбанки в
Швейцарии приостановили финансирование сделок по контрактам компании _Р.Максвелла_ ввиду неполучения платежей по
выделенным в 1979 г. льготным кредитам.

Во исполнение поручения Инстанции о содействии по нашей
линии _Р.Максвеллу_ в утверждении влияния в ведущих изданиях
США и Великобритании, полагали бы целесообразным учесть
эту задолженность перед совзагранбанками в сумме _8 млн._
долл. США в счет выделенных нам в 1979/80 гг. СМ СССР лимитов
на проведение _спецмероприятий за рубежом_.

В связи с вышеизложенным также сообщаем, что согласно
полученной нами достоверной информации, погашение предоставленных кредитов будет, как и ранее, проведено "Нэшнл Вестминстер
Банк" не позднее 1 октября с.г.

Прошу Ваших указаний о незамедлительном возобновлении
операций совзагранбанков с этими фирмами.

Первый заместитель Председателя   С.ЦВИГУН

Верно:
Нач. Секретариата—пом. 1-го зам. пред.

Поздоровский Г.А.

Отпечатано в 4 экз.:
1. Адресату.
2. Секретариат КГБ СССР.
3. 2 Гл. Упр. /т. Григоренко Г.Ф./.

Исп.: Волков А.А.
тел. 224-49-04

15-ам
25.01.80г.

ROBERT MAXWELL

Second document

Like the first document on Robert Maxwell only a senior KGB officer, in this case A. A.Volkov, has completed the document by writing in the highly sensitive information and then underlining it. In the document Volkov includes his telephone number in KGB headquarters. The use of the term 'Authority' in KGB documents can often be misleading. It usually relates to the head of the KGB but in some instances it can refer to the Russian Premier or Central Committee of the USSR. Semyon Tsvigun, the author of this document, was the First Deputy Chairman of the KGB and the brother-in-law of Leonid Brezhnev. His death in January 1982 was sudden. It was officially reported that he had committed suicide by taking cyanide, but that was never independently confirmed. One theory was that he was executed after being implemented in a corruption scandal that involved the Kremlin. The reference to 'soft credits' relates to credit extended on generous or subsidised terms.

Translation in full:

Top Secret
Copy No. 2
285

June 24, 1980   *1071-Ts*

For the attention of the Minister of Finance of the USSR
Comrade Garbuzov, V.F.

Dear Vasily Federovich!

In accordance with your instruction the Soviet foreign banks <u>in Switzerland</u> have suspended the financing of the transactions relating to contracts of <u>R. Maxwell's</u> companies due to non payment, for soft credits extended to them in 1979.

In implementing the order from the highest Authority on assistance to <u>R. Maxwell</u>, in our line of business, which is to strengthen influence in leading American and British publications, it would be deemed expedient to treat this debt to the Soviet foreign banks amounting to <u>$8 million</u> on account of the limits allocated to us for 1979/1980 by the USSR Council of Ministers for carrying out <u>special measures abroad.</u>

In connection with the above we also inform you that in accordance with reliable *information received by us, repayment of these credits should be made, as in the past, by the <u>National Westminster Bank</u>, not later than October 1 this year.*

We ask for your instructions on the immediate resumption of the operations of the Soviet foreign banks with these companies.

First Deputy Chairman

S.Tsvigun

Correct:

Head of the Secretary – assistant to first Deputy Chairman

Pozdoroski, J.A.

[Pozdoroski has signed the document]

Typed in four copies:
1. Addressee
2. Secretariat of KGB USSR
3. 2nd Chief Directorate (to Comrade Grigorenko, G.F)

Implemented by Volkov A.A.
Telephone: 224-49-04

15-DM
23.6.80g

The Winners of the Stalin Prize

After the testing of the atomic bomb in August 1949 Stalin instructed Beria to draw up a list of scientists and engineers to be considered for the award of Stalin's Prize. Beria deliberately excluded many who made a valuable contribution. This is the final list agreed by Stalin.

The 39 winners of Stalin Prize, 1st degree:

Semen P. Aleksandrov, Vladimir I. Alferov, Andrei A. Bochvar, Ilya I. Chernyayev, Shalva S. Danelia, Aleksandr Ya. Dementyev, Nikolai A. Dolezhal, Nikolai L. Dukhov, Nikolai M. Esakiya, Georgii N. Flerov, Boris V. Gromov, Yuli B. Khariton, Nikolai M. Khaustov, Georgi N. Kotelnikov, Zelik M. Krasnopolski, Ivan K. Kuznetsov, Igor V. Kurchatov, Grigori V. Mishenkov, Boris A. Nikitin, Vsevolod D. Nikolski, Andrian V. Nelyubin, Roman V. Nifontov, Sergei S. Panchev, Aleksandr S. Polikovski, Aleksandr Kh. Ratner, Nicholas V. Riehl, Mikhail A. Sadovski, Viktor I. Shadrin, Andrei A. Shafranov, Kirill I. Shchelkin, Viktor M. Shishov, Iosif E. Starik, Veniamin A. Tsukerman, Aleksandr P. Vinogradov, Anton N. Volski, Boris I. Yakushenkov, Aleksandr S. Zaimovski, Yakov B. Zeldovich, Daniil F. Zimin

The 112 winners of Stalin Prize, 2nd degree:

Aleksei S. Abramov, Georgi V. Akimov, Anatoli P. Aleksandrov, Nikolai P. Aleksakhin, Lev V. Altshuller, Aleksei A. Andreyev, Alfred Ya. Apin, Evgeni N. Babulevich, Yuri Ya. Bazilevski, Grigori K. Bannikov, Boris N. Borisoglebski, Anton V. Byalobzheski, Anatoli A. Chernyakov, Viktor A. Davidenko, Pavel A. Delens, Pavel G. Dobia, Boris G. Dubovski, Leonid R. Dulin, Mikhail A. Elyashevich, Amo S. Elyan, Ivan Ya. Emelyanov, Zinaida V. Ershova, Saveli M. Feinberg, Gleb M. Frank, David A. Frank-Kamenetski, Simkha A. Frankshtein, Aleksandr N. Frumkin, Vasili S. Fursov, Andrei A. Gershun, Yuri N. Golovanov, Valentin N. Gorshkov, Isai I. Gurevich, Vladimir N. Gusev, Aleksandr I. Gutov, Mikhail V. Iolko, Boris M. Isayev, Nikolai A. Isakov, Aleksei A. Karpukhin, Samvel G. Kacharyants, Nikolai F. Kvaskov, Pavel V. Kevlishvili, Valentin A. Kerzhanovich, Samuel B. Kormer, Mikhail S. Kozadayev, Nikolai S. Kozlov, Vladimir S. Komelkov, Yuri N. Koshkin, Konstantin K. Krupnikov, Grigori P. Kryukov, Boris V. Kurchatov, Lev D. Landau, Rostislav P. Lastovski, Boris N. Ledenev, Ovsei I. Leipunski, Avgust A. Letavet, Izrail L. Lyudmirski, Boris V. Malkin, Anatoli Ya. Malski, Sergei N. Matveyev, Grigori V. Matis, Nikolai P. Melnikov, Iosif Kh. Mints, Vyacheslav V. Mishke, Vladimir I. Mostovoi, Boris P. Nikolski, Viktor M. Nekrutkin, Mikhail S. Ozerski, Boris A. Olisov, Petr N. Palei, Grigori P. Pankratov, Moisei I. Pevzner, Boris S. Pozdnyakov, Aleksei I. Popov, Anatoli F. Popov, Pavel F. Pokhia, Yuri A. Prokofyev, Fedor G. Prokhorov, Khaim

Sh. Proshitski, Boris T. Pushkin, Simon Z. Roginski, Emmanuil I. Rome, Avraam Z. Rothshild, Lev I. Rusinov, Dmitri I. Ryabchikov, Aleksandr I. Shalnikov, Anatoli I. Savin, Ilya I. Salamatov, Nikolai N. Svirshevski, Konstantin A. Semendyayev, Nikolai N. Semenov, Sergei A. Skvortsov, Efim P. Slavski, Vasili V. Smirnov, Mikhail P. Solmov, Vladimir I. Stolyarov, Georgi L. Shnirman, Werner V. Schutze, Ivan V. Tananayev, Aleksandr L. Tarakanov, Nikolai A. Terletski, Gerbert V. Time, Fedor V. Tulyankin, Mikhail Ya. Vasilyev, Vsevolod V. Veinberg, Girsha A. Vinn-Feivel, Gunter V. Virtz, Dmitri T. Vorobyev, Vladimir P. Yudayev, Grigori N. Yakovlev, Viktor I. Zhuchikhin, Evgeni I. Zababakhin, Yakov I. Zilberman

The 25 winners of Stalin Prize, 3rd degree:

Nikolai I. Aleksandrov, Aleksandr R. Belov, Nikolai S. Chugreyev, Sergei S. Chugunov, Boris V. Florinski, Vladimir V. Goncharov, Aleksandr Z. Kachkachev, Aleksei V. Kotikov, Nesanel S. Lurye, Vladimir N. Maslov, Mikhail V. Poplavko-Mikhailov, Nikolai F. Pravdyuk, Aleksei N. Protopopov, Vasili V. Rylin, Andrei G. Samoilov, Andrei E. Semenov, Mikhail P. Sergeyev, Dmitri P. Shirshov, Nikolai A. Silin, Leonid P. Spasski, Diodor M. Tarasov, Mikhail V. Ugryumov, Viktor V. Vazinger, Evgeni K. Zavoiski, Savva I. Zolotukhin

Colonel Vladimir Borisovich Barkovsky, one of the greatest KGB spymasters, shaking hands with the author in the coffee shop of the National Hotel, Moscow. He alone knew how Russian Intelligence stole the atomic secrets of the West to build Stalin's bomb that was exploded in Semipalatinsk, Kazakhstan, on August 29, 1949 – an event that stunned the world, turning the USSR into the nuclear equal of the United States. Barkovsky was also fully aware of the value of the 'atomic' notebook, detailing the secrets of Hitler's atomic bomb programme, found in the briefcase of Major Hans van der Velde in the Ukrainian village of Krivaya Kosa in the early hours of February 23, 1942.

Without Barkovsky's help, advice and support this book could not have been written.

Vladimir Barkovsky died on July 21, 2003 in Moscow's hospital for KGB and FSB officers. Even his death was shrouded in mystery as veteran KGB colleagues were not immediately informed of his passing and were not invited to the funeral. His obituary in a Russian newspaper specialising in intelligence matters was not published until October. Barkovsky's death brought the final curtain down on an exceptional rewarding era for the Russian Intelligence Services.